INSTRUCTOR'S SOLUTIONS MANUAL

SOLUTIONS PREPARED BY TWIN PRIME EDITORIAL

A SURVEY OF MATHEMATICS WITH APPLICATIONS

EIGHTH EDITION

AND

EXPANDED EIGHTH EDITION

Allen R. Angel
Monroe Community College

Christine D. Abbott
Monroe Community College

Dennis C. Runde
Manatee Community College, Bradenton

PEARSON
Addison
Wesley

Boston San Francisco New York
London Toronto Sydney Tokyo Singapore Madrid
Mexico City Munich Paris Cape Town Hong Kong Montreal

Reproduced by Pearson Addison-Wesley from electronic files supplied by the author.

Copyright © 2009 Pearson Education, Inc.
Publishing as Pearson Addison-Wesley, 75 Arlington Street, Boston, MA 02116.

ISBN-13: 978-0-321-51092-1
ISBN-10: 0-321-51092-5

2 3 4 5 6 BB 10 09

PEARSON
Addison
Wesley

Table of Contents

CHAPTER ONE

CRITICAL THINKING SKILLS

Exercise Set 1.1

1. a) 1, 2, 3, 4, 5, …
    b) Counting numbers

2. a) If $a \div b$ has a remainder of zero, then a is divisible by b.
    b) 4, 8, 12
    c) 9, 18, 27

3. **Inductive reasoning** is the process of reasoning to a general conclusion through observations of specific cases.

4. **Deductive reasoning** is the process of reasoning to a specific conclusion from a general statement.

5. A **counterexample** is a specific case that satisfies the conditions of the conjecture but shows the conjecture is false.

6. A **conjecture** is a belief based on specific observations that has not been proven or disproven.

7. Inductive reasoning

8. Deductive reasoning

9. Inductive reasoning, because a general conclusion was made from observation of specific cases.

10. Inductive reasoning, because a general conclusion was made from observation of specific cases.

11. $5 \times 7 = 35$

12. $13 \times 14 = 182$

13. $1 \quad 5(=1+4) \quad 10(=4+6) \quad 10(=6+4) \quad 5(=4+1)$

14. $100,000 = 10^5$

15.

16.

17.

18.

19. 25, 30, 35 (Add 5 to previous number.)

20. 7, 4, 1 (Subtract 3 from previous number.)

21. −1, 1, −1 (Alternate −1 and 1.)

22. −3, −5, −7 (Subtract 2 from previous number.)

23. $\dfrac{1}{16}, \dfrac{1}{64}, \dfrac{1}{256}$ (Multiply previous number by $\dfrac{1}{4}$.)

24. 2500, −12,500, 62,500 (Multiply previous number by −5.)

25. 36, 49, 64 (The numbers in the sequence are the squares of the counting numbers.)

26. 21, 28, 36 ($15 + 6 = 21$, $21 + 7 = 28$, $28 + 8 = 36$)

1

27. 34, 55, 89 (Each number in the sequence is the sum of the previous two numbers.)

28. $\dfrac{243}{256}, -\dfrac{729}{1024}, \dfrac{2187}{4096}$ (Multiply previous number by $-\dfrac{3}{4}$.)

29. There are three letters in the pattern.
$39 \times 3 = 117$, so the 117th entry is the second R in the pattern. Therefore, the 118th entry is Y.

30. a) Answers will vary.
 b) The sum of the digits is 9.
 c) When a one- or two-digit number is multiplied by 9, repeated summing of the digits in the product yields the number 9.

31. a) 36, 49, 64

 b) Square the numbers 6, 7, 8, 9 and 10.

 c) $8 \times 8 = 64$ $9 \times 9 = 81$
 72 is not a square number since it falls between the two square numbers 64 and 81.

32. a) 28 and 36
 b) To find the 7th triangular number, add 7 to the 6th triangular number. To find the 8th triangular number, add 8 to the 7th triangular number. To find the 9th triangular number, add 9 to the 8th triangular number. To find the 10th triangular number, add 10 to the 9th triangular number. To find the 11th triangular number, add 11 to the 10th triangular number.
 c)
 $36 + 9 = 45; 45 + 10 = 55; 55 + 11 = 66; 66 + 12 = 78$

 72 is not a triangular number since it falls between the consecutive triangular numbers 66 and 78.

33. Blue: 1, 5, 7, 10, 12   Purple: 2, 4, 6, 9, 11   Yellow: 3, 8

34. a) 19 (Each new row has two additional triangles.)
 b) $1+3+5+7+9+11+13+15+17+19 = 100$

35. a) $\approx \$6$ billion   b) We are using observation of specific cases to make a prediction.

36. a) $\approx \$45$ b) $\approx \$51$
 c) We are using observation of specific cases to make a prediction.

37.

P	B	P	B
B	P	B	P
P	B	P	B
B	P	B	P

38.

39. a) You should obtain the original number.
 b) You should obtain the original number.
 c) Conjecture: The result is always the original number.
 d) $n, 8n, 8n+16, \dfrac{8n+16}{8} = \dfrac{8n}{8} + \dfrac{16}{8} = n+2, n+2-2 = n$

40. a) You should obtain twice the original number.
 b) You should obtain twice the original number.
 c) Conjecture: The result is always twice the original number.
 d) $n, 4n, 4n+6, \dfrac{4n+6}{2} = \dfrac{4n}{2} + \dfrac{6}{2} = 2n+3, 2n+3-3 = 2n$

41. a) You should obtain the number 5.

   b) You should obtain the number 5.

   c) Conjecture: No matter what number is chosen, the result is always the number 5.

   d) $n, n+1, n+(n+1) = 2n+1, 2n+1+9 = 2n+10, \dfrac{2n+10}{2} = \dfrac{2n}{2} + \dfrac{10}{2} = n+5, n+5-n = 5$

42. a) You should obtain the number 0.

   b) You should obtain the number 0.

   c) Conjecture: No matter what number is chosen, the result is always the number 0.

   d) $n, n+10, \dfrac{n+10}{5}, 5\left(\dfrac{n+10}{5}\right) = n+10, n+10-10 = n, n-n = 0$

43. $3+5 = 8$ is one counterexample.

44. $5 \div 2 = 2\frac{1}{2}$, which is not a counting number.

45. Two is a counting number. The sum of 2 and 3 is 5. Five divided by two is $\dfrac{5}{2}$, which is not an even number.

46. One and three are counting numbers. The product of 1 and 3 is 3, which is not divisible by 2.

47. One and two are counting numbers. The difference of 1 and 2 is $1-2 = -1$, which is not a counting number.

48. The sum of the odd numbers 1 and 5 is 6, which is not divisible by 4.

49. a) The sum of the measures of the interior angles should be $180°$.

   b) Yes, the sum of the measures of the interior angles should be $180°$.

   c) Conjecture: The sum of the measures of the interior angles of a triangle is $180°$.

50. a) The sum of the measures of the interior angles should be $360°$.

   b) Yes, the sum of the measures of the interior angles should be $360°$.

   c) Conjecture: The sum of the measures of the interior angles of a quadrilateral is $360°$.

51. 129, the numbers in positions are found as follows: $\begin{matrix} a & b \\ c & a+b+c \end{matrix}$

52. 1881, 8008, 8118 (They look the same when looked at in a mirror.)

53. c

Exercise Set 1.2
(Note: Answers in this section will vary depending on how you round your numbers. The answers may differ from the answers in the back of the textbook. However, your answers should be something near the answers given. All answers are approximate.)

1. $523 + 47.8 + 821.6 + 733 + 92.7 \approx 520 + 50 + 820 + 730 + 90 = 2210$

2. $3.76 + 76 + 821.7 + 654.93 + 321 + 0.89 \approx 0 + 80 + 820 + 650 + 320 + 0 = 1870$

3.
$$297,700 \times 4087 \approx 300,000 \times 4000 = 1,200,000,000$$

4. $1854 \times 0.0096 \approx 1900 \times 0.01 = 19$

5. $\dfrac{405}{0.049} \approx \dfrac{400}{0.05} = 8000$

6. $297.521 - 85.964 \approx 300 - 90 = 210$

7. $0.63 \times 1523 \approx 0.6 \times 1500 = 900$

8. $51,608 \times 6981 \approx 50,000 \times 7000 = 350,000,000$

9. 9% of $2164 \approx 10\%$ of $2000 = 0.10 \times 2000 = 200$

10. 18% of $1570 \approx 20\%$ of $1600 = 320$

11. $592 \times 2070 \times 992.62$
    $\approx 600 \times 2000 \times 1000 = 1,200,000,000$

12. $296.3 \div 0.0096 \approx 300 \div 0.01 = 30,000$

13. $27 \text{ hours} \times \$8.25 \text{ per hour}$

$\approx 30 \text{ hours} \times \$8 \text{ per hour} = \$240$

14. $13 \times \$0.15 \approx 10 \times \$0.15 = \$1.50$

15. $\$4.23 + \$2.79 + \$0.79 + \$7.62 + \$12.38 + \$4.99$

$\approx 4.20 + 2.80 + 0.80 + 7.60 + 12.40 + 5.00 = \$32.80$

16. $7\% \text{ of } \$599 \approx 7\% \text{ of } 600 = 0.07 \times \$600 = \$42$

17. $57 \text{ miles per hour for } 3.2 \text{ hours}$
$\approx 60 \text{ miles per hour for } 3 \text{ hours}$
$= 60 \times 3 = 180 \text{ miles}$

18.   One fourth of an annual salary of $47,600

$\approx \frac{1}{4} \times \$48,000 = \$12,000$

19. $27,453 - 14,292 \approx 27,500 - 14,300 = 13,200 \text{ lb}$

20. $\frac{3.25 \text{ lb}}{6} \approx \frac{3.00 \text{ lb}}{6} = 0.5 \text{ lb}$

21. $15\% \text{ of } \$26.32 \approx 15\% \text{ of } \$26 = 0.15 \times \$26 = \$3.90$

22. $\frac{173 \text{ mi}}{7} \approx \frac{175}{7} = 25 \text{ mi}$

23. $\frac{\$400}{\$23} \approx \frac{\$400}{\$25} = 16$

24. $\frac{\$2900}{12} \approx \frac{\$3000}{12} = \$250$

25.

$(\$29.99 + \$36.99 + \$59.99 + \$49.00) - \$139.99$
$\approx (\$30 + \$37 + \$60 + \$50) - \$140 = \$177 - \$140$
$= \$37$

26.   Team A: $189 + 172 + 191 \approx 190 + 170 + 190 = 550$
Team B: $183 + 229 + 167 \approx 180 + 230 + 170 = 580$
$580 - 550 = 30 \text{ lb}$

27. $11 \times 8 \times \$1.50 \approx 10 \times 8 \times \$1.50$
$= 10 \times \$12 = \$120$

28. $3.8 \text{ grubs per square foot} \times (60 \text{ ft} \times 80.2 \text{ ft})$

$\approx 4 \text{ grubs per square foot} \times (60 \times 80 \text{ square feet})$

$= 4 \times 4800 \text{ grubs} = 19,200 \text{ grubs}$

29. $100 \text{ Mexican pesos} = 100 \times 0.089 \text{ U.S. dollars}$

$\approx 100 \times 0.09 \text{ U.S. dollars} = 9 \text{ U.S. dollars}$
$\$50 - \$9 = \$41$

30. $\$973 + 6(\$61) + 6(\$97) + 6(\$150)$

$\approx \$970 + 6(\$60) + 6(\$100) + 6(\$150)$

$= \$970 + \$360 + \$600 + \$900 = \$2830$

31. $\approx 20 \text{ miles}$

32. $\approx 30 \text{ miles}$

33.   a) 100
b) 50
c) 125

34.   a) 24 million
b) 1.2 million

35.   a) 5 million
b) 98 million
c) $98 \text{ million} - 33 \text{ million} = 65 \text{ million}$
d) $19 \text{ million} + 79 \text{ million} + 84 \text{ million} +$
    $65 \text{ million} + 33 \text{ million} = 280 \text{ million}$

36.   a) 19%
b) 25%
c) $20\% \text{ of } 179 \text{ lb} \approx 20\% \text{ of } 180 = 0.2 \times 180 = 36 \text{ lb}$

37.   a) 85%
b) $68\% - 53\% = 15\%$
c) $85\% \text{ of } 70 \text{ million acres} = 59,500,000 \text{ acres}$
d) No, since we are not given the area of each
    state.

38.   a) $2(410) + 4(545)$

$\approx 2(400) + 4(550) = 800 + 2200 = 3000 \text{ calories}$
b) Running: $4(920) \approx 4(925) = 3700 \text{ calories}$
Casual bike riding: $4(300) = 1200 \text{ calories}$,
$3700 - 1200 = 2500 \text{ calories}$
c) $3(545) + 3(545) \approx 3(550) + 3(550)$
$= 1650 + 1650 = 3300 \text{ calories per week}$,
$3300 \text{ calories per week} (52 \text{ weeks})$
$\approx 3000 \times 50 = 150,000 \text{ calories}$

39. 25

40. 30

41. ≈ 160 bananas

42. ≈ 90 berries

43. 150°

44. 315°

45. 10%

46. 25%

47. 9 square units

48. 12 square units

49. 150 feet

50. $5(62) = 310$ in. or $\dfrac{310}{12} \approx 25.8$ ft

51.-59. Answers will vary.

60. There are 118 ridges around the edge.

61. There are 336 dimples on a regulation golf ball.

62. a) Answers will vary.

b) 60 seconds per minute $\times$ 60 minutes per hour

$\times$ 24 hours per day $= 60 \times 60 \times 24$ seconds per day

$= 86,400$ seconds per day,

$\dfrac{1,000,000}{86,400} = 11.57407407 \approx 11.6$ days

Exercise Set 1.3

1. $\dfrac{1 \text{ in.}}{18 \text{ mi}} = \dfrac{4.25 \text{ in.}}{x \text{ mi}}$

$1x = 18(4.25)$

$x = 76.5$ mi

2. $\dfrac{1 \text{ in.}}{12 \text{ ft}} = \dfrac{x \text{ in.}}{82 \text{ ft}}$

$12x = 1(82)$

$\dfrac{12x}{12} = \dfrac{82}{12}$

$x = \dfrac{82}{12} = 6\dfrac{10}{12} = 6\dfrac{5}{6}$ in. or ≈ 6.83 in.

3. $\dfrac{3 \text{ ft}}{1.2 \text{ ft}} = \dfrac{48.4 \text{ ft}}{x \text{ ft}}$

$3x = 1.2(48.4)$

$\dfrac{3x}{3} = \dfrac{58.08}{3}$

$x = \dfrac{58.08}{3} = 19.36$ ft

4. $\dfrac{1 \text{ bag}}{6000 \text{ ft}^2} = \dfrac{x \text{ bags}}{32,000 \text{ ft}^2}$

$6000x = 1(32,000)$

$\dfrac{6000x}{6000} = \dfrac{32,000}{6000}$

$x = \dfrac{32,000}{6000} = 5.\overline{3} \approx 5.33$ bags

5. 5.7% of $\$27,461 = 0.057 \times \$27,461 = \$1565$

$\$27,461 + \$1565 = \$29,026$

6. Cost per person with 5 people: $\dfrac{\$445}{5} = \$89$

Cost per person with 6 people: $\dfrac{\$510}{6} = \$85$

$\$89 - \$85 = \$4$ savings

7. a) 31.2% of $150,000 $= 0.312 \times \$150,000$
$$= \$46,800$$
$\$150,000 + \$46,800 = \$196,800$

   b) CA: 25.4% of $200,000 $= 0.254 \times \$200,000$
$$= \$50,800$$
NH: 12.1% of $200,000 $= 0.121 \times \$200,000$
$$= \$24,200$$
$\$50,800 - \$24,200 = \$26,600$

   c) 22.4% of $180,000 $= 0.224 \times \$180,000$
$$= \$40,320$$
$\$180,000 + \$40,320 = \$220,320$

8. a) Retirees: 63% of 48 million $= 0.63 \times 48$
$$= 30.24 \text{ million}$$
Disabled: 13% of 48 million $= 0.13 \times 48$
$$= 6.24 \text{ million}$$
$30.24 - 6.24 = 24$ million

   b) Survivors: 14% of 48 million $= 0.14 \times 48$
$$= 6.72 \text{ million}$$
Spouses etc.: 10% of 48 million $= 0.10 \times 48$
$$= 4.80 \text{ million}$$
$6.71 - 4.80 = 1.92$ million

9. Denise parks her car for eight hours per day.
$5[\$2.50 + \$1.00(7 \text{ hours per day})]$
$= 5[\$2.50 + \$7.00] = 5(\$9.50) = \$47.50$
Savings: $\$47.50 - \$35.00 = \$12.50$

10. Package 1: $\dfrac{\$27}{17} \approx \$1.17$ per picture

   Package 2: $\dfrac{\$17}{10} = \$1.70$ per picture

   Package 1 offers the better price per picture.

11. $\$120 + \$80(15) = \$120 + \$1200 = \$1320$

   Savings: $\$1320 - \$1250 = \$70$

12. 2005: $\$20 \times 2$ million $= \$40$ million
2006: $\$20 + 0.25 \times \$20 = \$25$
$\$25 \times 2$ million $= \$50$ million
$50 - 40 = \$10$ million

13. 15 year mortgage: $\$840.62(12)(15) = \$151,311.60$

   30 year mortgage: $\$620.28(12)(30) = \$223,300.80$

   Savings: $\$223,300.80 - \$151,311.60 = \$71,989.20$

14. Points needed for 80 average: $80(5) = 400$ points

   Wallace's points so far:
$79 + 93 + 91 + 68 = 331$ points

   Grade needed on fifth exam: $400 - 331 = 69$

15. a) $\dfrac{86.5}{34} \approx 2.54; \dfrac{91.5}{36} \approx 2.54; \dfrac{96.5}{38} \approx 2.54;$

$\dfrac{101.5}{40} \approx 2.54; \dfrac{106.5}{42} \approx 2.54 \ldots$

So, $48(2.54) \approx 122.$

   b) Answers will vary. A close approximation can be obtained by multiplying the U.S. sizes by 2.54.

16. a) $10 \cdot 10 \cdot 10 \cdot 10 = 10,000$
   b) 1 in 10,000

17. a) $\dfrac{460}{50} = 9.2$ min

   b) $\dfrac{1550}{25} = 62$ min

   c) $\dfrac{1400}{35} = 40$ min

   d) $\dfrac{1550}{80} + \dfrac{2200}{80} = \dfrac{3750}{80} \approx 47$ min

18. $38,687.0 \text{ mi} - 38,451.4 \text{ mi} = 235.6 \text{ mi}$

$\dfrac{235.6 \text{ mi}}{12.6 \text{ gal}} \approx 18.698 \approx 18.7 \text{ mpg}$

19. a) $1.5 trillion

b) $\dfrac{\$2.2 \text{ trillion}}{108,819,000}$

$\approx \dfrac{\$2,200,000,000,000}{100,000,000} = \$22,000$

20. a) $40 \times \$8.50 \times 52 = \$17,680$

b) Each week he makes $40 \times \$8.50 = \$340$.

$\dfrac{\$1275}{\$340} = 3.75$ weeks

21. By mail: $(\$52.80 + \$5.60 + \$8.56) \times 4$

$= \$66.96 \times 4 = \$267.84$

Tire store: $\$324 + 0.08 \times \$324$

$= \$324 + \$25.92 = \$349.92$

Savings: $\$349.92 - \$267.84 = \$82.08$

22. $(1 \text{ yd})^2 = (3 \text{ ft})^2 = 9 \text{ ft}^2$

$2400 \times 9 = 21,600 \text{ ft}^2$

$\dfrac{1 \text{ gal}}{350 \text{ ft}^2} = \dfrac{x \text{ gal}}{21,600 \text{ ft}^2}$

$350x = 1(21,600)$

$\dfrac{350x}{350} = \dfrac{21,600}{350}$

$x = \dfrac{21,600}{350} \approx 61.71 \approx 62$ gal

23. a) $\$620(0.12) = \$74.40$

b) $\$1200(0.22) = \$264$

c) The store lost $\$1200 - \$1000 = \$200$ on the purchase.
Store's profit: $\$264 - \$200 = \$64$

24. Steve and Maureen paid more than $8440 but less than $24,040, so they paid $8440 plus 25% of the amount over $61,300.

$\$13,365 - \$8440 = \$4925$

The amount over $61,300 was $\dfrac{\$4925}{0.25} = \$19,700$

$\$61,300 + \$19,700 = \$81,000$

25. a) $0.1 \text{ cm}^3 \times 60 \text{ sec} \times 60 \text{ min} \times 24 \text{ hr} \times 365 \text{ days}$

$= 3,153,600 \text{ cm}^3$

b) $30 \text{ cm} \times 20 \text{ cm} \times 20 \text{ cm} = 12,000 \text{ cm}^3$

$0.1 \text{ cm}^3 \times 60 \text{ sec} \times 60 \text{ min} \times 24 \text{ hr} = 8640$

$\dfrac{12,000}{8640} = 1.3\overline{8} \approx 1.4$ days

26. a) $1 \text{ oz} \times 60 \text{ min} \times 24 \text{ hr} \times 365 \text{ days} = 525,600 \text{ oz}$

$\dfrac{525,600}{128} = 4106.25$ gal

b) $\dfrac{4106.25}{1000} \times \$11.20 = 4.10625 \times \$11.20 = \$45.99$

27. a) Short: $\$30 \times 5 = \$150$
Long: $\$15 \times 5 = \$75$
$\$150 - \$75 = \$75$; Jeff saves $75.

b) $6 for first hour, plus $3 \times \$3$ for remaining 3 hours, for a total of $15.

c) Short: $\$6 + 4 \times \$3 = \$18$
Long: $15
Long term is cheaper by $3.

28. a) $\dfrac{20,000}{20.8} - \dfrac{20,000}{21.6} \approx 961.538 - 925.926$

$= 35.612 \approx 35.61$ gal

b) $35.61 \times \$3.00 = \$106.83$

c) $140,000,000 \times 35.61 = 4,985,400,000$ gal

29. a) Yes, divide the total emissions by the emissions per capita.

b) $\dfrac{5912.2}{19.8} \approx 298.596$ million ≈ 298.6 million

c) $\dfrac{4707.3}{3.6} \approx 1307.583$ million ≈ 1.3076 billion

30. Cost after 1 year: $\$799 + 0.06(\$799)$

$= \$799 + \$49.94 = \$846.94$

Cost after 2 years: $\$846.94 + 0.06(\$846.94)$

$= \$846.94 + \$50.82 = \$897.76$

31. Value after first year: $1000+0.10(\$1000)$

$=\$1000+\$100=\$1100$

Value after second year: $\$1100-0.10(\$1100)$

$=\$1100-\$110=\$990$

$990 is less than the intial investment of $1000.

32. After paying the $100 deductible, Yungchen must pay 20% of the cost of x-rays.

First x-ray:

$\$100+0.20(\$540)=\$100+\$108=\$208$

Second x-ray: $0.20(\$920)=\$184$

Total: $\$208+\$184=\$392$

33. a) $\dfrac{\$200}{\$41}\approx 4.87804878$ The maximum number of 10 packs is 4.

$\$200-(4\times\$41)=\$200-\$164=\$36$, $\dfrac{\$36}{\$17}=2.117647059$ Deirdre can also buy two 4 packs.

10 packs	4 packs	Number of rolls	Cost
4	2	$4(10)+2(4)=48$	$4(\$41)+2(\$17)=\$198$
3	4	46	$191
2	6	44	$184
1	9	46	$194
0	11	44	$187

Maximum number of rolls of film is 48.

b) The cost is $198 when she purchases four 10 packs and two 4 packs.

34. a) $\dfrac{\$50}{\$5.76}\approx 8.680\overline{5}$ The maximum number of 4 packs of 36 exposures is 8.

$\$50-(8\times\$5.76)=\$50-\$46.08=\$3.92$. So, Erika cannot buy any 24 exposures.

4 packs of 36 exp.	4 packs of 24 exp.	Number of exposures	Cost
8	0	$8(36)+0(24)=288$	$8(\$5.76)+0(\$4.08)=\$46.08$
7	2	300	$48.48
6	3	288	$46.80
5	5	300	$49.20
4	6	288	$47.52
3	8	300	$49.92
2	9	288	$48.24
1	10	276	$46.56
0	12	288	$48.96

2 packs of 24 exposures and 7 packs of 36 exposures, or 5 packs of 24 exposures and 5 packs of 36 exposures, or 8 packs of 24 exposures and 3 packs of 36 exposures

b) 300 exposures in each case

c) The minimum cost is $48.48 when she purchases 2 packs of 24 exposures and 7 packs of 36 exposures.

35. a) water/milk: $3(1) = 3$ cups   salt: $3\left(\dfrac{1}{8}\right) = \dfrac{3}{8}$ tsp

Cream of wheat: $3(3) = 9$ tbsp $= \dfrac{9}{16}$ cup (because 16 tbsp = 1 cup)

b) water/milk: $\dfrac{2 + 3.75}{2} = \dfrac{5.75}{2} = 2.875$ cups $= 2\dfrac{7}{8}$ cups

salt: $\dfrac{0.25 + 0.5}{2} = \dfrac{0.75}{2} = 0.375$ tsp $= \dfrac{3}{8}$ tsp

cream of wheat: $\dfrac{0.5 + 0.75}{2} = \dfrac{1.25}{2} = 0.625$ cups $= \dfrac{5}{8}$ cup $= \dfrac{5}{8}(16$ tbsp$) = 10$ tbsp

c) water/milk: $3\dfrac{3}{4} - 1 = \dfrac{15}{4} - \dfrac{4}{4} = \dfrac{11}{4} = 2\dfrac{3}{4}$ cups

salt: $\dfrac{1}{2} - \dfrac{1}{8} = \dfrac{4}{8} - \dfrac{1}{8} = \dfrac{3}{8}$ tsp   cream of wheat: $\dfrac{3}{4} - \dfrac{3}{16} = \dfrac{12}{16} - \dfrac{3}{16} = \dfrac{9}{16}$ cup = 9 tbsp

d) Differences exist in water/milk because the amount for 4 servings is not twice that for 2 servings. Differences also exist in Cream of Wheat because $\dfrac{1}{2}$ cup is not twice 3 tbsp.

36. a) rice: $\dfrac{1}{2}(4) = 2$ cups   b) rice: $1(2) = 2$ cups

water: $1\dfrac{1}{3}(4) = \dfrac{4}{3}(4) = \dfrac{16}{3} = 5\dfrac{1}{3}$ cups   water: $2\dfrac{1}{4}(2) = \dfrac{9}{4}(2) = \dfrac{18}{4} = 4\dfrac{2}{4} = 4\dfrac{1}{2}$ cups

salt: $\dfrac{1}{4}(4) = 1$ tsp   salt: $\dfrac{1}{2}(2) = 1$ tsp

butter/margarine: $1(4) = 4$ tsp   butter/margarine: $2(2) = 4$ tsp

c) rice: $\dfrac{1}{2} + 1\dfrac{1}{2} = \dfrac{1}{2} + \dfrac{3}{2} = \dfrac{4}{2} = 2$ cups

water: $1\dfrac{1}{3} + 3\dfrac{1}{3} = \dfrac{4}{3} + \dfrac{10}{3} = \dfrac{14}{3} = 4\dfrac{2}{3}$ cups

salt: $\dfrac{1}{4} + \dfrac{3}{4} = \dfrac{4}{4} = 1$ tsp

butter/margarine: 1 tsp + 1 tbsp = 1 tsp + 3 tsp = 4 tsp

d) rice: $3 - 1 = 2$ cups

water: $6 - 2\dfrac{1}{4} = \dfrac{24}{4} - \dfrac{9}{4} = \dfrac{15}{4} = 3\dfrac{3}{4}$ cups

salt: $1\dfrac{1}{2} - \dfrac{1}{2} = 1$ tsp

butter/margarine: 2 tbsp $= 2(3\text{tsp}) = 6$ tsp

6 tsp $-$ 2 tsp $= 4$ tsp

e) Differences exist in water because the amount for 4 servings is not twice that for 2 servings.

37. $1\ \text{ft}^2$ would be 12 in. by 12 in.

Thus, $1\ \text{ft}^2 = 12$ in. $\times 12$ in. $= 144$ in.^{2}

38. $1\ \text{ft}^3 = 12$ in. $\times 12$ in. $\times 12$ in. $= 1728$ in.^{3}

39. Area of original rectangle = lw

    Area of new rectangle = $(2l)(2w) = 4lw$

    Thus, if the length and width of a rectangle are doubled, the area is 4 times as large.

40. Volume of original cube = lwh

    Volume of new cube = $(2l)(2w)(2h) = 8lwh$ Thus, if the length, width, and height of a cube are doubled, the volume is 8 times as large or increases eight-fold.

41. 11 ft is one-sixth of the pole, so the length is $6 \times 11\,\text{ft} = 66\,\text{ft}$.

42.
$$\frac{10 \text{ pieces}}{\$x} = \frac{1000 \text{ pieces}}{\$10}$$
$$1000x = 10(10)$$
$$\frac{1000x}{1000} = \frac{100}{1000}$$
$$x = \frac{100}{1000} = \$0.10 = 10\cancel{c}$$

43. Left side: $1(-6) = -6$ Right side: $1(2) = 2$

    $\quad 2(-2) = -4$ $1(3) = 3$

    $\quad -6 + -4 = -10$ $1(6) = 6$

    $2 + 3 + 6 = 11$

    Place it at -1 so the left side would total $-10 + -1 = -11$.

44. 3

45. $30,000 is the difference between one-fourth of the cost and one-fifth of the cost.

    $\frac{1}{4} - \frac{1}{5} = \frac{1}{20}$; $20 \times \$3000 = \$60,000$.

    The yacht costs $60,000.

46. $10; 2002, 2112, 2222, 2332, 2442, 2552,$ $2662, 2772, 2882, 2992$

47. a) $(4 \times 4) + (3 \times 3) + (2 \times 2) + (1 \times 1)$

    $= 16 + 9 + 4 + 1 = 30$

    b) $(7 \times 7) + (6 \times 6) + (5 \times 5) + 30$

    $= 49 + 36 + 25 + 30 = 140$

48. a) Place the object, 1 g, and 3 g on one side and 9 g on the other side.

    b) Place the object, 9 g, and 3 g on one side and 27 g and 1 g on the other side.

49.

50. Eight pieces

51.

8	6	16
18	10	2
4	14	12

52.

15	1	11
5	9	13
7	17	3

53. $6 + 10 + 8 + 4 = 28; 3 + 7 + 5 + 1 = 16;$

    $10 + 14 + 12 + 8 = 44$

    The sum of the four corner entries is 4 times the number in the center of the middle row.

54. 21, 12, 33

Multiply the number in the center of the middle row by 3.

56. $35 - 15 = 20$ cubes

58. Each shakes with four people.

55. 63, 36, 99

Multiply the number in the center of the middle row by 9.

57. $3 \times 2 \times 1 = 6$ ways

59.

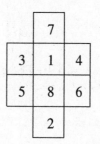

Other answers are possible, but 1 and 8 must appear in the center.

60.

(The diagram shows the number of times each part is used.)

61.

1	2	3	4	5
2	3	4	5	1
3	4	5	1	2
4	5	1	2	3
5	1	2	3	4

Other answers are possible.

62. With umbrella policy:

Mustang reduced premium: $\$1648 - \$90 = \$1558$

Focus reduced premium:

$\$1530 - 0.12(\$1530)$

$= \$1530 - \$183.60 = \$1346.40$

Total for umbrella policy:

$\$1558 + \$1346.40 + \$450 = \$3354.40$

Without umbrella policy: $\$1648 + \$1530 = \$3178$

Net amount for umbrella policy:

$\$3354.40 - \$3178 = \$176.40$

64. $16 + 16 + 4 + 4 + 4 = 44$

63. Mary is the skier.

65. Areas of the colored regions are:

1×1, 1×1, 2×2, 3×3, 5×5, 8×8, 13×13,

21×21; $1 + 1 + 4 + 9 + 25 + 64 + 169 + 441$

$= 714$ square units

66. 1 giraffe = 2 frogs

1 giraffe = 3 lions

3 lions = 2 frogs

Therefore, $\dfrac{3}{3}$ lion = $\dfrac{2}{3}$ frog.

Therefore, 1 lion = $\dfrac{2}{3}$ frog.

1 lion = 2 ostriches

Therefore, $\dfrac{2}{3}$ frog = 2 ostriches.

$\dfrac{2}{3}\left(\dfrac{3}{2}\right)$ frog = $2\left(\dfrac{3}{2}\right)$ ostriches

Therefore, 1 frog = 3 ostriches.

67. Let x be the amount Samantha had to start.

After first store: $x - \dfrac{1}{2}x - 20 = \dfrac{1}{2}x - 20$

After second store: $\dfrac{1}{2}\left(\dfrac{1}{2}x - 20\right) - 20 = \dfrac{1}{4}x - 30$

This is equal to $0, so the original amount was $120.

68. Thomas would have opened the box labeled *grapes and cherries*. Because all the boxes are labeled incorrectly, whichever fruit he pulls from the box of grapes and cherries, will be the only fruit in that box. If he pulled a grape, he labeled the box *grape*. If he pulled a cherry, he labeled the box *cherries*. That left two boxes whose original labels were incorrect. Because all labels must be changed, there was only one way for Thomas to assign the two remaining labels.

Review Exercises

1. 31, 36, 41 (Add 5 to previous number.)

2. 25, 36, 49 (next three perfect squares)

3. -48, 96, -192 (Multiply previous number by -2.)

4. 25, 32, 40 (19 + 6 = 25, 25 + 7 = 32, 32 + 8 = 40)

5. 10, 4, -3 (subtract 1, then 2, then 3, ...)

6. $\dfrac{3}{8}, \dfrac{3}{16}, \dfrac{3}{32}$ (Multiply previous number by $\dfrac{1}{2}$.)

7.

8.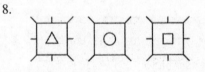

9. c

10. a) The final number is twice the original number.

b) The final number is twice the original number.

c) Conjecture: The final number is twice the original number.

d) $n, 10n, 10n + 5, \dfrac{10n + 5}{5} = \dfrac{10n}{5} + \dfrac{5}{5} = 2n + 1, 2n + 1 - 1 = 2n$

11. This process will always result in an answer of 3. $n, n + 5, 6(n + 5) = 6n + 30, 6n + 30 - 12$

$= 6n + 18, \dfrac{6n + 18}{2} = \dfrac{6n}{2} + \dfrac{18}{2} = 3n + 9, \dfrac{3n + 9}{3} = \dfrac{3n}{3} + \dfrac{9}{3} = n + 3, n + 3 - n = 3$

12. $1^2 + 2^2 = 5, 5$ is an odd number.

(Note: Answers for Ex. 13 - 25 will vary depending on how you round your numbers. The answers may differ from the answers in the back of the textbook. However, your answers should be something near the answers given. All answers are approximate.)

13. $210,302 \times 1992 \approx 210,000 \times 2000 = 420,000,000$

14. $215.9 + 128.752 + 3.6 + 861 + 729$

$\approx 250 + 150 + 0 + 850 + 750 = 2000$

15. 21% of $1012 \approx 20\%$ of 1000

$= 0.20 \times 1000 = 200$

16. Answers will vary.

17. $74 \times \$3.99 \approx 75 \times \$4.00 = \$300$

18. 6% of \$589 $\approx 6\%$ of $600 = 0.06 \times 600 = \$36$

19. $\dfrac{1.1 \text{ mi}}{22 \text{ min}} \approx \dfrac{1 \text{ mi}}{20 \text{ min}} = \dfrac{3 \text{ mi}}{60 \text{ min}} = 3 \text{ mph}$

21. $5 \text{ in.} = \dfrac{20}{4} \text{ in.} = 20\left(\dfrac{1}{4}\right) \text{ in.} = 20(0.1) \text{ mi} = 2 \text{ mi}$

23. 0.8 million

25. Length $= 1.75$ in., $1.75(12.5) = 21.875 \approx 22$ ft

    Height $= 0.625$ in., $0.625(12.5) = 7.8125 \approx 8$ ft

27. $4(\$2.69) = \$10.76$ for four six-packs

    Savings: $\$10.76 - \$9.60 = \$1.16$

29. To produce the 52 Oscars he found:

    $52 \times \$327 = \$17,004$

    He was awarded

    $\$50,000 - \$17,004 = \$32,996$ more.

31. 10% of $\$530 = 0.10 \times \$530 = \$53$

    $\$53 \times 7 = \$371$

    Savings: $\$371 - \$60 = \$311$

33. $\$4500 - 0.30(\$4500) = \$4500 - \$1350$

    $= \$3150$ take-home

    28% of $\$3150 = 0.28 \times \$3150 = \$882$

35. 3 P.M. -4 hr $= 11$ A.M.

    July 26, 11:00 A.M.

20. $\$2.49 + \$0.79 + \$1.89 + \$0.10 + \$2.19 + \$6.75$

    $\approx \$2 + \$1 + \$2 + \$0 + \$2 + \$7 = \$14.00$

22. 0.15 million

24. 13 square units

26. $\$2.00 + 7(\$1.50) = \$2.00 + \$10.50 = \$12.50$

    Change: $\$20.00 - \$12.50 = \$7.50$

28. Akala's: 2 hr $= 120$ min, $\dfrac{120}{15} = 8, 8 \times \$15 = \$120$

    Berkman's: 2 hr $= 120$ min, $\dfrac{120}{30} = 4$,

    $4 \times \$25 = \$100$

    Berkman's is the better deal by
    $\$120 - \$100 = \$20.00$.

30. a) $\dfrac{30}{2500} = \dfrac{x}{24,000}$; $x = \dfrac{30 \times 24,000}{2500} = 288$ lb

    b) $\dfrac{150}{30} = 5$ bags, and $5 \times 2500 = 12,500$ ft^2

32. $\dfrac{1.5 \text{ mg}}{10 \text{ lb}} = \dfrac{x \text{ mg}}{47 \text{ lb}}$

    $10x = 47(1.5)$

    $\dfrac{10x}{10} = \dfrac{70.5}{10}$

    $x = 7.05$ mg

34. 9 A.M. Eastern is 6 A.M. Pacific,
    from 6 A.M. Pacific to 1:35 P.M. Pacific
    is 7 hr 35 min , 7 hr 35 min $-$ 50 min stop
    $= 6$ hr 45 min

36. a) 1 in.$\times$1 in. $= 2.54$ cm $\times 2.54$ cm

    $= 6.4516 \text{ cm}^2 \approx 6.45 \text{ cm}^2$

    b) 1 in.$\times$1 in.$\times$1 in.

    $= 2.54 \text{ cm} \times 2.54 \text{ cm} \times 2.54 \text{ cm}$

    $= 16.387064 \text{ cm}^3 \approx 16.39 \text{ cm}^3$

    c) $\dfrac{1 \text{ in.}}{2.54 \text{ cm}} = \dfrac{x \text{ in.}}{1 \text{ cm}}$

    $2.54x = 1(1)$

    $\dfrac{2.54x}{2.54} = \dfrac{1}{2.54}$

    $x = 0.3937... \approx 0.39$ in.

37. Each figure has an additional two dots. To get the hundredth figure, 97 more figures must be drawn, $97(2) = 194$ dots added to the third figure. Thus, $194 + 7 = 201$.

38.

21	7	8	18
10	16	15	13
14	12	11	17
9	19	20	6

39.

23	25	15
13	21	29
27	17	19

40. 59 min 59 sec   Since it doubles every second, the jar was half full 1 second earlier than 1 hour.

41. 6

42. Nothing. Each friend paid $9 for a total of $27; $25 to the hotel, $2 to the clerk.
$25 for the room + $3 for each friend + $2 for the clerk = $30

43. Let $x =$ the total weight of the four women
$$\frac{x}{4} = 130, \quad x = 520, \quad \frac{520 + 180}{5} = \frac{700}{5} = 140 \text{ lb}$$

44. Yes; 3 quarters and 4 dimes, or 1 half dollar, 1 quarter and 4 dimes, or 1 quarter and 9 dimes.
Other answers are possible.

45. $6 \text{ cm} \times 6 \text{ cm} \times 6 \text{ cm} = 216 \text{ cm}^3$

46. Place six coins in each pan with one coin off to the side. If it balances, the heavier coin is the one on the side. If the pan does not balance, take the six coins on the heavier side and split them into two groups of three. Select the three heavier coins and weigh two coins. If the pan balances, it is the third coin. If the pan does not balance, you can identify the heavier coin.

47. $\dfrac{n(n+1)}{2} = \dfrac{500(501)}{2} = \dfrac{250,500}{2} = 125,250$

48. 16 blue: 4 green $\rightarrow$ 8 blue, 2 yellow $\rightarrow$ 5 blue, 2 white $\rightarrow$ 3 blue

49. 90: 101, 111, 121, 131, 141, 151, 161, 171, 181, 191, ...

50. The fifth figure will be an octagon with sides of equal length. Inside the octagon will be a seven sided figure with each side of equal length. The figure will have one antenna.

51. 61: The sixth figure will have 6 rows of 6 tiles and 5 rows of 5 tiles ($6 \times 6 + 5 \times 5 = 36 + 25 = 61$).

52. Some possible answers are given below. There are other possibilities.

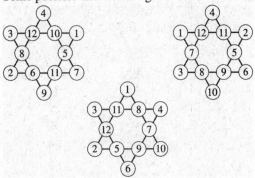

53. a) 2

   b) There are 3 choices for the first spot. Once that person is standing, there are 2 choices for the second spot and 1 for the third. Thus, $3 \times 2 \times 1 = 6$.

   c) $4 \times 3 \times 2 \times 1 = 24$

   d) $5 \times 4 \times 3 \times 2 \times 1 = 120$

   e) $n(n-1)(n-2)\cdots1$, (or $n!$), where n = the number of people in line

Chapter Test

1. 19, 23, 27   (Add 4 to previous number.)

2. $\dfrac{1}{16}, \dfrac{1}{32}, \dfrac{1}{64}$ (Multiply previous number by $\dfrac{1}{2}$.)

3. a) The result is the original number plus 1.

   b) The result is the original number plus 1.

   c) Conjecture: The result will always be the original number plus 1.

   d) $n, 5n, 5n+10, \dfrac{5n+10}{5} = \dfrac{5n}{5} + \dfrac{10}{5} = n+2, n+2-1 = n+1$

(Note: Answers for #4 - #6 will vary depending on how you round your numbers. The answers may differ from the answers in the back of the textbook. However, your answers should be something near the answers given. All answers are approximate.)

4. $0.18 \times 58,000 \approx 0.2 \times 60,000 = 12,000$

5. $\dfrac{210,000}{0.12} \approx \dfrac{210,000}{0.1} \approx 2,100,000$

6. 9 square units

7. a) $\dfrac{130 \text{ lb}}{63 \text{ in.}} \approx 2.0635$

   $\dfrac{2.0635}{63 \text{ in.}} = 0.032754$

   $0.032754 \times 703 \approx 23.03$

   b) He is in the at risk range.

8. $\$74.39 - \$59.99 = \$14.40$

   $\dfrac{\$14.40}{\$0.40} = 36$; 36 additional minutes

9. $\dfrac{\$15}{\$2.59} \approx 5.79$

   The maximum number of 6 packs is 5.

   $\$15.00 - (5 \times \$2.59) = \$15.00 - \$12.95 = \$2.05$

   $\dfrac{\$2.05}{\$0.80} = 2.5625$

   Thus, two individual cans can be purchased.

6 packs	Indiv. cans	Number of cans
5	2	32
4	5	29
3	9	27
2	12	24
1	15	21
0	18	18

   The maximum number of cans is 32.

10. 1 cut yields 2 equal pieces. Cut each of these 2 equal pieces to get 4 equal pieces.

3 cuts → 3(2.5 min) = 7.5 min

11. 2.5 in. by 1.875 in.

$\approx 2.5 \times 15.8$ by $1.875 \times 15.8 = 39.5$ in. by 29.625 in.

≈ 39.5 in. by 29.6 in.

(The actual dimensions are 100.5 cm by 76.5 cm.)

12. $12.75 × 40 = $510

$12.75 × 1.5 × 10 = $191.25

$510 + $191.25 = $701.25

$701.25 − $652.25 = $49.00

13.

40	15	20
5	25	45
30	35	10

14. Mary drove the first 15 miles at 60 mph which took $\frac{15}{60} = \frac{1}{4}$ hr, and the second 15 miles at 30 mph which took $\frac{15}{30} = \frac{1}{2}$ hr for a total time of $\frac{3}{4}$ hr. If she drove the entire 30 miles at 45 mph, the trip would take $\frac{30}{45} = \frac{2}{3}$ hr (40 min) which is less than $\frac{3}{4}$ hr (45 min).

15. $2 \times 6 \times 8 \times 9 \times 13 = 11,232$; 11 does not divide 11,232.

16. 243 jelly beans; $260 - 17 = 243, 234 + 9 = 243, 274 - 31 = 243$

17. a) 3 × $3.99 = $11.97

b) $9\left($1.75 \times 0.75\right) = 11.8125 \approx 11.81

c) $11.97 − $11.81 = $0.16 Using the coupon is least expensive by $0.16.

18. 24 (The first position can hold any of four letters, the second any of the three remaining letters, and so on. $4 \times 3 \times 2 \times 1 = 24$

Group Projects

1. a) $\dfrac{\$325}{3} \approx \$108.33$

    b) Let $x =$ the amount before tax

    $x + 0.07x = 325$

    $\dfrac{1.07x}{1.07} = \dfrac{325}{1.07}$

    $x = 303.7383178 \approx \$303.74$

    $\dfrac{\$303.74}{3} = 101.24\overline{6} \approx \$101.25$

    c) Inductive reasoning - arriving at a general conclusion from specific cases

    d) Combination set: $\$62.00 - (\$62.00 \times 0.10) = \$62.00 - \$6.20 = \$55.80$

    Individual sets: $2 \times \$36.00 = \$72.00, \$72.00 - (\$72.00 \times 0.20) = \$72.00 - \$14.40 = \$57.60$

    Therefore, the combination set is cheaper.

    e) Combination with tax: $\$55.80 \times 1.07 \approx \$59.71$

    Individual set with tax: $\$57.60 \times 1.07 \approx \$61.63$

    $\$61.63 - \$59.71 = \$1.92$

2. a) – d) Answers will vary.

    e) $400 \text{ mi} \div 50 \text{ mi/hr} = 8 \text{ hrs}, 9 \text{ A.M.} + 8 \text{ hrs} = 5 \text{ P.M.}$

    f) – h) Answers will vary.

3.

Order	Name	Apparel
1	Ernie	holster
2	Zeke	vest
3	Jed	chaps
4	Tex	Stetson

CHAPTER TWO

SETS

Exercise Set 2.1

1. A **set** is a collection of objects.
2. An **ellipsis** is three dots in a set indicating the elements continue in the same manner.
3. Description: the set of counting numbers less than 7

   Roster form: $\{1,2,3,4,5,6\}$

   Set-builder notation: $\{x|x \in N \text{ and } x < 7\}$

4. An **infinite** set is a set that is not finite.
5. A set is **finite** if it either contains no elements or the number of elements in the set is a natural number.
6. Set A is **equal** to set B, symbolized by $A = B$, if and only if they contain exactly the same elements.
7. Two sets are **equivalent** if they contain the same number of elements.
8. The **cardinal number** of a set A, symbolized by $n(A)$, is the number of elements in set A.
9. A set that contains no elements is called the **empty set** or **null set**.
10. $\{\ \},\varnothing$
11. A **universal set**, symbolized by U, is a set that contains all the elements for any specific discussion.
12. Set A and set B can be placed in **one-to-one correspondence** if every element of set A can be matched with exactly one element of set B and every element of set B can be matched with exactly one element of set A.
13. Not well defined, "best" is interpreted differently by different people.
14. Not well defined, "easiest" is interpreted differently by different people.
15. Well defined, the contents can be clearly determined.
16. Well defined, the contents can be clearly determined.
17. Well defined, the contents can be clearly determined.
18. Not well defined, "most interesting" is interpreted differently by different people.
19. Infinite, the number of elements in the set is not a natural number.
20. Finite, the number of elements in the set is a natural number.
21. Infinite, the number of elements in the set is not a natural number.
22. Infinite, the number of elements in the set is not a natural number.
23. Infinite, the number of elements in the set is not a natural number.
24. Finite, the number of elements in the set is a natural number.
25. $\{$ Maine, Maryland, Massachusetts, Michigan, Minnesota, Misssissippi, Missouri, Montana $\}$
26. $\{$Atlantic, Pacific, Arctic, Indian$\}$
27. $\{11,12,13,14,\ldots,177\}$
28. $C = \{4\}$
29. $B = \{2,4,6,8,\ldots\}$
30. $\{\ \}$ or $\varnothing$
31. $\{\ \}$ or $\varnothing$
32. $\{$ Alaska, Hawaii $\}$
33. $E = \{14,15,16,17,\ldots,84\}$
34. $\{$ Alaska, Hawaii $\}$

35. { Switzerland, Denmark, Sweden, United Kingdom, Germany, New Zealand }

36. { Australia, Czech Republic, China }

37. { Switzerland, Denmark, Sweden, United Kingdom, Germany }

38. { Turkey, Peru, Canada, Chile, Japan, Australia, Czech Republic }

39. { 2004, 2005 }

40. { 1996, 1997, 1998, 1999, 2000 }

41. { 1998, 1999, 2000 }

42. { } or $\varnothing$

43. $B = \{x \mid x \in N \text{ and } 4 < x < 13\}$ or

   $B = \{x \mid x \in N \text{ and } 5 \leq x \leq 12\}$

44. $A = \{x \mid x \in N \text{ and } x < 10\}$ or

   $A = \{x \mid x \in N \text{ and } x \leq 9\}$

45. $C = \{x \mid x \in N \text{ and } x \text{ is a multiple of } 3\}$

46. $D = \{x \mid x \in N \text{ and } x \text{ is a multiple of } 5\}$

47. $E = \{x \mid x \in N \text{ and } x \text{ is odd}\}$

48. $A = \{x \mid x \text{ is Independence Day}\}$

49. $C = \{x \mid x \text{ is February}\}$

50. $F = \{x \mid x \in N \text{ and } 14 < x < 101\}$ or $F = \{x \mid x \in N \text{ and } 15 \leq x \leq 100\}$

51. Set A is the set of natural numbers less than or equal to 7.

52. Set D is the set of natural numbers that are multiples of 3.

53. Set V is the set of vowels in the English alphabet.

54. Set S is the set of the seven dwarfs in *Snow White and the Seven Dwarfs*.

55. Set T is the set of species of trees.

56. Set E is the set of natural numbers greater than or equal to 4 and less than 11.

57. Set S is the set of seasons.

58. Set B is the set of members of the Beatles.

59. { Johnson & Johnson, Google, Home Depot }

60. { United Airlines, McDonald's }

61. { United Airlines }

62. {Johnson & Johnson, Google, Home Depot, Target,

   Coca-Cola, Toyota, Microsoft, Southwest Airlines }

63. { 1996, 1997, 1998, 1999 }

64. {1996, 1997, 1998, 1999, 2000, 2001, 2002,

   2003, 2004}

65. {1998, 1999, 2000, 2001, 2002, 2003, 2004 }

66. { } or $\varnothing$

67. False; $\{e\}$ is a set, and not an element of the set.

68. True; b is an element of the set.

69. False; h is not an element of the set.

70. True; Mickey Mouse is an element of the set.

71. False; 3 is an element of the set.

72. False; the capital of Hawaii is Honolulu, not Maui.

73. True; *Titanic* is an element of the set.

74. False; 2 is an even natural number.

75. $n(A) = 4$

76. $n(B) = 6$

77. $n(C) = 0$

78. $n(D) = 5$

79. Both; A and B contain exactly the same elements.

80. Equivalent; both sets contain the same number of elements, 3.

81. Neither; the sets have a different number of elements.

82. Neither; not all cats are Siamese.

83. Equivalent; both sets contain the same number of elements, 3.

84. Equivalent; both sets contain the same number of elements, 50.

85. a) Set A is the set of natural numbers greater than 2. Set B is the set of all numbers greater than 2.

   b) Set A contains only natural numbers. Set B contains other types of numbers, including fractions and decimal numbers.

   c) $A = \{3, 4, 5, 6, \ldots\}$

   d) No

86. a) Set A is the set of natural numbers greater than 2 and less than or equal to 5. Set B is the set of numbers greater than 2 and less than or equal to 5.

   b) Set A contains only natural numbers. Set B contains other types of numbers, including fractions and decimal numbers.

   c) $A = \{3, 4, 5\}$

   d) No

87. Cardinal; 12 tells how many.

88. Ordinal; 25 tells the relative position of the chart.

89. Ordinal; sixteenth tells Lincoln's relative position.

90. Cardinal; 35 tells how many dollars she spent.

91. Answers will vary.

92. Answers will vary. Examples: the set of people in the class who were born on the moon, the set of automobiles that get 400 miles on a gallon of gas, the set of fish that can talk

93. Answers will vary.

94. Answers will vary. Here are some examples.

   a) The set of men. The set of actors. The set of people over 12 years old. The set of people with two legs. The set of people who have been in a movie.

   b) The set of all the people in the world.

Exercise Set 2.2

1. Set A is a **subset** of set B, symbolized by $A \subseteq B$, if and only if all the elements of set A are also elements of set B.

2. Set A is a **proper subset** of set B, symbolized by $A \subset B$, if and only if all the elements of set A are also elements of set B and set $A \neq$ set B.

3. If $A \subseteq B$, then every element of set A is also an element of set B. If $A \subset B$, then every element of set A is also an element of set B and set $A \neq$ set B.

4. 2^n, where n is the number of elements in the set.

5. $2^n - 1$, where n is the number of elements in the set.

6. No, if two sets are equal one cannot be a proper subset of the other.

7. False; Spanish is an element of the set, not a subset.

8. False; the empty set is a subset of $\{$ salt, pepper, basil, garlic powder $\}$.

9. True; the empty set is a subset of every set.

10. False; red is an element of the set, not a proper subset.

11. True; 5 is not an element of $\{2, 4, 6\}$.

12. False; social worker is not in the second set.

13. False; the set $\{\varnothing\}$ contains the element $\varnothing$.

14. True; $\{$ motorboat, kayak $\}$ is a subset of $\{$ kayak, fishing boat, sailboat, motorboat $\}$.

15. True; $\{\ \}$ and $\varnothing$ each represent the empty set.

16. False; 0 is a number and $\{\ \}$ is a set.

17. False; the set $\{0\}$ contains the element 0.

18. True; $\{3,8,11\}$ is a subset of $\{3,8,11\}$.

19. False; $\{$swimming$\}$ is a set, not an element.

20. True; $\{3,5,9\} = \{3,9,5\}$.

21. True; the empty set is a subset of every set, including itself.

22. True; the elements of the set are themselves sets.

23. False; no set is a proper subset of itself.

24. True; $\{b,a,t\}$ is a subset of $\{t,a,b\}$.

25. $B \subseteq A, B \subset A$

26. $A = B, A \subseteq B, B \subseteq A$

27. $A \subseteq B, A \subset B$

28. None

29. $B \subseteq A, B \subset A$

30. $B \subseteq A, B \subset A$

31. $A = B, A \subseteq B, B \subseteq A$

32. $B \subseteq A, B \subset A$

33. $\{\ \}$ is the only subset.

34. $\{\ \}, \{\bigcirc\}$

35. $\{\ \}, \{$pen$\}, \{$pencil$\}, \{$pen, pencil$\}$

36. $\{\ \}, \{$ steak $\}, \{$ pork $\}, \{$ chicken $\}, \{$ steak, pork $\},$ $\{$ steak, chicken $\}, \{$ pork, chicken $\},$ $\{$ steak, pork, chicken $\}$

37. a) $\{\ \}, \{a\}, \{b\}, \{c\}, \{d\}, \{a,b\}, \{a,c\}, \{a,d\},$ $\{b,c\}, \{b,d\}, \{c,d\}, \{a,b,c\}, \{a,b,d\},$ $\{a,c,d\}, \{b,c,d\}, \{a,b,c,d\}$

   b) All the sets in part (a) are proper subsets of A except $\{a,b,c,d\}$.

38. a) $2^9 = 2 \times 2 \times 2 \times 2 \times 2 \times 2 \times 2 \times 2 \times 2 = 512$ subsets

   b) $2^9 - 1 = 512 - 1 = 511$ proper subsets

39. False; A could be equal to B.

40. True; every proper subset is a subset.

41. True; every set is a subset of itself.

42. False; no set is a proper subset of itself.

43. True; $\varnothing$ is a proper subset of every set except itself.

44. True; $\varnothing$ is a subset of every set.

45. True; every set is a subset of the universal set.

46. False; a set cannot be a proper subset of itself.

47. True; $\varnothing$ is a proper subset of every set except itself and $U \neq \varnothing$.

48. False; the only subset of $\varnothing$ is itself and $U \neq \varnothing$.

49. True; $\varnothing$ is a subset of every set.

50. False; U is not a subset of $\varnothing$.

51. The number of different variations of the house is equal to the number of subsets of $\{$deck, jacuzzi, security system, hardwood flooring$\}$, which is $2^4 = 2 \times 2 \times 2 \times 2 = 16$.

52. The number of options is equal to the number of subsets of $\{$ cucumber, onion, tomato, carrot, green pepper, olive, mushroom $\}$, which is $2^7 = 2 \times 2 \times 2 \times 2 \times 2 \times 2 \times 2 = 128$.

53. The number of different variations is equal to the number of subsets of $\{$call waiting, call forwarding, caller identification, three way calling, voice mail, fax line$\}$,

   which is $2^6 = 2 \times 2 \times 2 \times 2 \times 2 \times 2 = 64$.

54. The number of variations is equal to the number of subsets of $\{$ketchup, mustard, relish, hot sauce, onions, lettuce, tomato$\}$, which is $2^7 = 2 \times 2 \times 2 \times 2 \times 2 \times 2 \times 2 = 128$.

55. $E = F$ since they are both subsets of each other.

56. If there is a one-to-one correspondence between boys and girls, then the sets are equivalent.

57. a) Yes.

   b) No, c is an element of set D.

   c) Yes, each element of $\{a,b\}$ is an element of set D.

58. a) Each person has 2 choices, namely yes or no. $2 \times 2 \times 2 \times 2 = 16$

   b) YYYY, YYYN, YYNY, YNYY, NYYY, YYNN, YNYN, YNNY, NYNY, NNYY, NYYN, YNNN, NYNN, NNYN, NNNY, NNNN

   c) 5 out of 16

59. A one element set has one proper subset, namely the empty set. A one element set has two subsets, namely itself and the empty set. One is one-half of two. Thus, the set must have one element.

60. Yes

61. Yes

62. No

Section 2.3

1.

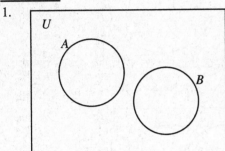

2.

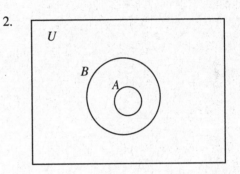

3.

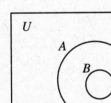

4.

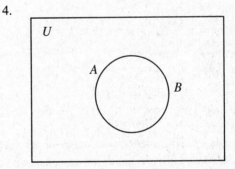

5.

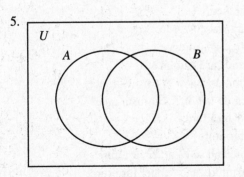

6. Combine the elements from set A and set B into one set. List any element that is contained in both sets only once.

7. Determine the elements that are in the universal set that are not in set A.

8. I, II, III

9. Select the elements common to both set A and set B.

10. II

11. a) *Or* is generally interpreted to mean *union*.

   b) *And* is generally interpreted to mean *intersection*.

12. $n(A \cup B) = n(A) + n(B) - n(A \cap B)$

13. The difference of two sets A and B is the set of elements that belong to set A but not to set B.

14. a) The Cartesian product of set A and set B is the set of all ordered pairs of the form (a, b), where $a \in A$ and $b \in B$.

   b) $m \times n$

15.
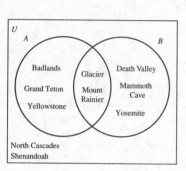

16.
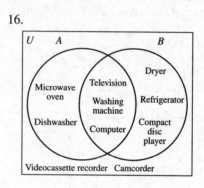

17.
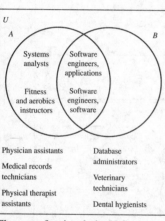

18.
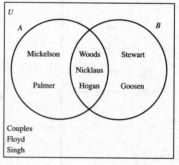

19. The set of animals in U.S. zoos that are not in the San Diego Zoo.

20. The set of U.S. colleges and universities that are not in the state of Mississippi

21. The set of insurance companies in the U.S. that do not offer life insurance

22. The set of insurance companies in the U.S. that do not offer car insurance

23. The set of insurance companies in the U.S. that offer life insurance or car insurance

24. The set of insurance companies in the U.S. that offer life insurance and car insurance

25. The set of insurance companies in the U.S. that offer life insurance and do not offer car insurance

26. The set of insurance companies in the U.S. that offer life insurance or do not offer car insurance

27. The set of furniture stores in the U.S. that sell mattresses and outdoor furniture

28. The set of furniture stores in the U.S. that sell mattresses or leather furniture

29. The set of furniture stores in the U.S. that do not sell outdoor furniture and sell leather furniture

30. The set of furniture stores in the U.S. that sell mattresses, outdoor furniture, and leather furniture

31. The set of furniture stores in the U.S. that sell mattresses or outdoor furniture or leather furniture

32. The set of furniture stores in the U.S. that do not sell mattresses or do not sell leather furniture

33. $A = \{ w, b, c, t, a, h \}$

34. $B = \{ a, h, f, r, d, g \}$

35. $A \cap B = \{ w, b, c, t, a, h \} \cap \{ a, h, f, r, d, g \} = \{ a, h \}$

36. $U = \{ w, b, c, t, a, h, f, r, d, g, p, m, z \}$

37. $A \cup B = \{ w, b, c, t, a, h \} \cup \{ a, h, f, r, d, g \} = \{ w, b, c, t, a, h, f, r, d, g \}$

38. $(A \cup B)'$: From #37, $A \cup B = \{ w, b, c, t, a, h, f, r, d, g \}$. $(A \cup B)' = \{ w, b, c, t, a, h, f, r, d, g \}' = \{ p, m, z \}$

39. $A' \cap B' = \{ w, c, b, t, a, h \} \{ a, h, f, r, d, g \} \cap \{ w, c, b, t, p, m, z \} = \{ p, m, z \}$

40. $(A \cap B)'$: From #35, $A \cap B = \{ a, h \}$. $(A \cap B)' = \{ a, h \}' = \{ w, c, b, t, f, r, d, g, p, m, z \}$

41. $A = \{ L, \Delta, @, *, \$ \}$

42. $B = \{ *, \$, R, \square, \alpha \}$

43. $U = \{ L, \Delta, @, *, \$, R, \square, \alpha, \infty, Z, \Sigma \}$

44. $A \cap B = \{ L, \Delta, @, *, \$ \} \cap \{ *, \$, R, \square, \alpha \} = \{ *, \$ \}$

45. $A' \cup B = \{ R, \square, \alpha, \infty, Z, \Sigma \} \cup \{ *, \$, R, \square, \alpha \} = \{ R, \square, \alpha, \infty, Z, \Sigma, *, \$ \}$

46. $A \cup B' = \{ L, \Delta, @, *, \$ \} \cup \{ *, \$, R, \square, \alpha \}' = \{ L, \Delta, @, *, \$ \} \cup \{ L, \Delta, @, \infty, \Sigma, Z \} = \{ L, \Delta, @, *, \$, \infty, \Sigma, Z \}$

47. $A' \cap B = \{ L, \Delta, @, *, \$ \}' \cap \{ *, \$, R, \square, \alpha \} = \{ R, \square, \alpha, \infty, Z, \Sigma \} \cap \{ *, \$, R, \square, \alpha \} = \{ R, \square, \alpha \}$

48. $(A \cup B)'$: From the diagram, $(A \cup B)' = \{ \infty, Z, \Sigma \}$

49. $A \cup B = \{ 1, 2, 4, 5, 8 \} \cup \{ 2, 3, 4, 6 \} = \{ 1, 2, 3, 4, 5, 6, 8 \}$

50. $A \cap B = \{ 1, 2, 4, 5, 8 \} \cap \{ 2, 3, 4, 6 \} = \{ 2, 4 \}$

51. $B' = \{ 2, 3, 4, 6 \}' = \{ 1, 5, 7, 8 \}$

52. $A \cup B' = \{ 1, 2, 4, 5, 8 \} \cup \{ 2, 3, 4, 6 \}' = \{ 1, 2, 4, 5, 8 \} \cup \{ 1, 5, 7, 8 \} = \{ 1, 2, 4, 5, 7, 8 \}$

53. $(A \cup B)'$ From #49, $A \cup B = \{ 1, 2, 3, 4, 5, 6, 8 \}$. $(A \cup B)' = \{ 1, 2, 3, 4, 5, 6, 8 \}' = \{ 7 \}$

54. $A' \cap B' = \{ 1, 2, 4, 5, 8 \}' \cap \{ 2, 3, 4, 6 \}' = \{ 3, 6, 7 \} \cap \{ 1, 5, 7, 8 \} = \{ 7 \}$

55. $(A \cup B)' \cap B$: From #53, $(A \cup B)' = \{ 7 \}$. $(A \cup B)' \cap B = \{ 7 \} \cap \{ 2, 3, 4, 6 \} = \{ \ \}$

56. $(A \cup B) \cap (A \cup B)' = \{ \ \}$ (The intersection of a set and its complement is always empty.)

57. $(B \cup A)' \cap (B' \cup A')$: From #53, $(A \cup B)' = (B \cup A)' = \{ 7 \}$.

$(B \cup A)' \cap (B' \cup A') = \{ 7 \} \cap \left[\{ 2, 3, 4, 6 \}' \cup \{ 1, 2, 4, 5, 8 \}' \right] = \{ 7 \} \cap \left(\{ 1, 5, 7, 8 \} \cup \{ 3, 6, 7 \} \right)$

$= \{ 7 \} \cap \{ 1, 3, 5, 6, 7, 8 \} = \{ 7 \}$

58. $A' \cup (A \cap B)$: From #50, $A \cap B = \{ 2, 4 \}$. $A' \cup (A \cap B) = \{ 1, 2, 4, 5, 8 \}' \cup \{ 2, 4 \} = \{ 3, 6, 7 \} \cup \{ 2, 4 \} = \{ 2, 3, 4, 6, 7 \}$

59. $B' = \{ b, c, d, f, g \}' = \{ a, e, h, i, j, k \}$

60. $B \cup C = \{ b, c, d, f, g \} \cup \{ a, b, f, i, j \} = \{ a, b, c, d, f, g, i, j \}$

61. $A \cap C = \{ a, c, d, f, g, i \} \cap \{ a, b, f, i, j \} = \{ a, f, i \}$

62. $A' \cup B'$: $A' = \{ b, e, h, j, k \}$, $B' = \{ a, e, h, i, j, k \}$. $A' \cup B' = \{ b, e, h, j, k \} \cup \{ a, e, h, i, j, k \} = \{ a, b, e, h, i, j, k \}$

63. $(A \cap C)'$: From #61, $A \cap C = \{ a, f, i \}$. $(A \cap C)' = \{ a, f, i \}' = \{ b, c, d, e, g, h, j, k \}$

64. $(A \cap B) \cup C = (\{ a, c, d, f, g, i \} \cap \{ b, c, d, f, g \}) \cup \{ a, b, f, i, j \} = \{ c, d, f, g \} \cup \{ a, b, f, i, j \}$
$= \{ a, b, c, d, f, g, i, j \}$

65. $AU(C\cap B)' = \{a,c,d,f,g,i\}\cup(\{a,b,f,i,j\}\cap\{b,c,d,f,g\})' = \{a,c,d,f,g,i\}\cup\{b,f\}'$

$= \{a,c,d,f,g,i\}\cup\{a,c,d,e,g,h,i,j,k\} = \{a,c,d,e,f,g,h,i,j,k\}$

66. $AU(C'\cup B') = \{a,c,d,f,g,i\}\cup\left(\{a,b,f,i,j\}'\cup\{b,c,d,f,g\}'\right)$

$= \{a,c,d,f,g,i\}\cup(\{c,d,e,g,h,k\}\cup\{a,e,h,i,j,k\}) = \{a,c,d,f,g,i\}\cup\{a,c,d,e,g,h,i,j,k\}$

$= \{a,c,d,e,f,g,h,i,j,k\}$

67. $(A'\cup C)\cup(A\cap B) = \left(\{a,c,d,f,g,i\}'\cup\{a,b,f,i,j\}\right)\cup(\{a,c,d,f,g,i\}\cap\{b,c,d,f,g\})$

$= (\{b,e,h,j,k\}\cup\{a,b,f,i,j\})\cup\{c,d,f,g\} = \{a,b,e,f,h,i,j,k\}\cup\{c,d,f,g\}$

$= \{a,b,c,d,e,f,g,h,i,j,k\}$, or U

68. $(C\cap B)\cap(A'\cap B)$: From #65, $C\cap B = \{b,f\}$.

$(C\cap B)\cap(A'\cap B) = \{b,f\}\cap\left(\{a,c,d,f,g,i\}'\cap\{b,c,d,f,g\}\right) = \{b,f\}\cap(\{b,e,h,j,k\}\cap\{b,c,d,f,g\})$

$= \{b,f\}\cap\{b\} = \{b\}$

For exercises 69-76: $U = \{1,2,3,4,5,6,7,8,9,10\}$, $A = \{1,2,4,6,9\}$, $B = \{1,3,4,5,8\}$, $C = \{4,5,9\}$

69. $A - B = \{1,2,4,6,9\} - \{1,3,4,5,8\} = \{2,6,9\}$

70. $A - C = \{1,2,4,6,9\} - \{4,5,9\} = \{1,2,6\}$

71. $A - B'$: This leaves only $A\cap B$, which is $\{1,4\}$

72. $A' - C = \{3,5,7,8,10\} - \{4,5,9\} = \{3,7,8,10\}$

73. $(A - B)' = \{2,6,9\}' = \{1,3,4,5,7,8,10\}$

74. $(A - B)' - C = \{1,3,4,5,7,8,10\} - \{4,5,9\} = \{1,3,7,8,10\}$

75. $C - A' = \{4,5,9\} - \{3,5,7,8,10\} = \{4,9\}$

76. $(C - A)' - B = \{5\}' - \{1,3,4,5,8\} = \{2,6,7,9,10\}$

For exercises 77-82: $A = \{a,b,c\}$ and $B = \{1,2\}$

77. $\{(a,1),(a,2),(b,1),(b,2),(c,1),(c,2)\}$

78. $\{(1,a),(1,b),(1,c),(2,a),(2,b),(2,c)\}$

79. No; the ordered pairs are not the same.

80. 6   81. 6   82. Yes

83. $A\cap B = \{1,3,5,7,9\}\cap\{2,4,6,8\} = \{\ \}$

84. $A\cup B = \{1,3,5,7,9\}\cup\{2,4,6,8\} = \{1,2,3,4,5,6,7,8,9\}$, or U

85. $A'\cup B = \{1,3,5,7,9\}'\cup\{2,4,6,8\} = \{2,4,6,8\}\cup\{2,4,6,8\} = \{2,4,6,8\}$, or B

86. $(B\cup C)' = (\{2,4,6,8\}\cup\{1,2,3,4,5\})' = \{1,2,3,4,5,6,8\}' = \{7,9\}$

87. $A\cap C' = \{1,3,5,7,9\}\cap\{1,2,3,4,5\}' = \{1,3,5,7,9\}\cap\{6,7,8,9\} = \{7,9\}$

88. $A\cap B' = \{1,3,5,7,9\}\cap\{2,4,6,8\}' = \{1,3,5,7,9\}\cap\{1,3,5,7,9\} = \{1,3,5,7,9\}$, or A

89. $(B \cap C)' = (\{2,4,6,8\} \cap \{1,2,3,4,5\})' = \{2,4\}' = \{1,3,5,6,7,8,9\}$

90. $(A \cup C) \cap B = (\{1,3,5,7,9\} \cup \{1,2,3,4,5\}) \cap \{2,4,6,8\} = \{1,2,3,4,5,7,9\} \cap \{2,4,6,8\} = \{2,4\}$

91. $(C' \cup A) \cap B = \left[\{1,2,3,4,5\}' \cup \{1,3,5,7,9\}\right] \cap \{2,4,6,8\} = (\{6,7,8,9\} \cup \{1,3,5,7,9\}) \cap \{2,4,6,8\}$

$= \{1,3,5,6,7,8,9\} \cap \{2,4,6,8\} = \{6,8\}$

92. $(C \cap B) \cup A$: From #89, $C \cap B = \{2,4\}$. $(C \cap B) \cup A = \{2,4\} \cup \{1,3,5,7,9\} = \{1,2,3,4,5,7,9\}$

93. $(A \cap B)' \cup C$: From #83, $A \cap B = \{\ \}$.

$(A \cap B)' \cup C = \{\ \}' \cup \{1,2,3,4,5\} = \{1,2,3,4,5,6,7,8,9\} \cup \{1,2,3,4,5\} = \{1,2,3,4,5,6,7,8,9\}$, or U

94. $(A' \cup C) \cap B = \left[\{1,3,5,7,9\}' \cup \{1,2,3,4,5\}\right] \cap \{2,4,6,8\} = (\{2,4,6,8\} \cup \{1,2,3,4,5\}) \cap \{2,4,6,8\}$

$= \{1,2,3,4,5,6,8\} \cap \{2,4,6,8\} = \{2,4,6,8\}$, or B

95. $(A' \cup B') \cap C = \left[\{1,3,5,7,9\}' \cup \{2,4,6,8\}'\right] \cap \{1,2,3,4,5\}$

$= (\{2,4,6,8\} \cup \{1,3,5,7,9\}) \cap \{1,2,3,4,5\} = \{1,2,3,4,5,6,7,8,9\} \cap \{1,2,3,4,5\} = \{1,2,3,4,5\}$, or C

96. $(A' \cap C) \cup (A \cap B)$: From #83, $A \cap B = \{\ \}$.

$(A' \cap C) \cup (A \cap B) = \left[\{1,3,5,7,9\}' \cap \{1,2,3,4,5\}\right] \cup \{\ \} = (\{2,4,6,8\} \cap \{1,2,3,4,5\}) \cup \{\ \}$

$= \{2,4\} \cup \{\ \} = \{2,4\}$

97. A set and its complement will always be disjoint since the complement of a set is all of the elements in the universal set that are not in the set. Therefore, a set and its complement will have no elements in common.

For example, if $U = \{1,2,3\}$, $A = \{1,2\}$, and $A' = \{3\}$, then $A \cap A' = \{\ \}$.

98. $n(A \cap B) = 0$ when A and B are disjoint sets. For example, if $U = \{1,2,3,4,5,6\}$, $A = \{1,3\}$, $B = \{2,4\}$,

then $A \cap B = \{\ \}$. $n(A \cap B) = 0$

99. Let $A = \{$customers who owned dogs$\}$ and $B = \{$customers who owned cats$\}$.

$n(A \cup B) = n(A) + n(B) - n(A \cap B) = 27 + 38 - 16 = 49$

100. Let $A = \{$students who sang in the chorus$\}$ and $B = \{$students who played in the stage band$\}$.

$n(A \cup B) = n(A) + n(B) - n(A \cap B)$

$46 = n(A) + 30 - 4$

$46 = n(A) + 26$

$20 = n(A)$

101. a) $A \cup B = \{a,b,c,d\} \cup \{b,d,e,f,g,h\} = \{a,b,c,d,e,f,g,h\}$, $n(A \cup B) = 8$,

$A \cap B = \{a,b,c,d\} \cap \{b,d,e,f,g,h\} = \{b,d\}$, $n(A \cap B) = 2$.

$n(A) + n(B) - n(A \cap B) = 4 + 6 - 2 = 8$

Therefore, $n(A \cup B) = n(A) + n(B) - n(A \cap B)$.

b) Answers will vary.

c) Elements in the intersection of A and B are counted twice in $n(A) + n(B)$.

102. $A \cap B'$ defines Region I. $A \cap B$ defines Region II. $A' \cap B$ defines Region III.

$A' \cap B'$ or $(A \cup B)'$ defines Region IV.

103. $A \cup B = \{1, 2, 3, 4, \ldots\} \cup \{4, 8, 12, 16, \ldots\} = \{1, 2, 3, 4, \ldots\}$, or A

104. $A \cap B = \{1, 2, 3, 4, \ldots\} \cap \{4, 8, 12, 16, \ldots\} = \{4, 8, 12, 16, \ldots\}$, or B

105. $B \cap C = \{4, 8, 12, 16, \ldots\} \cap \{2, 4, 6, 8, \ldots\} = \{4, 8, 12, 16, \ldots\}$, or B

106. $B \cup C = \{4, 8, 12, 16, \ldots\} \cup \{2, 4, 6, 8, \ldots\} = \{2, 4, 6, 8, \ldots\}$, or C

107. $A \cap C = \{1, 2, 3, 4, \ldots\} \cap \{2, 4, 6, 8, \ldots\} = \{2, 4, 6, 8, \ldots\}$, or C

108. $A' \cap C = \{1, 2, 3, 4, \ldots\}' \cap \{2, 4, 6, 8, \ldots\} = \{0\} \cap \{2, 4, 6, 8, \ldots\} = \{\ \}$

109. $B' \cap C = \{4, 8, 12, 16, \ldots\}' \cap \{2, 4, 6, 8, \ldots\} = \{0, 1, 2, 3, 5, 6, 7, 9, 10, 11, 13, 14, 15, \ldots\} \cap \{2, 4, 6, 8, \ldots\}$
$= \{2, 6, 10, 14, 18, \ldots\}$

110. $(B \cup C)' \cup C$: From #106, $B \cup C = C$. $(B \cup C)' \cup C = C' \cup C = \{2, 4, 6, 8, \ldots\}' \cup \{2, 4, 6, 8, \ldots\}$
$= \{0, 1, 2, 3, 4, \ldots\}$, or U

111. $(A \cap C) \cap B'$: From #107, $A \cap C = C$. $(A \cap C) \cap B' = C \cap B'$.
From #109, $B' \cap C = C \cap B' = \{2, 6, 10, 14, 18, \ldots\}$

112. $U' \cap (A \cup B)$: From #103, $A \cup B = A$. $U' \cap (A \cup B) = U' \cap A = \{\ \} \cap \{1, 2, 3, 4, \ldots\} = \{\ \}$

113. $A \cup A' = U$

114. $A \cap A' = \varnothing$

115. $A \cup \varnothing = A$

116. $A \cap \varnothing = \varnothing$

117. $A' \cup U = U$

118. $A \cap U = A$

119. $A \cup U = U$

120. $A \cup U' = A \cup \{\ \} = A$

121. If $A \cap B = B$, then $B \subseteq A$.

122. If $A \cup B = B$, then $A \subseteq B$.

123. If $A \cap B = \varnothing$, then A and B are disjoint sets.

124. If $A \cup B = A$, then $B \subseteq A$.

125. If $A \cap B = A$, then $A \subseteq B$.

126. If $A \cup B = \varnothing$, then $A = \varnothing$ and $B = \varnothing$.
Therefore, they are equal sets.

Exercise Set 2.4

1. 8

2. Region V, the intersection of all three sets

3. Regions II, IV, VI

4. $B \cap C$ is represented by regions V and VI. If $B \cap C$ contains 12 elements and region V contains 4 elements, then region VI contains $12 - 4 = 8$ elements.

5. $A \cap B$ is represented by regions II and V. If $A \cap B$ contains 9 elements and region V contains 4 elements, then region II contains $9 - 4 = 5$ elements.

6. $(A \cup B)' = A' \cap B'; (A \cap B)' = A' \cup B'$

7.   a) Yes

$$A \cup B = \{1,4,5\} \cup \{1,4,5\} = \{1,4,5\}$$

$$A \cap B = \{1,4,5\} \cap \{1,4,5\} = \{1,4,5\}$$

b) No

c) No

c)

$A \cup B$		$A \cap B$	
Set	Regions	Set	Regions
A	I, II	A	I, II
B	II, III	B	II, III
$A \cup B$	I, II, III	$A \cap B$	II

Since the two statements are not represented by the same regions, $A \cup B \neq A \cap B$ for all sets A and B.

8.   Deductive reasoning.

9.

10.

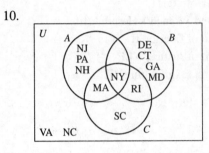

11.

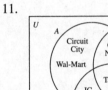

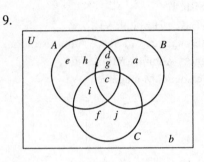

12.

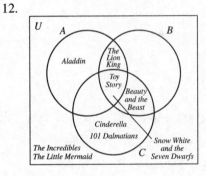

13.

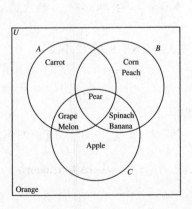

14.

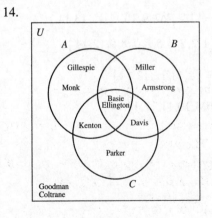

15.

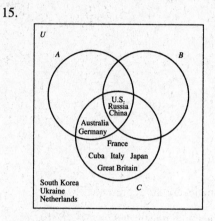

16.

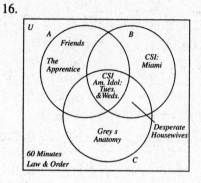

17. Mayo Clinic, V	18. UCLA Medical Center, IV
19. Methodist Hospital, I	20. Barnes-Jewish, II
21. Brigham and Women's Hospital, III	22. Yale–New Haven Hospital, VIII
23. Department of Energy, II	24. National Aeronautics and Space Administration, V
25. Department of Justice, VIII	26. Small Business Administration, VII
27. Department of Agriculture, III	28. Office of Personnel Management, VI

29. VI	30. VIII
31. III	32. IV
33. III	34. I
35. V	36. III
37. II	38. VIII
39. VII	40. VI
41. I	42. VII
43. VIII	44. V
45. VI	46. III

47. $A = \{1, 3, 4, 5, 7, 9\}$

48. $U = \{1, 2, 3, 4, 5, 6, 7, 8, 9, 10, 11, 12, 13, 14\}$

49. $B = \{2, 3, 4, 5, 6, 8, 12, 14\}$

50. $C = \{4, 5, 6, 7, 8, 10\}$

51. $A \cap B = \{3, 4, 5\}$

52. $A \cap C = \{4, 5, 7\}$

53. $(B \cap C)' = \{1, 2, 3, 7, 9, 10, 11, 12, 13, 14\}$

54. $A \cap B \cap C = \{4, 5\}$

55. $A \cup B = \{1, 2, 3, 4, 5, 6, 7, 8, 9, 12, 14\}$

56. $B \cup C = \{2, 3, 4, 5, 6, 7, 8, 10, 12, 14\}$

57. $(A \cup C)' = \{2, 11, 12, 13, 14\}$

58. $A \cap (B \cup C) = \{3, 4, 5, 7\}$

59. $A' = \{2, 6, 8, 10, 11, 12, 13, 14\}$

60. $(A \cup B \cup C)' = \{11, 13\}$

61. $(A \cup B)'$ $A' \cap B'$

Set	Regions	Set	Regions
A	I, II	A	I, II
B	II, III	A'	III, IV
$A \cup B$	I, II, III	B	II, III
$(A \cup B)'$	IV	B'	I, IV
		$A' \cap B'$	IV

Both statements are represented by the same region, IV, of the Venn diagram. Therefore, $(A \cup B)' = A' \cap B'$ for all sets A and B.

62. $(A \cap B)'$ $A' \cup B$

Set	Regions	Set	Regions
A	I, II	A	I, II
B	II, III	A'	III, IV
$A \cap B$	II	B	II, III
$(A \cap B)'$	I, III, IV	$A' \cup B$	II, III, IV

Since the two statements are not represented by the same regions, it is not true that $(A \cap B)' = A' \cup B$ for all sets A and B.

63. $A' \cup B'$ $A \cap B$

Set	Regions	Set	Regions
A	I, II	A	I, II
A'	III, IV	B	II, III
B	II, III	$A \cap B$	II
B'	I, IV		
$A' \cup B'$	I, III, IV		

Since the two statements are not represented by the same regions, it is not true that $A' \cup B' = A \cap B$ for all sets A and B.

64. $(A \cup B)'$ $(A \cap B)'$

Set	Regions	Set	Regions
A	I, II	A	I, II
B	II, III	B	II, III
$A \cup B$	I, II, III	$A \cap B$	II
$(A \cup B)'$	IV	$(A \cap B)'$	I, III, IV

Since the two statements are not represented by the same regions, it is not true that $(A \cup B)' = (A \cap B)'$ for all sets A and B.

65. $A' \cap B'$ $(A \cap B)'$

Set	Regions	Set	Regions
A	I, II	A	I, II
A'	III, IV	B	II, III
B	II, III	$A \cap B$	II
B'	I, IV	$(A \cap B)'$	1, III, IV
$A' \cap B'$	IV		

Since the two statements are not represented by the same regions, it is not true that $A' \cap B' = (A \cap B)'$ for all sets A and B.

66. $A' \cap B'$ $A \cup B'$

Set	Regions	Set	Regions
A	I, II	A	I, II
A'	III, IV	B	II, III
B	II, III	B'	I, IV
B'	I, IV	$A \cup B'$	I, II, IV
$A' \cap B'$	IV		

Since the two statements are not represented by the same regions, it is not true that $A' \cap B' = A \cup B'$ for all sets A and B.

67. $\left(A' \cap B\right)'$ $A \cup B'$

Set	Regions	Set	Regions
A	I, II	A	I, II
A'	III, IV	B	II, III
B	II, III	B'	I, IV
$A' \cap B$	III	$A \cup B'$	I, II, IV
$\left(A' \cap B\right)'$	I, II, IV		

Both statements are represented by the same regions, I, II, IV, of the Venn diagram. Therefore,

$\left(A' \cap B\right)' = A \cup B'$ for all sets A and B.

68. $A' \cap B'$ $\left(A' \cap B'\right)'$

Set	Regions	Set	Regions
A	I, II	A	I, II
A'	III, IV	A'	III, IV
B	II, III	B	II, III
B'	I, IV	B'	I, IV
$A' \cap B'$	IV	$A' \cap B'$	IV
		$\left(A' \cap B'\right)'$	I, II, III

Since the two statements are not represented by the same regions, it is not true that $A' \cap B' = \left(A' \cap B'\right)'$ for all sets A and B.

69. $A \cap (B \cup C)$ $(A \cap B) \cup C$

Set	Regions	Set	Regions
B	II, III, V, VI	A	I, II, IV, V
C	IV, V, VI, VII	B	II, III, V, VI
$B \cup C$	II, III, IV, V, VI, VII	$A \cap B$	II, V
A	I, II, IV, V	C	IV, V, VI, VII
$A \cap (B \cup C)$	II, IV, V	$(A \cap B) \cup C$	II, IV, V, VI, VII

Since the two statements are not represented by the same regions, it is not true that $A \cap (B \cup C) = (A \cap B) \cup C$ for all sets $A, B,$ and C.

70. $A \cup (B \cap C)$ $(B \cap C) \cup A$

Set	Regions	Set	Regions
B	II, III, V, VI	B	II, III, V, VI
C	IV, V, VI, VII	C	IV, V, VI, VII
$B \cap C$	V, VI	$B \cap C$	V, VI
A	I, II, IV, V	A	I, II, IV, V
$A \cup (B \cap C)$	I, II, IV, V, VI	$(B \cap C) \cup A$	I, II, IV, V, VI

Both statements are represented by the same regions, I, II, IV, V, VI, of the Venn diagram. Therefore, $A \cup (B \cap C) = (B \cap C) \cup A$ for all sets $A, B,$ and C.

71. $A \cap (B \cup C)$ $(B \cup C) \cap A$

Set	Regions	Set	Regions
B	II, III, V, VI	B	II, III, V, VI
C	IV, V, VI, VII	C	IV, V, VI, VII
$B \cup C$	II, III, IV, V, VI, VII	$B \cup C$	II, III, IV, V, VI, VII
A	I, II, IV, V	A	I, II, IV, V
$A \cap (B \cup C)$	II, IV, V	$(B \cup C) \cap A$	II, IV, V

Both statements are represented by the same regions, II, IV, V, of the Venn diagram. Therefore, $A \cap (B \cup C) = (B \cup C) \cap A$ for all sets $A, B,$ and C.

72. $A \cup (B \cap C)'$ $A' \cap (B \cup C)$

Set	Regions	Set	Regions
B	II, III, V, VI	B	II, III, V, VI
C	IV , V, VI, VII	C	IV, V, VI, VII
$B \cap C$	V, VI	$B \cup C$	II, III, IV, V, VI, VII
$(B \cap C)'$	I, II, III, IV, VII, VIII	A	I, II, IV, V
A	I, II, IV, V	A'	III, VI, VII, VIII
$A \cup (B \cap C)'$	I, II, III, IV, V, VII, VIII	$A' \cap (B \cup C)$	III, VI, VII

Since the two statements are not represented by the same regions, it is not true that $A \cup (B \cap C)' = A' \cap (B \cup C)$ for all sets $A, B,$ and C.

73. $A \cap (B \cup C)$ $(A \cap B) \cup (A \cap C)$

Set	Regions	Set	Regions
B	II, III, V, VI	A	I, II, IV, V
C	IV, V, VI, VII	B	II, III, V, VI
$B \cup C$	II, III, IV, V, VI, VII	$A \cap B$	II, V
A	I, II, IV, V	C	IV, V, VI, VII
$A \cap (B \cup C)$	II, IV, V	$A \cap C$	IV, V
		$(A \cap B) \cup (A \cap C)$	II, IV, V

Both statements are represented by the same regions, II, IV, V, of the Venn diagram.

Therefore, $A \cap (B \cup C) = (A \cap B) \cup (A \cap C)$ for all sets $A, B,$ and C.

74. $A \cup (B \cap C)$ $(A \cup B) \cap (A \cup C)$

Set	Regions	Set	Regions
B	II, III, V, VI	A	I, II, IV, V
C	IV, V, VI, VII	B	II, III, V, VI
$B \cap C$	V, VI	$A \cup B$	I, II, III, IV, V, VI
A	I, II, IV, V	C	IV, V, VI, VII
$A \cup (B \cap C)$	I, II, IV, V, VI	$A \cup C$	I, II, IV, V, VI, VII
		$(A \cup B) \cap (A \cup C)$	I, II, IV, V, VI

Both statements are represented by the same regions, I, II, IV, V, VI, of the Venn diagram.

Therefore, $A \cup (B \cap C) = (A \cup B) \cap (A \cup C)$ for all sets $A, B,$ and C.

75. $A \cap (B \cup C)'$ $A \cap (B' \cap C')$

Set	Regions
B	II, III, V, VI
C	IV, V, VI, VII
$B \cup C$	II, III, IV, V, VI, VII
$(B \cup C)'$	I, VIII
A	I, II, IV, V
$A \cap (B \cup C)'$	I

Set	Regions
B	II, III, V, VI
B'	I, IV, VII, VIII
C	IV, V, VI, VII
C'	I, II, III, VIII
$B' \cap C'$	I, VIII
A	I, II, IV, V
$A \cap (B' \cap C')$	I

Both statements are represented by the same region, I, of the Venn diagram.

Therefore, $A \cap (B \cup C)' = A \cap (B' \cap C')$ for all sets $A, B,$ and C.

76. $(A \cup B) \cap (B \cup C)$ $B \cup (A \cap C)$

Set	Regions
A	I, II, IV, V
B	II, III, V, VI
$A \cup B$	I, II, III, IV, V, VI
C	IV, V, VI, VII
$B \cup C$	II, III, IV, V, VI, VII
$(A \cup B) \cap (B \cup C)$	II, III, IV, V, VI

Set	Regions
A	I, II, IV, V
C	IV, V, VI, VII
$A \cap C$	IV, V
B	II, III, V, VI
$B \cup (A \cap C)$	II, III, IV, V, VI

Both statements are represented by the same regions, II, III, IV, V, VI, of the Venn diagram.

Therefore, $(A \cup B) \cap (B \cup C) = B \cup (A \cap C)$ for all sets $A, B,$ and C.

77. $(A \cup B)' \cap C$ $(A' \cup C) \cap (B' \cup C)$

Set	Regions
A	I, II, IV, V
B	II, III, V, VI
$A \cup B$	I, II, III, IV, V, VI
$(A \cup B)'$	VII, VIII
C	IV, V, VI, VII
$(A \cup B)' \cap C$	VII

Set	Regions
A	I, II, IV, V
A'	III, VI, VII, VIII
C	IV, V, VI, VII
$A' \cup C$	III, IV, V, VI, VII, VIII
B	II, III, V, VI
B'	I, IV, VII, VIII
$B' \cup C$	I, IV, V, VI, VII, VIII
$(A' \cup C) \cap (B' \cup C)$	IV, V, VI, VII, VIII

Since the two statements are not represented by the same regions, it is not true that $(A \cup B)' \cap C = (A' \cup C) \cap (B' \cup C)$ for all sets $A, B,$ and C.

78. $(C \cap B)' \cup (A \cap B)'$ $A \cap (B \cap C)$

Set	Regions	Set	Regions
C	IV, V, VI, VII	B	II, III, V, VI
B	II, III, V, VI	C	IV, V, VI, VII
$C \cap B$	V, VI	$B \cap C$	V, VI
$(C \cap B)'$	I, II, III, IV, VII, VIII	A	I, II, IV, V
A	I, II, IV, V	$A \cap (B \cap C)$	V
$A \cap B$	II, V		
$(A \cap B)'$	I, III, IV, VI, VII, VIII		
$(C \cap B)' \cup (A \cap B)'$	I, II, III, IV, VI, VII, VIII		

Since the two statements are not represented by the same regions, it is not true that $(C \cap B)' \cup (A \cap B)' = A \cap (B \cap C)$ for all sets $A, B,$ and C.

79. $(A \cup B)'$

80. $A \cap B'$

81. $(A \cup B) \cap C'$

82. $(A \cap B) \cup (B \cap C)$

83. a) $(A \cup B) \cap C = (\{1,2,3,4\} \cup \{3,6,7\}) \cap \{6,7,9\} = \{1,2,3,4,6,7\} \cap \{6,7,9\} = \{6,7\}$

   $(A \cap C) \cup (B \cap C) = (\{1,2,3,4\} \cap \{6,7,9\}) \cup (\{3,6,7\} \cap \{6,7,9\}) = \varnothing \cup \{6,7\} = \{6,7\}$

   Therefore, for the specific sets, $(A \cup B) \cap C = (A \cap C) \cup (B \cap C)$.

   b) Answers will vary.

   c) $(A \cup B) \cap C$ $(A \cap C) \cup (B \cap C)$

Set	Regions	Set	Regions
A	I, II, IV, V	A	I, II, IV, V
B	II, III, V, VI	C	IV, V, VI, VII
$A \cup B$	I, II, III, IV, V, VI	$A \cap C$	IV, V
C	IV, V, VI, VII	B	II, III, V, VI
$(A \cup B) \cap C$	IV, V, VI	$B \cap C$	V, VI
		$(A \cap C) \cup (B \cap C)$	IV, V, VI

Both statements are represented by the same regions, IV, V, VI, of the Venn diagram.

Therefore, $(A \cup B) \cap C = (A \cap C) \cup (B \cap C)$ for all sets $A, B,$ and C.

84. a) $(A \cup C)' \cap B = (\{a, c, d, e, f\} \cup \{a, b, c, d, e\})' \cap \{c, d\} = \{a, b, c, d, e, f\}' \cap \{c, d\}$

  $= \{g, h, i\} \cap \{c, d\} = \varnothing$

  $(A \cap C)' \cap B = (\{a, c, d, e, f\} \cap \{a, b, c, d, e\})' \cap \{c, d\} = \{a, c, d, e\}' \cap \{c, d\} = \{b, f, g, h, i\} \cap \{c, d\} = \varnothing$

  Therefore, for the specific sets, $(A \cup C)' \cap B = (A \cap C)' \cap B$.

  b) Answers will vary.

  c) $(A \cup C)' \cap B$ $(A \cap C)' \cap B$

Set	Regions	Set	Regions
A	I, II, IV, V	A	I, II, IV, V
C	IV, V, VI, VII	C	IV, V, VI, VII
$A \cup C$	I, II, IV, V, VI, VII	$A \cap C$	IV, V
$(A \cup C)'$	III, VIII	$(A \cap C)'$	I, II, III, VI, VII, VIII
B	II, III, V, VI	B	II, III, V, VI
$(A \cup C)' \cap B$	III	$(A \cap C)' \cap B$	II, III, VI

Since the two statements are not represented by the same regions, $(A \cup C)' \cap B \neq (A \cap C)' \cap B$

for all sets $A, B,$ and C.

85.

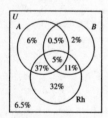

86.

Region	Set	Region	Set
I	$A \cap B' \cap C'$	V	$A \cap B \cap C$
II	$A \cap B \cap C'$	VI	$A' \cap B \cap C$
III	$A' \cap B \cap C'$	VII	$A' \cap B' \cap C$
IV	$A \cap B' \cap C$	VIII	$A' \cap B' \cap C'$

87. a) A : Office Building Construction Projects, B : Plumbing Projects, C : Budget Greater Than $300,000

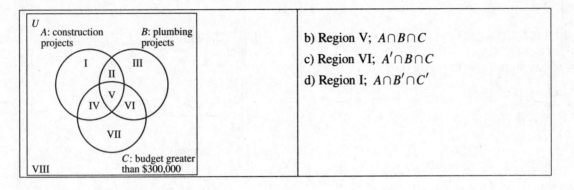

b) Region V; $A \cap B \cap C$

c) Region VI; $A' \cap B \cap C$

d) Region I; $A \cap B' \cap C'$

88. $n(A \cup B \cup C) = n(A) + n(B) + n(C) - 2n(A \cap B \cap C) - n(A \cap B \cap C') - n(A \cap B' \cap C) - n(A' \cap B \cap C)$

89. a)

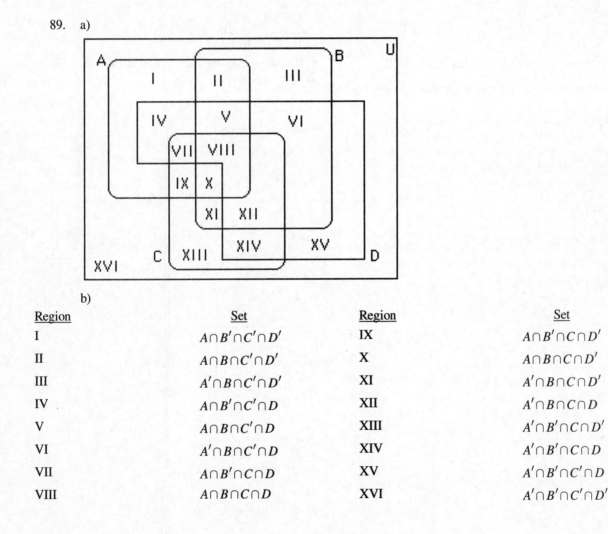

b)

Region	Set	Region	Set
I	$A \cap B' \cap C' \cap D'$	IX	$A \cap B' \cap C \cap D'$
II	$A \cap B \cap C' \cap D'$	X	$A \cap B \cap C \cap D'$
III	$A' \cap B \cap C' \cap D'$	XI	$A' \cap B \cap C \cap D'$
IV	$A \cap B' \cap C' \cap D$	XII	$A' \cap B \cap C \cap D$
V	$A \cap B \cap C' \cap D$	XIII	$A' \cap B' \cap C \cap D'$
VI	$A' \cap B \cap C' \cap D$	XIV	$A' \cap B' \cap C \cap D$
VII	$A \cap B' \cap C \cap D$	XV	$A' \cap B' \cap C' \cap D$
VIII	$A \cap B \cap C \cap D$	XVI	$A' \cap B' \cap C' \cap D'$

Exercise Set 2.5

1.

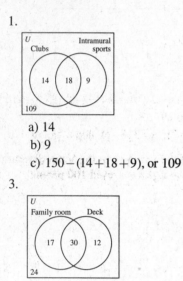

a) 14
b) 9
c) $150-(14+18+9)$, or 109

2.

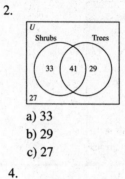

a) 33
b) 29
c) 27

3.

a) 17   b) 12
c) 59, the sum of the numbers in Regions I, II, III

4.

a) 38   b) 26
c) 106, the sum of the numbers in Regions I, II, III
d) $125-106$, or 19.

5.

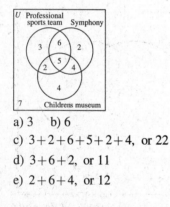

a) 3   b) 6
c) $3+2+6+5+2+4$, or 22
d) $3+6+2$, or 11
e) $2+6+4$, or 12

6.

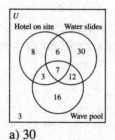

a) 30
b) $8+30+16$, or 54
c) $85-3$, or 82
d) $3+6+12$, or 21   e) 3

7.

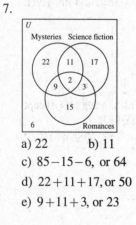

a) 22   b) 11
c) $85-15-6$, or 64
d) $22+11+17$, or 50
e) $9+11+3$, or 23

8.

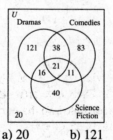

a) 20   b) 121
c) $121+83+40$, or 244
d) $16+38+11$, or 65
e) $350-20-40$, or 290

9.

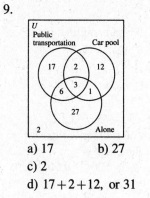

a) 17   b) 27

c) 2

d) 17 + 2 + 12, or 31   e) 2

10.

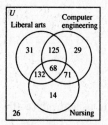

a) 496, the sum of the numbers in all the regions

b) 132   c) 29

d) 132 + 125 + 71, , or 328   e) 496 − 26, or 470

11.

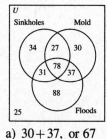

a) 30 + 37, or 67

b) 350 − 25 − 88, or 237

c) 37   d) 25

12. No. The sum of the numbers in the Venn diagram is 99. Dennis claims he surveyed 100 people.

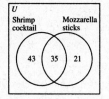

13. The Venn diagram shows the number of cars driven by women is 37, the sum of the numbers in Regions II, IV, V. This exceeds the 35 women the agent claims to have surveyed.

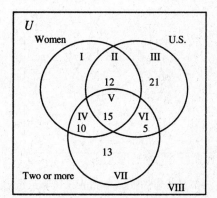

14. First fill in 15, 20 and 35 on the Venn diagram. Referring to the labels in the Venn diagram and the given information, we see that

$a + c = 140$

$b + c = 125$

$a + b + c = 185 − 15 = 170$

Adding the first two equations and subtracting the third from this sum gives $c = 125 + 140 − 170 = 95$.
Then $a = 45$ and $b = 30$. Then $d = 210 − 45 − 95 − 20 = 50$. We now have labeled all the regions except the region outside the three circles, so the number of parks with at least one of the features is
$15 + 45 + 20 + 30 + 95 + 50 + 35$, or 290. Thus the number with none of the features is $300 − 290$, or 10.

a) 290

b) 95

c) 10

d) 30 + 45 + 50, or 125.

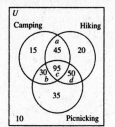

15. First fill in 15, 20 and 35 on the Venn diagram. Referring to the labels in the Venn diagram and the given information, we see that

$$a + c = 60$$
$$b + c = 50$$
$$a + b + c = 200 - 125 = 75$$

Adding the first two equations and subtracting the third from this sum gives $c = 60 + 50 - 75 = 35$. Then $a = 25$ and $b = 15$. Then $d = 180 - 110 - 25 - 35 = 10$. We now have labeled all the regions except the region outside the three circles, so the number of farmers growing at least one of the crops is $125 + 25 + 110 + 15 + 35 + 10 + 90$, or 410. Thus the number growing none of the crops is $500 - 410$, or 90.

a) 410

b) 35

c) 90

d) $15 + 25 + 10$, or 50

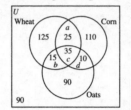

16. From the given information we can generate the Venn diagram. First fill in 4 for Region V. Then since the intersections in pairs all have 6 elements, we can fill in 2 for each of Regions II, IV, and VI. This already accounts for the 10 elements $A \cup B \cup C$, so the remaining 2 elements in U must be in Region VIII.

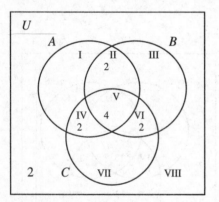

a) 10, the sum of the numbers in Regions I, II, III, IV, V, VI

b) 10, the sum of the numbers in Regions III, IV, V, VI, VIII

c) 6, the sum of the numbers in Regions I, III, IV, VI, VIII

Exercise Set 2.6

1. An **infinite set** is a set that can be placed in a one-to-one correspondence with a proper subset of itself.

2. a) A set is **countable** if it is finite or if it can be placed in a one-to-one correspondence with the set of counting numbers.

   b) Any set that can be placed in a one-to-one correspondence with the set of counting numbers has cardinality $\aleph_0$.

3. $\{5, 6, 7, 8, 9, \ldots, n + 4, \ldots\}$
   $\quad \downarrow \downarrow \downarrow \downarrow \downarrow \qquad \downarrow$
   $\{8, 9, 10, 11, 12, \ldots, n + 7, \ldots\}$

4. $\{20, 21, 22, 23, 24, \ldots, n + 19, \ldots\}$
   $\quad \downarrow \downarrow \downarrow \downarrow \downarrow \qquad \downarrow$
   $\{23, 24, 25, 26, 27, \ldots, n + 22, \ldots\}$

5. $\{3, 5, 7, 9, 11, ..., 2n + 1, ...\}$
    ↓ ↓ ↓ ↓ ↓   ↓
    $\{5, 7, 9, 11, 13, ..., 2n + 3, ...\}$

6. $\{20, 22, 24, 26, 28, ..., 2n + 18, ...\}$
    ↓ ↓ ↓ ↓ ↓   ↓
    $\{22, 24, 26, 28, 30, ..., 2n + 20, ...\}$

7. $\{3, 7, 11, 15, 19, ..., 4n - 1, ...\}$
    ↓ ↓ ↓ ↓ ↓   ↓
    $\{7, 11, 15, 19, 23, ..., 4n + 3, ...\}$

8. $\{4, 8, 12, 16, 20, ..., 4n, ...\}$
    ↓ ↓ ↓ ↓ ↓   ↓
    $\{8, 12, 16, 20, 24, ..., 4n + 4, ...\}$

9. $\{6, 11, 16, 21, 26, ..., 5n+1, ...\}$
    ↓ ↓ ↓ ↓ ↓   ↓
    $\{11, 16, 21, 26, 31, ..., 5n+6, ...\}$

10. $\left\{1, \dfrac{1}{2}, \dfrac{1}{3}, \dfrac{1}{4}, \dfrac{1}{5}, ..., \dfrac{1}{n}, ...\right\}$
    ↓ ↓ ↓ ↓ ↓   ↓
    $\left\{\dfrac{1}{2}, \dfrac{1}{3}, \dfrac{1}{4}, \dfrac{1}{5}, \dfrac{1}{6}, ..., \dfrac{1}{n+1}, ...\right\}$

11. $\left\{\dfrac{1}{2}, \dfrac{1}{4}, \dfrac{1}{6}, \dfrac{1}{8}, ..., \dfrac{1}{2n}, ...\right\}$
    ↓ ↓ ↓ ↓   ↓
    $\left\{\dfrac{1}{4}, \dfrac{1}{6}, \dfrac{1}{8}, \dfrac{1}{10}, ..., \dfrac{1}{2n+2}, ...\right\}$

12. $\left\{\dfrac{6}{13}, \dfrac{7}{13}, \dfrac{8}{13}, \dfrac{9}{13}, \dfrac{10}{13}, ..., \dfrac{n+5}{13}, ...\right\}$
    ↓ ↓ ↓ ↓ ↓   ↓
    $\left\{\dfrac{7}{13}, \dfrac{8}{13}, \dfrac{9}{13}, \dfrac{10}{13}, \dfrac{11}{13}, ..., \dfrac{n+6}{13}, ...\right\}$

13. $\{1, 2, 3, 4, 5, ..., n, ...\}$
    ↓ ↓ ↓ ↓ ↓   ↓
    $\{3, 6, 9, 12, 15, ..., 3n, ...\}$

14. $\{1, 2, 3, 4, 5, ..., n, ...\}$
    ↓ ↓ ↓ ↓ ↓   ↓
    $\{50, 51, 52, 53, 54, ..., n + 49, ...\}$

15. $\{1, 2, 3, 4, 5, ..., n, ...\}$
    ↓ ↓ ↓ ↓ ↓   ↓
    $\{4, 6, 8, 10, 12, ..., 2n + 2, ...\}$

16. $\{1, 2, 3, 4, 5, ..., n, ...\}$
    ↓ ↓ ↓ ↓   ↓
    $\{0, 2, 4, 6, 8, ..., 2n - 2, ...\}$

17. $\{1, 2, 3, 4, 5, ..., n, ...\}$
    ↓ ↓ ↓ ↓ ↓   ↓
    $\{2, 5, 8, 11, 14, ..., 3n - 1, ...\}$

18. $\{1, 2, 3, 4, 5, ..., n, ...\}$
    ↓ ↓ ↓ ↓ ↓   ↓
    $\{6, 11, 16, 21, 26, ..., 5n + 1, ...\}$

19. $\{1, 2, 3, 4, 5, ..., n, ...\}$
    ↓ ↓ ↓ ↓ ↓   ↓
    $\{5, 9, 13, 17, 21, ..., 4n + 1, ...\}$

20. $\{1, 2, 3, 4, 5, ..., n, ...\}$
    ↓ ↓ ↓ ↓ ↓   ↓
    $\left\{\dfrac{1}{2}, \dfrac{1}{4}, \dfrac{1}{6}, \dfrac{1}{8}, \dfrac{1}{10}, ..., \dfrac{1}{2n}, ...\right\}$

21. $\{1, 2, 3, 4, 5, ..., n, ...\}$
    ↓ ↓ ↓ ↓ ↓   ↓
    $\left\{\dfrac{1}{3}, \dfrac{1}{4}, \dfrac{1}{5}, \dfrac{1}{6}, \dfrac{1}{7}, ..., \dfrac{1}{n+2}, ...\right\}$

22. $\{1, 2, 3, 4, 5, ..., n, ...\}$
    ↓ ↓ ↓ ↓ ↓   ↓
    $\left\{\dfrac{1}{2}, \dfrac{2}{3}, \dfrac{3}{4}, \dfrac{4}{5}, \dfrac{5}{6}, ..., \dfrac{n}{n+1}, ...\right\}$

23. $\{1, 2, 3, 4, 5, ..., n, ...\}$
    ↓ ↓ ↓ ↓ ↓   ↓
    $\{1, 4, 9, 16, 25, ..., n^2, ...\}$

24. $\{1, 2, 3, 4, 5, ..., n, ...\}$
    ↓ ↓ ↓ ↓ ↓   ↓
    $\{2, 4, 8, 16, 32, ..., 2^n, ...\}$

25. $\{1, 2, 3, 4, 5, ..., n, ...\}$
    ↓ ↓ ↓ ↓ ↓   ↓
    $\{3, 9, 27, 81, 243, ..., 3^n, ...\}$

26. $\{1, 2, 3, 4, 5, ..., n, ...\}$
    ↓ ↓ ↓ ↓ ↓   ↓
    $\left\{\dfrac{1}{3}, \dfrac{1}{6}, \dfrac{1}{12}, \dfrac{1}{24}, \dfrac{1}{48}, ..., \dfrac{1}{3 \times 2^{n-1}}, ...\right\}$

27. $=$

28. $=$

29. $=$

30. $=$

31. $=$

32. a) Answers will vary.
    b) No

Review Exercises

1. True

2. False; the word *best* makes the statement not well defined.

3. True

4. False; no set is a proper subset of itself.

5. False; the elements 6, 12, 18, 24, ... are members of both sets.

6. True

7. False; the two sets do not contain exactly the same elements.

8. True

9. True

10. True

11. True

12. True

13. True

14. True

15. $A = \{7, 9, 11, 13, 15\}$

16. $B = \{$ Colorado, Nebraska, Missouri, Oklahoma $\}$

17. $C = \{1, 2, 3, 4, ..., 161\}$

18. $D = \{9, 10, 11, 12, ..., 96\}$

19. $A = \{x \mid x \in N \text{ and } 52 < x < 100\}$

20. $B = \{x \mid x \in N \text{ and } x > 42\}$

21. $C = \{x \mid x \in N \text{ and } x < 5\}$

22. $D = \{x \mid x \in N \text{ and } 27 \leq x \leq 51\}$

23. A is the set of capital letters in the English alphabet from E through M, inclusive.

24. B is the set of U.S. coins with a value of less than one dollar.

25. C is the set of the last three lowercase letters in the English alphabet.

26. D is the set of numbers greater than or equal to 3 and less than 9.

27. $A \cap B = \{1, 3, 5, 7\} \cap \{5, 7, 9, 10\} = \{5, 7\}$

28. $A \cup B' = \{1, 3, 5, 7\} \cup \{5, 7, 9, 10\}' = \{1, 3, 5, 7\} \cup \{1, 2, 3, 4, 6, 8\} = \{1, 2, 3, 4, 5, 6, 7, 8\}$

29. $A' \cap B = \{1, 3, 5, 7\}' \cap \{5, 7, 9, 10\} = \{2, 4, 6, 8, 9, 10\} \cap \{5, 7, 9, 10\} = \{9, 10\}$

30. $(A \cup B)' \cup C = (\{1, 3, 5, 7\} \cup \{5, 7, 9, 10\})' \cup \{1, 7, 10\} = \{1, 3, 5, 7, 9, 10\}' \cup \{1, 7, 10\}$

    $= \{2, 4, 6, 8\} \cup \{1, 7, 10\} = \{1, 2, 4, 6, 7, 8, 10\}$

31. $A - B = \{1, 3, 5, 7\} - \{5, 7, 9, 10\} = \{1, 3\}$

32. $A - C' = \{1, 3, 5, 7\} - \{1, 7, 10\}' = \{1, 3, 5, 7\} - \{2, 3, 4, 5, 6, 8, 9\} = \{1, 7\}$

33. $\{(1, 1), (1, 7), (1, 10), (3, 1), (3, 7), (3, 10), (5, 1), (5, 7), (5, 10), (7, 1), (7, 7), (7, 10)\}$

34. $\{(5, 1), (5, 3), (5, 5), (5, 7), (7, 1), (7, 3), (7, 5), (7, 7), (9, 1), (9, 3), (9, 5), (9, 7), (10, 1), (10, 3), (10, 5), (10, 7)\}$

35. $2^4 = 2 \times 2 \times 2 \times 2 = 16$

36. $2^4 - 1 = (2 \times 2 \times 2 \times 2) - 1 = 16 - 1 = 15$

37.

38. $A \cup B = \{a, c, d, f, g, i, k, l\}$

39. $A \cap B' = \{i, k\}$

40. $A \cup B \cup C = \{a, b, c, d, f, g, h, i, k, l\}$

41. $A \cap B \cap C = \{f\}$

42. $(A \cup B) \cap C = \{a, f, i\}$

43. $(A \cap B) \cup C = \{a, b, d, f, h, i, l\}$

44. $(A' \cup B')'$ $A \cap B$

Set	Regions	Set	Regions
A	I, II	A	I, II
A'	III, IV	B	II, III
B	II, III	$A \cap B$	II
B'	I, IV		
$A' \cup B'$	I, III, IV		
$(A' \cup B')'$	II		

Both statements are represented by the same region, II, of the Venn diagram. Therefore, $(A' \cup B')' = A \cap B$ for all sets A and B.

45. $(A \cup B') \cup (A \cup C')$ $A \cup (B \cap C)'$

Set	Regions	Set	Regions
A	I, II, IV, V	B	II, III, V, VI
B	II, III, V, VI	C	IV, V, VI, VII
B'	I, IV, VII, VIII	$B \cap C$	V, VI
$A \cup B'$	I, II, IV, V, VII, VIII	$(B \cap C)'$	I, II, III, IV, VII, VIII
C	IV, V, VI, VII	A	I, II, IV, V
C'	I, II, III, VIII	$A \cup (B \cap C)'$	I, II, III, IV, V, VII, VIII
$A \cup C'$	I, II, III, IV, V, VIII		
$(A \cup B') \cup (A \cup C')$	I, II, III, IV, V, VII, VIII		

Both statements are represented by the same regions, I, II, III, IV, V, VII, VIII, of the Venn diagram.

Therefore, $(A \cup B') \cup (A \cup C') = A \cup (B \cap C)'$ for all sets $A, B,$ and C.

46. II

47. III

48. I

49. IV

50. IV

51. II

52. The company paid $450 since the sum of the numbers in Regions I through IV is 450.

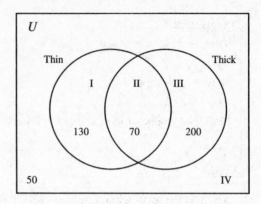

53. a) 315, the sum of the numbers in Regions I through VIII
    b) 10, Region III
    c) 30, Region II
    d) 110, the sum of the numbers in Regions III, VI, VII

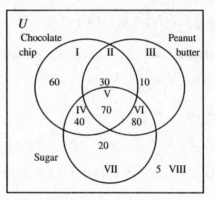

54. a) 38, Region I
    b) 298, the sum of the numbers in Regions I, III, VII
    c) 28, Region VI
    d) 236, the sum of the numbers in Regions I, IV, VII
    e) 106, the sum of the numbers in Regions II, IV, VI

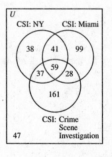

55. $\{2, 4, 6,\ 8,\ 10,\ ...,\ 2n,\ ...\}$
    $\downarrow \downarrow \downarrow \downarrow\ \downarrow\ \ \ \ \ \downarrow$
    $\{4, 6,\ 8, 10, 12,\ ...,\ 2n + 2,\ ...\}$

56. $\{3, 5, 7,\ 9,\ 11,\ ...,\ 2n + 1,\ ...\}$
    $\downarrow \downarrow \downarrow \downarrow\ \downarrow\ \ \ \ \ \downarrow$
    $\{5, 7, 9, 11, 13,\ ...,\ 2n + 3,\ ...\}$

57. $\{1, 2,\ 3,\ 4,\ 5,\ ...,\ \ \ n,\ ...\}$
    $\downarrow \downarrow \downarrow \downarrow \downarrow\ \ \ \ \ \downarrow$
    $\{5, 8,\ 11, 14, 17,\ ...,\ 3n + 2,\ ...\}$

58. $\{1, 2,\ 3,\ 4,\ \ 5,\ ...,\ \ \ n,\ ...\}$
    $\downarrow \downarrow \downarrow \downarrow\ \downarrow\ \ \ \ \ \downarrow$
    $\{4, 9, 14, 19, 24,\ ...,\ 5n - 1,\ ...\}$

Chapter Test

1. True

2. False; the sets do not contain exactly the same elements.

3. True

4. False; the second set has no subset that contains the element 7.

5. False; the empty set is a subset of every set.

6. False; the set has $2^4 = 2 \times 2 \times 2 \times 2 = 16$ subsets.

7. True

8. False; for any set A, $A \cup A' = U$, not $\{\ \}$.

9. True

10. $A = \{1, 2, 3, 4, 5, 6, 7, 8\}$

11. Set A is the set of natural numbers less than 9.

12. $A \cap B = \{3, 5, 7, 9\} \cap \{7, 9, 11, 13\} = \{7, 9\}$

13. $A \cup C' = \{3, 5, 7, 9\} \cup \{3, 11, 15\}' = \{3, 5, 7, 9\} \cup \{5, 7, 9, 13\} = \{3, 5, 7, 9, 13\}$

14. $A \cap (B \cap C)' = \{3, 5, 7, 9\} \cap (\{7, 9, 11, 13\} \cap \{3, 11, 15\})' = \{3, 5, 7, 9\} \cap \{11\}'$

    $= \{3, 5, 7, 9\} \cap \{3, 5, 7, 9, 13, 15\} = \{3, 5, 7, 9\}$, or A.

15. $n(A \cap B') = n(\{3, 5, 7, 9\} \cap \{7, 9, 11, 13\}') = n(\{3, 5, 7, 9\} \cap \{3, 5, 15\}) = n(\{3, 5\}) = 2$

16. $A - B = \{3, 5, 7, 9\} - \{7, 9, 11, 13\} = \{3, 5\}$

17. $A \times C = \{(3, 3), (3, 11), (3, 15), (5, 3), (5, 11), (5, 15), (7, 3), (7, 11), (7, 15), (9, 3), (9, 11), (9, 15)\}$

18.

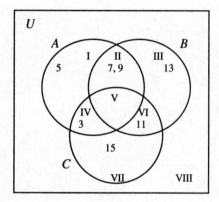

19. $A \cap (B \cup C')$ 　　　　　　　　　　　　　　　$(A \cap B) \cup (A \cap C')$

Set	Regions		Set	Regions
B	II, III, V, VI		A	I, II, IV, V
C	IV, V, VI, VII		B	II, III, V, VI
C'	I, II, III, VIII		$A \cap B$	II, V
$B \cup C'$	I, II, III, V, VI, VIII		C	IV, V, VI, VII
A	I, II, IV, V		C'	I, II, III, VIII
$A \cap (B \cup C')$	I, II, V		$A \cap C'$	I, II
			$(A \cap B) \cup (A \cap C')$	I, II, V

Both statements are represented by the same regions, I, II, V, of the Venn diagram.

Therefore, $A \cap (B \cup C') = (A \cap B) \cup (A \cap C')$ for all sets $A, B,$ and C.

20.

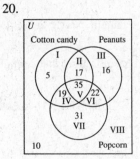

a) 52, the sum of the numbers in Regions I, III, VII

b) 10, Region VIII

c) 93, the sum of the numbers in Regions II, IV, V, VI

d) 17, Region II

e) 38, the sum of the numbers in Regions I, II, III

f) 31, Region VII

21. $\{7, 8,\ 9,\ 10, 11, \ldots, n + 6, \ldots\}$
     $\quad\downarrow\downarrow\ \downarrow\ \ \downarrow\ \ \ \downarrow\qquad\ \downarrow$
     $\{8, 9,\ 10, 11, 12, \ldots, n + 7, \ldots\}$

22. $\{1, 2, 3, 4,\ 5, \ldots,\ \ n, \ldots\}$
     $\quad\downarrow\downarrow\downarrow\downarrow\downarrow\qquad\ \downarrow$
     $\{1, 3, 5,\ 7, 9, \ldots, 2n - 1, \ldots\}$

Group Projects

1. a) A: Does not shed, B: Less than 16 in. tall, C: Good with kids

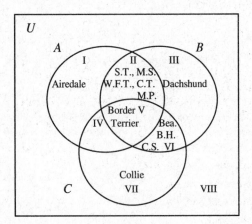

    b) Border terrier, Region V

2.   a) Animal   b) Chordate   c) Mammalia   d) Carnivore
     e) Felidae   f) Felis   g) Catus

3.

	First	Second	Third	Fourth	Fifth
a) Color	yellow	blue	red	ivory	green
b) Nationality	Norwegian	Afghan.	Senegalese	Spanish	Japanese
c) Food	apple	cheese	banana	peach	fish
d) Drink	vodka	tea	milk	whiskey	ale
e) Pet	fox	horse	snail	dog	zebra
f) Ale					

CHAPTER THREE

LOGIC

Exercise Set 3.1

1. a) A sentence that can be judged either true or false called a statement.
   b) A simple statement is a sentence that conveys one idea.
   c) Statements consisting of two or more simple statements are called compound statements.

3. *All*, *none* and *some* are quantifiers.

5. a) Some are   b) All are
   c) Some are not   d) None are

7. a) The *exclusive or* means that one or the other event can can occur, but not both. B) Yes; the *inclusive or* means that one or more events can occur simultaneously. c) The *inclusive or* is used in this chapter, unless otherwise stated.

9. compound; disjunction, $\vee$

11. compound; biconditional $\leftrightarrow$

13. compound; conjunction, $\wedge$

15. simple statement

17. compound; negation, $\sim$

19. compound; conjunction, $\wedge$

21. compound; negation, $\sim$

23. Some butterflies are not insects.

25. Some aldermen are running for mayor.

27. All turtles have claws.

29. Some bicycles have three wheels.

31. All pine trees produce pine cones.

33. No pedestrians are in the crosswalk.

35. $\sim p$

38. $\sim q \leftrightarrow \sim p$

41. $\sim p \wedge q$

44. $p \rightarrow \sim q$

47. Ken Jennings did not win more than $3 million.

49. Ken Jennings won 74 games of *Jeopardy!* and Ken Jennings won more than $3 million.

2. a) The negation of a true statement is always a <u>false</u> statement.
   b) The negation of a <u>false</u> statement is always a true statement.

4. Let *p*: The telephone has caller ID.
   The symbolic form is $\sim p$. The negation symbol, $\sim$, represents the word <u>not</u>.

6. a) $\rightarrow$ b) $\vee$ c) $\wedge$
   d) $\sim$ e) $\leftrightarrow$

8. When a compound statement contains more than one connective a comma can be used to indicate which simple statements are to be grouped together. When writing a statement symbolically, the simple statements on the same side of the comma are to be grouped together within parentheses.

10. compound; conditional, $\rightarrow$

12. compound; negation, $\sim$

14. compound; conjunction, $\wedge$

16. compound; biconditional, $\leftrightarrow$

18. compound; conditional, $\rightarrow$

20. compound; conjunction, $\wedge$

22. compound; conditional, $\rightarrow$

24. Some houses are not wired using parallel circuits.

26. No diet sodas contain saccharin.

28. Some teachers made the roster.

30. Some horses do not have manes.

32. Someone likes asparagus.

34. All dogs with long hair get cold.

37. $\sim q \vee \sim p$

40. $\sim q \wedge p$

43. $\sim q \leftrightarrow p$

46. $\sim (\sim q \rightarrow p)$

48. Ken Jennings did not win 74 games of *Jeopardy!*

50. Ken Jennings won more than $3 million or Ken Jennings won 74 games of *Jeopardy!*

51. If Ken Jennings did not win 74 games of *Jeopardy!* then Ken Jennings won more than $3 million.

52. Ken Jennings did not win 74 games of *Jeopardy!* if and only if Ken Jennings did not win $3 million.

53. Ken Jennings did not win 74 games of *Jeopardy!* or Ken Jennings did not win more than $3 million.

54. It is false that Ken Jennings won more than $3 million or Ken Jennings won 74 games of *Jeopardy!*

55. It is false that Ken Jennings won 74 games of *Jeopardy!* and Ken Jennings won more than $3 million.

56. Ken Jennings did not win 74 games of *Jeopardy!* and Ken Jennings did not win more than $3 million.

57. $(p \land \sim q) \lor r$

58. $(\sim p \land q) \land r$

59. $(p \land q) \lor r$

60. $(r \land q) \to p$

61. $p \to (q \lor \sim r)$

62. $(\sim p \leftrightarrow \sim q) \lor \sim r$

63. $(r \leftrightarrow q) \land p$

64. $\sim (r \to \sim q)$

65. $q \to (p \leftrightarrow r)$

66. $(r \lor \sim q) \leftrightarrow p$

67. The water is 70° or the sun is shining, and we do not go swimming.

68. The water is 70° and the sun is shining, or we go swimming.

69. The water is not 70°, and the sun is shining or we go swimming.

70. If the sun is shining then the water is 70°, or we go swimming.

71. If we do not go swimming, then the sun is shining and the water is 70°.

72. If the sun is shining and we go swimming, then the water is 70°.

73. If the sun is shining then we go swimming, and the water is 70°.

74. If the water is not 70°, then the sun is shining or we go swimming.

75. The sun is shinning if and only if the water is 70°, and we go swimming.

76. If the sun is shining, then the water is 70° if and only if we go swimming.

77. Not permissible. In the list of choices, the connective "or" is the exclusive or, thus one can order either the soup or the salad but not both items.

78. Permissible.

79. Not permissible. Potatoes and pasta cannot be ordered together.

80. Not permissible. Potatoes and pasta cannot be ordered together.

81. a) *w*: I bought the watch in Tijuana; *p*: I paid $100; $w \land \sim p$

    b) conjunction

82. a) *c*: conference is in Las Vegas; *s*: we can see Wayne Newton; *p*: we can play poker; $c \to (s \lor p)$

    b) conditional

83. a) *b*: below speed limit; *p*: pulled over; $\sim (b \to \sim p)$

    b) negation

84. a) *d*: dinner is ready; *e*: can eat; *r*: can go to restaurant; $(d \to e) \lor \sim r$

    b) disjunction

85. a) *f*: food has fiber; *v*: food has vitamins; *h*: be healthy; $(f \lor v) \to h$

    b) conditional

86. a) *c*: Corliss is teaching.; *f*: Faye in math lab. *w*: a weekend; $(c \to f) \leftrightarrow \sim w$

    b) biconditional

87. a) *c*: may take course; *f*: fail previous exam; *p*: passed placement test; $c \leftrightarrow (\sim f \lor p)$

    b) biconditional

88. a) *g*: car has gas; *b*: battery charged; *s*: car will start; $(g \land b) \to s$

    b) conditional

89. a) *c*: classroom is empty; *w*: is the weekend; *s*: is 7:00 a.m.; $(c \leftrightarrow w) \lor s$

    b) disjunction

90. This statement is a paradox.

91. Answers will vary.

92.

7	1	9	4	8	2	5	6	3
5	4	6	7	3	9	8	1	2
2	3	8	6	5	1	4	9	7
8	2	4	3	9	5	1	7	6
6	7	5	1	2	4	3	8	9
1	9	3	8	6	7	2	4	5
9	6	1	5	4	3	7	2	8
3	8	7	2	1	6	9	5	4
4	5	2	9	7	8	6	3	1

Exercise Set 3.2

1. a) $2^2 = 2 \times 2 = 4$ distinct cases

   b)

	p	q
Case 1:	T	T
Case 2	T	F
Case 3	F	T
Case 4	F	F

2. a) $2^3 = 2 \times 2 \times 2 = 8$ distinct cases

   b)

	p	q	r
case 1:	T	T	T
case 2:	T	T	F
case 3:	T	F	T
case 4:	T	F	F
case 5:	F	T	T
case 6:	F	T	F
case 7:	F	F	T
case 8:	F	F	F

3. a)

p	q	p	∧	q
T	T	T	T	T
T	F	T	F	F
F	T	F	F	T
F	F	F	F	F
		1	3	2

4. 2^5, or 32

   b) Only in case 1, when both simple statements are true.

   c)

p	q	p	∨	q
T	T	T	T	T
T	F	T	T	F
F	T	F	T	T
F	F	F	F	F
		1	3	2

   d) Only in Case 4, in which both simple statements are false.

5.

p	p	∧	~p
T	T	F	F
F	F	F	T
	1	3	2

6.

p	p	∨	~p
T	T	T	F
F	F	T	T
	1	3	2

7.

p	q	q	∨	~p
T	T	T	T	F
T	F	F	F	T
F	T	T	T	T
F	F	F	T	T
		1	3	2

8.

p	q	p	∧	~q
T	T	T	F	F
T	F	T	T	T
F	T	T	F	F
F	F	F	F	T
		1	3	2

9.

p	q	~p	∨	~q
T	T	F	F	F
T	F	F	T	T
F	T	T	T	F
F	F	T	T	T
		1	3	2

10.

p	q	~	(p	∨	~q	)
T	T	F	T	T	F	
T	F	F	T	T	T	
F	T	T	F	F	F	
F	F	F	F	T	T	
		4	1	3	2	

11.

p	q	~(p	∧	~ q)
T	T	T	T	F F
T	F	F	T	T T
F	T	T	F	F F
F	F	T	F	F T
		4	1	3 2

12.

p	q	~(~ p	∧	~ q)
T	T	T F	F	F
T	F	T F	F	T
F	T	T T	F	F
F	F	F T	T	T
		4 1	3	2

13.

p	q	r	~q	∨	(p	∧	r)
T	T	T	F	T	T	T	T
T	T	F	F	F	T	F	F
T	F	T	T	T	T	T	T
T	F	F	T	T	T	F	F
F	T	T	F	F	F	F	T
F	T	F	F	F	F	F	F
F	F	T	T	T	F	F	T
F	F	F	T	T	F	F	F
			1	5	2	4	3

14.

p	q	r	(p	∨	~ q)	∧	r
T	T	T	T	T	F	T	T
T	T	F	T	T	F	F	F
T	F	T	T	T	T	T	T
T	F	F	T	T	T	F	F
F	T	T	F	F	F	F	T
F	T	F	F	F	F	F	F
F	F	T	F	T	T	T	T
F	F	F	F	T	T	F	F
			1	3	2	5	4

15.

p	q	r	r	∨	(p	∧	~ q)
T	T	T	T	T	T	F	F
T	T	F	F	F	T	F	F
T	F	T	T	T	T	T	T
T	F	F	F	T	T	T	T
F	T	T	T	T	F	F	F
F	F	T	F	F	F	F	F
F	F	T	T	T	F	F	T
F	F	F	F	F	F	F	T
			1	5	2	4	3

16.

p	q	r	(r	∧	q)	∧	~ p
T	T	T	T			F	F
T	T	F	F			F	F
T	F	T	F			F	F
T	F	F	F			F	F
F	T	T	T			T	T
F	T	F	F			F	T
F	F	T	F			F	T
F	F	F	F			F	T
			1			3	2

17.

p	q	r	~ q ∧ (r ∨ ~ p)
T	T	T	F F T T F
T	T	F	F F F F F
T	F	T	T T T T F
T	F	F	T F F F F
F	T	T	F F T T T
F	T	F	F F F T T
F	F	T	T T T T T
F	F	F	T T F T T
			1 5 2 4 3

18.

p	q	r	~ p ∧ (q ∨ r)
T	T	T	F F T T T
T	T	F	F F T T F
T	F	T	F F F T T
T	F	F	F F F F F
F	T	T	T T T T T
F	T	F	T T T T F
F	F	T	T T F T T
F	F	F	T F F F F
			1 5 2 4 3

19.

p	q	r	(~ q ∧ r) ∨ p
T	T	T	F F T T T
T	T	F	F F F T T
T	F	T	T T T T T
T	F	F	T F F T T
F	T	T	F F T F F
F	T	F	F F F F F
F	F	T	T T T T F
F	F	F	T F F F F
			1 3 2 5 4

20.

p	q	r	~ r ∨ (~ p ∧ q)
T	T	T	F F F F T
T	T	F	T T F F T
T	F	T	F F F F F
T	F	F	T T F F F
F	T	T	F T T T T
F	T	F	T T T T T
F	F	T	F F T F F
F	F	F	T T T F F
			4 5 1 3 2

21. p: The cookies are warm.

   q: The milk is cold.

   In symbolic form the statement is p ∧ q.

p	q	p ∧ q
T	T	T
T	F	F
F	T	F
F	F	F
		1

22. p: The zoo is open.

   q: It is a nice day.

   In symbolic form the statement is p ∧ ~ q.

p	q	p	∧	~ q
T	T	T	F	F
T	F	T	T	T
F	T	F	F	F
F	F	F	F	T
		1	3	2

23. p: I have a new cell phone.

   q: I have a new battery.

   In symbolic form the statement is p ∧ ~ q.

p	q	p	∧	~ q
T	T	T	F	F
T	F	T	T	T
F	T	F	F	F
F	F	F	F	T
		1	3	2

24. p: Wanda Garner is the president.

   q: Judy Ackerman is the treasurer.

   In symbolic form the statement is ~ (p ∨ q).

p	q	~	(p	∨	q)
T	T	F	T	T	T
T	F	F	T	T	F
F	T	F	F	T	T
F	F	T	F	F	F
		4	1	3	2

25. p: Jasper Adams is the tutor.

q: Mark Russo is a secretary.

In symbolic form the statement is ~ (p ∧ q).

p	q	~ (p ∧ q)
T	T	F T T T
T	F	T T F F
F	T	T F F T
F	F	T F F F
		4 1 3 2

26. p: Mike made pizza.

q: Dennis made a chef salad.

r : Gil burned the lemon squares.

In symbolic form the statement is (p ∧ q) ∧ r.

p	q	r	(p ∧ q) ∧ r
T	T	T	T TT T T
T	T	F	T TT F F
T	F	T	T FF F T
T	F	F	T FF F F
F	T	T	F FT F T
F	T	F	F FT F F
F	F	T	F FF F T
F	F	F	F FF F F
			1 3 2 5 4

27. p: The copier is out of toner.

q: The lens is dirty.

r : The corona wires are broken.

The statement is p ∨ (q ∨ r).

p	q	r	p ∨ (q ∨ r)
T	T	T	T T T
T	T	F	T T T
T	F	T	T T T
T	F	F	T T F
F	T	T	F T T
F	T	F	F T T
F	F	T	F T T
F	F	F	F F F
			2 3 1

28. p: I am hungry.

q: I want to eat a healthy lunch.

r : I want to eat in a hurry.

The statement is p ∧ (q ∧ r).

p	q	r	p ∧ (q ∧ r)
T	T	T	T T T
T	T	F	T F F
T	F	T	T F F
T	F	F	T F F
F	T	T	F F T
F	T	F	F F F
F	F	T	F F F
F	F	F	F F F
			2 3 1

29. p: Congress must act on the bill.

q: The President signs the bill.

In symbolic form, the statement is

p ∧ (q ∨ ~ q).

p	q	p ∧(q∨ ~q)
T	T	TT TT F
T	F	TT FT T
F	T	FF TT F
F	F	FF FT T
		1 5 24 3

30. p: Gordon likes the PowerMac G4 Cube.

q: Gordon likes the iBook.

r : Gordon likes the Pentium IV.

In symbolic form, the statement is

(p ∧ q) ∧ ~ r.

p	q	r	(p ∧ q) ∧ ~ r
T	T	T	T TT F F
T	T	F	T TT T T
T	F	T	T FF F F
T	F	F	T FF F T
F	T	T	F FT F F
F	T	F	F FT F T
F	F	T	F FF F F
F	F	F	F FF F T
			1 3 2 5 4

31. (a) (~ p ∧ r) ∧ q
        (F ∧ T) ∧ F
          F ∧ F
            F
    Therefore the statement is false.
    (b) (~ p ∧ r) ∧ q
        (T ∧ T) ∧ T
          T   ∧ T
            T
    Therefore the statement is true.

33. (a) (~ p ∨ ~q) ∨ ~ r
        (F ∨ T) ∨ F
           T ∨ F
             T
    Therefore the statement is true.
    (b) (~ p ∨ ~q) ∨ ~ r
        (T ∨ F) ∨ F
           T ∨ F
             T
    Therefore the statement is true.

35. (a) (p ∨ ~q) ∧ ~ (p ∧ ~ r)
        (T ∨ T) ∧ ~ (T ∧ F)
           T   ∧   ~F
               T
    Therefore the statement is true.
    (b) (p ∨ ~q) ∧ ~(p ∧ ~ r)
        (F ∨ F) ∧ (F ∧ F)
           F   ∧   ~F
               F
    Therefore the statement is false.

37. (a) (~ r ∧ p) ∨ q
        (F ∧ T) ∨ F
           F   ∨ F
             F
    Therefore the statement is false.
    (b) (~ r ∧ p) ∨ q
        (F ∧ F) ∨ T
           F   ∨ T
             T
    Therefore the statement is true.

32. (a) ~ p ∨ (q ∨ r)
        F ∨ (F ∧ T)
        F ∨   F
            F
    Therefore the statement is false.
    (b) ~ p ∨ (q ∧ r)
        T ∨ (T ∧ T)
        T ∨   T
            T
    Therefore the statement is true.

34. (a) (~ q ∧ ~p) ∨ ~ r
        (T ∧ F) ∨ F
           F   ∨ F
             F
    Therefore the statement is false.
    (b) (~ q ∧ ~p) ∨ ~ r
        (F ∧ T) ∨ F
           F   ∨ F
             F
    Therefore the statement is false.

36. (a) (p ∧ ~q) ∨ r
        (T ∧ T) ∨ T
           T   ∨ T
             T
    Therefore the statement is true.
    (b) (p ∧ ~q) ∨ r
        (F ∧ F) ∨ T
           F   ∨ T
             T
    Therefore the statement is true.

38. (a) ~q ∨ (r ∧ p)
        T ∨ (T ∧ T)
        T ∨   T
            T
    Therefore the statement is true.
    (b) ~q ∨ (r ∧ p)
        F ∨ (T ∧ F)
        F ∨   F
            F
    Therefore the statement is false.

39. (a) $(\sim q \vee \sim p) \wedge r$

    $(T \vee F) \wedge T$

      $T \quad \wedge T$

        T

Therefore the statement is true.

(b) $(\sim q \vee \sim p) \wedge r$

    $(F \vee T) \wedge T$

      $T \quad \wedge T$

        T

Therefore the statement is true.

40. (a) $(\sim r \vee \sim p) \vee \sim q$

    $(F \vee F) \vee T$

      $F \quad \vee T$

        T

Therefore the statement is true.

(b) $(\sim r \vee \sim p) \vee \sim q$

    $(F \vee T) \vee F$

      $T \quad \vee F$

        T

Therefore the statement is true.

41. (a) $(\sim p \vee \sim q) \vee (\sim r \vee q)$

    $(F \vee T) \vee (F \vee F)$

      $T \quad \vee \quad F$

        T

Therefore the statement is true.

(b) $(\sim p \vee \sim q) \vee (\sim r \vee q)$

    $(T \vee F) \vee (F \vee T)$

      $T \quad \vee \quad T$

        T

Therefore the statement is true.

42. (a) $(\sim r \wedge \sim q) \wedge (\sim r \vee \sim p)$

    $(F \wedge T) \wedge (F \vee F)$

      $F \quad \wedge \quad F$

        F

Therefore the statement is false.

(b) $(\sim r \wedge \sim q) \wedge (\sim r \vee \sim p)$

    $(F \wedge F) \wedge (F \vee T)$

      $F \quad \wedge \quad T$

        F

Therefore the statement is false.

43. $18 \div 3 = 9$ or $56 \div 8 = 7$

    $F \quad \vee \quad T$

       T

Therefore the statement is true.

44. $17 \geq 17$ and $-3 > -2$

    $T \quad \wedge \quad F$

      F

Therefore the statement is false.

45. E: Virginia borders the Atlantic Ocean.

    C: California borders the Indian Ocean.

    $E \quad \vee \quad C$

    $T \quad \vee \quad F$

      T

Therefore the statement is true.

46. H: Hawaii is the 50th state.

    A: Alaska lies on the equator.

    B: Birmingham is the capital of Missouri.

    $(H \vee A) \wedge B$

    $(T \vee F) \wedge F$

      $T \quad \wedge F$

Therefore the statement is false.

47. S: Steven Spielberg is a movie director.

    H: Tom Hanks is an actor.

    M: John Madden is a sports announcer.

    $(S \wedge H) \wedge \sim M$

    $(T \wedge T) \wedge \quad F$

      $T \quad \wedge F$

        F

Therefore the statement is false.

48. Q: Quebec is in Texas.

    T: Toronto is in California.

    C: Cedar Rapids is in Iowa.

    $(Q \vee T) \wedge C$

    $(F \vee F) \wedge T$

      $F \quad \wedge T$

        F

Therefore the statement is false.

49. IQ: Iraq is in Africa.
    IN: Iran is in South America.
    S: Syria is in the Middle East.

    (IQ ∨ IN) ∧ S
    (F ∨ F) ∧ T
        F   ∧ T
              F

    Therefore the statement is false.

50. H: Holstein is a breed of cattle.
    C: Collie is a breed of dog.
    B: Beagle is a breed of cat.

    (H ∧ C) ∨ ~B
    (T ∧ T) ∨ T
        T   ∨ T
            T

    Therefore the statement is true.

51. p: The United States had the lowest per capita CO_2 emissions.
    q: The United States had the lowest per capita CO_2 emissions.

    p ∧ q
    F ∧ F
    False

52. p: The United States had more CO_2 emissions than China and Russia had combined.
    q: The United States had more CO_2 emissions than Russia, Japan and India had combined.

    p ∨ q
    T ∨ F
    True

53. p: India had lower per capita CO_2 emissions than Japan.
    q: China had lower per capita CO_2 emissions than India.

    p ∨ q
    T ∨ F
    True

54. p: Russia had lower per capita CO_2 emissions than the United States.
    q: Russia had higher per capita CO_2 emissions than the Japan.

    p ∧ q
    T ∧ T
    True

55. p: 30% of Americans get 6 hours of sleep.
    q: 9% get 5 hours of sleep.

    ~ (p ∧ q)
    ~ (F ∧ T)
       ~F
      True

56. p: 25% of Americans get 6 hours of sleep.
    q: 30% of Americans get 7 hours of sleep.
    r: 9% of Americans get 5 hours of sleep.

    p ∧ (q ∨ ~ r)
    T ∧ (T ∨ ~ T)
    T ∧ (T ∨ F)
    T ∧   T
      True

57. p: 13% of Americans get ≤ 5 hrs. of sleep.
    q: 32% of Americans get ≥ 6 hrs. of sleep.
    r: 30% of Americans get ≥ 8 hrs. of sleep.

    (p ∨ q) ∧ r
    (T ∨ F) ∧ F
       T   ∧ F
      False

58. p: > 50% of Americans get ≤ 7 hrs. of sleep.
    q: > 25% of Americans get ≤ 6 hrs. of sleep.

    p ∧ q)
    T ∧ T
    True

59. p ∧ ~q; true when p is true and q is false.

60. ~p ∧ q; true when p is false and q is true.

61. p ∨ ~q; true when p is true or when p and q are both false.

62. ~p ∨ ~q; true except when p and q are both true.

63. (r ∨ q) ∧ p; true when p is true and when either r or q is true.

64. (p ∧ q) ∨ r; true except when p, q, r have truth values TFF, FTF, or FFF.

65. q ∨ (p ∧ ~r); true except when p, q, r have truth values TFF, FTF, or FFF.

66. ~p ∧ (~r ∧ q); true when p is false, r is false and q is true.

67. (a) Mr. Duncan qualifies for the loan.
       Mrs. Tuttle qualifies for the loan.
    (b) The Rusineks do not qualify
       because their gross income is too low.

68. (a) The Argentos qualify for the loan.
    (b) Ms. McVey does not qualify because
       her gross income is too low. Ms. Fox
       and Mr. Siewert do not qualify
       because their assets are too low.

69. (a) Wing Park qualifies for the special
       fare.
    (b) The other 4 do not qualify:
       Gina V. returns after 04/01;
       Kara S. returns on Monday;
       Christos S. does not stay
       at least one Saturday; and
       Alex C. returns on Monday.

70.

p	q	r	~	[(~	(p ∨ q))	∨	(q ∧ r)]
T	T	T	F	F	T	T	T
T	T	F	T	F	T	F	F
T	F	T	T	F	T	F	F
T	F	F	T	F	T	F	F
F	T	T	F	F	T	T	T
F	T	F	T	F	T	F	F
F	F	T	F	T	F	T	F
F	F	F	F	T	F	T	F
			5	2	1	4	3

71.

p	q	r	[(q ∧ ~ r)	∧	(~ p ∨ ~ q)]	∨	(p ∨ ~ r)
T	T	T	F	F	F	T	T
T	T	F	T	F	F	T	T
T	F	T	F	F	T	T	T
T	F	F	F	F	T	T	T
F	T	T	F	F	T	F	F
F	T	F	T	T	T	T	T
F	F	T	F	F	T	F	F
F	F	F	F	F	T	T	T
			1	3	2	5	4

72. (a) $2^4 = 16$ distinct cases

72. (b)

p	q	r	s
T	T	T	T
T	T	T	F
T	T	F	T
T	T	F	F
T	F	T	T
T	F	T	F
T	F	F	T
T	F	F	F
F	T	T	T
F	T	T	F
F	T	F	T
F	T	F	F
F	F	T	T
F	F	T	F
F	F	F	T
F	F	F	F

72. (c)

p	q	r	s	(q ∧ p)	∨	(~r ∧ s)
T	T	T	T	T	T	F
T	T	T	F	T	T	F
T	T	F	T	T	T	T
T	T	F	F	T	T	F
T	F	T	T	F	F	F
T	F	T	F	F	F	F
T	F	F	T	F	T	T
T	F	F	F	F	F	F
F	T	T	T	F	F	F
F	T	T	F	F	F	F
F	T	F	T	F	T	T
F	T	F	F	F	F	F
F	F	T	T	F	F	F
F	F	T	F	F	F	F
F	F	F	T	F	T	T
F	F	F	F	F	F	F

72. (d)

p	q	r	s	(~r ∧ ~s)∧(~p ∨ q)		
T	T	T	T	F	F	T
T	T	T	F	F	F	T
T	T	F	T	F	F	T
T	T	F	F	T	T	T
T	F	T	T	F	F	F
T	F	T	F	F	F	F
T	F	F	T	F	F	F
T	F	F	F	T	F	F
F	T	T	T	F	F	T
F	T	T	F	F	F	T
F	T	F	T	F	F	T
F	T	F	F	T	T	T
F	F	T	T	F	F	T
F	F	T	F	F	F	T
F	F	F	T	F	F	T
F	F	F	F	T	T	T

73. Yes

p	q	r	(p ∧~q) ∨ r			(q ∧ ~r) ∨ p		
T	T	T	F	T	T	F	T	T
T	T	F	F	F	F	T	T	T
T	F	T	T	T	T	F	T	T
T	F	F	T	T	F	F	T	T
F	T	T	F	T	T	F	F	F
F	T	F	F	F	F	T	T	F
F	F	T	F	T	T	F	F	F
F	F	F	F	F	F	F	F	F

74. Answers will vary.

Exercise Set 3.3

1. a)

p	q	p	→	q
T	T	T	T	T
T	F	T	F	F
F	T	F	T	T
F	F	F	T	F
		1	3	2

1. c)

p	q	p ↔ q		
T	T	T	T	T
T	F	T	F	F
F	T	F	F	T
F	F	F	T	F
		1	3	2

b) The conditional statement is false only in the case when antecedent is true and the consequent is false, otherwise it is true.

d) The biconditional statement is true when the statements to the left and right of the biconditional symbol match, otherwise, false.

2. a) The antecedent
   b) The consequent

3. a) Substitute the truth values for the simple statement. Then evaluate the compound
   statement for that specific case.

   b) $[(p \leftrightarrow q) \vee (\sim r \rightarrow q)] \rightarrow \sim r$

   $[(T \leftrightarrow T) \vee (\sim T \rightarrow T)] \rightarrow \sim T$

   $[\quad T \quad \vee (\sim T \rightarrow T)] \rightarrow T$

   $[\quad T \quad \vee \quad T \quad] \rightarrow T$

   $\qquad\qquad T \qquad\qquad \rightarrow T$

   $\qquad\qquad\qquad T$

   In this specific case the statement is true.

4. A tautology is a compound statement that is true in every case.

5. A self-contradiction is a compound statement that is false in every case.

6. An implication is a <u>conditional</u> statement that is a tautology.

7.

p	q	$\sim p \rightarrow q$		
T	T	F	T	T
T	F	F	T	F
F	T	T	T	T
F	F	T	F	F
		1	3	2

8.

p	q	$\sim p \rightarrow \sim q$		
T	T	F	T	F
T	F	F	T	T
F	T	T	F	F
F	F	T	T	T
		1	3	2

9.

p	q	$\sim (p \rightarrow \sim q)$	
T	T	T	F
T	F	F	T
F	T	F	T
F	F	F	T
		2	1

10.

p	q	$\sim (\sim p \leftrightarrow q)$	
T	T	T	F
T	F	F	T
F	T	F	T
F	F	T	F
		2	1

11.

p	q	$\sim q$	$\leftrightarrow$	p
T	T	F	F	T
T	F	T	T	T
F	T	F	T	F
F	F	T	F	F
		1	3	2

12.

p	q	(p	$\leftrightarrow$	q)	$\rightarrow$	p
T	T		T		T	T
T	F		F		T	T
F	T		F		T	F
F	F		T		F	F
			1		3	2

13.

p	q	p	$\leftrightarrow$	(q $\vee$ p)
T	T	T	T	T
T	F	T	T	T
F	T	F	F	T
F	F	F	T	F
		1	3	2

14.

p	q	$(\sim q \wedge p) \rightarrow \sim q$				
T	T	F	F T	T	F	
T	F	T	T T	T	T	
F	T	F	F F	T	F	
F	F	T	F F	T	T	
		1	3 2	5	4	

15.

p	q	$q \rightarrow (p \rightarrow \sim q)$				
T	T	T F	T F	F
T	F	F T	T T	T
F	T	T T	F T	F
F	F	F T	F T	T
		4 5	1 3	2

16.

p	q	$(p \vee q)$	$\leftrightarrow$	$(p \wedge q)$
T	T	T	T	T
T	F	T	F	F
F	T	T	F	F
F	F	F	T	F
		1	3	2

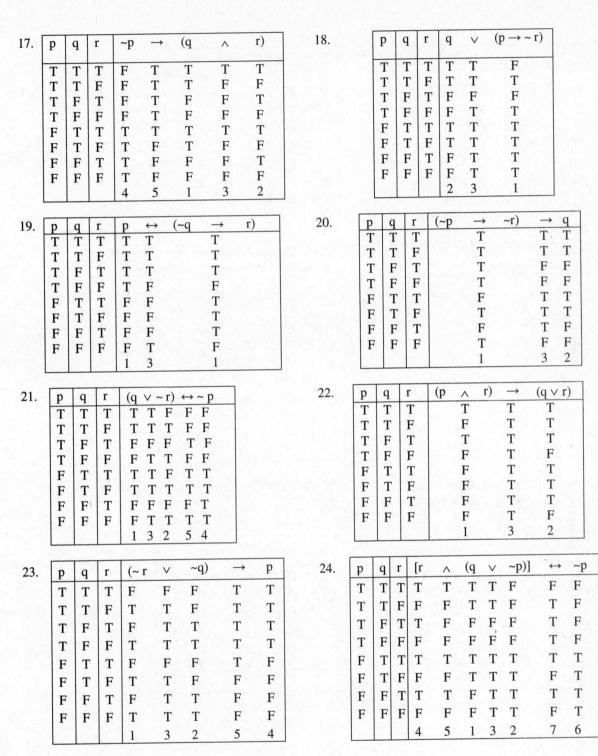

17.

p	q	r	~p	→	(q	∧	r)
T	T	T	F	T	T	T	T
T	T	F	F	T	T	F	F
T	F	T	F	T	F	F	T
T	F	F	F	T	F	F	F
F	T	T	T	T	T	T	T
F	T	F	T	F	T	F	F
F	F	T	T	F	F	F	T
F	F	F	T	F	F	F	F
			4	5	1	3	2

18.

p	q	r	q	∨	(p	→	~r)
T	T	T	T	T			F
T	T	F	T	T			T
T	F	T	F	F			F
T	F	F	F	T			T
F	T	T	T	T			T
F	T	F	T	T			T
F	F	T	F	T			T
F	F	F	F	T			T
			2	3			1

19.

p	q	r	p	↔	(~q	→	r)
T	T	T	T	T			T
T	T	F	T	T			T
T	F	T	T	T			T
T	F	F	T	F			F
F	T	T	F	F			T
F	T	F	F	F			T
F	F	T	F	F			T
F	F	F	F	T			F
			1	3			1

20.

p	q	r	(~p	→	~r)	→	q
T	T	T		T		T	T
T	T	F		T		T	T
T	F	T		T		F	F
T	F	F		T		F	F
F	T	T		F		T	T
F	T	F		T		T	T
F	F	T		F		T	T
F	F	F		T		F	F
				1		3	2

21.

p	q	r	(q	∨	~r)	↔	~p
T	T	T	T	T	F	F	F
T	T	F	T	T	T	F	F
T	F	T	F	F	F	T	F
T	F	F	F	T	T	F	F
F	T	T	T	T	F	T	T
F	T	F	T	T	T	T	T
F	F	T	F	F	F	F	T
F	F	F	F	T	T	T	T
			1	3	2	5	4

22.

p	q	r	(p	∧	r)	→	(q	∨	r)
T	T	T		T		T		T	
T	T	F		F		T		T	
T	F	T		T		T		T	
T	F	F		F		T		F	
F	T	T		F		T		T	
F	T	F		F		T		T	
F	F	T		F		T		T	
F	F	F		F		T		F	
				1		3		2	

23.

p	q	r	(~r	∨	~q)	→	p
T	T	T	F	F	F	T	T
T	T	F	T	T	F	T	T
T	F	T	F	T	T	T	T
T	F	F	T	T	T	T	T
F	T	T	F	F	F	T	F
F	T	F	T	T	F	F	F
F	F	T	F	T	T	F	F
F	F	F	T	T	T	F	F
			1	3	2	5	4

24.

p	q	r	[r	∧	(q	∨	~p)]	↔	~p
T	T	T	T	T	T	T	F	F	F
T	T	F	F	F	T	T	F	T	F
T	F	T	T	F	F	F	F	T	F
T	F	F	F	F	F	F	F	T	F
F	T	T	T	T	T	T	T	T	T
F	T	F	F	F	T	T	T	F	T
F	F	T	T	T	F	T	T	T	T
F	F	F	F	F	F	T	T	F	T
			4	5	1	3	2	7	6

25.

p	q	r	(p	→	q)	↔	(~q	→	~r)
T	T	T		T		T	F	T	F
T	T	F		T		T	F	T	T
T	F	T		F		T	T	F	F
T	F	F		F		F	T	T	T
F	T	T		T		T	F	T	F
F	T	F		T		T	F	T	T
F	F	T		T		F	T	F	F
F	F	F		T		T	T	T	T
				1		5	2	4	3

26.

p	q	r	(~p	↔	~q)	→	(~q	↔	r)
T	T	T	F	T	F	F	F	F	T
T	T	F	F	T	F	T	F	T	F
T	F	T	F	F	T	T	T	T	T
T	F	F	F	F	T	T	T	F	F
F	T	T	T	F	F	T	F	F	T
F	T	F	T	F	F	T	F	T	F
F	F	T	T	T	T	T	T	T	T
F	F	F	T	T	T	F	T	F	F
			1	3	2	7	4	6	5

27. p: I take niacin; q: I will stay healthy;
r: I will have lower cholesterol

p	q	r	p	→	(q	∧	r)
T	T	T	T	T			T
T	T	F	T	F			F
T	F	T	T	F			F
T	F	F	T	F			F
F	T	T	F	T			T
F	T	F	F	T			F
F	F	T	F	T			F
F	F	F	F	T			F
			1	3			2

28. p: the goalie will make the save; q: the stopper is in position; r: the forward can handle the ball

p	q	r	(p	↔	q)	∨	~r
T	T	T		T		T	F
T	T	F		T		T	T
T	F	T		F		F	F
T	F	F		F		T	T
F	T	T		F		F	F
F	T	F		F		T	T
F	F	T		T		T	F
F	F	F		T		T	T
				1		3	2

29. p: election was fair; q: polling station stayed open until 8 P.M.; r: we will request a recount

p	q	r	(p	↔	q)	∨	r
T	T	T		T		T	T
T	T	F		T		T	F
T	F	T		F		T	T
T	F	F		F		F	F
F	T	T		F		T	T
F	T	F		F		F	F
F	F	T		T		T	T
F	F	F		T		T	F
				1		3	2

30. p: the dam holds; q: we can go fishing; r: the pole is broken

p	q	r	(p	→	q)	↔	~r
T	T	T		T		F	F
T	T	F		T		T	T
T	F	T		F		T	F
T	F	F		F		F	T
F	T	T		T		F	F
F	T	F		T		T	T
F	F	T		T		F	F
F	F	F		T		T	T
				1		3	2

31. p: Mary Andrews sends me an e-mail;
q: we can call her; r: we can write to Mom

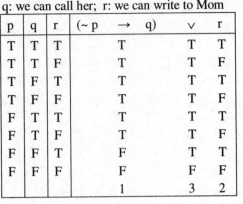

p	q	r	(~p	→	q)	∨	r
T	T	T		T		T	T
T	T	F		T		T	F
T	F	T		T		T	T
T	F	F		T		T	F
F	T	T		T		T	T
F	T	F		T		T	F
F	F	T		F		T	T
F	F	F		F		F	F
				1		3	2

32. p: Eileen Jones went to lunch; q: she can take a message; r: we will have to go home

p	q	r	~	[p	→	(~q	∧	r)]
T	T	T	T	T	F		F	
T	T	F	T	T	F		F	
T	F	T	F	T	T		T	
T	F	F	T	T	F		F	
F	T	T	F	F	T		F	
F	T	F	F	F	T		F	
F	F	T	F	F	T		T	
F	F	F	T	F	T		F	
			4	1	3		2	

33.

p	p	→	~p
T	T	F	F
F	F	T	T
	1	3	2

neither

34.

p	q	p ∧ ~ q	↔	~ p
T	T	F	T	F
T	F	T	F	F
F	T	F	F	T
F	F	F	F	T
		1	3	2

neither

35.

p	q	p	∧	(q ∧ ~ p)
T	T	T	F	F
T	F	T	F	F
F	T	F	F	T
F	F	F	F	F
		1	3	2

self-contradiction

36.

p	q	(p ∧ ~ q)	→	q
T	T	F	T	T
T	F	T	F	F
F	T	F	T	T
F	F	F	T	F
		1	3	2

neither

37.

p	q	(~ q	→	p)	∨	~ q
T	T		T		T	F
T	F		T		T	T
F	T		T		T	F
F	F		F		T	T
			1		3	2

tautology

38.

p	q	r	[(p → q)	∨	r]	↔	[(p ∧ q)	→	r]
T	T	T	T	T	T	T	T	T	T
T	T	F	T	T	F	F	T	F	F
T	F	T	F	T	T	T	F	T	T
T	F	F	F	F	F	T	F	T	F
F	T	T	T	T	T	T	F	T	T
F	T	F	T	T	F	T	F	T	F
F	F	T	T	T	T	T	F	T	T
F	F	F	T	T	F	T	F	T	F
			1	3	2	7	4	6	5

neither

39.

p	q	~p	→	(p ∨ q)
T	T	F	T	T
T	F	F	T	T
F	T	T	T	T
F	F	T	F	F
		1	3	2

not an implication

40.

p	q	(p ∧ q)	→	(~ p ∨ q)
T	T	T	T	T
T	F	F	T	F
F	T	F	T	T
F	F	F	T	T
		1	3	2

an implication

41.

p	q	(q ∧ p)	→	(p ∧ q)
T	T	T	T	T
T	F	F	T	F
F	T	F	T	F
F	F	F	T	F
		1	3	2

an implication

42.

p	q	r	(p ∨ q)	→	(p ∨ ~ r)
T	T	T	T	T	T
T	T	F	T	T	T
T	F	T	T	T	T
T	F	F	T	T	T
F	T	T	T	F	F
F	T	F	T	T	T
F	F	T	F	T	F
F	F	F	F	T	T
			1	3	2

not an implication

43.

p	q	[(p → q)	∧	(q → p)]	→	(p ↔ q)
T	T	T	T	T	T	T
T	F	F	F	T	T	F
T	T	T	F	F	T	F
T	F	T	T	T	T	T
		1	3	2	5	4

an implication

44.

p	q	r	[(p ∨ q)	∧	r]	→	(p ∨ q)
T	T	T	T	T	T	T	T
T	T	F	T	F	F	T	T
T	F	T	T	F	T	T	T
T	F	F	T	F	F	T	T
F	T	T	T	T	T	T	T
F	T	F	T	F	F	T	T
F	F	T	F	F	T	T	F
F	F	F	F	F	F	T	F
			1	3	2	5	4

an implication

45. $\sim p \to (q \to r)$
$F \to (F \to T)$
$T \to \quad T$
$\quad T$

46. $(p \vee q) \to \sim r$
$T \quad \to F$
$\quad F$

47. $q \leftrightarrow (\sim p \vee r)$
$F \leftrightarrow \quad T$
$\quad F$

48. $r \to (\sim p \leftrightarrow \sim q)$
$T \to (\ F \leftrightarrow T)$
$T \to \quad F$
$\quad F$

49. $(\sim p \wedge \sim q) \vee \sim r$
$(F \wedge \ T) \vee F$
$\quad F \quad \vee F$
$\quad F$

50. $\sim [\ p \to (q \wedge r)]$
$\sim [T \to (F \wedge T)]$
$\sim [T \to \quad F$
$\quad \sim F$
$\quad T$

51. $(p \wedge r) \leftrightarrow (p \vee \sim q)$
$(T \wedge T) \leftrightarrow (T \vee T)$
$\quad T \quad \leftrightarrow \quad T$
$\quad T$

52. $(\sim p \vee q) \to \sim r$
$(F \vee F) \to F$
$\quad F \quad \to F$
$\quad T$

53. $(\sim p \leftrightarrow r) \vee (\sim q \leftrightarrow r)$
$(F \leftrightarrow T) \vee (T \leftrightarrow T)$
$\quad T \quad \vee \quad T$
$\quad T$

54. $(r \to \sim p) \wedge (q \ \to \sim r)$
$(T \to \ F) \wedge (F \to F)$
$\quad F \quad \wedge \quad T$
$\quad F$

55. $\sim [(p \vee q) \leftrightarrow (p \to \sim r)]$
$\sim [(T \vee F) \leftrightarrow (T \to F)]$
$\quad \sim [T \quad \leftrightarrow \quad F]$
$\quad \sim F$
$\quad T$

56. $[(\sim r \to \sim q) \vee (p \wedge \sim r)] \to q$
$[(F \to \ T) \vee (T \wedge \ F)] \to F$
$[T \quad \vee \quad F] \quad \to F$
$\quad T \to F$
$\quad F$

57. If $2 + 7 = 9$, then $15 - 3 = 12$.
$\quad T \to T$
$\quad T$

58. If $\frac{3}{4} < 1$ and $\frac{7}{8} > 1$, then $\frac{15}{16} < 1$.
$\quad (T \wedge F) \to T$
$\quad F \ \to T$
$\quad T$

59. A cat has whiskers or a fish can swim, and a chicken lays eggs.
$\quad (T \vee T) \wedge T$
$\quad T \ \wedge T$
$\quad T$

60. Tallahassee is in Florida and Atlanta is in Georgia, or Chicago is in Mississippi.
$\quad (T \wedge T) \vee F$
$\quad T \ \vee F$
$\quad T$

61. Apple makes computers, if and only if Nike makes sports shoes or Rolex makes watches.
$\quad T \leftrightarrow (T \vee T)$
$\quad T \leftrightarrow \quad T$
$\quad T$

62. Spike Lee is a movie director, or if Halle Berry is a schoolteacher, then George Clooney is a circus clown.
$\quad T \vee (F \to F)$
$\quad T \vee \quad T$
$\quad T$

63. Valentine's Day is in February or President's Day is in March, and Thanksgiving Day is in November.
$(T \lor F) \land T$
    $T \land T$
       T

64. Honda makes automobiles or Honda makes motorcycles, if and only if Toyota makes cereal.
$(T \lor T) \leftrightarrow F$
    $T \quad \leftrightarrow F$
       F

65. Io has a diameter of 1000–3161 miles, or Thebe may have water, and Io may have atmosphere.
$(T \lor F) \land T$
    $T \land T$
       T

66. Titan may have water and Titan may have atmosphere, if and only if Janus may have water.
$(T \land T) \leftrightarrow F$
    $T \quad \leftrightarrow F$
       F

67. Phoebe has a larger diameter than Rhea if and only if Callisto may have water ice, and Calypso has a diameter of 6–49 miles.
$(F \leftrightarrow T) \land T$
    $F \quad \land T$
       F

68. If Jupiter has 16 moons or Saturn does not have 18 moons, then Saturn has 7 moons that may have water ice.
$(T \lor F) \to T$
    $T \quad \to T$
       T

69. The most common cosmetic surgery procedure for females is liposuction or the most common procedure for males is eyelid surger, and 20% of male cosmetic surgery is for nose reshaping.
$(T \lor F) \land F$
    $T \quad \land F$
       F

70. 7% of female cosmetic surgeries are for face-lifts and 10% of male surgeries are for face-lifts, if and only if males have a higher percent of eyelid surgeries than females.
$(T \land F) \leftrightarrow F$
    $F \quad \leftrightarrow F$
       T

For 71–76, *p*: Muhundan spoke at the teachers' conference.
    q: Muhundan received the outstanding teacher award
    Assume *p* and *q* are true.

71. $q \to p$
    $T \to T$
      T

72. $p \to \sim q$
    $T \to F$
      F

73. $\sim q \to p$
    $F \to T$
      T

74. $\sim p \leftrightarrow q$
    $F \leftrightarrow T$
      F

75. $q \to p$
    $T \to T$
      T

76. $\sim q \to \sim p$
    $F \to F$
      T

77. No, the statement only states what will occur if your sister gets straight A's. If your sister does not get straight A's, your parents may still get her a computer.

78. No, the statement only states what will occur if the interview goes well. If the interview does not go well, you may or may not get the job.

79.

p	q	r	[p ∨	(q	→	~ r)]	↔	(p ∧ ~ q)
T	T	T	T		F	F	F	F
T	T	F	T		T	T	F	F
T	F	T	T		T	F	T	T
T	F	F	T		T	T	T	T
F	T	T	F		F	F	T	F
F	T	F	T		T	T	F	F
F	F	T	T		T	F	F	F
F	F	F	T		T	T	F	F
			3	2	1		5	4

80.

p	q	r	[(r → ~q)	→	~p]	∨	(q ↔ ~ r)
T	T	T	F	T	F	T	F
T	T	F	T	F	F	T	T
T	F	T	T	F	F	T	T
T	F	F	T	F	F	F	F
F	T	T	F	T	T	T	F
F	T	F	T	T	T	T	T
F	F	T	T	T	T	T	T
F	F	F	T	T	T	T	F
			1	3	2	5	4

81. The statement may be expressed as $(p \to q) \lor (\sim p \to q)$, where p: It is a head and q: I win.

p	q	(p → q)	∨	(~ p → q)
T	T	T	T	T
T	F	F	T	T
F	T	T	T	T
F	F	F	T	F
		1	3	2

The statement is a tautology.

82.

p	q	r	s	(a) (p ∨ q)	→	(r ∧ s)	(b) (q → ~p)	∨	(r ↔ s)
T	T	T	T	T	T	T	F	T	T
T	T	T	F	T	F	F	F	F	F
T	T	F	T	T	F	F	F	F	F
T	T	F	F	T	F	F	F	T	T
T	F	T	T	T	T	T	T	T	T
T	F	T	F	T	F	F	T	T	F
T	F	F	T	T	F	F	T	T	F
T	F	F	F	T	F	F	T	T	T
F	T	T	T	T	T	T	T	T	T
F	T	T	F	T	F	F	T	T	F
F	T	F	T	T	F	F	T	T	F
F	T	F	F	T	F	F	T	T	T
F	F	T	T	F	T	T	T	T	T
F	F	T	F	F	T	F	T	T	F
F	F	F	T	F	T	F	T	T	F
F	F	F	F	F	T	F	T	T	T
				1	3	2	1	3	2

83.

Tiger	Boots	Sam	Sue
Blue	Yellow	Red	Green
Nine Lives	Whiskas	Friskies	Meow Mix

84. The birth order is Mary, Annie, Katie; Katie and Mary are telling the truth.

Exercise Set 3.4

1. a) Two statements are equivalent if both statements have exactly the same truth values in the answer column of the truth table.

1. b) Construct a truth table for each statement and then compare the columns. If they are identical, then the statements are equivalent. If the answer columns are not identical, then the statements are not equivalent.

2. The two statements must be equivalent. A biconditional is a tautology only when the statements on each side of the biconditional are equivalent.

3. $\sim (p \wedge q) \Leftrightarrow \sim p \vee \sim q$
   $\sim (p \vee q) \Leftrightarrow \sim p \wedge \sim q$

4. a) $q \to p$ b) $\sim p \to \sim q$ c) $\sim q \to \sim p$

5. converse $\Leftrightarrow$ inverse;   conditional $\Leftrightarrow$ contrapositive

6. $p \to q$ is equivalent to $\sim p \wedge q$.

7. If $p \to q$ is equivalent to $\sim p \vee q$, then $\sim(p \to q)$ is equivalent to $\sim(\sim p \vee q)$, which by De Morgan's second law is equivalent to $[\sim(\sim p)] \wedge \sim q$, which is equivalent to $p \wedge \sim q$.

8. T $p \leftrightarrow q \Leftrightarrow (p \to q) \wedge (q \to p)$

9. $\sim(p \wedge q) \Leftrightarrow \sim p \vee q$ (by law 1) and this is not equivalent to $\sim p \wedge q$.

10. $\sim(p \vee \sim q) \Leftrightarrow \sim p \wedge \sim(\sim q)$ (by law 2) and this is equivalent to $\sim p \wedge q$.

11. $\sim(p \wedge q) \Leftrightarrow \sim p \vee \sim q$ by law 1 and $\sim(q \vee \sim p) \Leftrightarrow \sim q \wedge \sim(\sim p) \Leftrightarrow \sim q \wedge p$ by law 2. $\sim p \vee \sim q$ is not equivalent to $\sim q \wedge p$, since if p and q are both false, the first statement is true and the second is false.

12. Using law 1 on the statement $\sim(p \wedge q)$, we get $\sim(p \wedge q) \Leftrightarrow \sim p \vee \sim q$, so the two given statements are equivalent.

13. Equivalent by law 2.

14. $\sim(p \wedge q) \Leftrightarrow \sim p \vee \sim q$ by law 1 and this is not equivalent to $\sim p \wedge \sim q$, since if p is true and q is false, the first statement is true but the second is false.

15. Yes, equivalent

16. Yes,
    $q \to \sim(p \wedge \sim r) \leftrightarrow q \to \sim p \vee \sim(\sim r) \leftrightarrow q \to \sim p \vee r$

17. Yes, $\sim (p \to \sim q) \Leftrightarrow \sim (\sim p \vee \sim q) \Leftrightarrow p \wedge q$

18. Yes, $\sim (\sim p \to q) \Leftrightarrow \sim (p \vee q) \Leftrightarrow \sim p \wedge \sim q$

19.

p	q	p → q	~ p ∨ q	
T	T	T	F T	T
T	F	F	F F	F
F	T	T	T T	T
F	F	T	T T	F
		1	1 3	2

The statements are equivalent.

20.

p	q	~ (p → q)	p ∧ ~ q
T	T	F T	F
T	F	T F	T
F	T	F T	F
F	F	F T	F
		2 1	1

The statements are equivalent.

21.

p	q	~ q → ~ p	p → q
T	T	F T F	T
T	F	T F F	F
F	T	F T T	T
F	F	T T T	T
		1 3 2	1

The statements are equivalent.

22.

p	q	q → p	~ p → ~ q
T	T	T	F T F
T	F	T	F F T
F	T	F	T F F
F	F	T	T T T
		1	1 3 2

The statements are equivalent.

23.

p	q	r	(p ∨ q) ∨ r	p ∨ (q ∨ r)
T	T	T	T TT	T T T
T	T	F	T TF	T T T
T	F	T	T TT	T T T
T	F	F	T TF	T T F
F	T	T	T TT	F T T
F	T	F	T TF	F T T
F	F	T	F TT	F T T
F	F	F	F FF	F F F
			1 3 2	2 3 1

The statements are equivalent.

24.

p	q	r	p ∨ (q ∧ r)	~ p → (q ∧ r)
T	T	T	T T T	F T T
T	T	F	T T F	F T F
T	F	T	T T F	F T F
T	F	F	T T F	F T F
F	T	T	F T T	T T T
F	T	F	F F F	T F F
F	F	T	F F F	T F F
F	F	F	F F F	T F F
			2 3 1	1 3 2

The statements are equivalent.

25.

p	q	r	p ∧ (q ∨ r)	(p ∧ q) ∨ r
T	T	T	T T T T T	T T T T T
T	T	F	T T T T F	T T T T T
T	F	T	T T F T T	T F F T T
T	F	F	T F F F F	T F F F F
F	T	T	F F T T T	F F T T T
F	T	F	F F T T F	F F T F F
F	F	T	F F F T T	F F F T T
F	F	F	F F F F F	F F F F F
			1 5 2 4 3	1 3 2 5 4

The statements are not equivalent.

26.

p	q	r	~ (q → p) ∨ r	(p ∨ q) ∧ ~ r
T	T	T	F T T T	T F F
T	T	F	F T F F	T T T
T	F	T	F T T T	T F F
T	F	F	F T F F	T T T
F	T	T	T F T T	T F F
F	T	F	T F T F	T T T
F	F	T	F T T T	F F F
F	F	F	F T F F	F F T
			2 1 4 3	1 3 2

The statements are not equivalent.

27.

p	q	r	(p → q) ∧ (q → r)	(p → q) → r
T	T	T	T T T	T T T
T	T	F	T F F	T F F
T	F	T	F F T	F T T
T	F	F	F F T	F T F
F	T	T	T T T	T T T
F	T	F	T F F	T F F
F	F	T	T T T	T T T
F	F	F	T T T	T F F
			1 3 2	1 3 2

The statements are not equivalent.

28.

p	q	r	~ q → (p ∧ r)	~ (p ∨ r) → q
T	T	T	F T T	F T T T
T	T	F	F T F	F T T T
T	F	T	T T T	F T T F
T	F	F	T F F	F T T F
F	T	T	F T F	F T T T
F	T	F	F T F	T F T T
F	F	T	T F F	F T T F
F	F	F	T F F	T F F F
			2 3 1	2 1 4 3

The statements are not equivalent.

29.

p	q	(p → q) ∧ (q → p)	p ↔ q
T	T	T T T	T
T	F	F F T	F
F	T	T F F	F
F	F	T T T	T
		1 3 2	1

The statements are equivalent.

30.

p	q	[~ (p → q)] ∧ [~ (q → p)]	~ (p ↔ q)
T	T	F T F F T	F T
T	F	T F F F T	T F
F	T	F T F T F	T F
F	F	F T F F T	F T
		2 1 5 4 3	2 1

The statements are not equivalent.

31. p: The Rocky Mountains are in the East.

q: The Appalachian Mountains are in the West.

In symbolic form, the statement is ~ (p ∧ q).

Applying DeMorgan's Laws we get: ~ p ∨ ~ q.

The Rocky Mountains are not in the East or the Appalachian Mountains are not in the West.

32. p: Johanna Chan is the secretary.

q: Davidson Pierre is the treasurer.

In symbolic form, the statement is ~ (p ∨ q).

Applying DeMorgan's Laws we get: ~ p ∧ ~ q.

Johanna Chan is not the secretary and Davidson Pierre is not the treasurer.

33. p: The watch was a Swatch watch.
 q: The watch was a Swiss Army watch.
 In symbolic form, the statement is ~ p ∧ ~ q.
 Applying DeMorgan's Laws we get: ~ (p ∨ q).
 It is false that the watch was a Swatch watch
 or the watch was a Swiss Army watch.

34. p: The pot roast is hot.
 q: The pot roast is well done.
 In symbolic form, the statement is p ∧ ~ q .
 Applying DeMorgan's Laws we get: ~ (~ p ∨ q). It
 is false that the pot roast is not hot or it is well done.

35. p: The hotel has a weight room.
 q: The conference center has an auditorium.
 In symbolic form, the statement is ~ p ∨ ~ q.
 Applying DeMorgan's Laws we get: ~ (p ∧ q).
 It is false that the hotel has a weight room and
 the conference center has an auditorium.

36. p: Robert Farinelli is authorized WedgCor dealer.
 q: He is going to work for Prism Constr. Co.
 In symbolic form, the statement is p ∨ ~ q.
 Applying DeMorgan's Laws we get: ~ (~ p ∧ q). It is
 false that Robert Farinelli isn't an authorized WedgCor
 Dealer and he is going to work for Prism Constr. Co.

37. p: Ashely takes the new job.
 q: Ashely will move.
 r: Ashely will buy a new house in town.
 In symbolic form, the statement is
 p → (~q ∨ r). Applying DeMorgan's Laws
 we get: p → ~ (q ∧ ~r). If Ashely takes the
 new job, it is not true that she will move and will
 not buy a new house in town.

38. p: Phil Murphy buys us dinner.
 q: We will go to the top of the CN Tower.
 r: We will be able to walk to the Bistro Restaurant.
 In symbolic form the statement is p → (~ q ∧ r).
 Applying DeMorgan's Laws we get: p → ~ (q ∨ ~ r).
 If Phil Murphy buy us dinner, then it is false that
 we will go to the top of the CN Tower or
 we will not be able to walk to the Bistro Restaurant.

39. p: Ena selects a new textbook.
 q: Ena will have to write a new syllabus.
 In symbolic form, the statement is p → q.
 Since p → q ⇔ ~ p ∨ q, an equivalent
 Statement is: Ena does not select a new textbook
 or she will have to write a new syllabus.

40. p: Maxwell's favorite TV show is *Jimmy Neutron*.
 q: Maxwell's favorite TV show is *Danny Phantom*.
 In symbolic form, the statement is p ∨ q.
 Since ~p → q ⇔ p ∨ q, an equivalent statement
 is: If *Jimmy Neutron* is not Maxwell's favorite TV show
 then *Danny Phantom* is his favorite TV show.

41. p: Bob the Tomato visited the nursing home.
 q: Bob the Tomato visited the Cub Scout
 meeting.
 In symbolic form, the statement is p ∨~ q.
 Since ~p → ~q ⇔ ~ p ∨q, an equivalent
 Statement is: If Bob the Tomato did not visit
 the nursing home, then he did not visit the
 Cub Scout meeting.

42. p: Joanne goes to the Lightning game.
 q: Joanne will go to the Devil Rays game.
 In symbolic form, the statement is p → ~ q.
 Since p → ~q ⇔ ~ p ∨ ~q, an equivalent statement
 is: Joanne does not go to the Lighning game or she will
 not go to the Devil Rays game.

43. p: The plumbers meet in Kansas City.
 q: The *Rainmakers* will provide the
 entertainment.
 In symbolic form, the statement is p → q .
 p → q ⇔ ~ p ∨ q . The plumbers do not
 meet in KC or the *Rainmakers* will provide
 the entertainment.

44. p: Mary Beth Headlee organized the conference.
 q: John Waters works at Sinclair Community College.
 In symbolic form, the statement is p ∨~ q.
 ~ p → ~ q ⇔ p ∨ ~ q . If Mary Beth Headlee did
 not organize the conference, then John Waters does
 not work at SCC.

45. p: Chase is hiding.
    q: The pitcher is broken.
    In symbolic form, the statement is ~p ∨ q .
    ~p ∨ q ⇔ p → q. If Chase is hiding, then the pitcher is broken.

46. p: Weezer is on the radio.
    q: Tim Ollendick is working.
    In symbolic form, the statement is ~p → q.
    ~p → q ⇔ ~(~p) ∨ q ⇔ p ∨ q. Weezer is on the radio or Tim Ollendick is working.

47. p: We go to Cincinnati.
    q: We go to the zoo.
    In symbolic form, the statement is ~(p → q) .
    ~(p → q) ⇔ p ∧ ~ q.
    We go to Cincinnati and we will not go to the zoo.

48. p: General Electric makes the telephone.
    q: The telephone is made in the United States.
    In symbolic form, the statement is ~(p → q) .
    ~(p → q) ⇔ p ∧ ~ q.
    General Electric makes the telephone and it is not made in the United States.

49. p: I am cold.
    q: The heater is working.
    In symbolic form, the statement is p ∧ ~ q .
    p ∧ ~ q ⇔ ~(p → q) .
    It is false that if I am cold then the heater is working.

50. p: The Badgers beat the Nittany Lions.
    q: The Bucks beat the 76ers.
    In symbolic form, the statement is p ∧ q .
    p ∧ q ⇔ ~(p → ~q)
    It is false that if the Badgers beat the Nittany Lions then the Bucks did not beat the 76ers.

51. p: Borders has a sale.
    q: We will buy $100 worth of books.
    In symbolic form, the statement is ~(p → q) .
    ~(p → q) ⇔ p ∧ ~ q.
    Borders has a sale and we will not buy $100 worth of books.

52. p: Thompson is sick today.
    q: Allen went to school.
    In symbolic form, the statement is p ∧ ~ q .
    p ∧ ~ q ⇔ ~(p → q) .
    It is false that if Thompson is sick today then Allen went to school.

53. p: John Deere will hire new workers.
    q: Dubuque will retain the workers.
    In symbolic form, the statement is p ∧ q .
    p ∧ q ⇔ ~(p → ~q).
    It is false that if John Deere will hire new workers Dubuque will not retain the workers.

54. p: My cell phone is made by Motorola.
    q: My carrier is Alltel.
    In symbolic form, the statement is ~p ∧ q .
    ~p ∧ q ⇔ ~(~p → ~q).
    It is false that if my cell phone is not made by Motorola then my carrier is not Alltel.

55. Converse: If we can finish the quilt in 1 week, then we work every night.
    Inverse: If we do not work every night then we cannot finish the quilt in 1 week.
    Contrapositive: If we cannot finish the quilt in 1 week then we do not work every night.

56. Converse: If you need to change the battery, then your cell phone is beeping..
    Inverse: If your cell phone is not beeping, then you do not need to change the battery.
    Contrapositive: If you do not need to change the battery, then your cell phone is not beeping.

57. Converse: If I buy silver jewelry, then I go to Mexico.
    Inverse: If I do not go to Mexico, then I do not buy silver jewelry.
    Contrapositive: If I do not buy silver jewelry then I do not go to Mexico.

58. Converse: If Bob Dylan goes on tour, then he records a new CD.
    Inverse: If Bob Dylan does not record a new CD, then he does not go on tour.
    Contrapositive: If Bob Dylan does not go on tour, then he does not record a new CD.

59. Converse: If I scream, then that annoying paper clip (Clippie) shows up on my screen.
    Inverse: If Clippie does not show up on my screen, then I will not scream.
    Contrapositive: If I do not scream, then Clippie does not show up on my screen.

60. Converse: If we go down to the marina and take out a sailboat,
    then the sun is shining.
    Inverse: If the sun is not shining, then we do not go down to the marina or we do not take out a sailboat.
    Contrapositive: If we do not go down to the marina or we do not take out a sailboat, then the sun is not shining.

61. If a natural number is divisible by 10, then it is divisible by 5. True

62. If a quadrilateral is a parallelogram, then the opposite sides are parallel. True

63. If a natural number is not divisible by 6, then it is not divisible by 3. False

64. If n is a natural number, then 1/n is a natural number. False

65. If two lines are not parallel, then the two lines intersect in at least one point. True

66. If m is a counting number, then $\dfrac{ma}{mb} = \dfrac{a}{b}$. True

67. p: Bill Rush is the editor.
    q: Bill Rush is the vice president.
    In symbolic form, the statements are:
    a) ~ p ∨ q, b) q → ~ p, c) p → ~ q
    Statement (c) is the contrapositive of statement. (b). Therefore,
    statements (b) and (c) are equivalent.

p	q	~p ∨ q	q → ~p
T	T	F T T	T F F
T	F	F F F	F T F
F	T	T T T	T T T
F	F	T T F	F T T
		1 3 2	1 3 2

    Since the truth tables for (a) and (b) are different we conclude that only statements (b) and (c) are equivalent.

68. p: Fido is our dog's name.
    q: Rex is our dog's name.
    In symbolic form, the statements are:
    a) p → ~ q, b) ~ (p ∧ ~ q), c) ~ p ∨ q.
    If we use DeMorgan's Laws on statement (b) we get statement (c).
    Therefore, statements (b) and (c) are equivalent. If we look at the truth tables for all three statements we can see that only statements (b) and (c) are equivalent.

p	q	a) p → ~q	b) ~ (p ∧ ~ q)	c) ~p ∨ q
T	T	T F F	T T F F	F T T
T	F	T T T	F T T T	F F F
F	T	F T F	T F F F	T T T
F	F	F T T	T F F T	T T F
		1 3 2	4 1 3 2	1 3 2

69. p: The office is cool.

q: The computer is jammed.

In symbolic form, the statements are: a) ~ p ∧ q,

b) ~ p → ~ q, c) ~ (p ∨ ~ q). If we use DeMorgan's

Laws on statement (a), we get statement (c).

Therefore, statements (a) and (c) are equivalent.

If we look at the truth tables for statements (a),

(b), and (c), we see that only statements (a) and (c)

are equivalent.

		a)	b)	c)
p	q	~ p ∧ q	~ p → ~ q	~ (p ∨ ~ q)
T	T	F F T	F T F	F T T F
T	F	F F F	F T T	F T T T
F	T	T T T	T F F	T F F F
F	F	T F F	T T T	F F T T
		1 3 2	1 3 2	4 1 3 2

70. p: The test is written

q: The review sheet is ready.

In symbolic form, the statements are:

a) ~p ∨ ~ q, b) p → q, c) ~(q ∧ ~p)

p	q	~p ∨ ~ q	p → q	~(q ∧ ~p)
T	T	F F F	T T T	T T F F
T	F	F T T	T F F	T F F F
F	T	T T F	F T T	F T T T
F	F	T T T	F T F	T F F T
		1 3 2	1 2 3	4 1 2 3

Therefore, none of the statements are equivalent.

71. p: Today is Sunday.

q: The library is open.

In symbolic form, the statements are: a) ~ p ∨ q,

b) p → ~ q, c) q → ~ p. Looking at the truth table for

all three statements, we can determine that only

statements (b) and (c) are equivalent.

		a)	b)	c)
p	q	~ p ∨ q	p → ~ q	q → ~ p
T	T	F T T	T F F	T F F
T	F	F F F	T T T	F T F
F	T	T T T	F T F	T T T
F	F	T T F	F T T	F T T
		1 3 2	1 3 2	1 3 2

72. p: You are fishing at 1 PM.

q: You are driving a car at 1 PM.

In symbolic form, the statements are:

a) p → q, b) ~ p ∨ q, c) ~ (p ∧ ~ q).

Using the fact that p → q ⇔ ~ p ∨ q,

we see that (a) and (b) are equivalent

statements. If we use DeMorgan's Laws

on statement (b), we get statement (c).

Therefore all three statements are

equivalent.

73. p: The grass grows.

q: The trees are blooming.

In symbolic form, the statements are: a) p ∧ q,

b) q → ~ p, c) ~ q ∨ ~ p. Using the fact that p → q

⇔ ~ p ∨ q, on statement (b) we get ~ q ∨ ~ p.

Therefore, statements (b) and (c) are equivalent.

Looking at the truth table for statements (a) and (b)

we can conclude that only statements (b) and (c) are

equivalent.

p	q	p ∧ q	q → ~ p
T	T	T	T F F
T	F	F	F T F
F	T	F	T T T
F	F	F	F T T
		1	1 3 2

74. p: Johnny Patrick is chosen as department chair.

q: Johnny Patrick is the only candidate.

In symbolic form, the statements are:

a) p ↔ q, b) (p → q) ∧ (q→ p), and c) ~ p ∧~q .

p	q	p ↔ q	(p → q) ∧ (q→p)	~ p ∧~ q
T	T	T T T	T T T T T T T	F F F
T	F	T F F	T F F F F T T	F F T
F	T	F F T	F T T T F T F F	T F F
F	F	F T F	F T F T F T F	T T T
		1 3 2	1 3 2 7 4 6 5	1 3 2

Therefore, (a) is equivalent to (b).

75. p: You drink milk.

q: Your cholesterol count will be lower.

In symbolic form, the statements are:

a) ~ (~ p → q), b) q ↔ p, and c) ~ (p → ~ q) .

p	q	~ (~ p → q)	q ↔ p	~ (p → ~ q)
T	T	F FT T	T T T	T T F F
T	F	F FT F	F F T	F T T T
F	T	F T T T	T F F	F F T F
F	F	T TF F	F T F	F F T T
		4 1 3 2	1 3 2	4 1 3 2

Therefore, none of the statements are equivalent.

76. p: Bruce S. will go on tour.

q: Clarence plays the saxophone in his band.

In symbolic form, the statements are: a) ~p ↔ ~q,

b) ~ (p ↔ ~ q), and c) p → q .

p	q	~p ↔ ~q	~ (p ↔ ~ q)	p → q
T	T	F T F	T T F F	T T T
T	F	F F T	F T T T	T F F
F	T	T T F	F F T F	F T T
F	F	T T T	T F F T	F T T
		1 3 2	4 1 3 2	1 3 2

Therefore, (a) is equivalent to (b).

77. p: The pay is good.

q: Today is Monday.

r : I will take the job.

Looking at the truth tables for statements (a), (b), and (c), we see that none of the statements are equivalent.

			a)	b)	c)
p	q	r	(p ∧q) → r	~ r → ~(p ∨q)	(p ∧q) ∨ r
T	T	T	T T T	F T F T	T T T
T	T	F	T F F	T F F T	T T F
T	F	T	F T T	F T F T	F T T
T	F	F	F T F	T F F T	F F F
F	T	T	F T T	F T F T	F T T
F	T	F	F T F	T F F T	F F F
F	F	T	F T T	F T T F	F T T
F	F	F	F T F	T T T F	F F F
			1 3 2	1 4 3 2	1 3 2

78. p: You are 18 years old.

q: You are a citizen of the United States.

r : You can vote in a presidential election.

Looking at the truth tables for statements (a), (b), and (c), we can determine that none of these statements are equivalent.

			a)	b)	c)
p	q	r	(p ∧ q) → r	r ⇔ (q ∧ p)	~ r ∨ (p ∧ ~ q)
T	T	T	T T T	T T T	F F T F F
T	T	F	T F F	F F T	T T T F F
T	F	T	F T T	T F F	F T T T T
T	F	F	F T F	F T F	T T T T T
F	T	T	F T T	T F F	F F F F F
F	T	F	F T F	F T F	T T F F F
F	F	T	F T T	T F F	F F F F T
F	F	F	F T F	F T F	T T F F T
			1 3 2	1 3 2	1 5 2 4 3

79. p: The package was sent by Federal Express.

q: The package was sent by United Parcel Service.

r : The package arrived on time.

Using the fact that p → q ⇔ ~ p ∨q to rewrite statement (c), we get p ∨ (~ q ∧r). Therefore, statements (a) and (c) are equivalent. Looking at the truth table for statements (a) and (b), we can conclude that only statements (a) and (c) are equivalent.

			a)	b)
p	q	r	p ∨ (~ q ∧ r)	r ⇔ (p ∨ ~ q)
T	T	T	T T F F T	T T T T F
T	T	F	T T F F F	F F T T F
T	F	T	T T T T T	T T T T T
T	F	F	T T T F F	F F T T T
F	T	T	F F F F T	T F F F F
F	T	F	F F F F F	F T F F F
F	F	T	F T T T T	T T F T T
F	F	F	F F T F F	F F F T T
			1 5 2 4 3	1 5 2 4 3

80. p: We put the dog outside.

q: We feed the dog.

r : The dog will bark.

In symbolic form, the statements are:

a) (p ∨q) → ~ r, b) r → (~ p ∧~ q), and c) r → ~ (p ∨q). Statement (c) is the contrapositive of statement (b) and if we use DeMorgan's Laws on statement (b) we obtain statement (c). Therefore, statements (a), (b), and (c) are equivalent.

81. p: The car needs oil.
    q: The car needs gas.
    r : The car is new.
    In symbolic form, the statements are: a) $p \wedge (q \vee r)$,
    b) $p \wedge \sim (\sim q \wedge \sim r)$, and c) $p \rightarrow (q \vee \sim r)$. If we use
    DeMorgan's Laws on the disjunction in statement (a),
    we obtain $p \wedge \sim (\sim q \wedge \sim r)$. Therefore, statements (a)
    and (b) are equivalent. If we compare the truth tables
    for (a) and (c) we see that they are not equivalent.
    Therefore, only statements (a) and (b) are equivalent.

p	q	r	$p \wedge (q \vee r)$	$p \rightarrow (q \vee \sim r)$
T	T	T	TT T	TT TT F
T	T	F	TT T	TT TT T
T	F	T	TT T	TF FF F
T	F	F	TF F	TT FT T
F	T	T	FF T	FT TT F
F	T	F	FF T	FT TT T
F	F	T	FF T	FT FF F
F	F	F	FF F	FT FT T
			1 3 2	1 5 2 4 3

82. p: The mortgage rate went down.
    q: Tim purchased the house.
    r : The down payment was 10%.
    Looking at the truth tables for statements
    (a), (b), and (c), we can determine that
    none of these statements are equivalent.

p	q	r	a) $p \leftrightarrow (q \wedge r)$	b) $r \wedge (q \rightarrow p)$	c) $q \rightarrow (p \wedge \sim r)$
T	T	T	TT T	TT T	TF TF F
T	T	F	TF F	FF T	TT TT T
T	F	T	TF F	TT T	FT TF F
T	F	F	TF F	FF T	FT TT T
F	T	T	FF T	TF F	TF FF F
F	T	F	FT F	FF F	TF FF T
F	F	T	FT F	TT T	FT FF F
F	F	F	FT F	FF T	FT FF T
			1 3 2	1 3 2	1 5 2 4 3

83. True. If $p \rightarrow q$ is false, it must be of the form
    $T \rightarrow F$. Therefore, the converse must be of the form
    $F \rightarrow T$, which is true.

84. True. If $p \rightarrow q$ is false, it must be of the form $T \rightarrow F$.
    Therefore, the inverse must be of the form $F \rightarrow T$, which
    is true.

85. False. A conditional statement and its contrapositive
    always have the same truth values.

86. True. A conditional statement and its contrapositive
    always have the same truth values.

87. If we use DeMorgan's Laws to rewrite $\sim p \vee q$, we
    get $\sim (p \wedge \sim q)$. Since $\sim p \vee q \Leftrightarrow \sim (p \wedge \sim q)$ and
    $p \rightarrow q \Leftrightarrow \sim p \vee q$, we can conclude that $p \rightarrow q \Leftrightarrow$
    $\sim (p \wedge \sim q)$. Other answers are possible.

88. Since $\sim (\sim p) \Leftrightarrow p$, we have $\sim [\sim (p \vee \sim q)] \Leftrightarrow p \vee \sim q$.

89. Research problem -- Answers will vary.

90. a) $\sim p = 1 - p = 1 - 0.25 = 0.75$
    b) $\sim q = 1 - q = 1 - 0.20 = 0.80$
    c) $p \wedge q$ has a truth value equal to the lesser of
    $p = 0.75$ and $q = 0.20$. Thus $p \wedge q = 0.20$
    d) $p \vee q$ has truth value equal to the greater of
    $p = 0.25$ and $q = 0.20$. Thus $p \vee q = 0.25$
    e) $p \rightarrow q$ has truth value equal to the lesser of 1
    and $1 - p + q = 1 - 0.25 + 0.20 = 0.95$. Thus
    $p \rightarrow q = 0.95$
    f) $p \leftrightarrow q$ has a truth value equal to $1 - |p - q| =$
    $1 - (0.25 - 0.20) = 1 - 0.05 = 0.95$. Thus $p \leftrightarrow q$
    $= 0.95$

Exercise Set 3.5

1. a) An argument is valid when its conclusion
   necessarily follows from the given set of
   premises.
   b) An argument is invalid or a fallacy when the
   conclusion does not necessarily follow from
   premises.

2. If $(p_1 \wedge p_2) \rightarrow c$ is a tautology, then the argument is
   valid.

3. Yes. For example,

$$p \rightarrow q$$
$$\underline{q}$$
$$\therefore \ p$$

is an invalid argument, but if p happens to be true, then its conclusion is true.

4. Yes. It is not necessary for the premises or the conclusion to be true statements for the argument to be valid.

5. Yes. If the conclusion does not follow from the set of premises, then the argument is invalid.

6. Yes. If the conclusion follows from the set of premises, then the argument is valid, even if the premises are false.

7. a) $p \rightarrow q$ b) If sky is clear, then I'll go to game.

    $\underline{p}$ The sky is clear.

    $\therefore q$ I will go to the game.

8. a) $p \rightarrow q$ b) If the sky is clear, then it will be hot.

    $\underline{q \rightarrow r}$ If it is hot, then will wear shorts.

    $\therefore p \rightarrow r$ If sky is clear, then wear shorts.

9. a) $p \rightarrow q$ b) If soil is dry, then grass needs water.

    $\underline{\sim q}$ The grass does not need water.

    $\therefore \sim p$ The soil is not dry.

10. a) $p \vee q$ b) Pizza is served on time or is free.

    $\underline{\sim p}$ The pizza was not served on time.

    $\therefore q$ The pizza is free.

11. a) $p \rightarrow q$ b) If you wash my car, then I pay you $5.

    $\underline{q}$ I will give you $5.

    $\therefore p$ You washed my car.

12. a) $p \rightarrow q$ b) If you wash my car, then I pay you $5.

    $\underline{\sim p}$ You did not wash my car.

    $\therefore \sim q$ I will not give you $5.

13. This argument is the fallacy of the inverse, therefore it is invalid.

14.

c	d	$[(\,c \vee d)\,\wedge \sim c] \rightarrow d$
T	T	T T T F F T T
T	F	T F F F F T F
F	T	F T T T T F T
F	F	F T F F T T F
		1 3 2 5 4 7 6

The argument is valid.

15. This is the law of detachment, so it is a valid argument.

16. This argument is in the form of the law of syllogism, so it is valid.

17. This argument is a disjunctive syllogism and therefore is valid.

18. This argument is the law of contraposition and therefore it is valid.

19. This argument is the fallacy of the converse. Therefore it is invalid.

20. This argument is in the form of the law of syllogism, so it is valid.

21. This argument is the law of contraposition, so it is valid.

22. This argument is the fallacy of the converse. Therefore it is invalid.

23. This argument is the law of syllogism and therefore it is valid.

24. This argument is the fallacy of the inverse. Therefore it is invalid.

25.

p	q	r	[(p ↔ q) ∧ (q ∧ r)] → (p ∨ r)
T	T	T	T T T T T
T	T	F	T F F T T
T	F	T	F F F T T
T	F	F	F F F T T
F	T	T	F F T T T
F	T	F	F F F T F
F	F	T	T F F T T
F	F	F	T F F T F
			1 3 2 5 4

The argument is valid.

26.

p	q	r	[(p ↔ q) ∧ (q → r)] → (~ r → ~ p)
T	T	T	T T T T F T
T	T	F	T F F T T F F
T	F	T	F F T T F T F
T	F	F	F F T T T F F
F	T	T	F F T T F T T
F	T	F	F F F T T T T
F	F	T	T T T T F T T
F	F	F	T T T T T T T
			1 3 2 7 4 6 5

The argument is valid.

27.

p	q	r	[(r ↔ p) ∧ (~p ∧ q)] → (p ∧ r)
T	T	T	T F F F T T T
T	T	F	F F F F T T F
T	F	T	T F F F F T T
T	F	F	F F F F F T F
F	T	T	F F T T T T F
F	T	F	T T T T T F F
F	F	T	F F T F F T F
F	F	F	T F T F F T F
			1 5 2 4 3 7 6

The argument is invalid.

28.

p	q	r	[(p ∨ q) ∧ (r ∧ p)] → q
T	T	T	T T T T T
T	T	F	T F F T T
T	F	T	T T T F F
T	F	F	T F F T F
F	T	T	T F F T T
F	T	F	T F F T T
F	F	T	F F F T F
F	F	F	F F F T F
			1 3 2 5 4

The argument is invalid.

29.

p	q	r	[(p→ q) ∧ (q ∨ r) ∧ (r ∨ p)] → p
T	T	T	T T T T T T T
T	T	F	T T T T T T T
T	F	T	F F T F T T T
T	F	F	F F F F T T T
F	T	T	T T T T T F F
F	T	F	T T T F F T F
F	F	T	T T T T T F F
F	F	F	T F F F F T F
			1 3 2 5 4 7 6

The argument is invalid.

30. The conclusion $p \leftrightarrow q$ follows by the law of syllogism and therefore the conclusion $q \rightarrow p$ follows.

31.

p	q	r	[(p → q) ∧ (r → ~ p) ∧ (p ∨ r)] → (q ∨ ~ p)
T	T	T	T F TF F F T T TT F
T	T	F	T T FT F T T T TT F
T	F	T	F F TF F F T T FF F
T	F	F	F F FT F F T T FF F
F	T	T	T T TT T T T T TT T
F	T	F	T T FT T F F T TT T
F	F	T	T T TT T T T T FT T
F	F	F	T T FT T F F T FT T
			1 5 24 3 7 6 11 9 10 8

The argument is valid.

32.

p	q	r	[(p ↔ q) ∧ (p ∨ q) ∧ (q → r)] → (q ∨r)
T	T	T	T T T T T T T
T	T	F	T T T F F T T
T	F	T	F F T F T T T
T	F	F	F F T F T T F
F	T	T	F F T F T T T
F	T	F	F F T F F T T
F	F	T	T F F F T T T
F	F	F	T F F F T T F
			1 4 2 5 3 7 6

The argument is valid.

33. p: Will Smith wins an Academy Award.
q: Will Smith retires from acting.

$$p \rightarrow q$$
$$\underline{\sim p}$$
$$\therefore \ \sim q$$

The argument is invalid (fallacy of the inverse.).

34. p: The car is a Road Runner.
q: The car is fast.

$$p \rightarrow q$$
$$\underline{q}$$
$$\therefore \ p$$

The argument is invalid (fallacy of the converse).

35. p: The baby is a boy.
q: The baby will be named Alexander Martin.

$$p \rightarrow q$$
$$\underline{p}$$
$$\therefore \ q$$

The argument is valid (law of detachment).

36. p: I get my child to preschool by 8:45 a.m.
q: I take the 9:00 a.m. class.
r: I am done by 2:00 p.m.

$$[(p \rightarrow q) \land (q \rightarrow r)] \rightarrow (p \rightarrow r)$$

This argument is valid by the law of syllogism.

37. p: The guitar is a Les Paul model.
q: The guitar is made by Gibson.

$$p \rightarrow q$$
$$\underline{\sim q}$$
$$\therefore \ \sim p$$

This argument is valid by the law of contraposition.

38. p: We will go for a bike ride.
q: We will go shopping.

$$p \lor q$$
$$\underline{\sim q}$$
$$\therefore \ p$$

This argument is an example of disjunctive syllogism and is therefore valid.

39. p: We planted the garden by the first Friday in
    April.
  q: We will have potatoes by the Fourth of July.

$p \rightarrow q$

$\underline{q}$

$\therefore \ p$

This is the fallacy of the converse; thus
the argument is invalid.

41. p: Sarah Hughes will win an Olympic gold medal
    in figure skating.
  q: Joey Cheek will win an Olympic gold medal
    in speed skating.

$p \vee q$

$\underline{\sim p}$

$\therefore \ q$

The argument is a disjunctive syllogism and is
therefore valid

43. p: It is cold.
  q: The graduation will be held indoors.
  r: The fireworks will be postponed.

$[(p \rightarrow q) \wedge (q \rightarrow r)] \rightarrow (p \rightarrow r)$

This argument is valid because of the law of
syllogism.

40. p: You pass General Chemistry.
  q: You take Organic Chemistry.

$p \rightarrow q$

$\underline{p}$

$\therefore \ q$

This is the law of detachment, thus the
argument is valid.

42. p: Nicholas Thompson teaches this course.
  q: I will get a passing grade.

$p \rightarrow q$

$\underline{\sim q}$

$\therefore \ \sim p$

This argument is valid by the law of
contraposition.

44. f: The canteen is full
  w: We can go for a walk.
  t: We will get thirsty.

f	w	t	$[(f \rightarrow w) \wedge (w \wedge \sim t)] \rightarrow (w \rightarrow \sim f)$							
T	T	T	T	F	T	F	F	T	T	F	F
T	T	F	T	T	T	T	T	F	T	F	F
T	F	T	F	F	F	F	F	T	F	T	F
T	F	F	F	F	F	F	T	T	F	T	F
F	T	T	T	F	T	F	F	T	T	T	T
F	T	F	T	T	T	T	T	T	T	T	T
F	F	T	T	F	F	F	F	T	F	T	T
F	F	F	T	F	F	F	T	T	F	T	T
			1	5	2	4	3	9	6	8	7

The argument is invalid.

45. m: Marie works for the post office
  j: Jim works for target.
  t: Tommy gets an internship.

m	j	t	$[(m \wedge j) \wedge (j \rightarrow t)] \rightarrow (t \rightarrow m)$				
T	T	T	T	T	T	T	T
T	T	F	T	F	F	T	T
T	F	T	F	F	T	T	T
T	F	F	F	F	T	T	T
F	T	T	F	F	T	T	F
F	T	F	F	F	F	T	T
F	F	T	F	F	T	T	F
F	F	F	F	F	T	T	T
			1	3	2	5	4

The argument is valid.

46. c: Vitamin C helps your immune system.
  n: Niacin helps reduce cholesterol.
  e: Vitamin E enhances your skin.

c	n	e	$[(c \vee n) \wedge (n \rightarrow e)] \rightarrow (c \wedge e)$				
T	T	T	T	T	T	T	T
T	T	F	T	F	F	T	F
T	F	T	T	T	T	T	T
T	F	F	T	T	T	F	F
F	T	T	T	T	T	F	F
F	T	F	T	F	F	T	F
F	F	T	F	F	T	T	F
F	F	F	F	F	T	T	F
			1	3	2	5	4

The argument is invalid.

47. s: It is snowing.
g: I am going skiing.
c: I will wear a coat.

s	g	c	[(s ∧ g) ∧ (g → c)] → (s → c)
T	T	T	T T T T T
T	T	F	T F F T F
T	F	T	F F T T T
T	F	F	F F T T F
F	T	T	F F T T T
F	T	F	F F F T T
F	F	T	F F T T T
F	F	F	F F T T T
			1 3 2 5 4

The argument is valid.

48. g: The garden has vegetables.
f: The garden has flowers.

g	f	[(g ∨ f) ∧ (~f → g)] → (f ∨ g)
T	T	T T F T T T T
T	F	T T T T T T T
F	T	T T F T F T T
F	F	F F T F F T F
		1 5 2 4 3 7 6

The argument is valid.

49. h: The house has electric heat.
b: The Flynns will buy the house.
p: The price is less than $100,000.

h	b	p	[(h → b) ∧ (~p → ~b)] → (h → p)
T	T	T	T T F T F T T
T	T	F	T F T F F T F
T	F	T	F F F T T T T
T	F	F	F F T T T T F
F	T	T	T T F T F T T
F	T	F	T F T F F T T
F	F	T	T T F T T T T
F	F	F	T T T T T T T
			1 5 2 4 3 7 6

The argument is valid.

50. a: There is an atmosphere.
g: There is gravity.
w: An object has weight.

a	g	w	[(a → g) ∧ (w →g)] → (a → w)
T	T	T	T T T T T
T	T	F	T T T F F
T	F	T	F F F T T
T	F	F	F F T T F
F	T	T	T T T T T
F	T	F	T T T T T
F	F	T	T F F T T
F	F	F	T T T T T
			1 3 2 5 4

The argument is invalid.

51. p: The prescription is called in to Walgreen's.
q. You pick up the prescription at 4:00 p.m.

p → q
~ q
∴ ~p

The argument is the law of contraposition and is valid.

52. p: The printer has a clogged nozzle.
q. The printer has no toner.

p	q	[(p ∨ q) ∧ ~ q] → p
T	T	T T T F F T T
T	F	T T F T T T T
F	T	F T T F F T T
F	F	F F F T T T F
		1 3 2 5 4 7 6

The argument is valid.

53. s: Max is playing Game Boy with the sound off.
h: Max is wearing headphones.

s ∨ h
~s
∴ h

This argument is an example of disjunctive syllogism and is therefore valid.

54. c: The cat is in the room.
m: The mice are hiding.

c → m
~m
∴ ~c

This argument is the law of contraposition and is valid.

55. t: The test was easy.
    g: I received a good grade.

t	g	[(t ∧ g) ∧ (~t ∨ ~g)]	→	~t
T	T	T F F F F T	T	F
T	F	F F F T T T	T	F
F	T	F F T T F T	T	T
F	F	F F T T T T	T	T
		1 5 2 4 3	7	6

The argument is valid.

56. b: Bonnie passed the bar exam.   b → p
    p: Bonnie will practice law.   ~ p
                                        ∴~ b

This argument is the law of contraposition and is valid.

57. c: The baby is crying.
    h: The baby is hungry.

c	h	[(c ∧ ~h) ∧ (h → c)]	→	h
T	T	T F F F T	T	T
T	F	T T T T T	F	F
F	T	F F F F F	T	T
F	F	F F T F T	T	F
		1 3 2 5 4	7	6

The argument is invalid.

58. n: The car is new.
    a: The car has air conditioning.

n	a	[(n → a) ∧ (~n ∧ a)]	→	~n
T	T	T F F F T	T	F
T	F	F F F F F	T	F
F	T	T T T T T	T	T
F	F	T F T F F	T	T
		1 5 2 4 3	7	6

The argument is valid.

59. f: The football team wins the game.   f → d
    d: Dave played quarterback.   d → ~ s
    s: The team is in second place.   ∴ f → s

Using the law of syllogism f → ~s, so this argument is invalid.

60. e: The engineering courses are difficult.
    c: The chemistry labs are long.
    A: The art tests are easy.

e	c	a	[(e ∧ c) ∧ (c → a)]	→	(e ∧ ~a)
T	T	T	T T T	F	T F F
T	T	F	T F F	T	T T T
T	F	T	F F T	T	T F F
T	F	F	F F T	T	T T T
F	T	T	F F T	T	F F F
F	T	F	F F F	T	F F T
F	F	T	F F T	T	F F F
F	F	F	F F T	T	F F T
			1 3 2	7	4 6 5

The argument is invalid.

61. Your face will break out. (law of detachment)

62. The temperature did not hit 100 degrees. (law of contraposition)

63. I am stressed out. (disjunctive syllogism)

64. If I can get Nick to his piano lesson by 3:30 P.M., then we do not need to order pizza again. (law of syllogism)

65. You did not close the deal. (law of contraposition)

66. Allyson will take a nap. (law of detachment)

67. If you do not pay off your credit card bill, then the bank makes money. (law of syllogism)

68. p: Lynn wins the contest.

q: Lynn strikes oil.

r : Lynn will be rich.

s: Lynn will stop working.

p	q	r	s	[((p ∨ q)	→	r) ∧ (r	→ s)]	→ (~ s	→	~ p)
T	T	T	T	T	T T	T	T	T		T
T	T	T	F	T	T T	F	F	T		F
T	T	F	T	T	F F	F	T	T		T
T	T	F	F	T	F F	F	T	T		F
T	F	T	T	T	T T	T	T	T		T
T	F	T	F	T	T T	F	F	T		F
T	F	F	T	T	F F	F	T	T		T
T	F	F	F	T	F F	F	T	T		F
F	T	T	T	T	T T	T	T	T		T
F	T	T	F	T	T T	F	F	T		T
F	T	F	T	T	F F	F	T	T		T
F	T	F	F	T	F F	F	T	T		T
F	F	T	T	F	T T	T	T	T		T
F	F	T	F	F	T T	F	F	T		T
F	F	F	T	F	T F	T	T	T		T
F	F	F	F	F	T F	T	T	T		T
				1	3 2	5	4	7		6

The argument is valid.

69. No. An argument is <u>invalid</u> only when the conjunction of the premises is true and the conclusion is false.

70. p: I think.

q: I am.

p → q

~ q

∴ ~p

By the Fallacy of the Inverse, the argument is invalid.

Exercise Set 3.6

1. a) It is a valid argument.

   b) It is an invalid argument.

2. Symbolic arguments use the connectives "and," "or," "not," "but," "if-then," and "if and only if", while syllogistic arguments use the quantifiers "all," "some," and "none."

3. a)

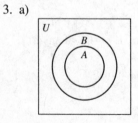

b)

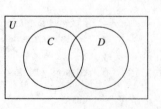

c)

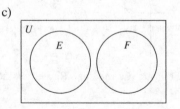

4. a) The conclusion necessarily follows from the premises.
    b) The conclusion does not necessarily follow from the premises.

6. Yes. An argument in which the conclusion does not necessarily follow from the given set of premises is invalid, even if the conclusion is a true statement.

5. Yes. If the conjunction of the premises is false in all cases, then the argument is valid regardless of the truth value of the conclusion.

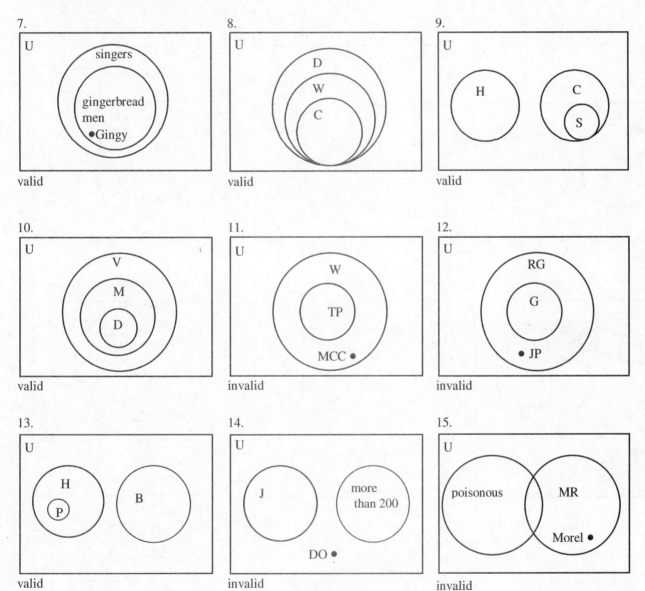

7.

U

singers

gingerbread men

•Gingy

valid

8.

U

D

W

C

valid

9.

U

H

C

S

valid

10.

U

V

M

D

valid

11.

U

W

TP

MCC •

invalid

12.

U

RG

G

• JP

invalid

13.

U

H

P

B

valid

14.

U

J

more than 200

DO •

invalid

15.

U

poisonous

MR

Morel •

invalid

16.

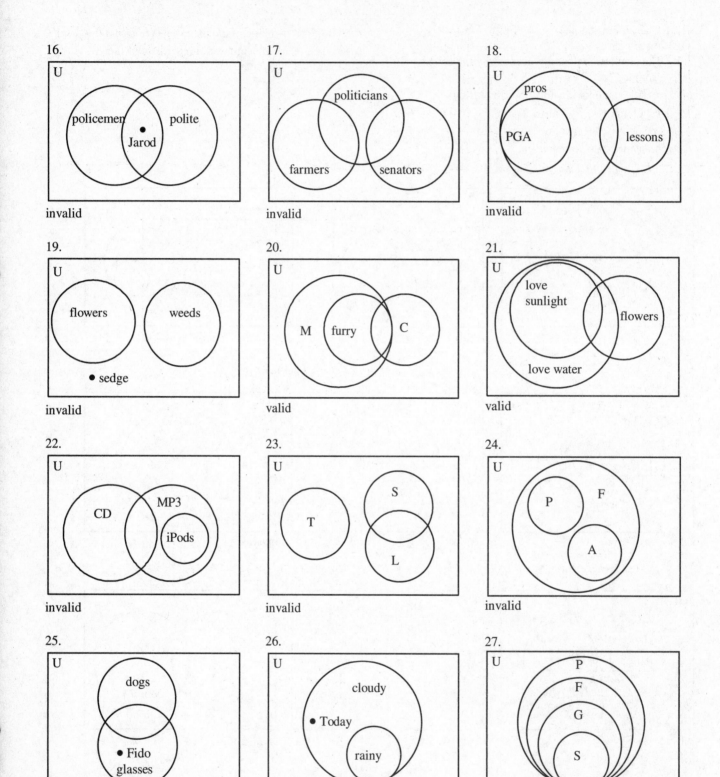

U

policemen   polite
• Jarod

invalid

17.

U

politicians

farmers   senators

invalid

18.

U

pros

PGA   lessons

invalid

19.

U

flowers   weeds

• sedge

invalid

20.

U

M   furry   C

valid

21.

U

love
sunlight   flowers

love water

valid

22.

U

CD   MP3
iPods

invalid

23.

U

T   S
L

invalid

24.

U

P   F
A

invalid

25.

U

dogs
• Fido
glasses

invalid

26.

U

cloudy
• Today
rainy

invalid

27.

U

P
F
G
S

valid

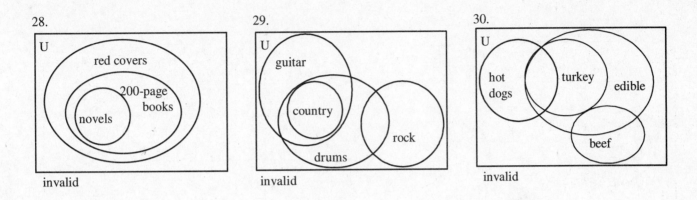

28.
invalid

29.
invalid

30.
invalid

31. $[(p \rightarrow q) \land (p \lor q)] \rightarrow \sim p$ can be expressed as a set statement by $[(P' \cup Q) \cap (P \cup Q)] \subseteq P'$. If this statement is true, then the argument is valid; otherwise, the argument is invalid.

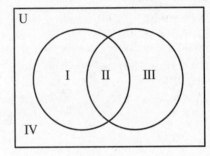

Set	Regions
$P' \cup Q$	II, III, IV
$P \cup Q$	I, II, III
$(P' \cup Q) \cap (P \cup Q)$	II, III
P'	III, IV

Since $(P' \cup Q) \cap (P \cup Q)$ is not a subset of P', the argument is invalid.

Exercise Set 3.7

1. a) In a series circuit, the current can take only one path.

   b) $\land$ (and)

3. One of the two switches will always be open.

5. $p \land q$

	Light	
p	q	$p \land q$
T	T	T
T	F	F
F	T	F
F	F	F

2. a) In a parellel circuit, there are two or more paths that the current can take.

   b) $\lor$ (or)

4. One of the switches will always be closed, and this allows current to flow to the bulb.

6. $(p \land q) \lor \overline{q}$

		Light		
p	q	$(p \land q)$	$\lor$	$\overline{q}$
T	T	T	T	F
T	F	F	T	T
F	T	F	F	F
F	F	F	T	T

7. $(p \vee q) \wedge \overline{q}$

			Light	
p	q	$(p \vee q)$	$\wedge$	$\overline{q}$
T	T	T	F	F
T	F	T	T	T
F	T	T	F	F
F	F	F	F	T

8. $(p \wedge q) \vee (\overline{p} \wedge q)$

				Light	
p	q	$\overline{p}$	$(p \wedge q)$	$\vee$	$(\overline{p} \wedge q)$
T	T	F	T	T	F
T	F	F	F	F	F
F	T	T	F	T	T
F	F	T	F	F	F

9. $(p \wedge q) \wedge [(p \wedge \overline{q}) \vee r]$

It is clear from the $(p \wedge q)$ condition that both p and q must be closed for the bulb to light. In this case the upper branch of the parallel portion of the circuit is open since it includes $\overline{q}$, so for the bulb to light, r must be closed. Thus the bulb lights only if p, q and r are all T.

10. $[(p \wedge r) \vee \overline{q}] \wedge (p \vee q)$

Suppose first that q is T. Then since $\overline{q}$ is F, the expression in brackets will be T only if both p and r are T. Thus one combination that lights the bulb is p, q, and r all T.

Now suppose that q is F and therefore $\overline{q}$ is T. Then for $(p \vee q)$ to be true, p must be T. But $\overline{q}$ provides a path through the part of the circuit corresponding to the expression in brackets, so the value of r doesn't matter. This gives two more possibilities: p is T, q is F, r is T, and p is T, q is F, and r is F.

11. $p \vee q \vee (r \wedge \overline{p})$

Reading from the circuit, we can see that the only case in which the bulb will *not* light is: p is F, q is F, and r is F.

12. $[(p \wedge \overline{q}) \vee (\overline{p} \wedge q)] \vee (p \wedge q)$

If either p or q is T, the expression in brackets will be T and current can travel through the corresponding part of the circuit to light the bulb. Thus the only case in with the bulb will *not* light is when p and q are both F.

13.

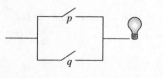

14.

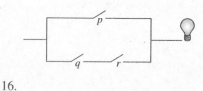

15.

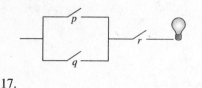

16.

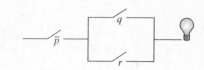

17.

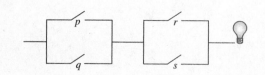

18.

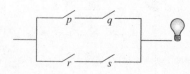

19.

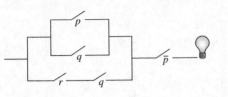

20.

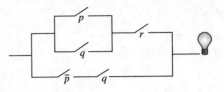

21. $p \vee q$; $\overline{p} \wedge \overline{q}$

Not equivalent; in fact, by De Morgan's laws,
$(p \vee q) \Leftrightarrow (\overline{\overline{p} \wedge \overline{q}})$, so the first circuit will light
the bulb exactly when the second one does not.

22. $p \wedge (q \vee r)$; $(p \wedge q) \vee (p \wedge r)$

p	q	r	p	∧	(q∨r)
T	T	T	T	T	T
T	T	F	T	T	T
T	F	T	T	T	T
T	F	F	T	F	F
F	T	T	F	F	T
F	T	F	F	F	T
F	F	T	F	F	T
F	F	F	F	F	F

p	q	r	(p∧q)	∨	(p∧r)
T	T	T	T	T	T
T	T	F	T	T	F
T	F	T	F	T	T
T	F	F	F	F	F
F	T	T	F	F	F
F	T	F	F	F	F
F	F	T	F	F	F
F	F	F	F	F	F

The next-to-last column of each table is the same, so the circuits are equivalent.

23. $[(p \wedge q) \vee r] \wedge p$; $(q \vee r) \wedge p$

Clearly both circuits light the bulb only if p is T.
In this case $p \wedge q$ has the same value as q alone,
so $(p \wedge q) \vee r$ will have the same value as $q \vee r$.
Thus the two circuits are equivalent.

24. $(p \vee r) \wedge (q \vee r)$; $(p \wedge q) \vee r$

p	q	r	(p∨r)	∧	(q∨r)
T	T	T	T	T	T
T	T	F	T	T	T
T	F	T	T	T	T
T	F	F	T	F	F
F	T	T	T	T	T
F	T	F	F	F	T
F	F	T	T	T	T
F	F	F	F	F	F

p	q	r	(p∧q)	∨	r
T	T	T	T	T	T
T	T	F	T	T	F
T	F	T	F	T	T
T	F	F	F	F	F
F	T	T	F	T	T
F	T	F	F	F	F
F	F	T	F	T	T
F	F	F	F	F	F

The next-to-last column of each table is the same, so the circuits are equivalent.

25. $(p \vee \overline{p}) \wedge q \wedge r; \quad p \wedge q \wedge r$

   Not equivalent, since the first circuit will light the bulb when p is F, q is T and r is T, while p being F breaks the second circuit.

26. $[(p \wedge q) \vee (r \wedge \overline{q})] \vee (r \wedge \overline{p}); \quad (p \vee r) \wedge (q \vee r)$

p	q	r	$[(p \wedge q)$	$\vee$	$(r \wedge \overline{q})]$	$\vee$	$(r \wedge \overline{p})$
T	T	T	T	T	F	T	F
T	T	F	T	T	F	T	F
T	F	T	F	T	T	T	F
T	F	F	F	F	F	F	F
F	T	T	F	F	F	T	T
F	T	F	F	F	F	F	F
F	F	T	F	T	T	T	T
F	F	F	F	F	F	F	F

p	q	r	$(p \vee r)$	$\wedge$	$(q \vee r)$
T	T	T	T	T	T
T	T	F	T	T	T
T	F	T	T	T	T
T	F	F	T	F	F
F	T	T	T	T	T
F	T	F	F	F	T
F	F	T	T	T	T
F	F	F	F	F	F

   The next-to-last column of each table is the same, so the circuits are equivalent.

27. a)

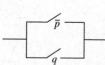

   b)

28. Answers will vary

Review Exercises

1. Some gift cards are exchangeable.

2. Some bears are not mammals.

3. No women are presidents.

4. All pine trees are green.

5. The coffee is Maxwell House or the coffee is hot.

6. The coffee is not hot and the coffee is strong.

7. If the coffee is hot, then the coffee is strong and it is not Maxwell House.

8. The coffee is Maxwell House if and only if the coffee is not strong.

9. The coffee is not Maxwell House, if and only if the coffee is strong and the coffee is not hot.

10. The coffee is Maxwell House or the coffee is not hot, and the coffee is not strong.

11. $r \wedge q$

12. $p \rightarrow r$

13. $(r \rightarrow q) \vee \sim p$

14. $(q \leftrightarrow p) \wedge \sim r$

15. $(r \wedge q) \vee \sim p$

16. $\sim (r \wedge q)$

17.

p	q	(p	∨	q)	∧	~ p
T	T		T		F	F
T	F		T		F	F
F	T		T		T	T
F	F		F		F	T
			1		3	2

18.

p	q	q	↔	(p	∨	~ q)
T	T	T	T	T	T	F
T	F	F	F	T	T	T
F	T	T	F	F	F	F
F	F	F	F	F	T	T
		1	5	2	4	3

19.

p	q	r	(p	∨	q)	↔	(p	∨	r)
T	T	T		T		T		T	
T	T	F		T		T		T	
T	F	T		T		T		T	
T	F	F		T		T		T	
F	T	T		T		T		T	
F	T	F		T		F		F	
F	F	T		F		F		T	
F	F	F		F		T		F	
				1		3		2	

20.

p	q	r	p	∧	(~ q	∨	r)
T	T	T	T	T	F	T	T
T	T	F	T	F	F	F	F
T	F	T	T	T	T	T	T
T	F	F	T	T	T	T	F
F	T	T	F	F	F	T	T
F	T	F	F	F	F	F	F
F	F	T	F	F	T	T	T
F	F	F	F	F	T	T	F
			4	5	1	3	2

21.

p	q	r	P	→	(q	∧	~ r)
T	T	T	T	F	T	F	F
T	T	F	T	T	T	T	T
T	F	T	T	F	F	F	F
T	F	F	T	F	F	F	T
F	T	T	F	T	T	F	F
F	T	F	F	T	T	T	T
F	F	T	F	T	F	F	F
F	F	F	F	T	F	F	T
			4	5	1	3	2

22.

p	q	r	(p ∧ q)	→	~ r
T	T	T	T	F	F
T	T	F	T	T	T
T	F	T	F	T	F
T	F	F	F	T	T
F	T	T	F	T	F
F	T	F	F	T	T
F	F	T	F	T	F
F	F	F	F	T	T
			1	3	2

23. The premises are true but the conclusion is false and T → F is false, so the statement is false.

24. Since $17 + 4 = 21$ and $3 - 9 = -6$, both of the statements joined by *and* are true, so the compound statement is true.

25. p: Oregon borders the Pacific Ocean.
q: California borders the Atlantic Ocean.
r: Minnesota is south of Texas.
(p ∨ q) → r
(T ∨ F) → F
   T → F
     F

26. p: $15 - 7 = 22$ (p ∨ q) ∧ r
q: $4 + 9 = 13$ (F ∨ T) ∧ T
r : $9 - 8 = 1$ T ∧ T
                          T

27. (p → ~ r) ∨ (p ∧ q)
(T → T) ∨ (T ∧ F)
   T   ∨ F
       T

28. (p ∨ q) ↔ (~ r ∧ p)
(T ∨ F) ↔ (T ∧ T)
  T   ↔   T
      T

29. ~ r ↔ [(p ∨ q) ↔ ~ p]
 T ↔ [(T ∨ F) ↔ F]
 T ↔ [T   ↔ F]
 T ↔   F
    F

30. ~ [(q ∧ r) → (~ p ∨ r)]
 ~ [(F ∧ F) → (F ∨ F)]
 ~ [F   →   F]
      ~ T
       F

31.

p	q	~ p ∨ ~ q	~ p ↔ q
T	T	F F F	F F T
T	F	F T T	F T F
F	T	T T F	T T T
F	F	T T T	T F F
		1 3 2	1 3 2

The statements are not equivalent.

32. Using the fact that (p → q) ⇔ (~ p ∨ q), we can conclude that ~ p → ~ q ⇔ p ∨ ~ q.

33.

p	q	r	~ p ∨ (q ∧ r)	(~ p ∨ q) ∧ (~ p ∨ r)
T	T	T	F T T	F T T T F T T
T	T	F	F F F	F T T F F F F
T	F	T	F F F	F F F F F T T
T	F	F	F F F	F F F F F F F
F	T	T	T T T	T T T T T T
F	T	F	T T F	T T T T T F
F	F	T	T T F	T T F T T T
F	F	F	T T F	T T F T T F
			2 3 1	1 3 2 7 4 6 5

The statements are equivalent.

34.

p	q	(~ q → p) ∧ p	~ (~ p ↔ q) ∨ p
T	T	F T T T T	T F F T T T
T	F	T T T T T	F F T F T T
F	T	F T F F F	F T T T F F
F	F	T F F F F	T T F F T F
		1 3 2 5 4	4 1 3 2 6 5

The statements are not equivalent.

35. p: Bobby Darin sang *Mack the Knife*.

q: Elvis wrote *Memphis*.
In symbolic form, the statement is p ∧ ~q. We are given that p ∧ ~q ⇔ ~(p → q). So an equivalent statement is: It is false that if Bobby Darin sang *Mack the Knife* then Elvis wrote *Memphis*.

36. p: Lynn Swann played for the Steelers.

q: Jack Tatum played for the Raiders.
In symbolic form, the statement is p ∨ q.
We are given that ~p ∨ q ⇔ (p → q), so p ∨ q ⇔ (~p → q). Thus an equivalent statement is: If Lynn Swann did not play for the Steelers then Jack Tatum played for the Raiders.

37. p: Altec Lansing only produces speakers.

q: Harmon Kardon only produces stereo receivers.
The symbolic form is ~ (p ∨ q).
Using De Morgan's Laws, we get
~ (p ∨ q) ⇔ ~ p ∧ ~ q.
Altec Lansing does not produce only speakers and Harmon Kardon does not produce only stereo receivers.

38. p: Travis Tritt won an Academy Award.

q: Randy Jackson does commercials for Milk Bone dog biscuits.
The symbolic form is ~ p ∧ ~ q.
Using De Morgan's Laws, we get
~ p ∧ ~ q ⇔ ~ (p ∨ q). It is false that Travis Tritt won an Academy Award or Randy Jackson does commercials for Milk Bone dog biscuits.

39. p: The temperature is above 32 degrees Fahrenheit.
q: We will go ice fishing at O'Leary's Lake.
The symbolic form is ~ p → q.
Using DeMorgan's Laws, we get ~ p → q ⇔ p ∨ q.
The temperature is above 32 degrees Fahrenheit or we will go ice fishing at O'Leary's Lake.

40. Converse: If you soften your opinion, then you hear a new voice today.

Inverse: If you don't hear a new voice today then you don't soften your opinion

Contrapositive: If you don't soften your opinion, then you don't hear a new voice today.

41. Converse: If we are going to learn the table's value then we take the table to *Antiques Roadshow*.

    Inverse: If we do not take the table to *Antiques Roadshow*, then we will not learn the table's value.

    Contrapositive: If we are not going to learn the table's value then we do not take the table to *Antiques Roadshow*.

42. Converse: If Maureen Gerald is helping at school, then she is not in attendance.

    Inverse: If Maureen Gerald is in attendance, then she is not helping at school.

    Contrapositive: If Maureen Gerald is not helping at school, then she is in attendance.

43. Converse: If we do not buy a desk at Miller's Furniture, then the desk is made by Winner's Only and is in the Rose catalog.

    Inverse: If we will buy a desk at Miller's furniture, then the desk is not made by Winner's Only or it is not in the Rose catalog.

    Contrapositive: If the desk is not made by Winner's Only or is not in the Rose catalog, then we will buy a desk at Miller's Furniture.

44. Converse: If I let you attend the prom, then you get straight A's on your report card.

    Inverse: If you do not get straight A's on your report card, then I will not let you attend the prom.

    Contrapositive: If I do not let you attend the prom, then you do not get straight A's on your report card.

45. p: You read 10 books in the summer.
    q: You reach your goal.
    In symbolic form, the statements are: a) $p \rightarrow q$, b) $\sim p \vee q$, and c) $\sim (p \wedge \sim q)$. Using the fact that $p \rightarrow q$ is equivalent to $\sim p \vee q$, statements (a) and (b) are equivalent. Using DeMorgan's Laws on statement (b) we get $\sim (p \wedge \sim q)$.

    Therefore all 3 statements are equivalent.

46. p: The screwdriver is on the workbench.
    q: The screwdriver is on the counter.
    In symbolic form, the statements are: a) $p \leftrightarrow \sim q$, b) $\sim q \rightarrow \sim p$, and c) $\sim (q \wedge \sim p)$. Looking at the truth tables for statements (a), (b), and (c) we can conclude that none of the statements are equivalent.

p	q	a) $p \leftrightarrow \sim q$			b) $\sim q \rightarrow \sim p$			c) $\sim (q \wedge \sim p)$			
T	T	T	F	F	F	T	F	T	T	F	F
T	F	T	T	T	T	F	F	T	F	F	F
F	T	F	T	F	F	T	T	F	T	T	T
F	F	F	F	T	T	T	T	T	F	F	T
		1	3	2	1	3	2	4	1	3	2

47. p: $2 + 3 = 6$.
    q: $3 + 1 = 5$.
    In symbolic form, the statements are: a) $p \rightarrow q$,
    b) $p \leftrightarrow \sim q$, and c) $\sim q \rightarrow \sim p$.
    Statement (c) is the contrapositive of statement
    (a). Therefore statements (a) and (c) are equivalent.
    For p and q false, (a) and (c) are true but (b) is false,
    so (b) is not equivalent to (a) and (c).

48. p: The sale is on Tuesday.
    q: I have money.
    r : I will go to the sale.
    In symbolic form the statements are: a) $(p \wedge q) \rightarrow r$,
    b) $r \rightarrow (p \wedge q)$, and c) $r \vee (p \wedge q)$. The truth table for
    statements (a), (b), and (c) shows that none of the
    statements are equivalent.

p	q	r	$(p \wedge q) \rightarrow r$			$r \rightarrow (p \wedge q)$			$r \vee (p \wedge q)$		
T	T	T	T	T	T	T	T	T	T	T	T
T	T	F	T	F	F	F	T	T	F	T	T
T	F	T	F	T	T	T	F	F	T	T	F
T	F	F	F	T	F	F	T	F	F	F	F
F	T	T	F	T	T	T	F	F	T	T	F
F	T	F	F	T	F	F	T	F	F	F	F
F	F	T	F	T	T	T	F	F	T	T	F
F	F	F	F	T	F	F	T	F	F	F	F
			1	3	2	1	3	2	1	3	2

49.

p	q	$[(p \rightarrow q) \wedge \sim p] \rightarrow q$				
T	T	T	F	F	T	T
T	F	F	F	F	T	F
F	T	T	T	T	T	T
F	F	T	T	T	F	F
		1	3	2	5	4

The argument is invalid.

50.

p	q	r	$[(p \wedge q) \wedge (q \rightarrow r)] \rightarrow (p \rightarrow r)$				
T	T	T	T	T	T	T	T
T	T	F	T	F	F	T	F
T	F	T	F	F	T	T	T
T	F	F	F	F	T	T	F
F	T	T	F	F	T	T	T
F	T	F	F	F	F	T	T
F	F	T	F	F	T	T	T
F	F	F	F	F	T	T	T
			1	3	2	5	4

The argument is valid.

51. p: Jose Macias is the manager.
   q: Kevin Geis is the coach.
   r: Tim Weisman is the umpire

   $p \rightarrow q$
   $\underline{q \rightarrow r}$
   $\therefore\; p \rightarrow r$

   This argument is in the form of the law of syllogism so it is valid.

52. p: We eat at Joe's. $p \rightarrow q$
    p: We get heartburn. $\underline{q \vee r}$
    r : We take Tums. $\therefore\; \sim q$

    If p is F, q is T, and r is either T or F, the premises are both true but the conclusion is false, so the argument is invalid.

53.

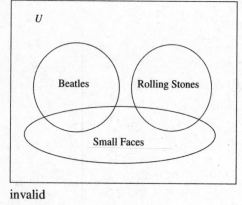

invalid

54.

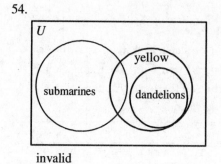

invalid

55.

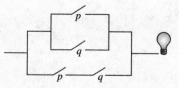

invalid

56.

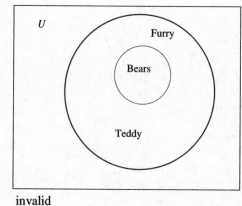

invalid

57. a) $p \wedge \left[(q \wedge r) \vee \bar{p}\right]$

   b) For the bulb to be on, the first switch on the left must be closed, so p is T. The eliminates the bottom branch of the parallel portion, so both switches on the top branch must be closed. Thus the bulb lights exactly when p, q, and r are all T

58.

59. Symbolically the two circuits are $(p \vee q) \wedge (\overline{q} \vee \overline{p})$ and $(p \wedge \overline{q}) \vee (q \wedge \overline{p})$.

p	q	$\overline{p}$	$\overline{q}$	$(p \vee q)$	$\wedge$	$(\overline{q} \vee \overline{p})$	p	q	$\overline{p}$	$\overline{q}$	$(p \wedge \overline{q})$	$\vee$	$(q \wedge \overline{p})$
T	T	F	F	T	F	F	T	T	F	F	F	F	F
T	F	F	T	T	T	T	T	F	F	T	T	T	F
F	T	T	F	T	T	T	F	T	T	F	F	T	T
F	F	T	T	F	F	T	F	F	T	T	F	F	F

The next-to last columns of these truth tables are identical, so the circuits are equivalent.

Chapter Test

1. $(p \wedge r) \vee \sim q$

2. $(r \rightarrow q) \vee \sim p$

3. $\sim (r \leftrightarrow \sim q)$

4. Ann is not the secretary and Elaine is the president, if and only if Dick is not the vice president.

5. If Ann is the secretary or Dick is not the vice president, then Elaine is the president.

6.

p	q	r	[~ (p → r)] ∧ q			
T	T	T	F	T	F	T
T	T	F	T	F	T	T
T	F	T	F	T	F	F
T	F	F	T	F	F	F
F	T	T	F	T	F	T
F	T	F	F	T	F	T
F	F	T	F	T	F	F
F	F	F	F	T	F	F
			2	1	4	3

7.

p	q	r	(q ↔ ~ r) ∨ p				
T	T	T	T	F	F	T	T
T	T	F	T	T	T	T	T
T	F	T	F	T	F	T	T
T	F	F	F	F	T	T	T
F	T	T	T	F	F	F	F
F	T	F	T	T	T	T	F
F	F	T	F	T	F	T	F
F	F	F	F	F	T	F	F
			1	3	2	5	4

8. p: $2 + 6 = 8$
   q: $7 - 12 = 5$
   $p \vee q$
   $T \vee F$
   T

9. p: A scissors can cut paper.
   q: A dime equals 2 nickels.
   r : Louisville is a city in Kentucky.
   $(p \vee q) \leftrightarrow r$
   $(T \vee T) \leftrightarrow T$
   $T \quad \leftrightarrow T$
   T

10. $(r \vee q) \leftrightarrow (p \wedge \sim q)$
    $(T \vee F) \leftrightarrow (T \wedge T)$
    $T \quad \leftrightarrow \quad T$
    T

11. $[\sim(r \rightarrow \sim p)] \wedge (q \rightarrow p)$
    $[\sim(T \rightarrow F)] \wedge (F \rightarrow T)$
    $[\quad \sim(F)\quad] \wedge \quad T$
    $\qquad T \qquad \wedge \quad T$
    $\qquad\qquad T$

12. By DeMorgan's Laws ,
    $\sim p \vee q \Leftrightarrow \sim (\sim (\sim p) \wedge \sim q)$.
    and this is equivalent to
    $\sim(p \wedge \sim q)$.

13. p: The bird is red.
    q: It is a cardinal.
    In symbolic form the statements
    are: a) $p \rightarrow q$, b) $\sim p \vee q$,
    and c) $\sim p \rightarrow \sim q$.
    Statement (c) is the inverse of
    statement (a) and thus they cannot
    be equivalent. Using the fact that
    $p \rightarrow q \Leftrightarrow \sim p \vee q$, to rewrite
    statement (a) we get $\sim p \vee q$.
    Therefore statements (a) and (b)
    are equivalent.

14. p: The test is today.   q: The concert is tonight. In symbolic form the
    statements are: a) $\sim (p \vee q)$, b) $\sim p \wedge \sim q$, and $\sim p \rightarrow \sim q$.
    Applying DeMorgan's Law to statement (a) we get: $\sim p \wedge \sim q$.
    Therefore statements (a) and (b) are equivalent. When we compare
    the truth tables for statements (a), (b), and (c) we see that only
    statements (a) and (b) are equivalent.

p	q	$\sim$	(p $\vee$ q)	$\sim$ p	$\wedge$	$\sim$ q	$\sim$ p	$\rightarrow$	$\sim$ q
T	T	F	T	F	F	F	F	T	F
T	F	F	T	F	F	T	F	T	T
F	T	F	T	T	F	F	T	F	F
F	F	T	F	T	T	T	T	T	T
		2	1	1	3	2	1	3	2

15. s: The soccer team won the game.
    f: Sue played fullback.
    p: The team is in second place.
    This argument is the law of
    syllogism and therefore it is
    valid.
    $$s \rightarrow f$$
    $$\underline{f \rightarrow p}$$
    $$s \rightarrow p$$
    This argument is the law of
    syllogism and therefore it is valid.

16.

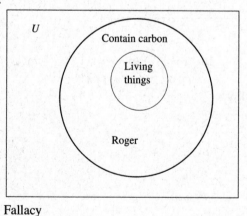

Fallacy

17. Some highways are not roads

18. Nick did not play football or Max
    did not play baseball.

19. Converse: If today is Saturday, then the
    garbage truck comes.
    Inverse: If the garbage truck does not
    come today, then today is not Saturday.
    Contrapositive: If today is not Saturday,
    then the garbage truck does not come.

20.

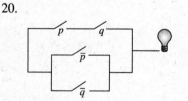

Group Projects

1. a) 4,   p closed, q closed   p closed, q open
            p open, q closed   p open, q open

b)

p	q	p∧q
1	1	1
1	0	0
0	1	0
0	0	0

c) If a closed switch is represented as T and an open
   switch is represented as F, and the bulb lighting as T,
   and the bulb not lighting as F, then the table would be
   identical to the truth table for p ∧q.

d)

p	q	p∨q
1	1	1
1	0	1
0	1	1
0	0	0

f) (p ∧ q) ∨ r

g)

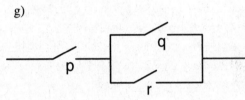

2. a) The tables have the same truth values as the *not, and*
      and *or* tables respectively.
   b) 0   c) 1   d) 0
   e) $I_a = 0$, $I_b = 1$ or $I_a = 1$, $I_b = 0$

.f)

I_a	I_b	O
1	1	1
1	0	0
0	1	1
0	0	1

CHAPTER FOUR

SYSTEMS OF NUMERATION

Exercise Set 4.1

1. A **number** is a quantity, and it answers the question, "How many?" A **numeral** is a symbol used to represent the number.

2. $\cap$, x, ✝, ι, 10

3. A **system of numeration** consists of a set of numerals and a scheme or rule for combining the numerals to represent numbers.

4. $\mathcal{O}$, C, 百, ρ, 100

5. The Hindu-Arabic numeration system

6. In an **additive system**, the sum of the values of the numerals equals the number.

7. In a **multiplicative system**, there are numerals for each number less than the base and for powers of the base. Each numeral less than the base is multiplied by a numeral for the power of the base, and these products are added to obtain the number.

8. In a **ciphered system**, the number represented by a particular set of numerals is the sum of the values of the numerals.

9. $100+100+100+10+10+10+10$
   $+1+1+1+1+1=345$

10. $1000+100+100+10+1+1+1=1213$

11. $1000+1000+100+100+100+100+10+10$
    $+1+1+1=2423$

12. $10,000+10,000+10,000+10,000+1000$
    $+100+100+10=41,210$

13. $100,000+100,000+100,000+10,000$
    $+10,000+10,000+1000+1000+1000+1000$
    $+100+100+10+1+1+1+1=334,214$

14. $1,000,000+1,000,000+1,000,000+100,000$
    $+100,000+100,000+100+100+100+100$
    $+10+10+10+1=3,300,431$

15. $\cap\cap\cap\cap|||$

16. $99\cap|||||$

17. $\int\int\cap\cap|||||$

18. $\int 99999999\cap||$

19. ⋈⨝$|||||||\int\int\int$99999999$\cap\cap|||||$

20. 𐀀𐀀𐀀⋈⨝$|||\int\int\int\int\int$99999$\cap|||||$

21. $5+1+1+1=8$

22. $10+10+(10-1)=29$

23. $(50-10)+1+1+1=43$

24. $(500-100)+50+10+10+(5-1)=474$

25. $1000+100+100+10+10+10+5+1=1236$

26. $1000+(1000-100)+50+10+(5-1)=1964$

27. $1000+1000+(1000-100)+(50-10)+5+1$
    $=2946$

28. $1000+500+100+100+(50-10)+5+1$
    $=1746$

29. $10(1000)+1000+1000+500+100+50+10$
$+5+1=12,666$

30. $50(1000)+1000+(1000-100)+(50-10)$
$+(5-1)=51,944$

31. $9(1000)+(500-100)+50+10+(5-1)=9464$

32. $5(1000)+1000+100+100+100+10+10$
$+10+1+1+1=6333$

33. XXVII

34. LXXXIX

35. CCCXLI

36. CDLXXVII

37. MMV

38. $\overline{\overline{\text{IV}}}$CCLXXXV

39. $\overline{\text{IV}}$DCCXCIII

40. $\overline{\text{VI}}$CCLXXIV

41. $\overline{\text{IX}}$CMXCIX

42. $\overline{\text{XIV}}$CCCXV

43. $\overline{\text{XX}}$DCXLIV

44. $\overline{\text{XCIX}}$CMXCIX

45. $7(10)+4=74$

46. $6(10)+2=62$

47. $4(1000)+8(10)+1=4081$

48. $3(1000)+2(10)+9=3029$

49. $8(1000)+5(100)+5(10)=8550$

50. $3(1000)+4(100)+8(10)+7=3487$

51. $4(1000)+3=4003$

52. $5(1000)+6(100)+2=5602$

53. 五十三

54. 一百七十八

55. 三百七十八

56. 二千零一

57. 四千二百六十

58. 六千九百零五

59. 七千零五十六

60. 三千零九

61. $20 + 6 = 26$
63. $200 + 70 + 9 = 279$
65. $2 \times 1000 + 800 + 80 + 3 = 2883$
67. $\nu \, \theta$
69. $\psi \, \kappa$ digamma
71. $'\varepsilon \, \varepsilon$

62. $100 + 30 + 8 = 138$
64. $900 + 5 = 905$
66. $7 \times 1000 + 400 + 60 + 7 = 7467$
68. $\rho \, o \, \eta$
70. $'\beta \eta$
72. $'\theta$ sampi koppa θ

73. $1000 + 10 + 10 + 1 = 1021$, MXXI, $'\alpha \, \kappa \, \alpha$

一千零二十一

74. $1000 + (1000 - 100) + 10 + 10 + 10 + 5 + 1 = 1936$,

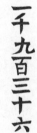

$'\alpha$ sampi λ digamma,

一千九百三十六

75. $5(100) + 2(10) + 7 = 527$,

𐅵𐅵𐅵𐅵𐅵ΝΙΙΙΙΙΙΙ, DXXVII, $\phi \, \kappa \, \zeta$

76. $400 + 20 + 2 = 422$, 𐅵𐅵𐅵𐅵ΝΙΙ, CDXXII,

四百二十二

77. $\overline{\text{CMXCIX}}$CMXCIX

78. a) – c) Answers will vary.

79. Advantage: You can write some numbers more compactly.
    Disadvantage: There are more numerals to memorize.
80. Advantage: Numbers are written in a more compact form.
    Disadvantage: There are more symbols to remember.
81. Advantage: You can write some numbers more compactly.
    Disadvantage: There are more numerals to memorize.
    The Hindu-Arabic system has fewer symbols, more compact notation, the inclusion of zero, and the
    capability of expressing decimal numbers and fractions.
82. Turn the book upside down.
83. MM
84. 1888, MDCCCLXXXVIII
85. a) , b) Answers will vary.

Exercise Set 4.2

1. Positional value system
2. A base 10 place-value system
3. $40 \rightarrow$ four tens, $400 \rightarrow$ four hundreds
4. Base 10, because we have 10 fingers.
5. a) 10
   b) 0, 1, 2, 3, 4, 5, 6, 7, 8, 9
6. A true positional-value system requires a base and a set of symbols, including a symbol for zero and one for each counting number less than the base.
7. Write each digit times its corresponding positional value.
8. It lacked a symbol for zero.
9. a) There may be confusion because numbers could be interpreted in different ways. For example, ❙ could be interpreted to be either 1 or 60.
   b) ❙❙   ❮❙❙❙ for both numbers; $133 = 2(60) + 13(1)$ and $7980 = 133(60)$
10. $(10+1)(1) = 11$ and $(10+1)(60) = 660$
11. $1, 20, 18 \times 20, 18 \times (20)^2, 18 \times (20)^3$
12. The Mayan system has a different base and the numbers are written vertically.

13. $(2 \times 10) + (3 \times 1)$
14. $(8 \times 10) + (4 \times 1)$
15. $(3 \times 100) + (5 \times 10) + (9 \times 1)$
16. $(5 \times 100) + (6 \times 10) + (2 \times 1)$
17. $(8 \times 100) + (9 \times 10) + (7 \times 1)$
18. $(3 \times 1000) + (7 \times 100) + (6 \times 10) + (9 \times 1)$
19. $(4 \times 1000) + (3 \times 100) + (8 \times 10) + (7 \times 1)$
20. $(2 \times 10,000) + (3 \times 1000) + (4 \times 100) + (6 \times 10) + (8 \times 1)$

21. $(1 \times 10,000) + (6 \times 1000) + (4 \times 100) + (0 \times 10) + (2 \times 1)$
22. $(1 \times 100,000) + (2 \times 10,000) + (5 \times 1000) + (6 \times 100) + (7 \times 10) + (8 \times 1)$
23. $(3 \times 100,000) + (4 \times 10,000) + (6 \times 1000) + (8 \times 100) + (6 \times 10) + (1 \times 1)$
24. $(3 \times 1,000,000) + (7 \times 100,000) + (6 \times 10,000) + (5 \times 1000) + (9 \times 100) + (3 \times 10) + (4 \times 1)$
25. $(10+1+1+1+1)(1) = 14$
26. $(10+(10-1))(1) = 19$
27. $(10+1+1+1)(60) + (1+1+1+1)(1) = 13(60) + 4(1) = 780 + 4 = 784$
28. $(10+1)(60) + ((10+10)-(1+1+1))(1) = 11(60) + (20-3)(1) = 660 + 17 = 677$
29. $1(60^2) + (10+10+1)(60) + (10-(1+1))(1) = 3600 + 21(60) + (10-2)(1) = 3600 + 1260 + 8 = 4868$
30. $10(60^2) + ((10+10)-(1+1+1))(60) + (1+1)(1) = 10(3600) + (20-3)(60) + 2 = 36,000 + 17(60) + 2$
    $= 36,000 + 1020 + 2 = 37,022$
31. 35 is 35 units. ❮❮❮❙❙❙❙❙
32. 129 is 2 group of 60 and 9 units remaining. ❙❙ ❮❙̃❙
33. 471 is 7 groups of 60 and 51 units remaining. ❮❙̃❙❙❙   ❮❮❮❮❮❙

34. 512 is 8 groups of 60 and 32 units remaining. ⟨𝐓𝐈𝐈 ⟨⟨⟨𝐈𝐈

35. 3685 is 1 group of 3600, 1 group of 60, and 25 units remaining. 𝐈 𝐈 ⟨⟨𝐈𝐈𝐈𝐈𝐈

36. 12435 is 3 groups of 3600, 27 groups of 60, and 15 units remaining. 𝐈𝐈𝐈 ⟨⟨⟨𝐓𝐈𝐈𝐈 ⟨𝐈𝐈𝐈𝐈𝐈

37. $2(20)+17(1) = 40+17 = 57$

38. $10(20)+7(1) = 200+7 = 207$

39. $13(18\times20)+0(20)+2(1) = 4680+0+2 = 4682$

40. $7(18\times20)+9(20)+7(1) = 2520+180+7 = 2707$

41. $11(18\times20)+2(20)+0(1) = 3960+40+0 = 4000$

42. $2(18\times20)+10(20)+10(1) = 720+200+10 = 930$

43.

44.
$$20 \overline{)\,257}$$
$$\underline{20}$$
$$57$$
$$\underline{40}$$
$$17$$

$$257 = 12(20)+17(1)$$

45.
$$20 \overline{)\,297}$$
$$\underline{280}$$
$$17$$

$$297 = 14(20)+17(1)$$

46.
$$360 \overline{)\,406} \qquad 20 \overline{)\,46}$$
$$\underline{360} \qquad\qquad \underline{40}$$
$$46 \qquad\qquad\quad 6$$

$$406 = 1(18\times20)+2(20)+6(1)$$

47.
$$360 \overline{)\,2163}$$
$$\underline{2160}$$
$$3$$

$$2163 = 6(360)+0(20)+3(1)$$

48.

	2			9			3	••

$7200 \overline{\smash{)}17{,}708}$ $17{,}708$ $360 \overline{\smash{)}3308}$ 3308 $20 \overline{\smash{)}68}$ ••••

$\underline{14{,}400}$ $\underline{3240}$ $\underline{60}$ •••

3308 68 8 •••

$$17{,}708 = 2\left(18 \times 20^2\right) + 9(18 \times 20) + 3(20) + 8(1)$$

49. Hindu-Arabic:

$5(18 \times 20) + 7(20) + 4(1) = 1800 + 140 + 4 = 1944$

Babylonian: $1944 = 32(60) + 24(1)$

❮❮❮❮❙❙ ❮❮❮❙❙❙❙

50. Hindu-Arabic: $10 + 10 + 10 + 1 + 1 + 1 = 33$

Mayan: $33 = 1(20) + 13(1)$ •

•••
‗

51. $\left(\triangle \times \ominus^2\right) + \left(\square \times \ominus\right) + \left(\Diamond \times 1\right)$

52. $\left(\ominus \times \ominus^3\right) + \left(\triangle \times \ominus^2\right) + \left(\Diamond \times \ominus\right) + \left(\square \times 1\right)$

53. a) No largest number; The positional values above 18×20 are $18 \times 20^2, 18 \times 20^3, \ldots$

b) $999{,}999 = 6\left(18 \times 20^3\right) + 18\left(18 \times 20^2\right) + 17(18 \times 20) + 13(20) + 19(1)$

•
‗
•••
‗
••
‗
•••
‗
••••

54. a) No largest number; The positional values are $\ldots, (60)^3, (60)^2, 60, 1$.

b) $999{,}999 = 4(60)^3 + 37(60)^2 + 46(60) + 39(1)$

❙❙❙❙   ❮❮❮❮❮❙̂❙❙❙   ❮❮❮❮❮❙❙❙❙❙❙   ❮❮❮❮❮❙̂❙

55. $2(60) + 23(1) = 120 + 23 = 143$

23

$143 + 23 = 166$

$166 = 2(60) + 46(1)$ ❙❙   ❮❮❮❮❮❮❙̂❙❙❙❙

56. $3(60)+33(1)=180+33=213$

    32

    $213-32=181$

    $181=3(60)+1(1)$ ▼▼▼   ▼

57. $7(18\times20)+6(20)+15(1)=2520+120+15=2655$

    $6(18\times20)+7(20)+13(1)=2160+140+13=2313$

    $2655+2313=4968$

    $4968=13(18\times20)+14(20)+8(1)$

58. $6(18\times20)+7(20)+13(1)=2160+140+13=2313$

    $2655-2313=342$

    $342=17(20)+2(1)$

59. Advantages: In general, a place-value system is more compact; large and small numbers can be written more easily; there are fewer symbols to memorize.

    Disadvantage: If many of the symbols in the numeral represent zero, then a place-value system may be less compact.

60. Answers will vary.

61. Answers will vary.

62. Answers will vary.

Exercise Set 4.3

1. a) Multiply each digit by its positional value and find the sum of these products.

    b) Divide the base 10 numeral by the highest power of the base that is smaller than the base 10 numeral. Record the quotient and repeat the procedure with the remainder, using the next lower power of the base. Continue until the remainder is smaller than the base. The list of quotients followed by the remainder is the numeral in the new base.

2. a) 0, 1

    b) 0, 1, 2, 3, 4, 5, 6, 7

    c) 0, 1, 2, 3, 4, 5, 6, 7, 8, 9, A, B

    d) 0, 1, 2, 3, 4, 5, 6, 7, 8, 9, A, B, C, D, E, F

3. a) The last digit is equal to the base; all digits should represent numbers smaller than the base.

    b) The only digits used in base 2 are 0 and 1, so 3 cannot be part of a base 2 numeral.

    c) There is no digit L in base 12.

    d) There is no digit G in base 16.

4. a) $10_2=(1\times2)+(0\times1)=2$

    b) $10_8=(1\times8)+(0\times1)=8$

    c) $10_{16}=(1\times16)+(0\times1)=16$

    d) $10_{32}=(1\times32)+(0\times1)=32$

5. $1_2=1\times1=1$

6. $10_2=(1\times2)+(0\times1)=2$

7. $23_5=(2\times5)+(3\times1)=13$

8. $41_5 = (4 \times 5) + (1 \times 1) = 21$

9. $270_8 = (2 \times 64) + (7 \times 8) + (0 \times 1) = 184$

10. $306_8 = (3 \times 64) + (0 \times 8) + (6 \times 1) = 198$

11. $309_{12} = (3 \times 144) + (0 \times 12) + (9 \times 1) = 441$

12. $1005_{12} = (1 \times 1728) + (0 \times 144) + (0 \times 12) + (5 \times 1) = 1733$

13. $573_{16} = (5 \times 256) + (7 \times 16) + (3 \times 1) = 1395$

14. $423_{16} = (4 \times 256) + (2 \times 16) + (3 \times 1) = 1059$

15. $110101_2 = 32 + 16 + 4 + 1 = 53$

16. $1110111_2 = 64 + 32 + 16 + 4 + 2 + 1 = 119$

17. $7654_8 = (7 \times 512) + (6 \times 64) + (5 \times 8) + (4 \times 1) = 4012$

18. $5032_8 = (5 \times 512) + (0 \times 64) + (3 \times 8) + (2 \times 1) = 2586$

19. $A91_{12} = (10 \times 144) + (9 \times 12) + 1 = 1549$

20. $B52_{12} = (11 \times 144) + (5 \times 12) + 2 = 1646$

21. $C679_{16} = (12 \times 4096) + (6 \times 256) + (7 \times 16) + 9 = 50,809$

22. $D20E_{16} = (13 \times 4096) + (2 \times 256) + (0 \times 16) + 14 = 53,774$

23. To convert 6 to base 2   ... 16 8 4 2 1

$$
\begin{array}{ccc}
\quad 1 & \quad 1 & \quad 0 \\
4\,\overline{)\,6} & 2\,\overline{)\,2} & 0\,\overline{)\,0} \\
\underline{\;4\;} & \underline{\;2\;} & \underline{\;0\;} \\
2 & 0 & 0
\end{array}
\qquad 6 = 110_2
$$

24. To convert 25 to base 2   ... 32 16 8 4 2 1

$$
\begin{array}{ccccc}
\quad 1 & \quad 1 & \quad 0 & \quad 0 & \quad 1 \\
16\,\overline{)\,25} & 8\,\overline{)\,9} & 4\,\overline{)\,1} & 2\,\overline{)\,1} & 1\,\overline{)\,1} \\
\underline{\;9\;} & \underline{\;8\;} & \underline{\;0\;} & \underline{\;0\;} & \underline{\;1\;} \\
0 & 1 & 1 & 1 & 0
\end{array}
\qquad 25 = 11001_2
$$

25. To convert 347 to base 3   ... 243 81 27 9 3 1

$$
\begin{array}{cccccc}
\quad 1 & \quad 1 & \quad 0 & \quad 2 & \quad 1 & \quad 2 \\
243\,\overline{)\,347} & 81\,\overline{)\,104} & 27\,\overline{)\,26} & 9\,\overline{)\,23} & 3\,\overline{)\,5} & 1\,\overline{)\,2} \\
\underline{\;243\;} & \underline{\;81\;} & \underline{\;0\;} & \underline{\;18\;} & \underline{\;3\;} & \underline{\;2\;} \\
104 & 23 & 23 & 5 & 2 & 0
\end{array}
\qquad 347 = 110212_3
$$

26. To convert 513 to base 3   ... 243 81 27 9 3 1

$$
\begin{array}{cccccc}
\quad 2 & \quad 0 & \quad 1 & \quad 0 & \quad 0 & \quad 0 \\
243\,\overline{)\,513} & 81\,\overline{)\,27} & 27\,\overline{)\,27} & 9\,\overline{)\,0} & 3\,\overline{)\,0} & 1\,\overline{)\,0} \\
\underline{\;486\;} & \underline{\;0\;} & \underline{\;27\;} & \underline{\;0\;} & \underline{\;0\;} & \underline{\;0\;} \\
27 & 27 & 0 & 0 & 0 & 0
\end{array}
\qquad 513 = 201000_3
$$

27. To convert 53 to base 4   ... 256 64 16 4 1

$$
\begin{array}{ccc}
\quad 3 & \quad 1 & \quad 1 \\
16\,\overline{)\,53} & 4\,\overline{)\,5} & 1\,\overline{)\,1} \\
\underline{\;48\;} & \underline{\;4\;} & \underline{\;1\;} \\
5 & 1 & 0
\end{array}
\qquad 53 = 311_4
$$

28. To convert 591 to base 4   ... 1024 256 64 16 4 1

$$
\begin{array}{r} 2 \\ 256\overline{)591} \\ \underline{512} \\ 79 \end{array}
\quad
\begin{array}{r} 1 \\ 64\overline{)79} \\ \underline{64} \\ 15 \end{array}
\quad
\begin{array}{r} 0 \\ 16\overline{)15} \\ \underline{0} \\ 15 \end{array}
\quad
\begin{array}{r} 3 \\ 4\overline{)15} \\ \underline{12} \\ 3 \end{array}
\quad
\begin{array}{r} 3 \\ 1\overline{)3} \\ \underline{3} \\ 0 \end{array}
$$

$591 = 21033_4$

29. To convert 102 to base 5   ... 625 125 25 5 1

$$
\begin{array}{r} 4 \\ 25\overline{)102} \\ \underline{100} \\ 2 \end{array}
\quad
\begin{array}{r} 0 \\ 5\overline{)2} \\ \underline{0} \\ 2 \end{array}
\quad
\begin{array}{r} 2 \\ 1\overline{)2} \\ \underline{2} \\ 0 \end{array}
$$

$102 = 402_5$

30. To convert 549 to base 7   ... 2401 343 49 7 1

$$
\begin{array}{r} 1 \\ 343\overline{)549} \\ \underline{343} \\ 206 \end{array}
\quad
\begin{array}{r} 4 \\ 49\overline{)206} \\ \underline{196} \\ 10 \end{array}
\quad
\begin{array}{r} 1 \\ 7\overline{)10} \\ \underline{7} \\ 3 \end{array}
\quad
\begin{array}{r} 3 \\ 1\overline{)3} \\ \underline{3} \\ 0 \end{array}
$$

$549 = 1413_7$

31. To convert 1098 to base 8   ... 4096 512 64 8 1

$$
\begin{array}{r} 2 \\ 512\overline{)1098} \\ \underline{1024} \\ 74 \end{array}
\quad
\begin{array}{r} 1 \\ 64\overline{)74} \\ \underline{64} \\ 10 \end{array}
\quad
\begin{array}{r} 1 \\ 8\overline{)10} \\ \underline{8} \\ 2 \end{array}
\quad
\begin{array}{r} 2 \\ 1\overline{)2} \\ \underline{2} \\ 0 \end{array}
$$

$1098 = 2112_8$

32. To convert 2921 to base 8   ... 4096 512 64 8 1

$$
\begin{array}{r} 5 \\ 512\overline{)2921} \\ \underline{2560} \\ 361 \end{array}
\quad
\begin{array}{r} 5 \\ 64\overline{)361} \\ \underline{320} \\ 41 \end{array}
\quad
\begin{array}{r} 5 \\ 8\overline{)41} \\ \underline{40} \\ 1 \end{array}
\quad
\begin{array}{r} 1 \\ 1\overline{)1} \\ \underline{1} \\ 0 \end{array}
$$

$2921 = 5551_8$

33. To convert 1432 to base 9   ... 6561 729 81 9 1

$$
\begin{array}{r} 1 \\ 729\overline{)1432} \\ \underline{729} \\ 703 \end{array}
\quad
\begin{array}{r} 8 \\ 81\overline{)703} \\ \underline{648} \\ 55 \end{array}
\quad
\begin{array}{r} 6 \\ 9\overline{)55} \\ \underline{54} \\ 1 \end{array}
\quad
\begin{array}{r} 1 \\ 1\overline{)1} \\ \underline{1} \\ 0 \end{array}
$$

$1432 = 1861_9$

34. To convert 2170 to base 9   ... 6561 729 81 9 1

$$
\begin{array}{r} 2 \\ 729\overline{)2170} \\ \underline{1458} \\ 712 \end{array}
\quad
\begin{array}{r} 8 \\ 81\overline{)712} \\ \underline{648} \\ 64 \end{array}
\quad
\begin{array}{r} 7 \\ 9\overline{)64} \\ \underline{63} \\ 1 \end{array}
\quad
\begin{array}{r} 1 \\ 1\overline{)1} \\ \underline{1} \\ 0 \end{array}
$$

$2170 = 2871_9$

35. To convert 9004 to base 12   ... 20,736 1728 144 12 1

$$
\begin{array}{r} 5 \\ 1728\overline{)9004} \\ \underline{8640} \\ 364 \end{array}
\quad
\begin{array}{r} 2 \\ 144\overline{)364} \\ \underline{288} \\ 76 \end{array}
\quad
\begin{array}{r} 6 \\ 12\overline{)76} \\ \underline{72} \\ 4 \end{array}
\quad
\begin{array}{r} 4 \\ 1\overline{)4} \\ \underline{4} \\ 0 \end{array}
$$

$9004 = 5264_{12}$

36. To convert 13,312 to base 12   ... 20,736 1728 144 12 1

$$\begin{array}{c} 7 \\ 1728\overline{|13{,}312} \\ \underline{12{,}096} \\ 1216 \end{array} \quad \begin{array}{c} 8 \\ 144\overline{|1216} \\ \underline{1152} \\ 64 \end{array} \quad \begin{array}{c} 5 \\ 12\overline{|64} \\ \underline{60} \\ 4 \end{array} \quad \begin{array}{c} 4 \\ 1\overline{|4} \\ \underline{4} \\ 0 \end{array}$$

$13{,}312 = 7854_{12}$

37. To convert 493 to base 16   ... 65,536 4096 256 16 1

$$\begin{array}{c} 1 \\ 256\overline{|493} \\ \underline{256} \\ 237 \end{array} \quad \begin{array}{c} 14 \;=E \\ 16\overline{|237} \\ \underline{224} \\ 13 \end{array} \quad \begin{array}{c} 13 \;=D \\ 1\overline{|13} \\ \underline{13} \\ 0 \end{array}$$

$493 = 1ED_{16}$

38. To convert 3243 to base 16   ... 65,536 4096 256 16 1

$$\begin{array}{c} 12 \;=C \\ 256\overline{|3243} \\ \underline{3072} \\ 171 \end{array} \quad \begin{array}{c} 10 \;=A \\ 16\overline{|171} \\ \underline{160} \\ 11 \end{array} \quad \begin{array}{c} 11 \;=B \\ 1\overline{|11} \\ \underline{11} \\ 0 \end{array}$$

$3243 = CAB_{16}$

39. To convert 9455 to base 16   ... 65,536 4096 256 16 1

$$\begin{array}{c} 2 \\ 4096\overline{|9455} \\ \underline{8192} \\ 1263 \end{array} \quad \begin{array}{c} 4 \\ 256\overline{|1263} \\ \underline{1024} \\ 239 \end{array} \quad \begin{array}{c} E \;=14 \\ 16\overline{|239} \\ \underline{224} \\ 15 \end{array} \quad \begin{array}{c} 15 \;=F \\ 1\overline{|15} \\ \underline{15} \\ 0 \end{array}$$

$9455 = 24EF_{16}$

40. To convert 39,885 to base 16   ... 65,536 4096 256 16 1

$$\begin{array}{c} 9 \\ 4096\overline{|39{,}885} \\ \underline{36864} \\ 3021 \end{array} \quad \begin{array}{c} 11 \;=B \\ 256\overline{|3021} \\ \underline{2816} \\ 205 \end{array} \quad \begin{array}{c} 12 \;=C \\ 16\overline{|205} \\ \underline{192} \\ 13 \end{array} \quad \begin{array}{c} 13 \;=D \\ 1\overline{|13} \\ \underline{13} \\ 0 \end{array}$$

$39{,}885 = 9BCD_{16}$

41. To convert 2009 to base 3   ... 2187 729 243 81 27 9 3 1

$$\begin{array}{c} 2 \\ 729\overline{|2009} \\ \underline{1458} \\ 551 \end{array} \; \begin{array}{c} 2 \\ 243\overline{|551} \\ \underline{486} \\ 65 \end{array} \; \begin{array}{c} 0 \\ 81\overline{|65} \\ \underline{0} \\ 65 \end{array} \; \begin{array}{c} 2 \\ 27\overline{|65} \\ \underline{54} \\ 11 \end{array} \; \begin{array}{c} 1 \\ 9\overline{|11} \\ \underline{9} \\ 2 \end{array} \; \begin{array}{c} 0 \\ 3\overline{|2} \\ \underline{0} \\ 2 \end{array} \; \begin{array}{c} 2 \\ 1\overline{|2} \\ \underline{2} \\ 0 \end{array}$$

$2009 = 2202102_{3}$

42. To convert 2009 to base 4   ... 1024 256 64 16 4 1

$$\begin{array}{c} 1 \\ 1024\overline{|2009} \\ \underline{1024} \\ 985 \end{array} \; \begin{array}{c} 3 \\ 256\overline{|985} \\ \underline{768} \\ 217 \end{array} \; \begin{array}{c} 3 \\ 64\overline{|217} \\ \underline{192} \\ 25 \end{array} \; \begin{array}{c} 1 \\ 16\overline{|25} \\ \underline{16} \\ 9 \end{array} \; \begin{array}{c} 2 \\ 4\overline{|9} \\ \underline{8} \\ 1 \end{array} \; \begin{array}{c} 1 \\ 1\overline{|1} \\ \underline{1} \\ 0 \end{array}$$

$2009 = 133121_{4}$

43. To convert 2009 to base 5   ... 3125 625 125 25 5 1

$$\begin{array}{c} 3 \\ 625\overline{|2009} \\ \underline{1875} \\ 134 \end{array} \; \begin{array}{c} 1 \\ 125\overline{|134} \\ \underline{125} \\ 9 \end{array} \; \begin{array}{c} 0 \\ 25\overline{|9} \\ \underline{0} \\ 9 \end{array} \; \begin{array}{c} 1 \\ 5\overline{|9} \\ \underline{9} \\ 4 \end{array} \; \begin{array}{c} 4 \\ 1\overline{|4} \\ \underline{4} \\ 0 \end{array}$$

$2009 = 31014_{5}$

44. To convert 2009 to base 6 … 1296 216 36 6 1

1	3	1	4	5
1296 ⟌ 2009	216 ⟌ 713	36 ⟌ 65	6 ⟌ 29	1 ⟌ 5
1296	648	36	24	5
713	65	29	5	0

$2009 = 13145_6$

45. To convert 2009 to base 7 … 2401 343 49 7 1

5	6	0	0
343 ⟌ 2009	49 ⟌ 294	7 ⟌ 0	1 ⟌ 0
1715	294	0	0
294	0	3	0

$2009 = 5600_7$

46. To convert 2009 to base 9 … 6561 729 81 9 1

2	6	7	2
729 ⟌ 2009	81 ⟌ 551	9 ⟌ 65	1 ⟌ 2
1458	486	63	2
551	65	2	0

$2009 = 2672_9$

47. To convert 2009 to base 11 … 14,641 1331 121 11 1

1	5	6	7
1331 ⟌ 2009	121 ⟌ 678	11 ⟌ 73	1 ⟌ 7
1331	605	66	7
678	73	7	7

$2009 = 1567_{11}$

48. To convert 2009 to base 13 … 2197 169 13 1

11 = B	11 = B	7
169 ⟌ 2009	13 ⟌ 150	1 ⟌ 7
1859	143	7
150	7	0

$2009 = BB7_{13}$

49. To convert 2009 to base 15 … 3375 225 15 1

8	13 = D	14 = E
225 ⟌ 2009	15 ⟌ 209	1 ⟌ 14
1800	195	14
209	14	0

$2009 = 8DE_{15}$

50. To convert 2009 to base 17 … 83521 289 17 1

6	16 = G	3
289 ⟌ 2009	17 ⟌ 275	1 ⟌ 3
1734	272	3
275	3	0

$2009 = 6G3_{17}$

51. $4(5)+3(1)=20+3=23$

52. $2(5)+3(1)=10+3=13$

53. $3(5^2)+0(5)+3(1)=3(25)+0+3$
$=75+0+3=78$

54. $2(5^2)+4(5)+3(1)=2(25)+20+3$
$=50+20+3=73$

55. To convert   ... 25   5   1

$$
\begin{array}{cc}
3=\ominus & 4=\oslash \\
5\,\overline{|\,19} & 1\,\overline{|\,4} \\
\underline{15} & \underline{4} \\
4 & 0
\end{array}
$$

$19=\ominus\,\oslash_5$

56. To convert   ... 25   5   1

$$
\begin{array}{cc}
4=\oslash & 3=\ominus \\
5\,\overline{|\,23} & 1\,\overline{|\,3} \\
\underline{20} & \underline{3} \\
3 & 0
\end{array}
$$

$23=\oslash\,\ominus_5$

57. To convert   ... 125   25   5   1

$$
\begin{array}{ccc}
2=\oslash & 4=\oslash & 4=\oslash \\
25\,\overline{|\,74} & 5\,\overline{|\,24} & 1\,\overline{|\,4} \\
\underline{50} & \underline{20} & \underline{4} \\
24 & 4 & 0
\end{array}
$$

$74=\oslash\,\oslash\,\oslash_5$

58. To convert   ... 125   25   5   1

$$
\begin{array}{ccc}
3=\ominus & 2=\oslash & 0=\bigcirc \\
25\,\overline{|\,85} & 5\,\overline{|\,10} & 1\,\overline{|\,0} \\
\underline{75} & \underline{10} & \underline{0} \\
10 & 0 & 0
\end{array}
$$

$85=\ominus\,\oslash\,\bigcirc_5$

59. $3(4)+2(1)=12+2=14$

60. $1(4)+3(1)=4+3=7$

61. $2(4^2)+1(4)+0(1)=2(16)+4+0=32+4+0=36$

62. $3(4^2)+2(4)+1(1)=3(16)+8+1=48+8+1=57$

For #63–66, blue $=0=$ b, red $=1=$ r, gold $=2=$ go, green $=3=$ gr

63. To convert   ... 16   4   1

$$
\begin{array}{cc}
2=\text{(go)} & 2=\text{(go)} \\
4\,\overline{|\,10} & 1\,\overline{|\,2} \\
\underline{8} & \underline{2} \\
2 & 0
\end{array}
$$

$10=\text{(go)}\ \text{(go)}_4$

64. To convert   ... 16 4 1

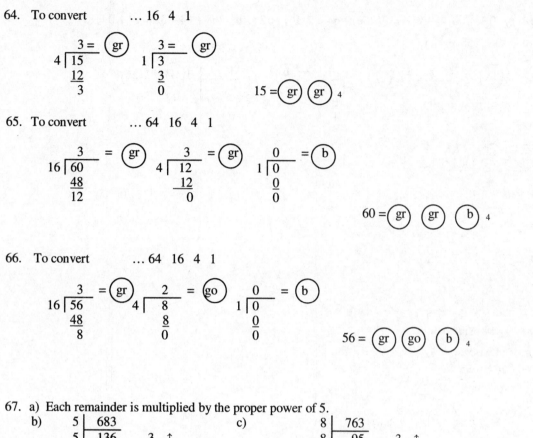

65. To convert   ... 64 16 4 1

66. To convert   ... 64 16 4 1

67. a) Each remainder is multiplied by the proper power of 5.

b)

5	683		
5	136	3	↑
5	27	1	↑
5	5	2	↑
5	1	0	↑
	0	1	↑

$683 = 10213_5$

c)

8	763		
8	95	3	↑
8	11	7	↑
8	1	3	↑
	0	1	↑

$763 = 1373_8$

68. a) $1_3, 2_3, 10_3, 11_3, 12_3, 20_3, 21_3, 22_3, 100_3, 101_3, 102_3, 110_3, 111_3, 112_3, 120_3, 121_3, 122_3, 200_3, 201_3, 202_3$

b) 1000_3

69. Answers will vary.

70. $2^7 = 2 \times 2 \times 2 \times 2 \times 2 \times 2 \times 2 = 128$

71. $1(b^2) + 1(b) + 1 = 43$

$b^2 + b + 1 = 43$

$b^2 + b - 42 = 0$

$(b+7)(b-6) = 0$

$b + 7 = 0$ or $b - 6 = 0$

$b = -7$ or $b = 6$

Since the base cannot be negative, $b = 6$.

72. $d(5^2) + d(5) + d(1) = 124$

$25d + 5d + d = 124$

$\dfrac{31d}{31} = \dfrac{124}{31}$

$d = 4$

73. a) $3(4^4)+1(4^3)+2(4^2)+3(4)+0(1)=3(256)+64+2(16)+12+0=768+64+32+12+0=876$

b) To convert   ... 256 64 16 4 1

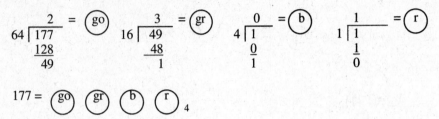

$$177 = \textcircled{go}\ \textcircled{gr}\ \textcircled{b}\ \textcircled{r}\ _4$$

74. Answers will vary.
75. Answers will vary.

Exercise Set 4.4

1. a) $b^0=1, b^1=b, b^2, b^3, b^4$

   b) $2^0=1, 2^1=2, 2^2, 2^3, 2^4$

2. $8^0=1, 8^1=8, 8^2=64$ using base 8.

3. No; there is no 3 in base 3.
4. No; there is no 6 in base 5.
5. Answers will vary.
6. Answers will vary.

7.
$$\begin{array}{r} 21_3 \\ 20_3 \\ \hline 111_3 \end{array}$$

8.
$$\begin{array}{r} 23_4 \\ 13_4 \\ \hline 102_4 \end{array}$$

9.
$$\begin{array}{r} 1234_5 \\ 341_5 \\ \hline 2130_5 \end{array}$$

10.
$$\begin{array}{r} 1101_2 \\ 111_2 \\ \hline 10100_2 \end{array}$$

11.
$$\begin{array}{r} 799_{12} \\ 218_{12} \\ \hline 9B5_{12} \end{array}$$

12.
$$\begin{array}{r} 222_3 \\ 22_3 \\ \hline 1021_3 \end{array}$$

13.
$$\begin{array}{r} 1112_3 \\ 1011_3 \\ \hline 2200_3 \end{array}$$

14.
$$\begin{array}{r} 470_{12} \\ 347_{12} \\ \hline 7B7_{12} \end{array}$$

15.
$$\begin{array}{r} 14631_7 \\ 6040_7 \\ \hline 24001_7 \end{array}$$

16.
$$\begin{array}{r} 1341_8 \\ 341_8 \\ \hline 1702_8 \end{array}$$

17.
$$\begin{array}{r} 1110_2 \\ 110_2 \\ \hline 10100_2 \end{array}$$

18.
$$\begin{array}{r} 43A_{16} \\ 496_{16} \\ \hline 8D0_{16} \end{array}$$

19.
$$\begin{array}{r} 201_3 \\ -120_3 \\ \hline 11_3 \end{array}$$

20.
$$\begin{array}{r} 512_6 \\ -421_6 \\ \hline 51_6 \end{array}$$

21.
$$\begin{array}{r} 2138_9 \\ -1207_9 \\ \hline 831_9 \end{array}$$

22.
$$\begin{array}{r} AB32_{12} \\ -207_{12} \\ \hline A927_{12} \end{array}$$

23.
$$\begin{array}{r} 1101_2 \\ -111_2 \\ \hline 110_2 \end{array}$$

24.
$$\begin{array}{r} 1221_3 \\ -202_3 \\ \hline 1012_3 \end{array}$$

25.
$$\begin{array}{r} 1001_2 \\ -110_2 \\ \hline 11_2 \end{array}$$

26.
$$\begin{array}{r} 2173_8 \\ -1654_8 \\ \hline 317_8 \end{array}$$

27.
$$\begin{array}{r} 4223_7 \\ -304_7 \\ \hline 3616_7 \end{array}$$

28.
$$\begin{array}{r} 4232_5 \\ -2341_5 \\ \hline 1341_5 \end{array}$$

29.
$$\begin{array}{r} 2100_3 \\ -1012_3 \\ \hline 1011_3 \end{array}$$

30.
$$\begin{array}{r} 4E7_{16} \\ -189_{16} \\ \hline 35E_{16} \end{array}$$

31.
$$\begin{array}{r} 22_3 \\ \times\ 2_3 \\ \hline 121_3 \end{array}$$

32.
$$\begin{array}{r} 124_5 \\ \times\ 3_5 \\ \hline 432_5 \end{array}$$

33.
$$\begin{array}{r} 647_8 \\ \times\ 5_8 \\ \hline 4103_8 \end{array}$$

34.
$$\begin{array}{r} 12_4 \\ \times\ 30_4 \\ \hline 000 \\ 102 \\ \hline 1020_4 \end{array}$$

35.
$$\begin{array}{r} 512_6 \\ \times\ 23_6 \\ \hline 2340 \\ \underline{1424} \\ 21020_6 \end{array}$$

36.
$$\begin{array}{r} 124_{12} \\ \times\ 6_{12} \\ \hline 720_{12} \end{array}$$

37.
$$\begin{array}{r} B12_{12} \\ \times\ 83_{12} \\ \hline 2936 \\ \underline{7494} \\ 77676_{12} \end{array}$$

38.
$$\begin{array}{r} 6A3_{12} \\ \times\ 24_{12} \\ \hline 2350 \\ \underline{1186} \\ 13BB0_{12} \end{array}$$

39.
$$\begin{array}{r} 111_2 \\ \times\ 101_2 \\ \hline 111 \\ 000 \\ \underline{111} \\ 100011_2 \end{array}$$

40.
$$\begin{array}{r} 584_9 \\ \times\ 24_9 \\ \hline 2567 \\ \underline{1278} \\ 15457_9 \end{array}$$

41.
$$\begin{array}{r} 316_7 \\ \times\ 16_7 \\ \hline 2541 \\ \underline{316} \\ 6031_7 \end{array}$$

42.
$$\begin{array}{r} 7A9_{12} \\ \times\ 12_{12} \\ \hline 1396 \\ \underline{7A9} \\ 9266_{12} \end{array}$$

43. $1_2 \times 1_2 = 1_2$

$$
\begin{array}{r}
101_2 \\
1_2 \overline{)\ 101_2} \\
\underline{1} \\
00 \\
\underline{0} \\
01 \\
\underline{01} \\
0
\end{array}
$$

44. $2_3 \times 1_3 = 2_3$ 21_3 R1₃
$2_3 \times 2_3 = 11_3$ $2_3 \overline{)\ 120_3}$
$2_3 \times 3_3 = 20_3$ $\underline{11}$
$2_3 \times 4_3 = 22_3$ 10
$2_3 \times 5_3 = 31_3$ $\underline{2}$
                           1

45. $2_6 \times 1_6 = 2_6$ 223_6 R1₆
$2_6 \times 2_6 = 4_6$ $2_6 \overline{)\ 451_6}$
$2_6 \times 3_6 = 10_6$ $\underline{4}$
$2_6 \times 4_6 = 12_6$ 5
$2_6 \times 5_6 = 14_6$ $\underline{4}$
                           11
                           $\underline{10}$
                           1

46. $7_9 \times 1_9 = 7_9$ 15_9 R4₉
$7_9 \times 2_9 = 15_9$ $7_9 \overline{)\ 123_9}$
$7_9 \times 3_9 = 23_9$ $\underline{7}$
$7_9 \times 4_9 = 31_9$ 43
$7_9 \times 5_9 = 38_9$ $\underline{38}$
$7_9 \times 6_9 = 46_9$ 4

47. $2_4 \times 1_4 = 2_4$ 123_4
$2_4 \times 2_4 = 10_4$ $2_4 \overline{)\ 312_4}$
$2_4 \times 3_4 = 12_4$ $\underline{2}$
                           11
                           $\underline{10}$
                           12
                           $\underline{12}$
                           0

48. $6_{12} \times 1_{12} = 6_{12}$ 86_{12} R1₁₂
$6_{12} \times 2_{12} = 10_{12}$ $6_{12} \overline{)\ 431_{12}}$
$6_{12} \times 3_{12} = 16_{12}$ $\underline{40}$
$6_{12} \times 4_{12} = 20_{12}$ 31
$6_{12} \times 5_{12} = 26_{12}$ $\underline{30}$
$6_{12} \times 6_{12} = 30_{12}$ 1
$6_{12} \times 7_{12} = 36_{12}$
$6_{12} \times 8_{12} = 40_{12}$

49. $2_4 \times 1_4 = 2_4$ 103_4 R1₄
$2_4 \times 2_4 = 10_4$ $2_4 \overline{)\ 213_4}$
$2_4 \times 3_4 = 12_4$ $\underline{2}$
                           01
                           $\underline{00}$
                           13
                           $\underline{12}$
                           1

50. $5_6 \times 1_6 = 5_6$ 24_6 R2₆
$5_6 \times 2_6 = 14_6$ $5_6 \overline{)\ 214_6}$
$5_6 \times 3_6 = 23_6$ $\underline{14}$
$5_6 \times 4_6 = 32_6$ 34
$5_6 \times 5_6 = 41_6$ $\underline{32}$
                           2

51. $3_5 \times 1_5 = 3_5$ 41_5 R1₅
$3_5 \times 2_5 = 11_5$ $3_5 \overline{)\ 224_5}$
$3_5 \times 3_5 = 14_5$ $\underline{22}$
$3_5 \times 4_5 = 22_5$ 04
                           $\underline{3}$
                           1

52.

$4_6 \times 1_6 = 4_6$

$4_6 \times 2_6 = 12_6$

$4_6 \times 3_6 = 20_6$

$4_6 \times 4_6 = 24_6$

$4_6 \times 5_6 = 32_6$

$$4_6 \overline{\smash{)}210_6} \quad 31_6 \quad R2_6$$
$$\underline{20}$$
$$10$$
$$\underline{4}$$
$$2$$

53.

$6_7 \times 1_7 = 6_7$

$6_7 \times 2_7 = 15_7$

$6_7 \times 3_7 = 24_7$

$6_7 \times 4_7 = 33_7$

$6_7 \times 5_7 = 42_7$

$6_7 \times 6_7 = 51_7$

$$6_7 \overline{\smash{)}404_7} \quad 45_7 \quad R2_7$$
$$\underline{33}$$
$$44$$
$$\underline{42}$$
$$2$$

54.

$3_7 \times 1_7 = 3_7$

$3_7 \times 2_7 = 6_7$

$3_7 \times 3_7 = 12_7$

$3_7 \times 4_7 = 15_7$

$3_7 \times 5_7 = 21_7$

$3_7 \times 6_7 = 24_7$

$$3_7 \overline{\smash{)}2101_7} \quad 500_7 \quad R1_7$$
$$\underline{21}$$
$$00$$
$$\underline{00}$$
$$01$$
$$\underline{00}$$
$$1$$

55.
$$\begin{array}{r} 3_5 \\ + 3_5 \\ \hline 11_5 \end{array} = \ominus \ominus_5$$

56.
$$\begin{array}{r} 2_5 \\ + 3_5 \\ \hline 10_5 \end{array} = \ominus \bigcirc_5$$

57.
$$\begin{array}{r} 23_5 \\ + 13_5 \\ \hline 41_5 \end{array} = \bigcirc \ominus_5$$

58.
$$\begin{array}{r} 21_5 \\ + 43_5 \\ \hline 114_5 \end{array} = \ominus \ominus \bigcirc_5$$

For #59-66, blue = 0 = b, red = 1 = r, gold = 2 = go, green = 3 = gr

59.
$$\begin{array}{r} 3_4 \\ + 2_4 \\ \hline 11_4 \end{array} = \left(r \right)\left(r \right)_4$$

60.
$$\begin{array}{r} 32_4 \\ + 11_4 \\ \hline 103_4 \end{array} = \left(r \right)\left(b \right)\left(gr \right)_4$$

61.
$$\begin{array}{r} 12_4 \\ + 30_4 \\ \hline 102_4 \end{array} = \left(r \right)\left(b \right)\left(go \right)_4$$

62.
$$\begin{array}{r} 130_4 \\ + 221_4 \\ \hline 1011_4 \end{array} = \left(r \right)\left(b \right)\left(r \right)\left(r \right)_4$$

63.
$$\begin{array}{r} 31_4 \\ - 13_4 \\ \hline 12_4 \end{array} = \left(r \right)\left(go \right)_4$$

64.
$$\begin{array}{r} 33_4 \\ - 12_4 \\ \hline 21_4 \end{array} = \left(go \right)\left(r \right)_4$$

65.
$$\begin{array}{r} 231_4 \\ - 103_4 \\ \hline 122_4 \end{array} = \left(r \right)\left(go \right)\left(go \right)_4$$

66.
$$\begin{array}{r} 301_4 \\ - 120_4 \\ \hline 121_4 \end{array} = \left(r \right)\left(go \right)\left(r \right)_4$$

67. $2302_5 = 2\left(5^3\right) + 3\left(5^2\right) + 0\left(5\right) + 2\left(1\right) = 2\left(125\right) + 3\left(25\right) + 0 + 2 = 250 + 75 + 0 + 2 = 327$

68.   To convert 327 to base 9

... 729   81   9   1

$$81 \overline{\smash{)}327} \quad 4$$
$$\underline{324}$$
$$3$$

$$9 \overline{\smash{)}3} \quad 0$$
$$\underline{0}$$
$$3$$

$$1 \overline{\smash{)}3} \quad 3$$
$$\underline{3}$$
$$0$$

$327 = 403_9$

$9^2 = \bullet \bullet \bullet \bullet$

$9^1 = $ none

$9^0 = \bullet \bullet \bullet$

69.

$$\begin{array}{r} FAB_{16} \\ \times \quad 4_{16} \\ \hline 2C \\ 28 \\ \underline{3C} \\ \hline 3EAC_{16} \end{array}$$

70. $D_{16} \times 1_{16} = D_4$

$$D_{16} \times 2_{16} = 1A_{16}$$
$$D_{16} \times 3_{16} = 27_{16}$$
$$D_{16} \times 4_{16} = 34_{16}$$
.
.
.
$$D_{16} \times A_{16} = 82_{16}$$

$$\begin{array}{r} 134A_{16} \quad RC_{16} \\ D_{16} \overline{\smash{\big)}\ FACE_{16}} \\ \underline{D} \\ 2A \\ \underline{27} \\ 3C \\ \underline{34} \\ 8E \\ \underline{82} \\ C \end{array}$$

71. $20_4 \times 1_4 = 20_4$

$$20_4 \times 2_4 = 100_4$$
$$20_4 \times 3_4 = 120_4$$

$$\begin{array}{r} 11_4 \quad R3_4 \\ 20_4 \overline{\smash{\big)}\ 223_4} \\ \underline{20} \\ 23 \\ \underline{20} \\ 3 \end{array}$$

72. $14_5 \times 1_5 = 14_5$

$$14_5 \times 2_5 = 33_5$$
$$14_5 \times 3_5 = 102_5$$
$$14_5 \times 4_5 = 121_5$$

$$\begin{array}{r} 13_5 \\ 14_5 \overline{\smash{\big)}\ 242_5} \\ \underline{14} \\ 102 \\ \underline{102} \\ 0 \end{array}$$

73.   a) 462_8
       $\underline{\times 35_8}$
       2772
       $\underline{1626}$
       21252_8

b) $462_8 = 4(8^2) + 6(8) + 2(1) = 4(64) + 48 + 2 = 256 + 48 + 2 = 306$

   $35_8 = 3(8) + 5(1) = 24 + 5 = 29$

c) $306 \times 29 = 8874$

d) $21252_8 = 2(8^4) + 1(8^3) + 2(8^2) + 5(8) + 2(1)$

   $= 2(4096) + 512 + 2(64) + 40 + 2$

   $= 8192 + 512 + 128 + 40 + 2 = 8874$

e) Yes, in part a), the numbers were multiplied in base 8 and then converted to base 10 in part d).
In part b), the numbers were converted to base 10 first, then multiplied in part c).

74. $b = 5$
75.   Orange = 0; purple = 1; turquoise = 2; red = 3
76.   Answers will vary.
77.   Answers will vary.

Exercise Set 4.5

1.   Duplation and mediation, lattice multiplication and Napier rods

2.   a) Answers will vary.

   b)   73 –   21
       ~~36~~ – ~~42~~
       ~~18~~ – ~~84~~
        9 –   168
       ~~4~~ – ~~336~~
       ~~2~~ – ~~672~~
        1 – 1344
              1533

3.   a)   Answers will vary.

   b)

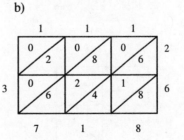

$143 \times 26 = 3718$

4.   a)   Answers will vary.
     b)

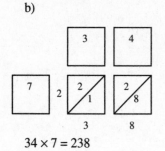

$34 \times 7 = 238$

5.   9 – 171
     4 – ~~342~~
     ~~2 – 684~~
     1 – 1368
         1539

6.   39 – 57
     19 – 114
     9 – 228
     4 – ~~456~~
     ~~2 – 912~~
     1 – 1824
         2223

7.   27 – 53
     13 – 106
     ~~6 – 212~~
     3 – 424
     1 – 848
         1431

8.   ~~138 – 41~~
     69 – 82
     ~~34 – 164~~
     17 – 328
     ~~8 – 656~~
     ~~4 – 1312~~
     ~~2 – 2624~~
     1 – 5248
         5658

9.   35 – 236
     17 – 472
     ~~8 – 944~~
     4 – ~~1888~~
     ~~2 – 3776~~
     1 – 7552
         8260

10. ~~96 – 53~~
     ~~48 – 106~~
     ~~24 – 212~~
     ~~12 – 424~~
     6 – 848
     3 – 1696
     1 – 3392
         5088

11. 93 – 93
     ~~46 – 186~~
     23 – 372
     11 – 744
     5 – 1488
     ~~2 – 2976~~
     1 – 5952
         8649

12. 49 – 124
     ~~24 – 248~~
     ~~12 – 496~~
     ~~6 – 992~~
     3 – 1984
     1 – 3968
         6076

13.

$5 \times 191 = 995$

14.

$6 \times 227 = 1362$

15.

$8 \times 469 = 3752$

16.

$9 \times 509 = 4581$

17.

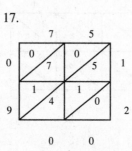

$75 \times 12 = 900$

18.

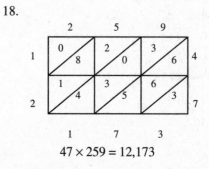

$47 \times 259 = 12,173$

19.

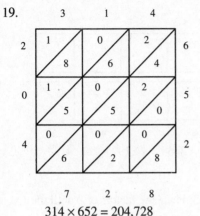

$314 \times 652 = 204{,}728$

20.

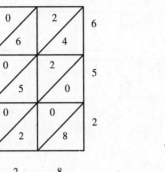

$634 \times 832 = 527{,}488$

21.

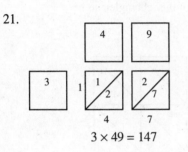

$3 \times 49 = 147$

22.

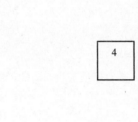

$4 \times 54 = 216$

23.

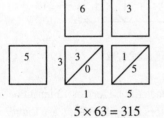

$5 \times 63 = 315$

24.

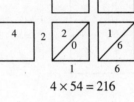

$6 \times 171 = 1026$

25.

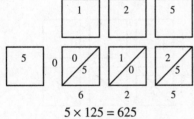

$5 \times 125 = 625$

26.

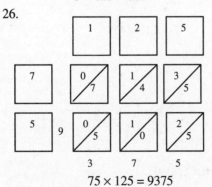

$75 \times 125 = 9375$

27.

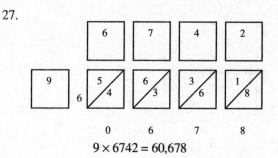

9 × 6742 = 60,678

28.

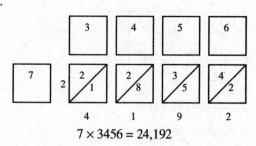

7 × 3456 = 24,192

29. a) 253 × 46; Place the factors of 8 until the
correct factors and placements are found
so the rest of the rectangle can be completed.

b)

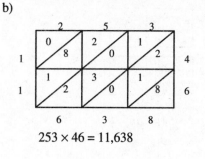

253 × 46 = 11,638

30. a) 475 × 263; Place the factors of 8 until the
correct factors and placements are found
so the rest of the rectangle can be
completed.

b)

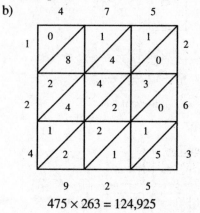

475 × 263 = 124,925

31. a) 4 × 382; Place the factors of 12 until the correct
factors and placements are found so the rest
can be completed.

b)

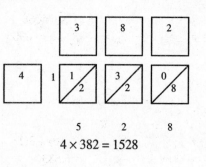

4 × 382 = 1528

32. a) 7 × 685; Place the factors of 42 until the
correct factors and placements are found
so the rest can be completed.

b)

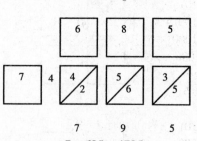

7 × 685 = 4795

33. 13 – 22
~~6 – 44~~
3 – 88
1 – <u>176</u>
286 =

34. ~~26 – 67~~
13 – 134
~~6 – 268~~
3 – 536
1 – <u>1072</u>
1742 = MDCCXLII

35.

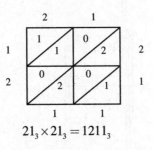

$21_3 \times 21_3 = 1211_3$

36.

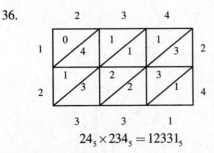

$24_5 \times 234_5 = 12331_5$

37. a) $1000 + 500 + 100 + 100 + 50 + 10 + 10 + 5 + 1 = 1776$
   b) Answers will vary.

38. Answers will vary.
39. Answers will vary.

Review Exercises

1. $1000 + 1000 + 100 + 10 + 10 + 1 = 2121$

2. $1000 + 100 + 100 + 10 + 1 + 1 + 1 + 1 = 1214$

3. $10 + 100 + 100 + 100 + 1 + 1000 = 1311$

4. $100 + 10 + 1000 + 1 + 1000 + 1 + 1 + 1 = 2114$

5. $1000 + 1000 + 100 + 100 + 100 + 10 + 1 + 1 + 1 + 1 = 2314$

6. $100 + 100 + 10 + 1 + 1000 + 1000 + 1 + 100 = 2312$

7. *bbba*

8. *cbbaaaaa*

9. *ccbbbbbbbbbaaa*

10. *ddaaaaaaaa*

11. *dddddccccccccbbbbba*

12. *ddcccbaaaa*

13. $3(10) + 2 = 30 + 2 = 32$

14. $8(10) + 5 = 80 + 5 = 85$

15. $7(100) + 4(10) + 9 = 700 + 40 + 9 = 749$

16. $4(1000) + 6(10) + 8 = 4000 + 60 + 8 = 4068$

17. $5(1000) + 6(100) + 4(10) + 8 = 5000 + 600 + 40 + 8 = 5648$

18. $6(1000) + 9(100) + 5 = 6000 + 900 + 5 = 6905$

19. *cxg*

20. *ayexg*

21. *hyfxb*

22. *czixd*

23. *fzd*

24. *bza*

25. $9(10) + 3(1) = 90 + 3 = 93$

26. $2(100) + 3(1) = 200 + 3 = 203$

27. $5(100) + 6(10) + 8(1) = 500 + 60 + 8 = 568$

28. $4(10,000) + 6(1000) + 8(100) + 8(10) + 3(1) = 40,000 + 6000 + 800 + 80 + 3 = 46,883$

29. $6(10,000) + 4(1000) + 4(100) + 8(10) + 1 = 60,000 + 4000 + 400 + 80 + 1 = 64,481$

30. $6(10,000) + 5(100) + 2(10) + 9(1) = 60,000 + 500 + 20 + 9 = 60,529$

31. la

32. tpd

33. vrc

34. BArg

35. ODvog

36. QFvrf

37.

38. MDCCLXXVI

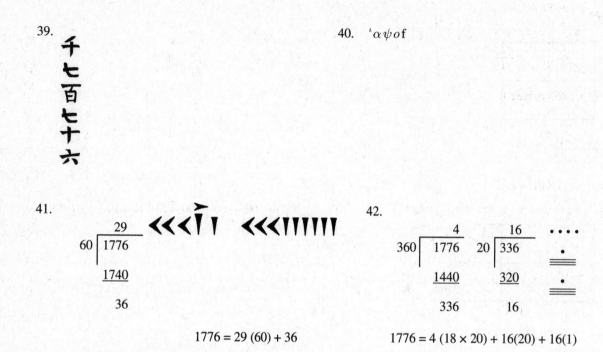

39.

40. $'\alpha\psi o f$

41.

$$60 \overline{\smash{\big)}\,1776} \quad \begin{array}{r} 29 \\ \hline \end{array}$$
$$\underline{1740}$$
$$36$$

$$1776 = 29\,(60) + 36$$

42.

$$360 \overline{\smash{\big)}\,1776} \quad \begin{array}{r} 4 \\ \hline \end{array} \qquad 20 \overline{\smash{\big)}\,336} \quad \begin{array}{r} 16 \\ \hline \end{array} \qquad \cdots$$
$$\underline{1440} \qquad\qquad \underline{320}$$
$$336 \qquad\qquad 16$$

$$1776 = 4\,(18 \times 20) + 16(20) + 16(1)$$

43. $100{,}000 + 100{,}000 + 10{,}000 + 10{,}000 + 1000 + 1000 + 10 + 10 + 10 + 1 + 1 + 1 + 1 + 1 = 222{,}035$

44. $8\,(1000) + 2\,(100) + 5\,(10) + 4 = 8000 + 200 + 50 + 4 = 8254$

45. $600 + 80 + 5 = 685$

46. $1000 + (1000 - 100) + (100 - 10) + 1 = 1000 + 900 + 90 + 1 = 1991$

47. $21(60) + (20 - 3) = 1260 + 17 = 1277$

48. $7(18 \times 20) + 8(20) + 10(1) = 7(360) + 160 + 10 = 2520 + 160 + 10 = 2690$

49. $47_8 = 4(8) + 7(1) = 32 + 7 = 39$

50. $101_2 = 1(2^2) + 0(2) + 1(1) = 4 + 0 + 1 = 5$

51. $130_4 = 1(4^2) + 3(4) + 0(1) = 16 + 12 + 0 = 28$

52. $3425_7 = 3(7^3) + 4(7^2) + 2(7) + 5(1) = 3(343) + 4(49) + 14 + 5 = 1029 + 196 + 14 + 5 = 1244$

53. $A94_{12} = 10(12^2) + 9(12) + 4(1) = 1440 + 108 + 4 = 1552$

54. $20220_3 = 2(3^4) + 0(3^3) + 2(3^2) + 2(3) + 0(1) = 2(81) + 0 + 2(9) + 6 + 0 = 162 + 0 + 18 + 6 + 0 = 186$

55. To convert 463 to base 2   … 512 256 128 64 32 16 8 4 2 1

$$256\overline{\smash{\big)}\,463}\;^{1} \quad 128\overline{\smash{\big)}\,207}\;^{1} \quad 64\overline{\smash{\big)}\,79}\;^{1} \quad 32\overline{\smash{\big)}\,15}\;^{0} \quad 16\overline{\smash{\big)}\,15}\;^{0} \quad 8\overline{\smash{\big)}\,15}\;^{1} \quad 4\overline{\smash{\big)}\,7}\;^{1} \quad 2\overline{\smash{\big)}\,3}\;^{1} \quad 1\overline{\smash{\big)}\,1}\;^{1}$$
$$\underline{256} \qquad \underline{128} \qquad \underline{64} \qquad \underline{\;0\;} \qquad \underline{\;0\;} \qquad \underline{\;8\;} \qquad \underline{\;4\;} \qquad \underline{\;2\;} \qquad \underline{\;1\;}$$
$$207 \qquad\;\; 79 \qquad\;\; 15 \qquad 15 \qquad 15 \qquad 7 \qquad 3 \qquad 1 \qquad 0$$

$$463 = 111001111_2$$

56. To convert 463 to base 3   … 729 243 81 27 9 3 1

$$243\overline{\smash{\big)}\,463}\;^{1} \quad 81\overline{\smash{\big)}\,220}\;^{2} \quad 27\overline{\smash{\big)}\,58}\;^{2} \quad 9\overline{\smash{\big)}\,4}\;^{0} \quad 3\overline{\smash{\big)}\,4}\;^{1} \quad 1\overline{\smash{\big)}\,1}\;^{1}$$
$$\underline{243} \qquad \underline{162} \qquad \underline{54} \qquad \underline{\;0\;} \qquad \underline{\;3\;} \qquad \underline{\;1\;}$$
$$220 \qquad\;\; 58 \qquad\;\; 4 \qquad\;\; 4 \qquad 1 \qquad 0 \qquad 463 = 122011_3$$

57. To convert 463 to base 4   ... 1024   256   64   16   4   1

$$
256\overline{\smash{\big)}463} \quad 64\overline{\smash{\big)}207} \quad 16\overline{\smash{\big)}15} \quad 4\overline{\smash{\big)}15} \quad 1\overline{\smash{\big)}3}
$$

1	3	0	3	3
256	192	0	12	3
207	15	15	3	0

$463 = 13033_4$

58. To convert 463 to base 8   ... 512   64   8   1

7	1	7
$64\overline{\smash{\big)}463}$	$8\overline{\smash{\big)}15}$	$1\overline{\smash{\big)}7}$
448	8	7
15	7	0

$463 = 717_8$

59. To convert 463 to base 12   ... 1728   144   12   1

3	2	7
$144\overline{\smash{\big)}463}$	$12\overline{\smash{\big)}31}$	$1\overline{\smash{\big)}7}$
432	24	7
31	7	0

$463 = 327_{12}$

60. To convert 463 to base 16   ... 65,536   4096   256   16   1

1	12 = C	15 = F
$256\overline{\smash{\big)}463}$	$16\overline{\smash{\big)}207}$	$1\overline{\smash{\big)}15}$
256	192	15
207	15	0

$493 = 1CF_{16}$

61.
$$
\begin{array}{r}
52_7 \\
55_7 \\
\hline
140_7
\end{array}
$$

62.
$$
\begin{array}{r}
10110_2 \\
11001_2 \\
\hline
101111_2
\end{array}
$$

63.
$$
\begin{array}{r}
9B_{12} \\
87_{12} \\
\hline
166_{12}
\end{array}
$$

64.
$$
\begin{array}{r}
2B9_{16} \\
456_{16} \\
\hline
70F_{16}
\end{array}
$$

65.
$$
\begin{array}{r}
3024_5 \\
4023_5 \\
\hline
12102_5
\end{array}
$$

66.
$$
\begin{array}{r}
3407_8 \\
7014_8 \\
\hline
12423_8
\end{array}
$$

67.
$$
\begin{array}{r}
4032_7 \\
-321_7 \\
\hline
3411_7
\end{array}
$$

68.
$$
\begin{array}{r}
1001_2 \\
-101_2 \\
\hline
100_2
\end{array}
$$

69.
$$
\begin{array}{r}
A7B_{12} \\
-95_{12} \\
\hline
9A6_{12}
\end{array}
$$

70.
$$
\begin{array}{r}
4321_5 \\
-442_5 \\
\hline
3324_5
\end{array}
$$

71.
$$
\begin{array}{r}
1713_8 \\
-1243_8 \\
\hline
450_8
\end{array}
$$

72.
$$
\begin{array}{r}
F64_{16} \\
-2A3_{16} \\
\hline
CC1_{16}
\end{array}
$$

73.
$$
\begin{array}{r}
1011_2 \\
\times\ 101_2 \\
\hline
1011 \\
0000 \\
1011 \\
\hline
110111_2
\end{array}
$$

74.
$$
\begin{array}{r}
221_3 \\
\times\ 22_3 \\
\hline
1212 \\
1212 \\
\hline
21102_3
\end{array}
$$

75.
$$
\begin{array}{r}
34_5 \\
\times 21_5 \\
\hline
34 \\
123 \\
\hline
1314_5
\end{array}
$$

76.
$$
\begin{array}{r}
476_8 \\
\times\ 23_8 \\
\hline
1672 \\
1174 \\
\hline
13632_8
\end{array}
$$

77.
$$
\begin{array}{r}
126_{12} \\
\times\ 47_{12} \\
\hline
856 \\
4A0 \\
\hline
5656_{12}
\end{array}
$$

78.
$$
\begin{array}{r}
1A3_{16} \\
\times\ 12_{16} \\
\hline
346 \\
1A3 \\
\hline
1D76_{16}
\end{array}
$$

79.

$2_3 \times 1_3 = 2_3$
$2_3 \times 2_3 = 11_3$
$2_3 \times 3_3 = 20_3$
$2_3 \times 4_3 = 22_3$

$$2_3 \overline{\smash{)}120_3} \quad \begin{array}{r} 21_3 \quad R\,1_3 \\ \underline{11} \\ 10 \\ \underline{2} \\ 1 \end{array}$$

80.

$2_4 \times 1_4 = 2_4$
$2_4 \times 2_4 = 10_4$
$2_4 \times 3_4 = 12_4$

$$2_4 \overline{\smash{)}320_4} \quad \begin{array}{r} 130_4 \\ \underline{2} \\ 12 \\ \underline{12} \\ 0 \\ \underline{0} \\ 0 \end{array}$$

81.

$3_5 \times 1_5 = 3_5$
$3_5 \times 2_5 = 11_5$
$3_5 \times 3_5 = 14_5$
$3_5 \times 4_5 = 22_5$

$$3_5 \overline{\smash{)}130_5} \quad \begin{array}{r} 23_5 \quad R1_5 \\ \underline{11} \\ 20 \\ \underline{14} \\ 1 \end{array}$$

82.

$4_6 \times 1_6 = 4_6$
$4_6 \times 2_6 = 12_6$
$4_6 \times 3_6 = 20_6$
$4_6 \times 4_6 = 24_6$
$4_6 \times 5_6 = 32_6$

$$4_6 \overline{\smash{)}3020_6} \quad \begin{array}{r} 433_6 \\ \underline{24} \\ 22 \\ \underline{20} \\ 20 \\ \underline{20} \\ 0 \end{array}$$

83.

$3_6 \times 1_6 = 3_6$
$3_6 \times 2_6 = 10_6$
$3_6 \times 3_6 = 13_6$
$3_6 \times 4_6 = 20_6$
$3_6 \times 5_6 = 23_6$

$$3_6 \overline{\smash{)}2034_6} \quad \begin{array}{r} 411_6 \quad R1_6 \\ \underline{20} \\ 03 \\ \underline{3} \\ 04 \\ \underline{3} \\ 1 \end{array}$$

84.

$6_8 \times 1_8 = 6_8$
$6_8 \times 2_8 = 14_8$
$6_8 \times 3_8 = 22_8$
$6_8 \times 4_8 = 30_8$
$6_8 \times 5_8 = 36_8$
$6_8 \times 6_8 = 44_8$
$6_8 \times 7_8 = 52_8$

$$6_8 \overline{\smash{)}5072_8} \quad \begin{array}{r} 664_8 \quad R2_8 \\ \underline{44} \\ 47 \\ \underline{44} \\ 32 \\ \underline{30} \\ 2 \end{array}$$

85.

~~142~~   ~~24~~
71 - 48
35 - 96
17 - 192
~~8~~   ~~384~~
~~4~~   ~~768~~
~~2~~   ~~1536~~
1 - <u>3072</u>
3408

86.

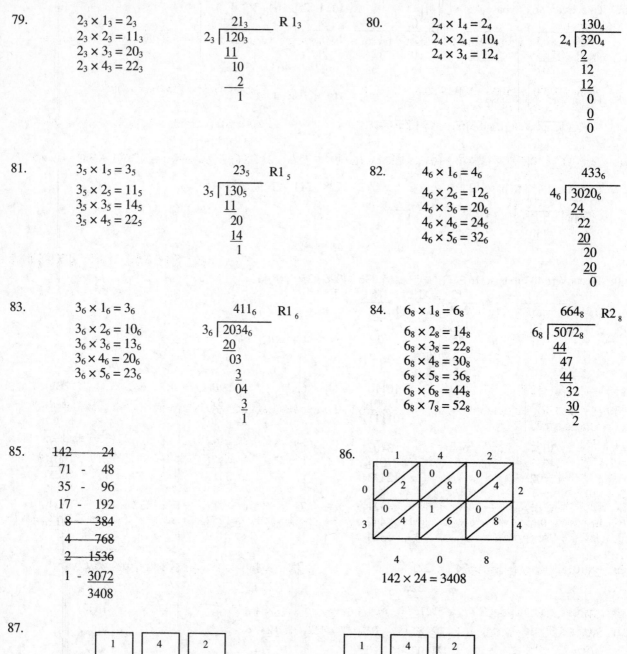

$142 \times 24 = 3408$

87.

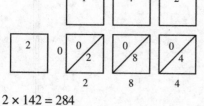

$2 \times 142 = 284$

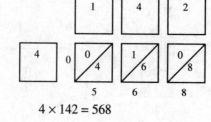

$4 \times 142 = 568$

$2 \times 142 = 284$, therefore $20 \times 142 = 2840$

Therefore, $142 \times 24 = 2840 + 568 = 3408$.

Chapter Test

1. A **number** is a quantity and answers the question "How many?" A **numeral** is a symbol used to represent the number.

2. $1000 + 1000 + (500 - 100) + 50 + 10 + 10 + 10 + (5 - 1) = 2484$

3. $21(60) + 15(1) = 1260 + 15 = 1275$

4. $8 (1000) + 0 + 9(10) = 8000 + 0 + 90 = 8090$

5. $2 (18 \times 20) + 12(20) + 9 (1) = 2 (360) + 240 + 9 = 720 + 240 + 9 = 969$

6. $100,000 + 10,000 + 10,000 + 1000 + 1000 + 100 + 10 + 10 + 10 + 10 + 1 + 1 = 122,142$

7. $2 (1000) + 700 + 40 + 5 = 2000 + 700 + 40 + 5 = 2745$

9. $\beta \upsilon o f$

8. ꩜꩜꧑ꢑ||||

10.

	3		17
360	1434	20	354
	1080		340
	354		14

$1434 = 3(18 \times 20) + 17(20) + 14(1)$

11.

	26
60	1596
	1560
	36

$1596 = 26(60) + 36(1)$

12. MMMDCCVI

13. In an additive system, the number represented by a particular set of numerals is the sum of the values of the numerals.

14. In a multiplicative system, there are numerals for each number less than the base and for powers of the base. Each numeral less than the base is multiplied by a numeral for the power of the base, and these products are added to obtain the number.

15. In a ciphered system, the number represented by a particular set of numerals is the sum of the values of the numerals. There are numerals for each number up to and including the base and multiples of the base.

16. In a place-value system, each number is multiplied by a power of the base. The position of the numeral indicates the power of the base by which it is multiplied.

17. $23_4 = 2 (4) + 3 (1) = 8 + 3 = 11$

18. $403_5 = 4(5^2) + 0(5) + 3(1) = 4(25) + 0 + 3 = 100 + 0 + 3 = 103$

19. $101101_2 = 1(2^5) + 0(2^4) + 1(2^3) + 1(2^2) + 0(2) + 1(1) = 32 + 0 + 8 + 4 + 0 + 1 = 45$

20. $3A7_{12} = 3(12^2) + 10(12) + 7(1) = 3(144) + 120 + 7 = 432 + 120 + 7 = 559$

21. To convert 36 to base 2   ... 64 32 16 8 4 2 1

	1		0		0		1		0		0
32	36	16	4	8	4	4	4	2	0	1	0
	32		0		0		4		0		0
	4		4		4		0		0		0

$36 = 100100_2$

22. To convert 93 to base 8   ... 512 64 8 1

	1		3		5
64	93	8	29	1	5
	64		24		5
	29		5		0

$93 = 135_8$

23. To convert 2356 to base 12   ... 20,736 1728 144 12 1

$$1728\overline{)\begin{array}{r}1\\2356\end{array}}\quad144\overline{)\begin{array}{r}4\\628\end{array}}\quad12\overline{)\begin{array}{r}4\\52\end{array}}\quad1\overline{)\begin{array}{r}4\\4\end{array}}$$

$$\begin{array}{r}\underline{1728}\\628\end{array}\qquad\begin{array}{r}\underline{576}\\52\end{array}\qquad\begin{array}{r}\underline{48}\\4\end{array}\qquad\begin{array}{r}\underline{4}\\0\end{array}\qquad 2356=1444_{12}$$

24. To convert 2938 to base 16   ... 65,536 4096 256 16 1

$$\phantom{256\overline{)}}\begin{array}{r}11\\\end{array}=B\qquad\begin{array}{r}7\\\end{array}\qquad\begin{array}{r}10\\\end{array}=A$$

$$256\overline{)\begin{array}{r}2938\end{array}}\quad16\overline{)\begin{array}{r}122\end{array}}\quad1\overline{)\begin{array}{r}10\end{array}}$$

$$\begin{array}{r}\underline{2401}\\122\end{array}\qquad\begin{array}{r}\underline{112}\\10\end{array}\qquad\begin{array}{r}\underline{10}\\0\end{array}\qquad 2938=B7A_{16}$$

25.
$$\begin{array}{r}1101_2\\+\underline{1011_2}\\11000_2\end{array}$$

26.
$$\begin{array}{r}324_6\\-\underline{142_6}\\142_6\end{array}$$

27.
$$\begin{array}{r}45_6\\\times\underline{23_6}\\223\\\underline{134}\\2003_6\end{array}$$

28.
$3_5 \times 1_5 = 3_5$
$3_5 \times 2_5 = 11_5$
$3_5 \times 3_5 = 14_5$
$3_5 \times 4_5 = 22_5$

$$3_5\overline{)\begin{array}{r}220_5\\1210_5\end{array}}$$
$$\begin{array}{r}\underline{11}\\11\\\underline{11}\\00\\\underline{00}\\0\end{array}$$

29. 35 - 28
     17 - 56
     ~~8~~ ~~112~~
     ~~4~~ ~~224~~
     ~~2~~ ~~448~~
     1 - 896
         980

30. $43 \times 196 = 8428$

Group Projects

1. a) 06470-9869-1
    b) i) 51593-4837-5   ii) 14527-8924-75-6

    c) i)

    ii)

    d) Answers will vary.

CHAPTER FIVE

NUMBER THEORY AND THE REAL NUMBER SYSTEM

Exercise Set 5.1

1. Number theory is the study of numbers and their properties.
2. If a and b are factors of c, then c ÷ a is an integer and c ÷ b is an integer.
3. a) *a* divides *b* means that *b* divided by *a* has a remainder of zero.
   b) *a* is divisible by *b* means that *a* divided by *b* has a remainder of zero.
4. A prime number is natural number greater than 1 that has exactly two factors (or divisors), itself and one.
5. A composite number is a natural number that is divisible by a number other than itself and 1. Any natural number that is not prime is composite.
6. Every composite number can be expressed as a unique product of prime numbers.

7. a) The least common multiple (LCM) of a set of natural numbers is the smallest natural number that is divisible (without remainder) by each element of the set.
   b) Determine the prime factorization of each number. Then find the product of the prime factors with the largest exponent that appear in any of the prime factorizations.
   c) The prime factors with the largest exponent that appear in any of the factorizations are 2^4 and 5. The LCM of 16 and 40 is $2^4 \cdot 5$, or 80.

$$
\begin{array}{c|c}
2 & 16 \\
2 & 8 \\
2 & 4 \\
  & 2 \\
\end{array}
$$
$$16 = 2^4$$

8. a) The greatest common divisor (GCD) of a set of natural numbers is the largest natural number that divides (without remainder) every number in that set.
   b) Determine the prime factorization of each number. Then find the product of the prime factors with the smallest exponent that appear in any of the prime factorizations.
   c) The prime factor with the smallest exponent that appear in any of the factorizations is 2^3. The GCD of 16 and 40 is $2^3 = 8$.

$$
\begin{array}{c|c}
5 & 40 \\
2 & 8 \\
2 & 4 \\
  & 2 \\
\end{array}
$$
$$40 = 2^3 \cdot 5$$

9. Mersenne Primes are prime numbers of the form $2^n - 1$ where n is a prime number.
10. A conjecture is a supposition that has not been proved nor disproved.
11. Goldbach's conjecture states that every even number greater than or equal to 4 can be represented as the sum of two (not necessarily distinct) prime numbers.
12. Twin primes are of the form p, p+2, where p is a prime number. An example is 5 & 7.

13. The prime numbers between 1 and 100 are: 2, 3, 5, 7, 11, 13, 17, 19, 23, 29, 31, 37, 41, 43, 47, 53, 59, 61, 67, 71, 73, 79, 83, 89, 97.

14.

1	(2)	(3)	4	(5)	6	(7)	8	9	10
(11)	12	(13)	14	15	16	(17)	18	(19)	20
21	22	(23)	24	25	26	27	28	(29)	30
(31)	32	33	34	35	36	(37)	38	39	40
(41)	42	(43)	44	45	46	(47)	48	49	50
51	52	(53)	54	55	56	57	58	(59)	60
(61)	62	63	64	65	66	(67)	68	69	70
(71)	72	(73)	74	75	76	77	78	(79)	80
81	82	(83)	84	85	86	87	88	(89)	90
91	92	93	94	95	96	(97)	98	99	100
(101)	102	(103)	104	105	106	(107)	108	(109)	110
111	112	(113)	114	115	116	117	118	119	120
121	122	123	124	125	126	(127)	128	129	130
(131)	132	133	134	135	136	(137)	138	(139)	140
141	142	143	144	145	146	147	148	(149)	150

The prime numbers between 1 and 150 are: 2, 3, 5, 7, 11, 13, 17, 19, 23, 29, 31, 37, 41, 43, 47, 53, 59, 61, 67, 71, 73, 79, 83, 87, 89, 97, 101, 103, 107, 109, 113, 127, 131, 137, 139, and 149.

15. True; since $27 \div 7 = 4$

16. False

17. False; 26 is a multiple of 13.

18. True; since $18 \div 6 = 3$.

19. False.

20. True; since $45 \div 15 = 3$.

21. True; if a number is divisible by 10, then it is also divisible by 5.

22. False; consider 15.

23. False; if a number is divisible by 3, then the sum of the number's digits is divisible by 3.

24. True.

25. True; since $2 \cdot 3 = 6$.

26. True; since $3 \cdot 4 = 12$.

27. Divisible by 3, 5 and 9.

28. Divisible by 3 and 9.

29. Divisible by 2, 3, 6 and 9.

30. Divisible by 2, 3, 4, 5, 6, 9, and 10.

31. Divisible by 2, 3, 4, 5, 6, 8, and 10.

32. Divisible by none of the numbers.

33. $2 \cdot 3 \cdot 4 \cdot 5 \cdot 6 = 720$. (other answers are possible)

34. $3 \cdot 4 \cdot 5 \cdot 9 \cdot 10 = 5400$. (other answers are possible

35.
$$
\begin{array}{r|r}
2 & 48 \\
2 & 24 \\
2 & 12 \\
2 & 6 \\
& 3
\end{array}
$$
$48 = 2^4 \cdot 3$

36.
$$
\begin{array}{r|r}
2 & 58 \\
& 29
\end{array}
$$
$58 = 2 \cdot 29$

37.
$$
\begin{array}{r|r}
2 & 168 \\
2 & 84 \\
2 & 42 \\
3 & 21 \\
& 7
\end{array}
$$
$168 = 2^3 \cdot 3 \cdot 7$

38.
$$
\begin{array}{r|r}
3 & 315 \\
3 & 105 \\
5 & 35 \\
& 7
\end{array}
$$
$315 = 3^2 \cdot 5 \cdot 7$

39.
$$
\begin{array}{r|r}
2 & 332 \\
2 & 166 \\
& 83
\end{array}
$$
$332 = 2^2 \cdot 83$

40.
$$
\begin{array}{r|r}
3 & 399 \\
7 & 133 \\
& 19
\end{array}
$$
$399 = 3 \cdot 7 \cdot 19$

41.
$$
\begin{array}{r|r}
3 & 513 \\
3 & 171 \\
3 & 57 \\
& 19
\end{array}
$$
$513 = 3^3 \cdot 19$

42.
$$
\begin{array}{r|r}
3 & 663 \\
13 & 221 \\
& 17
\end{array}
$$
$663 = 3 \cdot 13 \cdot 17$

43.
$$
\begin{array}{r|r}
2 & 1336 \\
2 & 668 \\
2 & 334 \\
& 167
\end{array}
$$
$1336 = 2^3 \cdot 167$

44.
$$
\begin{array}{r|r}
13 & 1313 \\
& 101
\end{array}
$$
$1313 = 13 \cdot 101$

45.
$$
\begin{array}{r|r}
3 & 2001 \\
23 & 667 \\
& 29
\end{array}
$$
$2001 = 3 \cdot 23 \cdot 29$

46.
$$
\begin{array}{r|r}
2 & 3190 \\
5 & 1595 \\
11 & 319 \\
& 29
\end{array}
$$
$3190 = 2 \cdot 5 \cdot 11 \cdot 29$

47. The prime factors of 21 and 18 are: $6 = 3 \cdot 2$, $15 = 3 \cdot 7$
a) The common factor is 3, thus, the GCD = 3.
b) The factors with the greatest exponent that appear in either are 2, 3, 7. Thus, the LCM = $2 \cdot 3 \cdot 7 = 42$.

48. The prime factors of 15 and 24 are: $15 = 3 \cdot 5$ and $24 = 2^3 \cdot 3$
a) The common factor is 3 thus, the GCD = 3
b) The factors with the greatest exponent that appear in either are 2^3, 3 and 5; the LCM $= 2^3 \cdot 3 \cdot 5 = 120$.

49. The prime factors of 20 and 35 are: $20 = 2^2 \cdot 5$, $35 = 5 \cdot 7$
a) The common factor is 5; thus the GCD = 5.
b) The factors with the greatest exponent that appear in either are: 2^2, 5 and 7; thus, the LCM = $2^2 \cdot 5 \cdot 7 = 140$

50. The prime factors of 32 and 224 are: $32 = 2^5$, $224 = 2^5 \cdot 7$
a) The common factor is: 2^5; thus, the GCD = $2^5 = 32$.
b) The factors with the greatest exponent that appear in either are: 2^5 and 7; thus, the LCM = $2^5 \cdot 7 = 224$

51. The prime factors of 40 and 900 are: $40 = 2^3 \cdot 5$, $900 = 2^2 \cdot 3^2 \cdot 5^2$
a) The common factors are: 2^2, 5; thus, the GCD = $2^2 \cdot 5 = 20$.
b) The factors with the greatest exponent that appear in either are: 2^3, 3^2, 5^2; thus, the LCM = $2^2 \cdot 3^2 \cdot 5^2 = 1800$

52. The prime factors of 120 and 240 are: $120 = 2^3 \cdot 3 \cdot 5$, $240 = 2^4 \cdot 3 \cdot 5$
a) The common factors are: 2^3, 3, 5; thus, the GCD = $2^3 \cdot 3 \cdot 5 = 120$.
b) The factors with the greatest exponent that appear in either are: 2^4, 3, 5; thus, the LCM = $2^4 \cdot 3 \cdot 5 = 240$

53. The prime factors of 96 and 212 are: $96 = 2^5 \cdot 3$, $212 = 2^2 \cdot 53$

a) The common factors are: 2^2; thus, the GCD $= 2^2 = 4$.

b) The factors with the greatest exponent that appear in either are: 2^5, 3, 53; thus, the LCM $= 2^5 \cdot 3 \cdot 53 = 5088$

54. The prime factors of 240 are: $2^4 \cdot 3 \cdot 5$.

The prime factors of 285 are: $3 \cdot 5 \cdot 19$

a) The common factors are 3 and 5; thus, the GCD $= 3 \cdot 5 = 15$.

b) The factors with the greatest exponent that appear in either are: 2^4, 3, 5, and 19; thus the LCM $= 2^4 \cdot 3 \cdot 5 \cdot 19 = 4560$.

55. The prime factors of 24, 48, and 128 are: $24 = 2^3 \cdot 3$, $48 = 2^4 \cdot 3$, $128 = 2^7$

a) The common factors are: 2^3; thus, the GCD $= 2^3 = 8$.

b) The factors with the greatest exponent that appear in any are: 2^7, 3; thus, LCM $= 2^7 \cdot 3 = 384$

56. The prime factors of 18, 78, and 198 are: $18 = 2 \cdot 3^2$, $78 = 2 \cdot 3 \cdot 13$, $198 = 2 \cdot 3^2 \cdot 11$

a) The common factors are: 2, 3; thus, the GCD $= 2 \cdot 3 = 6$.

b) The factors with the greatest exponent that appear in any are: 2, 3^2, 11, 13; thus, the LCM $= 2 \cdot 3^2 \cdot 11 \cdot 13 = 2574$

57. Use the list of primes generated in exercise 13. The next two sets of twin primes are: 17, 19, 29, 31.

58. No. Any other two consecutive natural numbers will include an even number, and even numbers greater than two are composite.

59. (a) 10, 21 Yes; (b) 22, 26 No; (c) 27, 28 Yes; (d) 85, 119 Yes

60. Use the formula $2^n - 1$, where n is a prime number. $2^2 - 1 = 3$, $2^3 - 1 = 7$, $2^5 - 1 = 31$, $2^7 - 1 = 127$, $2^{13} - 1 = 8191$.

61. Fermat number $= 2^{2^n} + 1$, where n is a natural number. $2^{2^1} + 1 = 5$, $2^{2^2} + 1 = 2^4 + 1 = 17$, $2^{2^3} + 1 = 2^8 + 1 = 257$. These numbers are prime.

62. $4 = 2 + 2$, $6 = 3 + 3$, $8 = 3 + 5$, $10 = 3 + 7$, $12 = 5 + 7$, $14 = 7 + 7$, $16 = 3 + 13$, $18 = 5 + 13$, $20 = 3 + 17$

63. $2 \times 60, 3 \times 40, 4 \times 30, 5 \times 24, 6 \times 20, 8 \times 15, 10 \times 12,$
$12 \times 10, 15 \times 8, 20 \times 6, 24 \times 5, 30 \times 4, 40 \times 3, 60 \times 2$

64. a) The possible committee sizes are: 4, 5, 10, 20, or 25.   b) The number of committees possible are: 25 committees of 4, 20 committees of 5, 10 committees of 10, 5 committees of 20, or 4 committees of 25.

65. The gcd of 30 and 14 is 210 days.

66. The gcd of 390 and 468 is 78 dolls.

67. The gcd of 70 and 175 is 35 cars.

68. The gcd of 432 and 360 is 72 cards.

69 The gcd of 150 and 180 is 30 trees.

70. The lcm of 3500 and 6000 is 42,000 miles.

71. The lcm of 5 and 6 is 30 days.

72. a) $5 = 6 - 1$ $7 = 6 + 1$ $11 = 12 - 1$ $13 = 12 + 1$ $17 = 18 - 1$ $19 = 18 + 1$ $23 = 24 - 1$
$29 = 30 - 1$

b) Conjecture: Every prime number greater than 3 differs by 1 from a multiple of the number 6.

c) The conjecture appears to be correct.

73. A number is divisible by 15 if both 3 and 5 divide the number.

74. A number is divisible by 22 if both 2 and 11 divide the number.

75. $40 \div 15 = 2$ with rem. $= 10$
    $15 \div 10 = 1$ with rem. $= 5$
    $10 \div 5 = 2$ with rem. $= 0$
    Thus, gcd of 15 and 40 is 5.

76. $28 \div 12 = 2$ with rem. $= 4$
    $12 \div 4 = 3$ with rem. $= 0$
    Thus, gcd of 12 and 28 is 4.

77. $105 \div 35 = 3$ with rem. $= 0$.
    Thus, gcd of 105 and 35 is 35.

78. $104 \div 78 = 1$ with rem. $= 26$.
    $78 \div 26 = 3$ with rem. $= 0$.
    Thus, gcd of 104 and 78 is 26.

79. $180 \div 150 = 1$ with rem. $= 30$.
    $150 \div 30 = 5$ with rem. $= 0$.
    Thus, the gcd of 150 and 180 is 30.

80. $560 \div 210 = 2$ w/rem. $= 140$.
    $210 \div 140 = 1$ w/rem. $= 70$.
    $140 \div 70 = 2$ w/rem. $= 0$.
    Thus, gcd of 210 and 560 is 70.

81. The proper factors of 12 are: 1, 2, 3, 4, and 6.
    $1 + 2 + 3 + 4 + 6 = 16 \neq 12$
    Thus, 12 is not a perfect #.

82. The proper factors of 28 are: 1, 2, 4, 7, and 14.
    $1 + 2 + 4 + 7 + 14 = 28$
    Thus, 28 is a perfect number.

83. The proper factors of 48 are: 1, 2, 3, 4, 6, 8, 12, 16, and 24.
    $1 + 2 + 3 + 4 + 6 + 8 + 12 + 16 + 24 = 76$
    Thus, 48 is not a perfect #.

84. The proper factors of 496 are: 1, 2, 4, 8, 16, 31, 62, 124, and 248.
    $1 + 2 + 4 + 8 + 16 + 31 + 62 + 124 + 248 = 496$
    Thus, 496 is a perfect #

85. a) $60 = 2^2 \cdot 3^1 \cdot 5^1$ Adding 1 to each exponent and then multiplying these numbers, we get $(2+1)(1+1)(1+1) = 3 \cdot 2 \cdot 2 = 12$ divisors of 60 b) They are 1, 2, 3, 4, 5, 6, 10, 12, 15, 20, 30, and 60.

86. No, 2 and 4 are not unique prime factors since $4 = 2 \cdot 2$. Any number that 4 divides, 2 will also divide, but 8 does not divide all numbers that are divisible by 4. Some examples are: 4, 12, and 20.

87. One of the numbers must be divisible by 3 and at least one must be even, so their product will be divisible by 2 and 3 and thus by 6.

88. The sum of the groups which have the same three digits will always be divisible by three.
    (i.e. $d + d + d = 3d$ and $3 | 3d$)

89. $54036 = (54,000 + 36)$; $54,000 \div 18 = 3,000$ and $36 \div 18 = 2$
    Thus, since $18 | 54000$ and $18 | 36$, $18 | 54036$.

90. $2^2 - 1 = 3, 2^3 - 1 = 7, 2^5 - 1 = 31, 2^7 - 1 = 127$ are prime numbers, but $2^{11} - 1 = 2,048 - 1 = 2,047$; and since $23 \cdot 89 = 2,047$, 2047 is not prime.

91. $8 = 2+3+3$, $9 = 3+3+3$, $10 = 2+3+5$, $11 = 2+2+7$, $12 = 2+5+5$, $13 = 3+3+7$, $14 = 2+5+7$, $15 = 3+5+7$, $16 = 2+7+7$, $17 = 5+5+7$, $18 = 2+5+11$, $19 = 3+5+11$, $20 = 2+7+11$.

92. (a) $329 \rightarrow 32 - 18 = 14; 7 | 14;$ yes
    (b) $553 \rightarrow 55 - 6 = 49; 7 | 49;$ yes
    (c) $583 \rightarrow 58 - 6 = 52; 7 \nmid 52;$ no
    (d) $4823 \rightarrow 482 - 6 = 476; 476 = 7 \cdot 68;$ yes

93. Denmark, Kangaroo, Orange. The sum of the digits minus 5 will always be 4, so the first letter for the country will always be D.

Exercise Set 5.2

1. Begin at zero, draw an arrow to the value of the first number. From the tip of that arrow draw another arrow by moving a number of spaces equal to the value of the second number. Be sure to move left if the number is negative and move right if the number is positive. The sum of the two numbers is at the tip of the second arrow.

2. $-n$; Additive Inverse = that number when added to n yields the Additive Identity (= 0); $n + (-n) = 0$

3. To rewrite a subtraction problem as an addition problem, rewrite the subtraction sign as an addition sign and change the second number to its additive inverse.

4. The quotient of two numbers with like signs is a positive number, and the quotient of two numbers with unlike signs is a negative number.

5. The product of two numbers with like signs is a positive number, and the product of two numbers with unlike signs is a negative number.

6. If we set $5 \div 0 = x$ and we cross multiply, we get the equation $0x = 5$. Since $0 \bullet x = 0$, we get $5 = 0$, which is a false statement, which means that there is no such number x. Therefore, division by 0 is not allowed.

7. $-4 + 7 = 3$

8. $3 + (-7) = -4$

9. $-9 + 5 = -4$

10. $(-2) + (-2) = -4$

11. $[6 + (-11)] + 0 = -5 + 0 = -5$

12. $(2 + 5) + (-4) = 7 + (-4) = 3$

13. $[(-3) + (-4)] + 9 =$
    $-7 + 9 = 2$

14. $[8 + (-3)] + (-2) =$
    $[5] + (-2) = 3$

15. $[(-23) + (-9)] + 11 =$
    $[-32] + 11 = -21$

16. $[5 + (-13)] + 18 =$
    $[-8] + 18 = 10$

17. $1 - 7 = -6$

18. $-4 - 8 = -12$

19. $-5 - 4 = -9$

20. $6 - (-3) = 9$

21. $-5 - (-3) = -5 + 3 = -2$

22. $-4 - 4 = -4 + (-4) = -8$

23. $14 - 20 = 14 + (-20) = -6$

24. $8 - (-3) = 8 + 3 = 11$

25. $[5 + (-3)] - 4 = 2 - 4 =$
    $2 + (-4) = -2$

26. $6 - (8 + 6) = 6 - 14 =$
    $6 + (-14) = -8$

27. $-5 \bullet 6 = -30$

28. $9(-3) = -18$

29. $(-8)(-8) = 64$

30. $-4(11) = -44$

31. $[(-8)(-2)] \bullet 6 = 16 \bullet 6 = 96$

32. $(4)(-5)(-6) = (-20)(-6)$
    $= 120$

33. $(5 \bullet 6)(-2) = (30)(-2) = -60$

34. $(-9)(-1)(-2) = (9)(-2)$
    $= -18$

35. $[(-3)(-6)] \bullet [(-5)(8)] =$
    $(18)(-40) = -720$

36. $[(-8)(4)(5)](-2) =$
    $[(-32)(5)](-2) = [-160](-2)$
    $= 320$

37. $-28 \div (-4) = 7$

38. $-72 \div 9 = -8$

39. $11 \div (-11) = -1$

40. $-100 \div 20 = -5$

41. $\dfrac{56}{-8} = -7$

42. $\dfrac{-75}{15} = -5$

43. $\dfrac{-210}{14} = -15$

44. $\dfrac{186}{-6} = -31$

45. $144 \div (-3) = -48$

46. $(-900) \div (-4) = 225$

47. True; every whole number is an integer.

48. False; Negative numbers are not whole numbers.

49. False; the difference of two negative integers may be positive, negative, or zero.

50. True.

51. True; the product of two integers with like signs is a positive integer.

52. False; the difference of a positive integer and a neg. integer may be +, - or zero.

53. True; the quotient of two integers with unlike signs is a negative number.

54. False; the quotient of any two integers with like signs is a positive number.

55. False; the sum of a positive integer and a negative integer could be pos., neg., or zero.

56. False; the product of two integers with unlike signs is always a negative integer.

57. $(7 + 11) \div 3 = 18 \div 3 = 6$

58. $(-8) \div [64 \div (-8)] =$
$(-8) \div [-8] = 1$

59. $[(-7)(-6)] - 22 =$
$42 - 22 = 20$

60. $[8(-2)] - 15 = -16 - 15 = -31$

61. $(4 - 8)(3) = (-4)(3) = -12$

62. $[18 \div (-2)](-3) = (-9)(-3)$
$= 27$

63. $[2 + (-17)] \div 3 = [-15] \div 3 = -5$

64. $(5 - 9) \div (-4) =$
$(-4) \div (-4) = 1$

65. $[(-22)(-3)] \div (2 - 13) =$
$= 66 \div (-11) = -6$

66. $[15(-4)] \div (-6) =$
$(-60) \div (-6) = 10$

67. $-9, -6, -3, 0, 3, 6$

68. $-10, -1, 0, 10, 100$

69. $-6, -5, -4, -3, -2, -1$

70. $-108, -76, -47, 33, 72, 106$

71. $11,250 - 95 + 61 - 65 - 42 =$
$11,250 + 61 - (95 + 65 + 42) =$
$11,311 - 202 = 11,109$

72. $0 + 100 - 40 + 90 - 20 + 80 =$
$60 + 90 - 20 + 80 = 210$ pts.

73. $14,495 - (-282) =$
$14,495 + 282 = 14,777$ feet

74. $-1000 + 600 - 700 - 400 =$
$-400 - 700 - 400 = -1500$;
1500 feet under water.

75. $-6 + 4 - 1 + 12 =$
$-7 + 16 = 9$; 9 yards; no

76. $134 - (-79.8) =$
$134 + 79.8 = 213.8°$ F.

77. a) $+1 - (-8) = +1 + 8 = 9.$
There is a 9 hr. time diff.
b) $-5 - (-7) = -5 + 7 = 2.$
There is a 2 hr. time diff.

78. $\dfrac{-a}{-b} = \dfrac{-1}{-1} \cdot \dfrac{a}{b} = \dfrac{a}{b}$

79.

$$\dfrac{-1+2-3+4-5+\ldots 99+100}{1-2+3-4+5\ldots+99-100} =$$

$$\dfrac{50}{-50} = -1$$

80. a) The next 3 pentagonal numbers are 35, 51, and 70.

b) The nth pentagonal number is obtained by adding the nth triangular # (see Section 1.1) to the nth square number (see Section 1.1) and subtracting n. For example, if n = 4, the 4th triangular number is 10

80. b) continued: and the 4th square number is 16. The sum of 10 and 16 is 26 and
$26 - n = 26 - 4 = 22$,
which is the 4th pentagonal #. The next 5 pentagonal numbers 35, 51, 70, 92, and 117.

c) Since 70 is the 7th pentagonal number and 92 is the 8th pentagonal number, 72 cannot be a pentagonal number.

81. $0 + 1 - 2 + 3 + 4 - 5 + 6 - 7 - 8 + 9 = 1$ (other answers are possible)

82. (a) $4 + 4 - 4 - 4 = 0$ $\dfrac{4+4}{4+4} = 1$ $\dfrac{4}{4} + \dfrac{4}{4} = 2$ $\dfrac{4+4+4}{4} = 3$

$4(4-4) + 4 = 4$ $\dfrac{4 \cdot 4 + 4}{4} = 5$ $4 + \dfrac{4+4}{4} = 6$ $4 + 4 - \dfrac{4}{4} = 7$

$4 \cdot 4 - 4 - 4 = 8$ $4 + 4 + \dfrac{4}{4} = 9$

(b) $4\left(4 - \dfrac{4}{4}\right) = 12$ $4 \bullet 4 - \dfrac{4}{4} = 15$ $\dfrac{4 \bullet 4 \bullet 4}{4} = 16$ (c) $\dfrac{44-4}{4} = 10$

$4 \bullet 4 - \dfrac{4}{4} = 17$ $\left(4 + \dfrac{4}{4}\right)4 = 20$

Exercise Set 5.3

1. Rational numbers is the set of all numbers of the form p/q, where p and q are integers, and $q \neq 0$.

2. a) Multiply and divide the number by the position value of the last nonzero digit to the right of the decimal point.

   b) $0.397 = \dfrac{1000(0.213)}{1000} = \dfrac{213}{1000}$

3. a) Divide both the numerator and the denominator by their greatest common divisor.

   b) $\dfrac{28}{35} = \dfrac{28 \div 7}{35 \div 7} = \dfrac{4}{5}$

4. Divide the numerator by the denominator. The quotient is the integer part of the mixed number.

   The fraction part of the mixed number is the remainder divided by the divisor.

5. For positive mixed numbers, multiply the denominator of the fraction by the integer preceding it.

   Add this product to the numerator. This sum is the numerator of the improper fraction; the denominator

   is the same as the denominator of the mixed number. For negative mixed numbers, you can temporarily

   ignore the negative sign, perform the conversion described above, and then reattach the negative sign.

6. a) The product of two fractions is found by multiplying the numerators and multiplying the denominators.

   b) $\dfrac{14}{15} \bullet \dfrac{25}{28} = \dfrac{350}{420} = \dfrac{350 \div 70}{420 \div 70} = \dfrac{5}{6}$

7. a) The reciprocal of a number is 1 divided by the number.

   b) The reciprocal of -2 is $\dfrac{1}{-2} = -\dfrac{1}{2}$

8. a) To divide two fractions, multiply the first fraction by the reciprocal of the second fraction.

   b) $\dfrac{14}{33} \div \dfrac{10}{21} = \dfrac{14}{33} \bullet \dfrac{21}{10} = \dfrac{294}{330} = \dfrac{294 \div 6}{330 \div 6} = \dfrac{49}{55}$

9. a) To add or subtract two fractions with a common denominator, we add or subtract their numerators and keep the common denominator.

   b) $\dfrac{11}{24} + \dfrac{3}{24} = \dfrac{14}{24} = \dfrac{14 \div 2}{24 \div 2} = \dfrac{7}{12}$ c) $\dfrac{37}{48} - \dfrac{13}{48} = \dfrac{24}{48} = \dfrac{24 \div 24}{48 \div 24} = \dfrac{1}{2}$

10. a) First rewrite each fraction with a common denominator. Then add or subtract the fractions.

   b) $\dfrac{2}{3}+\dfrac{5}{8}=\dfrac{16}{24}+\dfrac{15}{25}=\dfrac{31}{24}$ c) $\dfrac{5}{6}-\dfrac{2}{15}=\dfrac{5\cdot5}{6}-\dfrac{2\cdot2}{15}=\dfrac{25}{30}-\dfrac{4}{30}=\dfrac{21}{30}=\dfrac{7}{10}$

11. We can multiply a fraction by the number one in the form of c/c (where c is a nonzero integer) and the number will maintain the same value.

12. Yes. $\dfrac{21}{33}=\dfrac{21\div3}{33\div3}=\dfrac{7}{11}$

13. GCD of 5 and 10 is 5.

   $\dfrac{5}{10}=\dfrac{5\div5}{10\div5}=\dfrac{1}{2}$

14. GCD of 12 and 16 is 4.

   $\dfrac{12}{16}=\dfrac{12\div4}{16\div4}=\dfrac{3}{4}$

15. GCD of 24 and 54 is 6.

   $\dfrac{24}{54}=\dfrac{24\div6}{54\div6}=\dfrac{4}{9}$

16. GCD of 36 and 56 is 4.

   $\dfrac{36}{56}=\dfrac{36\div4}{56\div4}=\dfrac{9}{14}$

17. GCD of 95 and 125 is 5.

   $\dfrac{95}{125}=\dfrac{95\div5}{125\div5}=\dfrac{19}{25}$

18. GCD of 13 and 221 is 13.

   $\dfrac{13}{221}=\dfrac{13\div13}{221\div13}=\dfrac{1}{17}$

19. GCD of 112 and 176 is 16.

   $\dfrac{112}{176}=\dfrac{112\div16}{176\div16}=\dfrac{7}{11}$

20. GCD of 120 and 135 is 15.

   $\dfrac{120}{135}=\dfrac{120\div15}{135\div15}=\dfrac{8}{9}$

21. GCD of 45 and 495 is 45.

   $\dfrac{45}{495}=\dfrac{45\div45}{495\div45}=\dfrac{1}{11}$

22. GCD of 124 and 148 is 4.

   $\dfrac{124}{148}=\dfrac{124\div4}{148\div4}=\dfrac{31}{37}$

23.

   $3\dfrac{5}{8}=\dfrac{(8)(3)+5}{8}=\dfrac{24+5}{8}=\dfrac{29}{8}$

24. $2\dfrac{1}{4}=\dfrac{(4)(2)+1}{4}=\dfrac{8+1}{4}=\dfrac{9}{4}$

25. $-1\dfrac{15}{16}=-\dfrac{-((1)(16)+15)}{16}$

   $=-\dfrac{16+15}{16}=-\dfrac{31}{16}$

26. $-7\dfrac{1}{5}=-\dfrac{(7)(5)+1}{5}$

   $=-\dfrac{35+1}{5}=-\dfrac{36}{5}$

27. $-4\dfrac{15}{16}=-\dfrac{(4)(16)+15}{16}$

   $=-\dfrac{64+15}{16}=-\dfrac{79}{16}$

28. $11\dfrac{9}{16}=\dfrac{(11)(16)+9}{16}$

   $=\dfrac{176+9}{16}=\dfrac{185}{16}$

29. $1\dfrac{1}{8}=\dfrac{(1)(8)+1}{8}=\dfrac{8+1}{8}=\dfrac{9}{8}$

30. $2\dfrac{1}{4}=\dfrac{(2)(4)+1}{4}=\dfrac{8+1}{4}=\dfrac{9}{4}$

31. $1\dfrac{7}{8}=\dfrac{(1)(8)+7}{8}=\dfrac{8+7}{8}=\dfrac{15}{8}$

32. $1\dfrac{1}{2}=\dfrac{(1)(2)+1}{2}=\dfrac{2+1}{2}=\dfrac{3}{2}$

33. $\dfrac{13}{5}=\dfrac{10+3}{5}=\dfrac{(2)(5)+3}{5}=2\dfrac{3}{5}$

34. $\dfrac{23}{4}=\dfrac{20+3}{4}=\dfrac{(5)(4)+3}{4}=5\dfrac{3}{4}$

35. $-\dfrac{73}{6}=\dfrac{-(72+1)}{6}$

   $=\dfrac{-(12\cdot6+1)}{6}=-12\dfrac{1}{6}$

36. $-\dfrac{157}{12}=-\dfrac{156+1}{12}$

   $=-\dfrac{(13)(12)+1}{12}$

   $=-13\dfrac{1}{12}$

37. $-\dfrac{878}{15}=-\dfrac{870+8}{15}$

   $=-\dfrac{(58)(15)+8}{15}=-58\dfrac{8}{15}$

38. $\dfrac{1028}{21}=\dfrac{1008+20}{21}$

   $=\dfrac{(48)(21)+20}{21}=48\dfrac{20}{21}$

39. $\dfrac{7}{10} = 0.7$

40. $\dfrac{15}{16} = .9375$

41. $\dfrac{2}{9} = .\overline{2}$

42. $\dfrac{1}{6} = 0.1\overline{6}$

43. $\dfrac{3}{8} = 0.375$

44. $\dfrac{23}{7} = 3.\overline{285714}$

45. $\dfrac{13}{6} = 2.1\overline{6}$

46. $\dfrac{155}{15} = 7.\overline{6}$

47. $\dfrac{85}{15} = 5.\overline{6}$

48. $\dfrac{100}{9} = 11.\overline{1}$

49. $\dfrac{75}{100} = \dfrac{75 \div 25}{100 \div 25} = \dfrac{3}{4}$

50. $0.29 = \dfrac{29}{100}$

51. $0.045 = \dfrac{45}{1000} = \dfrac{45 \div 5}{1000 \div 5} = \dfrac{9}{200}$

52. $0.375 = \dfrac{375}{1000} = \dfrac{375 \div 125}{1000 \div 125} = \dfrac{3}{8}$

53. $0.2 = \dfrac{2}{10} = \dfrac{1}{5}$

54. $.251 = \dfrac{251}{1000}$

55. $0.0131 = \dfrac{131}{10,000}$

56. $.2345 = \dfrac{2345}{10000} = \dfrac{469}{2000}$

57. $.0001 = \dfrac{1}{10000}$

58. $0.0053 = \dfrac{53}{10,000}$

59. Let $n = 0.\overline{1}$, $\quad 10n = 1.\overline{1}$

$$10n = 1.\overline{1}$$
$$\underline{-n = 0.\overline{1}} \qquad \dfrac{9n}{9} = \dfrac{1}{9} = n$$
$$9n = 1.0$$

60. Let $n = 0.\overline{5}$, $\quad 10n = 5.\overline{5}$

$$10n = 5.\overline{5}$$
$$\underline{-n = 0.\overline{5}} \qquad \dfrac{9n}{9} = \dfrac{5}{9} = n$$
$$9n = 5.0$$

61. Let $n = 1.\overline{9}$, $\quad 10n = 19.\overline{9}$

$$10n = 19.\overline{9}$$
$$\underline{-n = 1.\overline{9}}$$
$$9n = 18.0$$
$$\dfrac{9n}{9} = \dfrac{18}{9} = 2 = n$$

62. Let $n = 0.\overline{23}$, $\quad 100n = 23.\overline{23}$

$$100n = 23.\overline{23}$$
$$\underline{-n = 0.\overline{23}}$$
$$99n = 23.00$$
$$\dfrac{99n}{99} = \dfrac{23}{99} = n$$

63. Let $n = 1.\overline{36}$, $\quad 100n = 136.\overline{36}$

$$100n = 136.\overline{36}$$
$$\underline{-n = 1.\overline{36}}$$
$$99n = 135.0$$
$$\dfrac{99n}{99} = \dfrac{135}{99} = \dfrac{15}{11} = n$$

64. Let
$$n = .\overline{135}, 1000n = 135.\overline{135}$$
$$1000n = 135.\overline{135}$$
$$\underline{-n = .\overline{135}}$$
$$999n = 135.0$$
$$\dfrac{999n}{999} = \dfrac{135}{999} = \dfrac{5}{37} = n$$

65. Let $n = 2.0\overline{5}$,

$10n = 20.\overline{5}, \quad 100n = 205.\overline{5}$

$100n = 205.\overline{5}$

$\underline{-10n = 20.\overline{5}}$

$90n = 185.0$

$\dfrac{90n}{90} = \dfrac{185}{90} = \dfrac{37}{18} = n$

66. Let $n = 2.4\overline{9}$, $\quad 100n = 249.\overline{9}$

$100n = 249.\overline{9}$

$\underline{-10n = 24.\overline{9}}$

$90n = 225.0$

$\dfrac{90n}{90} = \dfrac{245}{90} = \dfrac{5}{2} = n$

67. Let $\quad n = 3.4\overline{78}$,

$1000n = 3478.\overline{78}$

$1000n = 3478.\overline{78}$

$\underline{-10n = 34.\overline{78}}$

$990n = 3444.0$

$\dfrac{990n}{990} = \dfrac{3444}{990} = \dfrac{574}{165} = n$

68. Let $n = 4.1\overline{19}, 10n = 41.19,$

$1000n = 4119.\overline{19}$

$1000n = 4119.\overline{19}$

$\underline{-10n = 41.19}$

$990n = 4078.0$

$\dfrac{990n}{990} = \dfrac{4079}{990} = \dfrac{2039}{495} = n$

69. $\dfrac{1}{2} \cdot \dfrac{4}{5} = \dfrac{1 \cdot 4}{2 \cdot 5} = \dfrac{4}{10} = \dfrac{4 \div 2}{10 \div 2} = \dfrac{2}{5}$

70.

$\dfrac{2}{9} \div \dfrac{4}{7} = \dfrac{2}{9} \cdot \dfrac{7}{4} = \dfrac{14}{36} = \dfrac{14 \div 2}{36 \div 2} = \dfrac{7}{18}$

71. $\dfrac{-3}{8} \cdot \dfrac{-16}{15} = \dfrac{48}{120} = \dfrac{2}{5}$

72. $\left(-\dfrac{3}{5}\right) \div \dfrac{10}{21} = \left(-\dfrac{3}{5}\right) \cdot \dfrac{21}{10} = -\dfrac{63}{50}$

73. $\dfrac{7}{8} \div \dfrac{8}{7} = \dfrac{7}{8} \cdot \dfrac{7}{8} = \dfrac{49}{64}$

74. $\dfrac{3}{7} \div \dfrac{3}{7} = \dfrac{3}{7} \cdot \dfrac{7}{3} = \dfrac{21}{21} = 1$

75. $\left(\dfrac{3}{5} \cdot \dfrac{4}{7}\right) \div \dfrac{1}{3} = \dfrac{12}{35} \div \dfrac{1}{3} = \dfrac{12}{35} \cdot \dfrac{3}{1} = \dfrac{36}{35}$

76. $\left(\dfrac{4}{7} \div \dfrac{4}{5}\right) \cdot \dfrac{1}{7} = \left(\dfrac{4}{7} \cdot \dfrac{5}{4}\right) \cdot \dfrac{1}{7} = \dfrac{5}{7} \cdot \dfrac{1}{7} = \dfrac{5}{49}$

77. $\left[\left(-\dfrac{2}{3}\right)\left(\dfrac{5}{8}\right)\right] \div \left(-\dfrac{7}{16}\right) = \left(-\dfrac{10}{24}\right) \cdot \left(-\dfrac{16}{7}\right) = \dfrac{160}{168} = \dfrac{20}{21}$

78. $\left(\dfrac{7}{15} \cdot \dfrac{5}{8}\right) \div \left(\dfrac{7}{9} \cdot \dfrac{5}{2}\right) = \left(\dfrac{35}{120}\right) \div \left(\dfrac{35}{18}\right) = \dfrac{35}{120} \cdot \dfrac{18}{35} = \dfrac{18}{120} = \dfrac{3}{20}$

79. The lcm of 3 and 4 is 12.

$\dfrac{1}{4} + \dfrac{2}{3} = \left(\dfrac{1}{4} \cdot \dfrac{3}{3}\right) + \left(\dfrac{2}{3} \cdot \dfrac{4}{4}\right) = \dfrac{3}{12} + \dfrac{8}{12} = \dfrac{11}{12}$

80. The lcm of 6 and 8 is 24.

$\dfrac{7}{8} - \dfrac{1}{6} = \left(\dfrac{7}{8} \cdot \dfrac{3}{3}\right) - \left(\dfrac{1}{6} \cdot \dfrac{4}{4}\right) = \dfrac{21}{24} - \dfrac{4}{24} = \dfrac{17}{24}$

81. The lcm of 11 and 22 is 22.

$\dfrac{2}{11} + \dfrac{5}{22} = \left(\dfrac{2}{11} \cdot \dfrac{2}{2}\right) + \dfrac{5}{22} = \dfrac{4}{22} + \dfrac{5}{29} = \dfrac{9}{22}$

82. The lcm of 12 and 36 is 36.

$\dfrac{5}{12} + \dfrac{7}{36} = \left(\dfrac{5}{12} \cdot \dfrac{3}{3}\right) + \dfrac{7}{36} = \dfrac{15}{36} + \dfrac{7}{36} = \dfrac{22}{36} = \dfrac{22 \div 2}{36 \div 2} = \dfrac{11}{18}$

83. The lcm of 9 and 54 is 54.

$\dfrac{5}{9} - \dfrac{7}{54} = \left(\dfrac{5}{9} \cdot \dfrac{6}{6}\right) - \dfrac{7}{54} = \dfrac{30}{54} - \dfrac{7}{54} = \dfrac{23}{54}$

84. The lcm of 25 and 100 is 100.

$\dfrac{17}{25} - \dfrac{43}{100} = \left(\dfrac{17}{24} \cdot \dfrac{4}{4}\right) - \dfrac{43}{100} = \dfrac{68}{100} - \dfrac{43}{100} = \dfrac{25}{100}$

$= \dfrac{1}{4}$

85. The lcm of 12, 48, and 72 is 144.

$\dfrac{1}{12} + \dfrac{1}{48} + \dfrac{1}{72} = \left(\dfrac{1}{12} \cdot \dfrac{12}{12}\right) + \left(\dfrac{1}{48} \cdot \dfrac{3}{3}\right) + \left(\dfrac{1}{72} \cdot \dfrac{2}{2}\right)$

$= \dfrac{12}{144} + \dfrac{3}{144} + \dfrac{2}{144} = \dfrac{17}{144}$

86. The lcm of 5,15,and 75 is 75.

$$\frac{3}{5}+\frac{7}{15}+\frac{9}{75}=\left(\frac{3}{5}\cdot\frac{15}{15}\right)+\left(\frac{7}{15}\cdot\frac{5}{5}\right)+\frac{9}{75}$$

$$=\frac{45}{75}+\frac{35}{75}+\frac{9}{75}=\frac{89}{75}$$

87. The lcm of 30,40,and 50 is 600.

$$\frac{1}{30}-\frac{3}{40}-\frac{7}{50}=\left(\frac{1}{30}\cdot\frac{20}{20}\right)\left(\frac{3}{40}\cdot\frac{15}{15}\right)\left(\frac{7}{50}\cdot\frac{12}{12}\right)$$

$$=\frac{20}{600}-\frac{45}{600}-\frac{84}{600}=-\frac{109}{600}$$

88. The lcm of 25, 100, and 40 is 200.

$$\frac{4}{25}-\frac{9}{100}-\frac{7}{40}=\left(\frac{4}{25}\cdot\frac{8}{8}\right)\left(\frac{9}{100}\cdot\frac{2}{2}\right)\left(\frac{7}{40}\cdot\frac{5}{5}\right)$$

$$=\frac{32}{200}-\frac{18}{200}-\frac{35}{200}=-\frac{21}{200}$$

89. $\dfrac{2}{3}+\dfrac{1}{8}=\dfrac{2\cdot8+3\cdot1}{3\cdot8}=\dfrac{16+3}{23}=\dfrac{19}{24}$

90. $\dfrac{1}{5}+\dfrac{4}{9}=\dfrac{1\cdot9+5\cdot4}{5\cdot9}=\dfrac{9+20}{45}=\dfrac{29}{45}$

91. $\dfrac{5}{6}-\dfrac{7}{8}=\dfrac{5\cdot4-7\cdot3}{24}=\dfrac{20-21}{24}=\dfrac{-1}{24}$

92. $\dfrac{7}{3}-\dfrac{5}{12}=\dfrac{7\cdot12-3\cdot5}{3\cdot12}=\dfrac{84-15}{36}=\dfrac{69}{36}=\dfrac{23}{12}$

93. $\dfrac{3}{8}+\dfrac{5}{12}=\dfrac{3\cdot12+8\cdot5}{8\cdot12}=\dfrac{36+40}{96}=\dfrac{76}{96}=\dfrac{19}{24}$

94. $\left(\dfrac{2}{3}+\dfrac{1}{4}\right)-\dfrac{3}{5}=\left(\dfrac{2\cdot4+3\cdot1}{3\cdot4}\right)-\dfrac{3}{5}=\dfrac{8+3}{12}-\dfrac{3}{5}$

$$=\frac{11}{12}-\frac{3}{5}=\frac{11\cdot5-12\cdot3}{12\cdot5}=\frac{55-36}{60}=\frac{19}{60}$$

95. $\left(\dfrac{2}{3}\cdot\dfrac{9}{10}\right)+\dfrac{2}{5}=\dfrac{18}{30}+\dfrac{2}{5}=\dfrac{18}{30}+\left(\dfrac{2}{5}\cdot\dfrac{6}{6}\right)=$

$$=\frac{18}{30}+\frac{12}{30}=\frac{30}{30}=1$$

96. $\left(\dfrac{7}{6}\div\dfrac{4}{3}\right)-\dfrac{11}{12}=\left(\dfrac{7}{6}\cdot\dfrac{3}{4}\right)-\dfrac{11}{12}=\dfrac{21}{24}-\left(\dfrac{11}{12}\cdot\dfrac{2}{2}\right)=$

$$=\frac{21}{24}-\frac{22}{24}=\frac{-1}{24}$$

97. $\left(\dfrac{3}{4}+\dfrac{1}{6}\right)\div\left(2-\dfrac{7}{6}\right)=\left(\dfrac{3}{4}\cdot\dfrac{3}{3}+\dfrac{1}{6}\cdot\dfrac{2}{2}\right)\div\left(\dfrac{2}{1}\cdot\dfrac{6}{6}-\dfrac{7}{6}\right)=\left(\dfrac{9}{12}+\dfrac{2}{12}\right)\div\left(\dfrac{12}{6}-\dfrac{7}{6}\right)=\dfrac{11}{12}\div\dfrac{5}{6}=\dfrac{11}{12}\cdot\dfrac{6}{5}=\dfrac{66}{60}=\dfrac{11}{10}$

98. $\left(\dfrac{1}{3}\cdot\dfrac{3}{7}\right)+\left(\dfrac{3}{5}\cdot\dfrac{10}{11}\right)=\dfrac{3}{21}+\dfrac{30}{55}=\dfrac{1}{7}+\dfrac{6}{11}=\dfrac{1}{7}\cdot\dfrac{11}{11}+\dfrac{6}{11}\cdot\dfrac{7}{7}=\dfrac{11}{77}+\dfrac{42}{77}=\dfrac{53}{77}$

99. $\left(3\dfrac{4}{9}\right)\div\left(4+\dfrac{2}{3}\right)=\left(\dfrac{3}{1}\cdot\dfrac{9}{9}-\dfrac{4}{9}\right)\div\left(\dfrac{4}{1}\cdot\dfrac{3}{3}+\dfrac{2}{3}\right)=\left(\dfrac{27}{9}-\dfrac{4}{9}\right)\div\left(\dfrac{12}{3}+\dfrac{2}{3}\right)=\dfrac{23}{9}\div\dfrac{14}{3}=\dfrac{23}{9}\cdot\dfrac{3}{14}=\dfrac{69}{126}=\dfrac{23}{42}$

100. $\left(\dfrac{2}{5}\div\dfrac{4}{9}\right)\left(\dfrac{3}{5}\cdot6\right)=\left(\dfrac{2}{5}\cdot\dfrac{9}{4}\right)\left(\dfrac{3}{5}\cdot\dfrac{6}{1}\right)=\dfrac{18}{20}\cdot\dfrac{18}{5}=\dfrac{9}{10}\cdot\dfrac{18}{5}=\dfrac{162}{50}=\dfrac{81}{25}$

101. $\quad 71\dfrac{5}{8}\quad\rightarrow\quad 70\dfrac{13}{8}$

$$\quad\underline{-69\dfrac{7}{8}}\quad\rightarrow\quad\underline{-69\dfrac{7}{8}}$$

$$1\dfrac{6}{8}\rightarrow 1\dfrac{3}{4}\text{ inches}$$

102. The LCM of 2, 4, 6 is 12. $\dfrac{1}{2}+\dfrac{1}{4}+\dfrac{1}{6}=\left(\dfrac{1}{2}\cdot\dfrac{6}{6}\right)+\left(\dfrac{1}{4}\cdot\dfrac{3}{3}\right)+\left(\dfrac{1}{6}\cdot\dfrac{2}{2}\right)=\dfrac{6}{12}+\dfrac{3}{12}+\dfrac{2}{12}=\dfrac{11}{12}$;

$1-\dfrac{11}{12}=\dfrac{1}{12}$ musk thistles

103.
$14\left(8\dfrac{5}{8}\right)=14\left(\dfrac{69}{8}\right)=\dfrac{966}{8}=\dfrac{966\div2}{8\div2}=\dfrac{483}{4}=120.75''$

104.
$\left(1\dfrac{1}{2}\right)\left(\dfrac{1}{4}\right)=\left(\dfrac{3}{2}\right)\left(\dfrac{1}{4}\right)=\dfrac{3}{8}$ cups of snipped parsley

$\left(1\dfrac{1}{2}\right)\left(\dfrac{1}{8}\right)=\left(\dfrac{3}{2}\right)\left(\dfrac{1}{8}\right)=\dfrac{3}{16}$ tsp of pepper

$\left(1\dfrac{1}{2}\right)\left(\dfrac{1}{2}\right)=\left(\dfrac{3}{2}\right)\left(\dfrac{1}{2}\right)=\dfrac{3}{4}$ cups of sliced carrots

105.

$1-\left(\dfrac{1}{4}+\dfrac{1}{5}+\dfrac{1}{2}\right)2\dfrac{1}{4}+3\dfrac{7}{8}+4\dfrac{1}{4}=2\dfrac{4}{16}+3\dfrac{14}{16}+4\dfrac{4}{16}$

$=9\dfrac{22}{16}=10\dfrac{6}{16}$

$20\dfrac{5}{16}-10\dfrac{6}{16}=19\dfrac{21}{16}-10\dfrac{6}{16}=9\dfrac{15}{16}''$

106. The LCM of 4, 5, 3 is 60.

$\dfrac{1}{4}+\dfrac{2}{5}+\dfrac{1}{3}=\left(\dfrac{1}{4}\right)\left(\dfrac{15}{15}\right)+\left(\dfrac{2}{5}\right)\left(\dfrac{12}{12}\right)+\left(\dfrac{1}{3}\right)\left(\dfrac{20}{20}\right)$

$=\dfrac{15}{60}+\dfrac{24}{60}+\dfrac{20}{60}=\dfrac{59}{60}$

107.
$1-\left(\dfrac{1}{2}+\dfrac{2}{5}\right)=1-\left(\dfrac{5}{10}+\dfrac{4}{10}\right)=1-\dfrac{9}{10}=\dfrac{10}{10}-\dfrac{9}{10}=\dfrac{1}{10}$

Student tutors represent 0.1 of the budget.

108. $\left(1\dfrac{1}{4}\right)(15)=\left(\dfrac{5}{4}\right)\left(\dfrac{15}{1}\right)=\dfrac{75}{4}=18\dfrac{3}{4}$ cups

109.
$4\dfrac{1}{2}+30\dfrac{1}{4}+24\dfrac{1}{8}=4\dfrac{4}{8}+30\dfrac{2}{8}+24\dfrac{1}{8}=58\dfrac{7}{8}$ inches

110. $\left(24\dfrac{7}{8}\right)\div2=\dfrac{199}{8}\cdot\dfrac{1}{2}=\dfrac{199}{16}=12\dfrac{7}{16}$ in.

111. a) $1\dfrac{49}{60},2\dfrac{48}{60},9\dfrac{6}{60},6\dfrac{3}{60},2\dfrac{9}{60},\dfrac{22}{60}$

    b) $1\dfrac{49}{60}+2\dfrac{48}{60}+9\dfrac{6}{60}+6\dfrac{3}{60}+2\dfrac{9}{60}+\dfrac{22}{60}$

       $=(1+2+9+6+2+0)+\dfrac{49+48+6+3+9+22}{60}$

       $=20+\dfrac{137}{60}=22\dfrac{17}{60}$ or 22 hours, 17 minutes

112. a) $\dfrac{25}{60},7\dfrac{54}{60},3\dfrac{1}{60},1\dfrac{23}{60},\dfrac{28}{60}$

    b) $\dfrac{25}{60}+7\dfrac{54}{60}+3\dfrac{1}{60}+1\dfrac{23}{60}+\dfrac{28}{60}$

       $=(0+7+3+1+0)+\dfrac{25+54+1+23+28}{60}$

       $=11+\dfrac{131}{60}=13\dfrac{11}{60}$ or 13 hours, 11 minutes

113. $8\frac{3}{4}$ ft $= \left(\frac{35}{4}\cdot\frac{12}{1}\right)$ in. $= 105$ in.

$\left[105-(3)\left(\frac{1}{8}\right)\right]\div 4=\left[\frac{840}{8}-\frac{3}{8}\right]\div 4=\frac{837}{8}\bullet\frac{1}{4}=\frac{837}{32}=26\frac{5}{32}$.   The length of each piece is $26\frac{5}{32}$ in.

114. width = 8 ft. 3 in. = 96 in. + 3 in. = 99 in.; length = 10 ft. 8 in. = 120 in. + 8 in. = 128 in.

   a) perimeter = 2L + 2W = 2(128) + 2(99) = 454 in $\dfrac{454"}{12"/\text{ft.}}=37\frac{10}{12}$ft.$= 37$ ft. 10 in.

   b) width = 8ft. 3in. $= 8\frac{3}{12}$ ft. $= 8\frac{1}{4}$ ft. $= \frac{33}{4}$ ft .; length = 10ft. 8in. $= 10\frac{8}{12}$ ft. $= 10\frac{2}{3}$ ft. $= \frac{32}{3}$ ft

   Area $= L\times w = \dfrac{32}{3}\times\dfrac{33}{4}=\dfrac{1056}{12}=88$ sq.ft

   c) Volume $= L\cdot W\cdot H = \dfrac{32}{3}\times\dfrac{33}{4}\times\dfrac{55}{6}=\dfrac{58080}{72}=806\frac{2}{3}$ cu. ft.

115. a) $20+18\frac{3}{8}\div 2=20+9\frac{3}{16}=29\frac{3}{16}$in.   c) $26\frac{1}{4}+\left(6\frac{3}{4}-\frac{1}{4}\right)=26\frac{1}{4}+6\frac{2}{4}=32\frac{3}{4}$in.

   b) $26\frac{1}{4}+6\frac{3}{4}=33$ in.

116. original area $= 8\frac{1}{2}\bullet 9\frac{1}{4}=\frac{17}{2}\bullet\frac{37}{4}=\frac{629}{8}=78\frac{5}{8}$ sq. in.; new area $= 8\frac{1}{2}\bullet 10\frac{1}{4}=\frac{17}{2}\bullet\frac{41}{4}=\frac{697}{8}=87\frac{1}{8}$ sq. in.

   area increase $= 87\frac{1}{8}-78\frac{5}{8}=86\frac{9}{8}-78\frac{5}{8}=8\frac{4}{8}=8\frac{1}{2}$ sq. in.

117. $\dfrac{0.10+0.11}{2}=\dfrac{0.21}{2}=0.105$ 118. $\dfrac{5.03+5.003}{2}=\dfrac{10.033}{2}=5.0165$

119. $\dfrac{-2.176+(-2.175)}{2}=\dfrac{-4.351}{2}=-2.1755$ 120. $\dfrac{1.3457+1.34571}{2}=\dfrac{2.69141}{2}=1.345705$

121. $\dfrac{4.872+4.873}{2}=\dfrac{9.745}{2}=4.8725$ 122. $\dfrac{-3.7896+(-3.7895)}{2}=\dfrac{-7.5791}{2}=$

   -3.78955

123. $\left(\frac{1}{3}+\frac{2}{3}\right)\div 2=\frac{3}{3}\bullet\frac{1}{2}=\frac{3}{6}=\frac{1}{2}$ 124. $\left(\frac{2}{7}+\frac{3}{7}\right)\div 2=\frac{5}{7}\bullet\frac{1}{2}=\frac{5}{14}$

125. $\left(\frac{1}{100}+\frac{1}{10}\right)\div 2=\frac{11}{100}\bullet\frac{1}{2}=\frac{11}{200}$ 126. $\left(\frac{7}{13}+\frac{8}{13}\right)\div 2=\frac{15}{13}\bullet\frac{1}{2}=\frac{15}{26}$

127.
$\left(\frac{1}{10}+\frac{1}{100}\right)\div 2=\left(\frac{10}{100}+\frac{1}{100}\right)\bullet\frac{1}{2}=\frac{11}{100}\bullet\frac{1}{2}=\frac{11}{200}$ 128. $\left(\frac{1}{2}+\frac{2}{3}\right)\div 2=\left(\frac{3}{6}+\frac{4}{6}\right)\bullet\frac{1}{2}=\frac{7}{6}\bullet\frac{1}{2}=\frac{7}{12}$

129. a) Water (or milk): $\left(1+1\frac{3}{4}\right)\div 2=\left(\frac{4}{4}+\frac{7}{4}\right)\bullet\frac{1}{2}=\frac{11}{4}\bullet\frac{1}{2}=\frac{11}{8}=1\frac{3}{8}$ cup;

   Oats: $\left(\frac{1}{2}+1\right)\div 2=\frac{3}{2}\bullet\frac{1}{2}=\frac{3}{4}$ cup

   b) Water (or milk): $1+\frac{1}{2}=1\frac{1}{2}$ cup;

   Oats: $\frac{1}{2}+\frac{1}{2}\cdot\frac{1}{2}=\frac{3}{4}$ cup

130. a) 1   b) $0.\overline{9}$ c) $\frac{1}{3} = 0.\overline{3}$, $\frac{2}{3} = 0.\overline{6}$, $\frac{1}{3} + \frac{2}{3} = \frac{3}{3} = 1$, $0.\overline{3} + 0.\overline{6} = 0.\overline{9}$ d) $0.\overline{9} = 1$

131. a) $\frac{1}{8}$ b) $\frac{1}{16}$ c) 5 times   d) 6 times

Exercise Set 5.4

1. A rational number can be written as a ratio of two integers, p/q, with q not equal to zero. Numbers that cannot be written as the ratio of two integers are called irrational numbers.

2. The principal square root of a number n written $\sqrt{n}$, is the positive number that when multiplied by itself gives n.

3. A perfect square number is any number that is the square of a natural number.

4. The product rule for radical numbers: $\sqrt{a \cdot b} = \sqrt{a} \cdot \sqrt{b}$ $a \geq 0, b \geq 0$

   The quotient rule for radical numbers: $\frac{\sqrt{a}}{\sqrt{b}} = \sqrt{\frac{a}{b}}$ $a \geq 0, b \geq 0$

5. a) To add or subtract two or more square roots with the same radicand, add or subtract their coefficients and then multiply by the common radical.

   b) $3\sqrt{5} + 8\sqrt{5} - 6\sqrt{5} = 11\sqrt{5} - 6\sqrt{5} = 5\sqrt{5}$

6. A rationalized denominator contains no radical expressions.

7. a) Multiply both the numerator and denominator by the same number that will result in the radicand in the denominator becoming a perfect square.

   b) $\frac{2}{\sqrt{3}} = \frac{2}{\sqrt{3}} \cdot \frac{\sqrt{3}}{\sqrt{3}} = \frac{2\sqrt{3}}{\sqrt{9}} = \frac{2\sqrt{3}}{3}$

8. (a) Press $\left[\sqrt{}\,\right]$, then enter the number, then press $[\text{Enter}]$ or $[=]$.

   (b) $\sqrt{11} \approx 3.3166247904 \approx 3.32$

9. $\sqrt{25} = 5$ rational

10. $\sqrt{50} = \sqrt{25}\sqrt{2} = 5\sqrt{2}$ irrational

11. $\frac{3}{5}$ rational

12. Irrational; non-terminating, non-repeating decimal

13. Irrational; non-terminating, non-repeating decimal

14. Irrational; π is non-terminating, non-repeating.

15. Rational; quotient of two integers

16. Rational; terminating decimal

17. Irrational; non-terminating, non-repeating decimal

18. Rational; $\frac{\sqrt{5}}{\sqrt{5}} = 1$ 1 is an integer.

19. $\sqrt{16} = 4$

20. $\sqrt{144} = 12$

21. $\sqrt{100} = 10$

22. $-\sqrt{121} = -11$

23. $-\sqrt{169} = -13$

24. $\sqrt{25} = 5$

25. $-\sqrt{81} = -9$

26. $-\sqrt{36} = -6$

27. $-\sqrt{100} = -10$

28. $\sqrt{289} = 17$

29. 2, rational, integer, natural

30. -3, rational, integer

31. $\sqrt{25} = 5$, rat'l, integer., nat'l

32. $\frac{3}{8}$, rational

33. irrational

34. rational

35. rational

36. rational

37. rational

38. irrational

39. $\sqrt{12} = \sqrt{4}\sqrt{3} = 2\sqrt{3}$

40. $\sqrt{20} = \sqrt{4}\sqrt{5} = 2\sqrt{5}$

41. $\sqrt{48} = \sqrt{3}\sqrt{16} = 4\sqrt{3}$

42. $\sqrt{50} = \sqrt{25}\sqrt{2} = 5\sqrt{2}$

43. $\sqrt{63} = \sqrt{9}\sqrt{7} = 3\sqrt{7}$

44. $\sqrt{75} = \sqrt{25}\sqrt{3} = 5\sqrt{3}$

45. $\sqrt{84} = \sqrt{4}\sqrt{21} = 2\sqrt{21}$

46. $\sqrt{90} = \sqrt{9}\sqrt{10} = 3\sqrt{10}$

47. $\sqrt{162} = \sqrt{81}\sqrt{2} = 9\sqrt{2}$

48. $\sqrt{200} = \sqrt{100}\sqrt{2} = 10\sqrt{2}$

49. $3\sqrt{5} + 2\sqrt{5} = (3+2)\sqrt{5} = 5\sqrt{5}$

50.
$4\sqrt{6} - 7\sqrt{6} = (4-7)\sqrt{6} = -3\sqrt{6}$

51.

$5\sqrt{18} - 7\sqrt{8} = 5\left(\sqrt{9}\sqrt{2}\right) - 7\left(\sqrt{4}\sqrt{2}\right)$
$= 15\sqrt{2} - 14\sqrt{2} = (15-14)\sqrt{2} = \sqrt{2}$

52.
$2\sqrt{18} - 3\sqrt{50} = 2\left(\sqrt{9}\sqrt{2}\right) - 3\left(\sqrt{25}\sqrt{2}\right)$
$= 6\sqrt{2} - 15\sqrt{2} = (6-15)\sqrt{2} = -9\sqrt{2}$

53.
$4\sqrt{12} - 7\sqrt{27} = 4\sqrt{4}\sqrt{3} - 7\sqrt{9}\sqrt{3}$
$= 4\cdot 2\sqrt{3} - 7\cdot 3\sqrt{3} = 8\sqrt{3} - 21\sqrt{3}$
$= -13\sqrt{3}$

54.

$2\sqrt{7} + 5\sqrt{28} = 2\sqrt{7} + 5\cdot 2\sqrt{7}$
$= 2\sqrt{7} + 10\sqrt{7} = (2+10)\sqrt{7}$
$= 12\sqrt{7}$

55.

$5\sqrt{3} + 7\sqrt{12} - 3\sqrt{75}$
$= 5\sqrt{3} + 7\cdot 2\sqrt{3} - 3\cdot 5\sqrt{3}$
$= 5\sqrt{3} + 14\sqrt{3} - 15\sqrt{3}$
$= (5+14-15)\sqrt{3} = 4\sqrt{3}$

56.

$13\sqrt{2} + 2\sqrt{18} - 5\sqrt{32}$
$= 13\sqrt{2} + 2\cdot 3\sqrt{2} - 5\cdot 4\sqrt{2}$
$= 13\sqrt{2} + 6\sqrt{2} - 20\sqrt{2}$
$= (13+6-20)\sqrt{2} = -\sqrt{2}$

57.

$\sqrt{8} - 3\sqrt{50} + 9\sqrt{32}$
$= 2\sqrt{2} - 3\cdot 5\sqrt{2} + 9\cdot 4\sqrt{2}$
$= 2\sqrt{2} - 15\sqrt{2} + 36\sqrt{2}$
$= (2-15+36)\sqrt{2} = 23\sqrt{2}$

58.

$\sqrt{63} + 13\sqrt{98} - 5\sqrt{112}$
$= 3\sqrt{7} + 13\cdot 7\sqrt{2} - 5\cdot 4\sqrt{7}$
$= 3\sqrt{7} + 91\sqrt{2} - 20\sqrt{7}$
$= -17\sqrt{7} + 91\sqrt{2}$

59.

$\sqrt{3}\sqrt{27} = \sqrt{3\cdot 27} = \sqrt{81} = 9$

60. $\sqrt{5}\cdot\sqrt{15} = \sqrt{5}\sqrt{5}\sqrt{3}$
$= 5\sqrt{3}$

61. $\sqrt{6}\cdot\sqrt{10} = \sqrt{2}\sqrt{3}\sqrt{2}\sqrt{5}$
$= \sqrt{4}\sqrt{15} = 2\sqrt{15}$

62. $\sqrt{2}\sqrt{10} = \sqrt{2\cdot 10} = \sqrt{20}$
$= \sqrt{4}\sqrt{5} = 2\sqrt{5}$

63. $\sqrt{10}\cdot\sqrt{20} = \sqrt{200}$
$= \sqrt{100}\cdot\sqrt{2} = 10\sqrt{2}$

64. $\sqrt{11}\cdot\sqrt{33} = \sqrt{11}\cdot\sqrt{11}\cdot\sqrt{3}$
$= 11\sqrt{3}$

65. $\dfrac{\sqrt{20}}{\sqrt{5}} = \sqrt{\dfrac{20}{5}} = \sqrt{4} = 2$

66. $\dfrac{\sqrt{125}}{\sqrt{5}} = \sqrt{25} = 5$

67. $\dfrac{\sqrt{72}}{\sqrt{8}} = \sqrt{9} = 3$

68. $\dfrac{\sqrt{145}}{\sqrt{5}} = \sqrt{\dfrac{145}{5}} = \sqrt{29}$

69. $\dfrac{1}{\sqrt{5}} = \dfrac{1}{\sqrt{5}}\dfrac{\sqrt{5}}{\sqrt{5}} = \dfrac{\sqrt{5}}{5}$

70. $\dfrac{3}{\sqrt{3}} = \dfrac{3}{\sqrt{3}} \cdot \dfrac{\sqrt{3}}{\sqrt{3}} = \dfrac{3\sqrt{3}}{3} = \sqrt{3}$

71. $\dfrac{\sqrt{3}}{\sqrt{7}} \cdot \dfrac{\sqrt{7}}{\sqrt{7}} = \dfrac{\sqrt{21}}{7}$

72. $\dfrac{\sqrt{2}}{\sqrt{7}} = \dfrac{\sqrt{2}}{\sqrt{7}} \cdot \dfrac{\sqrt{7}}{\sqrt{7}} = \dfrac{\sqrt{14}}{7}$

73. $\dfrac{\sqrt{20}}{\sqrt{3}} = \dfrac{\sqrt{20}}{\sqrt{3}}\dfrac{\sqrt{3}}{\sqrt{3}} = \dfrac{\sqrt{60}}{\sqrt{9}}$
    $= \dfrac{\sqrt{4}\sqrt{15}}{3} = \dfrac{2\sqrt{15}}{3}$

74. $\dfrac{\sqrt{50}}{\sqrt{14}} = \sqrt{\dfrac{50}{14}} = \sqrt{\dfrac{25}{7}}$
    $= \dfrac{\sqrt{25}}{\sqrt{7}}\dfrac{\sqrt{7}}{\sqrt{7}} = \dfrac{5\sqrt{7}}{7}$

75. $\dfrac{\sqrt{5}}{\sqrt{3}} = \dfrac{\sqrt{5}}{\sqrt{3}} \cdot \dfrac{\sqrt{3}}{\sqrt{3}} = \dfrac{\sqrt{15}}{3}$

76. $\dfrac{\sqrt{15}}{\sqrt{3}} = \sqrt{5}$

77. $\dfrac{\sqrt{10}}{\sqrt{6}} \cdot \dfrac{\sqrt{6}}{\sqrt{6}} = \dfrac{\sqrt{60}}{6}$
    $= \dfrac{2\sqrt{15}}{6} = \dfrac{\sqrt{15}}{3}$

78. $\dfrac{\sqrt{2}}{\sqrt{27}} = \dfrac{\sqrt{2}}{\sqrt{27}} \cdot \dfrac{\sqrt{3}}{\sqrt{3}} = \dfrac{\sqrt{6}}{\sqrt{81}} = \dfrac{\sqrt{6}}{9}$

79. $\sqrt{5}$ is between 2 and 3 since $\sqrt{5}$ is between $\sqrt{4} = 2$ and $\sqrt{9} = 3$. $\sqrt{5}$ is between 2 and 2.5 since 5 is closer to 4 than to 9. Using a calculator $\sqrt{5} \approx 2.2$.

80. $\sqrt{17}$ is between 4 and 5 since $\sqrt{17}$ is between $\sqrt{16} = 4$ and $\sqrt{25} = 5$. $\sqrt{17}$ is between 4 and 4.5 since 17 is closer to 16 than to 25. Using a calculator $\sqrt{17} \approx 4.1$.

81. $\sqrt{107}$ is between 10 and 11 since $\sqrt{107}$ is between $\sqrt{100} = 10$ and $\sqrt{121} = 11$. $\sqrt{107}$ is between 10 and 10.5 since 107 is closer to 100 than to 121. Using a calculator $\sqrt{107} \approx 10.3$.

82. $\sqrt{135}$ is between 11 and 12 since $\sqrt{135}$ is between $\sqrt{121} = 11$ and $\sqrt{144} = 12$. $\sqrt{135}$ is between 11.5 and 12 since 135 is closer to 144 than to 121. Using a calculator $\sqrt{135} \approx 11.6$.

83. $\sqrt{170}$ is between 13 and 14 since $\sqrt{170}$ is between $\sqrt{169} = 13$ and $\sqrt{196} = 14$. $\sqrt{170}$ is between 13 and 13.5 since 170 is closer to 169 than to 196. Using a calculator $\sqrt{170} \approx 13.04$.

84. $\sqrt{200}$ is between 14 and 15 since $\sqrt{200}$ is between $\sqrt{196} = 14$ and $\sqrt{225} = 15$. $\sqrt{200}$ is between 14 and 14.5 since 200 is closer to 196 than to 225. Using a calculator $\sqrt{200} \approx 14.1$.

85. False. The result may be a rational number or an irrational number.

86. False. $\sqrt{p}$ is an irrational number for any prime number p.

87. True   88. True   89. False. The result may be a rational number or an irrational number.

90. False. The result may be a rational number or an irrational number.

91. $\sqrt{3} + 5\sqrt{3} = 6\sqrt{3}$

92. $\sqrt{2} + (-\sqrt{2}) = 0$

93. $\sqrt{2} \cdot \sqrt{3} = \sqrt{6}$

94. $\sqrt{3}\cdot\sqrt{3}=\sqrt{9}=3$ 95. No. $2\neq 1.414$ since $\sqrt{2}$ is an irrational number and 1.414 is a rational number.

96. $\sqrt{17}$ is irrational. Because
4.123 is rational, $\sqrt{17}\neq 4.123$.

97. No. 3.14 and $\dfrac{22}{7}$ are rational numbers, π is an
irrational number.

98. $\sqrt{9+16}\neq\sqrt{9}+\sqrt{16}$
$\quad\;\; \sqrt{25}\;\;\neq\;\; 3+\;4$
$\quad\quad\; 5\;\;\neq\;\; 7$

99. $\sqrt{4\cdot 16}=\sqrt{4}\sqrt{16}$
$\quad\;\; \sqrt{64}\;\; =\;\; 2\cdot 4$
$\quad\quad 8\;\; =\;\; 8$

100. $T=2\pi\sqrt{\dfrac{35}{980}}=2\pi\dfrac{\sqrt{35}}{\sqrt{980}}=2\pi\dfrac{\sqrt{5}\sqrt{7}}{\sqrt{5}\sqrt{196}}$

$\quad =2\pi\dfrac{\sqrt{7}}{14}=\dfrac{2\pi\sqrt{7}}{2\cdot 7}=\dfrac{\pi\sqrt{7}}{7}\approx 1.2$ seconds

101. a) $s=\sqrt{\dfrac{4}{0.04}}=\sqrt{100}=10$ mph

   b) $s=\sqrt{\dfrac{16}{0.04}}=\sqrt{400}=20$ mph

   c) $s=\sqrt{\dfrac{64}{0.04}}=\sqrt{1600}=40$ mph

   d) $s=\sqrt{\dfrac{256}{0.04}}=\sqrt{6400}=80$ mph

102. a) $t=\dfrac{\sqrt{100}}{4}=\dfrac{10}{4}=2.5$ sec

   b) $t=\dfrac{\sqrt{400}}{4}=\dfrac{20}{4}=5$ sec

   c) $t=\dfrac{\sqrt{900}}{4}=\dfrac{30}{4}=7.5$ sec

   d) $t=\dfrac{\sqrt{1600}}{4}=\dfrac{40}{4}=10$ sec

103. a) $\sqrt{0.04}=0.2$ a terminating
decimal and thus it is rational.

   b) $\sqrt{0.7}=\sqrt{\dfrac{7}{10}}=\dfrac{\sqrt{70}}{10}$; $\sqrt{70}$ is irrational since

   the only integers with rational square roots are
the perfect squares and 70 is not a perfect square.

   Thus $\dfrac{\sqrt{70}}{10}=\sqrt{0.7}$ is irrational.

104. No. The sum of two irrational numbers may not be irrational. (i.e. $-\sqrt{3}+\sqrt{3}\;=0$)

105. a) $\left(44\div\sqrt{4}\right)\div\sqrt{4}=\left(44\div 2\right)\div 2=22\div 2=11$

   b) $\left(44\div 4\right)+\sqrt{4}=11+2=13$

   c) $4+4+4+\sqrt{4}=12+2=14$

   d) $\sqrt{4}\left(4+4\right)+\sqrt{4}=2\left(8\right)+2=16+2=18$

Exercise Set 5.5

1. The set of real numbers is the union of the rational numbers and the irrational numbers.

2. All real numbers = $\mathbb{R}$

3. If the given operation is preformed on any two elements of the set and the result is an element of the set, then the set is <u>closed</u> under the given operation.

4. The order in which two numbers are added does not make a difference in the result.   Ex. $a + b = b + a$

5. The order in which two numbers are multiplied does not make a difference in the result.   Ex. $2 \cdot 3 = 3 \cdot 2$

6. The associative property of multiplication states that when multiplying three real numbers, parentheses may be placed around any two adjacent numbers.   Ex. $(2 \cdot 3) \cdot 4 = 2 \cdot (3 \cdot 4)$.

7. The associative property of addition states that when adding three real numbers, parentheses may be placed around any two adjacent numbers. $(a + b) + c = a + (b + c)$

8. The distributive property of multiplication over addition allows you to either add first and then multiply, or multiply first and then add. $a(b + c) = ab + ac$

9. Not closed. (e.g., $3 - 5 = -2$ is not a natural number).

10. Closed. The sum of two natural numbers is a natural number.

11. Closed. The product of two natural numbers is a natural number.

12. Not closed. (e.g. $3 \div 5 = \dfrac{3}{5} = 0.6$ is not a natural number).

13. Closed. The sum of two integers is an integer.

14. Closed. The difference of two integers is an integer.

15. Closed. The product of two integers is an integer.

16. Not closed. (e.g. $2 \div 5 = \dfrac{2}{5} = 0.4 = 0.4$ is not an integer).

17. Closed	18. Closed	19. Not closed	20. Closed
21. Not closed	22. Not closed	23. Not closed	24. Not closed
25. Closed	26. Closed	27. Closed	28. Not closed (for example, $3 \div 0$ is not a real number)

29. Commutative property of addition. The order $5 + x$ is changed to $x + 5$. .

30. $(x + 5) + 6 = x + (5 + 6)$;   Associative because the grouping of the three terms is changed.

31. $(-2) + (-3) = -5 = (-3) + (-2)$

32. $(-4) \cdot (-5) = 20 = (-5) \cdot (-4)$

33. No. $5 - 3 = 2$, but $3 - 5 = -2$

34. No. $6 \div 3 = 2$, but $3 \div 6 = \dfrac{1}{2}$

35. $[(-3) + (-5)] + (-7) = (-8) + (-7) = -15$
    $(-3) + [(-5) + (-7)] = (-3) + (-12) = -15$

36. $[(-3) \cdot (-5)] \cdot (-7) = (15) \cdot (-7) = -105$
    $(-3) \cdot [(-5) \cdot (-7)] = (-3) \cdot (35) = -105$

37. No.
    $(8 \div 4) \div 2 = 2 \div 2 = 1$, but $8 \div (4 \div 2) = 8 \div 2 = 4$

38. No. $(8 - 7) - 12 = 1 - 12 = -11$, but
    $8 - (7 - 12) = 8 - (-5) = 8 + 5 = 13$

39. No. $(8 \div 4) \div 2 = 2 \div 2 = 1$,
    but $8 \div (4 \div 2) = 8 \div 2 = 4$

40. No. $2 + (3 \cdot 4) = 2 + 12 = 14$, but $(2+3) \cdot (2+4)$
    $= 5 \cdot 6 = 30$

41. $3(y+5) = 3 \cdot y + 3 \cdot 5$
    Distributive property

42. $6 + 7 = 7 + 6$ Commutative property of addition

43. $(7 \cdot 8) \cdot 9 = 7 \cdot (8 \cdot 9)$
    Associative property of multiplication

44. $c + d = d + c$
    Commutative property of addition

45. $(24+7)+3 = 24+(7+3)$
    Associative property of addition

46. $4 \cdot (11 \cdot x) = (4 \cdot 11) \cdot x$
    Associative property of multiplication

47. $\sqrt{3} \cdot 7 = 7 \cdot \sqrt{3}$
    Commutative property of multiplication

48. $\frac{3}{8} + \left(\frac{1}{8} + \frac{3}{2} \right) = \left(\frac{3}{8} + \frac{1}{8} \right) + \frac{3}{2}$
    Associative property of addition

49. $-1(x+4) = (-1) \cdot x + (-1) \cdot 4$
    Distributive property

50. $(p+q)+r = p+(q+r)$
    Associative property of addition

51. $\sqrt{5} \cdot 2 = 2 \cdot \sqrt{5}$
    Commutative property of multiplication

52. $(r+s)+t = t+(r+s)$
    Commutative property of addition

53. $(r+s) \cdot t = (r \cdot t) + (s \cdot t)$
    Distributive property

54. $g \cdot (h+i) = (h+i) \cdot g$
    Commutative property of multiplication

55. $(f \cdot g) + (j \cdot h) = (g \cdot f) + (j \cdot h)$
    Commutative property of multiplication

56. $(k+l) \cdot (m+n) = (l+k) \cdot (m+n)$
    Commutative property of addition

57. $4(z+1) = 4z+4$

58. $-1(a+b) = -a-b$

59. $-\frac{3}{4}(x-12) = -\frac{3}{4}x + \frac{3}{4} \cdot 12 = -\frac{3}{4}x + 9$

60. $-x(-y+z) = (-x)(-y) + (-x)(z) = xy - xz$

61. $6\left(\frac{x}{2} + \frac{2}{3} \right) = \frac{6x}{2} + \frac{12}{3} = 3x+4$

62. $24\left(\frac{x}{3} - \frac{1}{8} \right) = \frac{24x}{3} - \frac{24}{8} = 8x-3$

63. $32\left(\frac{1}{16}x - \frac{1}{32} \right) = \frac{32x}{16} - \frac{32}{32} = 2x-1$

64. $15\left(\frac{2}{3}x - \frac{4}{5} \right) = \frac{30x}{3} - \frac{60}{5} = 10x-12$

65. $\sqrt{2}\left(\sqrt{8} - \sqrt{2} \right) = \sqrt{16} - \sqrt{4} = 4 - 2 = 2$

66. $-3\left(2 - \sqrt{3} \right) = -6 + 3\sqrt{3}$

67. $5\left(\sqrt{2} + \sqrt{3} \right) = 5\sqrt{2} + 5\sqrt{3}$

68. $\sqrt{5}\left(\sqrt{15} - \sqrt{20} \right) = \sqrt{75} - \sqrt{100} = 5\sqrt{3} - 10$

69. a) Distributive property
    b) Associative property of addition
71. a) Distributive property
    b) Associative property of addition;
    c) Commutative property of addition
    d) Associative property of addition
73. a) Distributive property
    b) Commutative property of addition;
    c) Associative property of addition
    d) Commutative property of addition
75. Yes. You can either feed your dog first or give your dog water first.
77. No. The clothes must be washed first before being dried.
79. Yes. Can be done in either order; either fill the car with gas or wash the windshield
81. No. Pressing the keys will have no effect if there are no batteries in place.
83. Yes. The order does not matter.
85. Yes. The order does not matter
87. Yes. The final result will be the same regardless of the order of the events.
89. Baking pizzelles: mixing eggs into the batter, or mixing sugar into the batter.; Yard work: mowing the lawn, or trimming the bushes

70. a) Distributive property
    b) Associative property of addition
72. a) Distributive property
    b) Associative property of addition;
    c) Commutative property of addition
    d) Associative property of addition
74. a) Distributive property
    b) Commutative property of addition;
    c) Associative property of addition
    d) Commutative property of addition
76. Yes. Can be done independently; no order needed
78. No. The PC must be turned on first before you can type a term paper.
80. No. The lamp must be turned on first before reading a book.
82. Yes. The order does not matter
84. Yes. The order does not matter.
86. No. The egg cannot be poured before it is cracked.
88. Yes. The meatloaf will taste the same regardless of the order the items are mixed.
90. Washing siding/washing windows/washing the car Writing letters to spouse, parents or friends
91. No. $0 \div a = 0$ but $a \div 0$ is undefined.

92. a) No. (Man eating) tiger is a tiger that eats men, and man (eating tiger) is a man that is eating a tiger.
    b) No. (Horse riding) monkey is a monkey that rides a horse, and horse (riding monkey) is a horse that rides a monkey.
    c) Answers will vary.

Exercise Set 5.6

1. 2 is the base and 3 is the exponent.

2. b^n is b multiplied by itself n times. $b^n = \underbrace{b \cdot b \cdot b \cdots b}_{n \text{ factors of } b}$

3. a) If m and n are natural numbers and a is any real number, then $a^m a^n = a^{m+n}$
   b) $2^3 \cdot 2^4 = 2^{3+4} = 2^7 = 128$

4. a) If m and n are natural numbers and a is any real number except 0, then $\dfrac{a^m}{a^n} = a^{m-n}$.

   b) $\dfrac{5^6}{5^4} = 5^{6-4} = 5^2 = 25$

5. a) If a is any real number except 0, then $a^0 = 1$.

   b) $7^0 = 1$

6. a) If n is a natural number and a is any real number except 0, then $a^{-n} = \dfrac{1}{a^n}$.

   b) $2^{-3} = \dfrac{1}{2^3} = \dfrac{1}{8}$

7. a) If m and n are natural numbers and a is any real number, then $\left(a^m\right)^n = a^{m \cdot n}$

   b) $\left(3^2\right)^4 = 3^{2 \cdot 4} = 3^8 = 6561$

8. Since 1 raised to any power equals 1, $1^{500} = 1$.

9. a) Since 1 raised to any exponent equals +1, then $-1^{500} = (-1)\left(1^{500}\right) = (-1)(1) = -1$

   b) Since -1 raised to an even exponent equals 1, then number $(-1)^{500} = \left((-1)^2\right)^{250} = (1)^{250} = 1$

   c) In -1^{501}, -1 is not raised to the 501st power, but +1 is; so $-1^{501} = (-1)\left(1^{501}\right) = (-1)(1) = -1$

   d) Since -1 is raised to an odd exponent is -1, then $(-1)^{501} = -1$

10. a) Move the decimal point in the original number to the right or left until you obtain a number greater than or equal to 1 and less than 10. Count the number of places the decimal was moved. If it was moved to the left, the count is a positive number and if it was moved to the right, the count is a negative number. Multiply the number obtained in the first step by 10 raised to the count number.

    b) $0.000739 = 7.39 \times 10^{-4}$. Note: the count number is -4.

    c) $1{,}940{,}000{,}000 = 1.94 \times 10^9$. Note: the count number is 9.

11. a) If the exponent is positive, move the decimal point in the number to the right the same number of places as the exponent adding zeros where necessary. If the exponent is negative, move the decimal point in the number to the left the same number of places as the exponent adding zeros where necessary.

    b) $2.91 \times 10^{-5} = 0.0000291$

    c) $7.02 \times 10^6 = 7{,}020{,}000$

12. a) The number is greater than or equal to 10.

    b) The number is greater than or equal to 1 but < 10.

    c) The number is less than 1.

13. a) $3^2 = 3 \cdot 3 = 9$

    b) $2^3 = 2 \cdot 2 \cdot 2 = 8$

14. a) $2^5 = 2 \cdot 2 \cdot 2 \cdot 2 \cdot 2 = 32$

    b) $5^2 = 5 \cdot 5 = 25$

15. a) $(-5)^2 - (-5)(-5) = 25$

    b) $-5^2 = -(5)(5) = -25$

16. a) $-3^2 = -(3)(3) = -9$

    b) $(-3)^2 = (-3)(-3) = 9$

17. a) $-2^4 = -(2)(2)(2)(2) = -16$

    b) $(-2)^4 = (-2)(-2)(-2)(-2) = 16$

18. a) $(-3)^4 = (-3)(-3)(-3)(-3) = 81$

    b) $-3^4 = -(3)(3)(3)(3) = -81$

19. a) $-4^3 = -(4)(4)(4) = -64$

    b) $(-4)^3 = (-4)(-4)(-4) = -64$

20. a) $(-2)^7 = -\left(2^7\right) = -128$

    (an odd power of a negative number is negative)

    b) $-2^7 = -\left(2^7\right) = -128$

21. a) $\left(\dfrac{1}{8}\right)^2 = \left(\dfrac{1}{8}\right)\left(\dfrac{1}{8}\right) = \dfrac{1}{64}$

    b) $\left(-\dfrac{3}{4}\right)^2 = \left(-\dfrac{3}{4}\right)\left(-\dfrac{3}{4}\right) = \dfrac{9}{16}$

22. a) $-\left(\dfrac{2}{3}\right)^2 = -\left(\dfrac{2}{3}\right)\left(\dfrac{2}{3}\right) = -\dfrac{4}{9}$

    b) $\left(\dfrac{1}{6}\right)^3 = \left(\dfrac{1}{6}\right)\left(\dfrac{1}{6}\right)\left(\dfrac{1}{6}\right) = \dfrac{1}{216}$

23. a) $1000^1 = 1000$

    b) $1^{1000} = 1$

24. a) $2008^1 = 2008$

    b) $1^{2008} = 1$

25. a) $3^2 \cdot 3^3 = 3^{2+3} = 3^5 = 243$

    b) $(-3)^2 \cdot (-3)^3 = (-3)^{2+3} = (-3)^5 = -243$

26. a) $2^3 \cdot 2 = 2^{3+1} = 2^4 = 16$

    b) $(-2)^3 \cdot (-2) = (-2)^{3+1} = (-2)^4 = 16$

27. a) $\dfrac{5^7}{5^5} = 5^{7-5} = 5^2 = 25$

    b) $\dfrac{(-5)^7}{(-5)^5} = (-5)^{7-5} = (-5)^2 = 25$

28. a) $\dfrac{4^5}{4^2} = 4^{5-2} = 4^3 = 64$

    b) $\dfrac{(-4)^5}{(-4)^2} = (-4)^{5-2} = (-4)^3 = -64$

29. a) $6^0 = 1$

    b) $-6^0 = -1$

30. a) $(-6)^0 = 1$

    b) $-(-6)^0 = -1$

31. a) $(6x)^0 = 1$

    b) $6x^0 = 6$

32. a) $-6x^0 = -6$

    b) $(-6x)^0 = 1$

33. a) $3^{-3} = \dfrac{1}{3^3} = \dfrac{1}{27}$

    b) $7^{-2} = \dfrac{1}{7^2} = \dfrac{1}{49}$

34. a) $5^{-1} = \dfrac{1}{5}$

    b) $2^{-4} = \dfrac{1}{2^4} = \dfrac{1}{16}$

35. a) $-9^{-2} = -\dfrac{1}{9^2} = -\dfrac{1}{81}$

    b) $(-9)^{-2} = \dfrac{1}{(-9)^2} = \dfrac{1}{81}$

36. a) $-5^{-2} = -\dfrac{1}{5^2} = -\dfrac{1}{25}$

    b) $(-5)^{-2} = \dfrac{1}{(-5)^2} = \dfrac{1}{25}$

37. a) $\left(2^2\right)^3 = 2^{2\times3} = 2^6 = 64$

    b) $\left(2^3\right)^2 = 2^{3\times2} = 2^6 = 64$

38. a) $\left(\left(\dfrac{1}{2}\right)^2\right)^3 = \left(\dfrac{1}{2}\right)^{2\times3} = \left(\dfrac{1}{2}\right)^6 = \dfrac{1}{64}$

    b) $\left(\left(-\dfrac{1}{2}\right)^2\right)^3 = \left(-\dfrac{1}{2}\right)^{2\times3} = \left(-\dfrac{1}{2}\right)^6 = \dfrac{1}{64}$

39. a) $4^3 \cdot 4^{-2} = 4^{3-2} = 4^1 = 4$

   b) $2^{-2} \cdot 2^{-2} = 2^{-2-2} = 2^{-4} = \dfrac{1}{2^4} = \dfrac{1}{16}$

40. a)

   $(-5)^{-2} \cdot (-5)^{-2} = (-5)^{-2-2} = (-5)^{-4} = \dfrac{1}{(-5)^4} = \dfrac{1}{625}$

   b)

   $(-1)^{-5}(-1)^{-5} = (-1)^{-5-5} = (-1)^{-10} = \dfrac{1}{(-1)^{10}} = 1$

41. $175000 = 1.75 \times 10^5$

42. $496000000 = 4.96 \times 10^8$

43. $0.00023 = 2.3 \times 10^{-4}$

44. $0.000034 = 3.4 \times 10^{-5}$

45. $0.56 = 5.6 \times 10^{-1}$

46. $0.00467 = 4.67 \times 10^{-3}$

47. $19000 = 1.9 \times 10^4$

48. $1260000000 = 1.26 \times 10^9$

49. $0.000186 = 1.86 \times 10^{-4}$

50. $0.0003 = 3.0 \times 10^{-4}$

51. $0.00000423 = 4.23 \times 10^{-6}$

52. $54000 = 5.4 \times 10^4$

53. $711 = 7.11 \times 10^2$

54. $0.02 = 2.0 \times 10^{-2}$

55. $0.153 = 1.53 \times 10^{-1}$

56. $416000 = 4.16 \times 10^5$

57. $1.7 \times 10^2 = 170$

58. $2.03 \times 10^4 = 20,300$

59. $1.097 \times 10^{-4} = 0.0001097$

60. $4.003 \times 10^7 = 40,030,000$

61. $8.62 \times 10^{-5} = 0.0000862$

62. $2.19 \times 10^{-4} = 0.000219$

63. $3.12 \times 10^{-1} = 0.312$

64. $4.6 \times 10^1 = 46$

65. $9.0 \times 10^6 = 9000000$

66. $7.3 \times 10^4 = 73000$

67. $2.31 \times 10^2 = 231$

68. $1.04 \times 10^{-2} = 0.0104$

69. $3.5 \times 10^4 = 35000$

70. $2.17 \times 10^{-6} = 0.00000217$

71. $1.0 \times 10^4 = 10000$

72. $1.0 \times 10^{-3} = 0.001$

73. $\left(3 \times 10^2\right)\left(2.5 \times 10^3\right) = 750,000$

74. $\left(2 \times 10^8\right)\left(3.9 \times 10^{-5}\right) = 7800$

75. $\left(5.1 \times 10^1\right)\left(3.0 \times 10^{-4}\right) = 15.3 \times 10^{-3} = 0.0153$

76. $\left(1.6 \times 10^{-2}\right)\left(4.0 \times 10^{-3}\right) = 6.4 \times 10^{-5} = 0.000064$

77. $\dfrac{7.5 \times 10^6}{3 \times 10^4} = 2.5 \times 10^2 = 250$

78. $\dfrac{5.2 \times 10^7}{4 \times 10^9} = 1.3 \times 10^{-2} = 0.013$

79. $\dfrac{8.4 \times 10^{-6}}{4.0 \times 10^{-3}} = 2.1 \times 10^{-3} = 0.0021$

80. $\dfrac{25.0 \times 10^3}{5.0 \times 10^{-2}} = 5.0 \times 10^5 = 500000$

81. $\dfrac{4.0 \times 10^5}{2.0 \times 10^4} = 2.0 \times 10^1 = 20$

82. $\dfrac{16.0 \times 10^3}{8.0 \times 10^{-3}} = 2.0 \times 10^6 = 2000000$

83. $\left(5 \times 10^6\right)\left(2 \times 10^4\right) = 10 \times 10^{10} = 1 \times 10^{11}$

84. $\left(1.5 \times 10^{-3}\right)\left(4 \times 10^6\right) = 6 \times 10^3$

85. $\left(3.0 \times 10^{-3}\right)\left(1.5 \times 10^{-4}\right) = 4.5 \times 10^{-7}$

86. $\left(2.3 \times 10^5\right)\left(3.0 \times 10^3\right) = 6.9 \times 10^8$

87. $\dfrac{5.6 \times 10^6}{8 \times 10^4} = 0.7 \times 10^2 = 7 \times 10^1$

88. $\dfrac{2.8 \times 10^4}{4 \times 10^{-3}} = 0.7 \times 10^7 = 7 \times 10^6$

89. $\dfrac{4.0 \times 10^{-5}}{2.0 \times 10^2} = 2.0 \times 10^{-7}$

90. $\dfrac{1.2 \times 10^{-3}}{6 \times 10^{-6}} = 0.2 \times 10^3 = 2.0 \times 10^2$

91. $\dfrac{1.5 \times 10^5}{5.0 \times 10^{-4}} = 0.3 \times 10^9 = 3.0 \times 10^8$

92. $\dfrac{2.4 \times 10^4}{8.0 \times 10^6} = 0.3 \times 10^{-2} = 3.0 \times 10^{-3}$

93. $3.6 \times 10^{-3}, 1.7, 9.8 \times 10^2, 1.03 \times 10^4$

94. $8.5 \times 10^{-5}, \ 1.3 \times 10^{-1}, \ 8.2 \times 10^3, \ 6.2 \times 10^4$

95. 8.3×10^{-5}; 0.00079; 4.1×10^{3}; $40,000$; Note: $0.00079 = 7.9 \times 10^{-4}$, $40,000 = 4 \times 10^{4}$

96. $1,962,000$; 4.79×10^{6}; 3.14×10^{7}; $267,000,000$

97. $\dfrac{2.990 \times 10^{8}}{6.522 \times 10^{9}} \approx 0.458 \times 10^{-1} \approx 0.046$

98. $\dfrac{1.307 \times 10^{9}}{6.522 \times 10^{9}} \approx 0.2004 \times 10^{0} \approx 0.200$

99. $\dfrac{1.095 \times 10^{9}}{6.522 \times 10^{9}} \approx 0.1679 \times 10^{0} \approx 0.168$

100. a) $\dfrac{5.67 \times 10^{12}}{2.73 \times 10^{8}} \approx 2.077 \times 10^{4} = 20,770$ or $20,770$

  b) $\$28,030 - \$20,770 = \$7,260$
  (We round the values in a) and b) since the population and the debt are given only to three figures.)

101. $\dfrac{7.6 \times 10^{65}}{2.806 \times 10^{14}} \approx 2.708 \times 10^{51}$; about 2.7×10^{51} sec

102. $\dfrac{1.24 \times 10^{13}}{2.99 \times 10^{8}} \approx 0.41472 \times 10^{5} = 41,472$, or $\$41,472$

103. $\dfrac{8.86 \times 10^{12}}{1.307 \times 10^{9}} \approx 6.779 \times 10^{3} = 6779$ or $\$6779$

104. $t = \dfrac{d}{r} = \dfrac{4.5 \times 10^{8}}{2.5 \times 10^{4}} = 1.8 \times 10^{4}$ 18,000 hrs.

105. $t = \dfrac{d}{r} = \dfrac{239000 \text{ mi}}{20000 \text{ mph}} = 11.95$ 11.95 hrs

106. $(500,000)(40,000,000,000) = (5 \times 10^{5})(4 \times 10^{10}) = 20 \times 10^{15} = 2 \times 10^{16}$
  2.0×10^{16} drops

107. $(50)(5,800,000) = (5 \times 10^{1})(5.8 \times 10^{6}) = 29 \times 10^{7} = 2.9 \times 10^{8}$
  2.9×10^{8} cells

108. $\dfrac{4.5 \times 10^{9}}{2.5 \times 10^{5}} = 1.8 \times 10^{4}$ or 18,000 times

109. $(100,000 \text{ cu ft/sec}) (60 \text{ sec/min}) (60 \text{ min/hr}) (24 \text{ hr}) = 8,640,000,000 \text{ ft}^{3}$ or 8.64×10^{9} cu ft

110. $(14)(2.38)(10^5) = 33.32 \times 10^5 = 3.332 \times 10^6$ or 3,332,000 miles

111. a) $(0.60)(1,200,000,000) = \$720,000,000$ b) $(0.25)(1,200,000,000) = \$300,000,000$
    c) $(0.10)(1,200,000,000) = \$120,000,000$ d) $(0.05)(1,200,000,000) = \$60,000,000$

112. a) $(0.40)(3,400,000,000) = \$1,360,000,000$ b) $(0.40)(3,400,000,000) = \$1,360,000,000$
    c) $(0.10)(3,400,000,000) = \$340,000,000$ d) $(0.10)(3,400,000,000) = \$340,000,000$

113. 1,000 times, since 1 meter $= 10^3$ millimeters $= 1,000$ millimeters

114. Since 1 gram $= 10^3$ milligrams and 1 gram $= 10^{-3}$ kilograms, 10^{-3} kilograms $= 10^3$ milligrams

$$\frac{10^{-3} \text{ Kilograms}}{10^{-3}} = \frac{10^3 \text{ milligrams}}{10^{-3}},$$ Thus, 1 kilogram $= 10^6$ milligrams

115. $\dfrac{2 \times 10^{30}}{6 \times 10^{24}} = 0.\overline{3} \times 10^6 \approx 300,000$ times

116. a) $1,000,000 = 1.0 \times 10^6$; $1,000,000,000 = 1.0 \times 10^9$; $1,000,000,000,000 = 1.0 \times 10^{12}$

  b) $\dfrac{1.0 \times 10^6}{1.0 \times 10^3} = 1.0 \times 10^3$ days or 1,000 days ≈ 2.74 years

  c) $\dfrac{1.0 \times 10^9}{1.0 \times 10^3} = 1.0 \times 10^6$ days or 1,000,000 days $\approx 2,740$ years

  d) $\dfrac{1.0 \times 10^{12}}{1.0 \times 10^3} = 1.0 \times 10^9$ days or 1,000,000,000 days $\approx 2,740,000$ years

  e) $\dfrac{1 \text{ billion}}{1 \text{ million}} = \dfrac{1.0 \times 10^9}{1.0 \times 10^6} = 1.0 \times 10^3 = 1,000$ times greater

117. a) $(1.86 \times 10^5 \text{ mi/sec})(60 \text{ sec/min})(60 \text{ min/hr})(24 \text{ hr/day})(365 \text{ days/yr})(1 \text{ yr})$

    $= (1.86 \times 10^5)(6 \times 10^1)(6 \times 10^1)(2.4 \times 10^1)(3.65 \times 10^2) = 586.5696 \times 10^{10} \approx 5.87 \times 10^{12}$ miles

  b) $t = \dfrac{d}{r} = \dfrac{9.3 \times 10^7}{1.86 \times 10^5} = 5.0 \times 10^2 = 500$ seconds or 8 min. 20 sec.

118. a) $E(0) = 2^{10} \times 2^0 = 2^{10} \times 1 = 1024$ bacteria   b) $E(1/2) = 2^{10} \times 2^{1/2} = 2^{10.5} \approx 1448$ bacteria

Exercise Set 5.7
1. A sequence is a list of numbers that are related to each other by a given rule. One example is 2, 4, 6, 8….
2. The terms of the sequence.
3. a) An arithmetic sequence is a sequence in which each term differs from the preceding term by a constant
       amount. One example is 1, 4, 7, 10,….
  b) A geometric sequence is one in which the ratio of any term to the term that directly precedes it is a constant.
       One example is 1, 3, 9, 27,….

4. a) $d = +5$,   b) $r = -3$

5. a) $a_n = n^{th}$ term of the sequence   b) a_1 = first term of a sequence   c) d = common difference in a sequence
   d) s_n = the sum of the first n terms of the arithmetic sequence

6. a) $a_n = n^{th}$ term of the sequence   b) a_1 = first term of a sequence   c) r = common ratio between consecutive
   terms   d) s_n = the sum of the first n terms of the geometric sequence

7. $a_1 = 5, d = 1$ 5, 6, 7, 8, 9

8. $a_1 = 4, d = 2$ 4, 6, 8, 10, 12

9. $a_1 = 12, d = -2$ 12, 10, 8, 6, 4

10. $a_1 = -11, d = 5$ −11, −6, −1, 4, 9

11. $a_1 = 5, d = -2$ 5, 3, 1, −1, −3

12. $a_1 = -3, d = -4$ −3, −7, −11, −15, −19

13. $a_1 = \frac{3}{4}, d = \frac{1}{4}$ $\frac{3}{4}, 1, \frac{5}{4}, \frac{3}{2}, \frac{7}{4}$

14. $a_1 = \frac{5}{2}, d = -\frac{3}{2}$ $\frac{5}{2}, 1, -\frac{1}{2}, -2, -\frac{7}{2}$

15. $a_4 = 4 + (5-1)1 = 4 + 4 = 8$

16. $a_8 = -5 + (8-1)(4) = -5 + 28 = 23$

17. $a_{10} = -5 + (10-1)(2) = -5 + 18 = 13$

18. $a_{12} = 7 + (12-1)(-3) = 7 + (11)(-3)$
    $= 7 - 33 = -26$

19. $a_{20} = \frac{4}{5} + (19)(-1) = \frac{4}{5} - 19 = \frac{4}{5} - \frac{95}{5} = -\frac{91}{5}$

20. $a_{14} = \frac{1}{3} + (14-1)\left(\frac{2}{3}\right) = \frac{1}{3} + \frac{26}{3} = \frac{27}{3} = 9$

21. $a_{22} = -23 + (22-1)\left(\frac{5}{7}\right) = -23 + 15 = -8$

22. $a_{15} = \frac{4}{3} + (14)\left(\frac{1}{3}\right) = \frac{4}{3} + \frac{14}{3} = \frac{18}{3} = 6$

23. $a_n = n$ $(a_1 = 1, d = 1)$

24. $a_n = 2n - 1$ $(a_1 = 1, d = 2)$

25. $a_n = 2n$ $(a_1 = 2, d = 2)$

26. $a_1 = -3, d = 3$
    $a_n = -3 + (n-1)3 = -3 + 3n - 3 = 3n - 6$

27. $a_1 = \frac{1}{4}, d = \frac{3}{4}$
    $a_n = \frac{1}{4} + (n-1)\left(\frac{3}{4}\right) = \frac{1}{4} + \frac{3}{4}n - \frac{3}{4} = \frac{3}{4}n - \frac{1}{2}$

28. $a_1 = -\frac{1}{4}, d = \frac{1}{4}$
    $a_n = -\frac{1}{4} + (n-1)\frac{1}{4} = -\frac{1}{4} + \frac{1}{4}n - \frac{1}{4} = \frac{1}{4}n - \frac{1}{2}$

29. $a_1 = -3, d = \frac{3}{2}$
    $a_n = -3 + (n-1)\left(\frac{3}{2}\right) = -3 + \frac{3}{2}n - \frac{3}{2} = \frac{3}{2}n = \frac{9}{2}$

30. $a_1 = -5, d = 3$
    $a_n = -5 + (n-1)3 = -5 + 3n - 3 = 3n - 8$

31. $s_{50} = \dfrac{n(a_1 + a_n)}{2} = \dfrac{50(1+50)}{2} = \dfrac{50(51)}{2}$
$= (25)(51) = 1275$

32. $s_{50} = \dfrac{50(2+100)}{2} = \dfrac{50(102)}{2} = (25)(102) = 2550$

33. $s_{50} = \dfrac{50(1+99)}{2} = \dfrac{50(100)}{2} = (25)(100) = 2500$

34. $s_9 = \dfrac{9(-4 + (-28))}{2} = \dfrac{9 \cdot (-32)}{2} = -144$

35. $s_8 = \dfrac{8(11 + (-24))}{2} = \dfrac{8 \cdot (-13)}{2} = -52$

36. $s_{19} = \dfrac{19\left(-\dfrac{1}{16} + \dfrac{17}{16}\right)}{2} = \dfrac{19 \cdot \left(\dfrac{16}{16}\right)}{2} = \dfrac{19}{2} = 9.5$

37. $s_{24} = \dfrac{24\left(\dfrac{1}{5} + \dfrac{24}{5}\right)}{2} = \dfrac{24 \cdot \left(\dfrac{25}{5}\right)}{2} = 12 \cdot 5 = 60$

38. $s_{21} = \dfrac{21\left(-\dfrac{3}{4} + \dfrac{17}{4}\right)}{2} = \dfrac{21 \cdot \left(\dfrac{14}{4}\right)}{2} = \dfrac{147}{4} = 36.75$

39. $a_1 = 1,\ r = 5$ 1, 5, 25, 125, 625

40. $a_1 = 1,\ r = 2$ 1, 2, 4, 8, 16

41. $a_1 = 2, r = -4$ 2, –4, 8, –16, 32

42. $a_1 = 8, r = \dfrac{1}{2}$ 8, 4, 2, 1, $\dfrac{1}{2}$

43. $a_1 = -3, r = -1$ –3, 3, –3, 3, –3

44. $a_1 = -6, r = -2$ –6, 12, –24, 48, –96

45. $a_1 = 81, r = -\dfrac{1}{3}$ 81, –27, 9, –3, 1

46. $a_1 = \dfrac{16}{15}, r = \dfrac{1}{2}$ $\dfrac{16}{15}, \dfrac{8}{15}, \dfrac{4}{15}, \dfrac{2}{15}, \dfrac{1}{15}$

47. $a_6 = 5(2)^5 = (5)(32) = 160$

48. $a_6 = 1(3)^5 = (1)(243) = 243$

49. $a_3 = 3\left(\dfrac{1}{2}\right)^2 = 3\left(\dfrac{1}{4}\right) = \dfrac{3}{4}$

50. $a_7 = -3(-3)^6 = -3(729) = -2187$

51. $a_7 = (-5) \cdot 3^6 = (-5)(729) = -3645$

52. $a_8 = \left(\dfrac{1}{2}\right)(-2)^7 = \left(\dfrac{1}{2}\right)(-128) = -64$

53. $a_{10} = (-2)(3)^9 = -39{,}366$

54. $a_{18} = (-5)(-2)^{17} = 655{,}360$

55. 1, 2, 4, 8 $a_n = 1(2)^{n-1} = 2^{n-1}$

56. 1, 3, 9, 29 $a_n = 1(3)^{n-1} = 3^{n-1}$

57. $-1, 1, -1, 1$ $a_n = (-1)(-1)^{n-1} = (-1)^n$

58. $-16, -8, -4, -2$ $a_n = a_1 r^{n-1} = -16\left(\dfrac{1}{2}\right)^{n-1}$

59. $2, 1, \dfrac{1}{2}, \dfrac{1}{4}$ $a_n = (2)\left(\dfrac{1}{2}\right)^{n-1}$

60. $-3, 6, -12, 24$ $a_n = (-3)(-2)^{n-1}$

61. $9, 3, 1, \dfrac{1}{3}$ $a_n = (9)\left(\dfrac{1}{3}\right)^{n-1}$

62. $-4, -\dfrac{8}{3}, -\dfrac{16}{9}, -\dfrac{32}{27}$ $a_n = (-4)\left(\dfrac{2}{3}\right)^{n-1}$

63. $s_5 = \dfrac{a_1(1-r^5)}{1-r} = \dfrac{6(1-2^5)}{1-2} = \dfrac{6(-31)}{-1} = 186$

64. $s_4 = \dfrac{a_1(1-r^4)}{1-r} = \dfrac{4(1-3^4)}{1-3} = \dfrac{4(-80)}{-2} = 160$

65. $s_6 = \dfrac{a_1(1-r^6)}{1-r} = \dfrac{(-3)(1-4^6)}{1-4} = \dfrac{(-3)(-4095)}{-3}$
$= -4095$

66. $s_9 = \dfrac{a_1(1-r^9)}{1-r} = \dfrac{-3(1-5^9)}{1-5} = \dfrac{-3(-1,953,124)}{-4}$
$= -1,464,843$

67. $s_{11} = \dfrac{a_1(1-r^{11})}{1-r} = \dfrac{-7(1-3^{11})}{1-3} = \dfrac{-7(-177,146)}{-2}$
$= -620,011$

68. $s_{15} = \dfrac{a_1(1-r^n)}{1-r} = \dfrac{-1(1-(2)^{15})}{1-2} = \dfrac{(-1)(1-32,768)}{-1}$
$= 1-32,768 = -32,767$

69. $s_{13} = \dfrac{(-1)(1-(-2)^{15})}{1-(-2)} = \dfrac{(-1)(1+32,768)}{3}$
$= \dfrac{(-1)(32,769)}{3} = -10,923$

70. $s_{10} = \dfrac{(512)\left(1-\left(\frac{1}{2}\right)^{10}\right)}{1-\frac{1}{2}} = \dfrac{(1024)\left(1-\frac{1}{1024}\right)}{\frac{1}{2}}$
$= 1024 - 1 = 1023$

71. $s_{100} = \dfrac{(100)(1+100)}{2} = \dfrac{(100)(101)}{2}$
$= 50(101) = 5050$

72. $s_{100} = \dfrac{(100)(1+199)}{2} = \dfrac{(100)(200)}{2}$
$= 50(200) = 10000$

73. $s_{100} = \dfrac{(100)(2+200)}{2} = \dfrac{(100)(202)}{2}$
$= 50(202) = 10100$

74.
$s_{50} = \dfrac{(50)(3+150)}{2} = \dfrac{(50)(153)}{2} = 25(153) = 3825$

75. a) $a_{12} = 96 + (11)(-3) = 96 - 33 = 63$ in.

b) $\dfrac{[12(96+63)]}{2} = \dfrac{(12)(159)}{2} = (6)(159) = 954$ in.

76. $s_{12} = \dfrac{12(1+12)}{2} = \dfrac{12(13)}{2} = \dfrac{156}{2} = 78$ times

77. a) Using the formula $a_n = a_1 + (n-1)d$, we get
$a_8 = 35,000 + (8-1)(1400) = \$44,800$

b) $\dfrac{8(35000+44800)}{2} = \dfrac{8(79800)}{2} = \$319,200$

78. $a_{11} = 72 + (10)(-6) = 72 - 60 = 12$ in.

79. 1, 2, 3,....   n=31
$s_{31} = \dfrac{31(1+31)}{2} = \dfrac{31(32)}{2} = 31(16) = 496$ PCs

80. $a_{10} = (8000)(1.08)^9 = 15992$ students

81. $a_6 = 200(0.8)^6 = 200(0.262144)^1 = 52.4288$ g

82. $a_{15} = a_1 r^{15} = 1(2)^{15} = 32,768$ layers

83. $a_{15} = 31,000(1.06)^{14} = \$70,088$

84. $a_5 = 30(0.8)^4 = 12.288$ ft.

85. This is a geometric sequence where $a_1 = 2000$ and $r = 3$. In ten years the stock will triple its value 5 times.
$a_6 = a_1 r^{6-1} = 2000(3)^5 = \$486,000$

86. Visitors have scored $\dfrac{8}{2}(1+8) = 36$ runs;   home team has scored $\dfrac{1(1-2^8)}{1-2} = 255$ runs

87. $\dfrac{82[1-(1/2)^6]}{1-(1/2)} = \dfrac{82[1-(1/64)]}{1/2} = \dfrac{82}{1} \cdot \dfrac{63}{64} \cdot \dfrac{2}{1} = 161.4375$

88. The arithmetic sequence $180^0, 360^0, 540^0, 720^0, \ldots$ has a common difference of 180.
Thus, $a_n = 180(n-2) = 180n - 360, \ n \geq 3$

89. 12, 18, 24, ... ,1608 is an arithmetic sequence with $a_1 = 12$ and $d = 6$. Using the expression for the nth term
of an arithmetic sequence $a_n = a_1 + (n-1)d$ or $1608 = 12 + (n-1)6$ and dividing both sides by 6 gives
$268 = 2 + n - 1$ or $n = 267$

90. Since $a_5 = a_1 r^4$ and $a_2 = a_1 r$, $a_5/a_2 = r^3$. Thus $r^3 = 648/24 = 27$ or $r = 3$.
Then $24 = a_2 = a_1 r = a_1(3)$ or $a_1 = 24/3 = 8$.

91. The total distance is 30 plus twice the sum of the terms of the geometric sequence having $a_1 = (30)(0.8) = 24$
and $r = 0.8$.   Thus $s_5 = \dfrac{24[1-(0.8)^5]}{(1-0.8)} = \dfrac{24[1-0.32768]}{0.2} = \dfrac{24(0.67232)}{0.2} = 80.6784.$
So the total distance is $30 + 2(80.6784) = 191.3568$ ft.

92. The sequence of bets during a losing streak is geometric.

a) $a_6 = a_1 r^{n-1} = 1(2)^{6-1} = 1(32) = \$32$ $s_5 = \dfrac{a_1\left(1-r^n\right)}{1-r} = \dfrac{1\left(1-2^5\right)}{1-2} = \dfrac{-31}{-1} = \$31$

b) $a_6 = a_1 r^{n-1} = 10(2)^{6-1} = 10(32) = \$320$ $s_5 = \dfrac{a_1\left(1-r^n\right)}{1-r} = \dfrac{10\left(1-2^5\right)}{1-2} = \dfrac{10(-31)}{-1} = \$310$

c) $a_{11} = a_1 r^{n-1} = 1(2)^{11-1} = 1(1024) = \$1,024$ $s_{10} = \dfrac{a_1\left(1-r^n\right)}{1-r} = \dfrac{1\left(1-2^{10}\right)}{1-2} = \dfrac{1(-1023)}{-1} = \$1,023$

d) $a_{11} = a_1 r^{n-1} = 10(2)^{11-1} = 10(1024) = \$10,240$ $s_{10} = \dfrac{a_1\left(1-r^n\right)}{1-r} = \dfrac{10\left(1-2^{10}\right)}{1-2} = \dfrac{10(-1023)}{-1} = \$10,230$

e) If you lose too many times in a row, then you will run out of money.

Exercise Set 5.8

1. Begin with the numbers 1, 1, then add 1 and 1 to get 2 and continue to add the previous two numbers in the sequence to get the next number in the sequence.

2. a) 1,2,3,5,8,13,21,34,55,89   b) $\dfrac{55}{34} = 1.61764 \approx 1.619$ c) $\dfrac{89}{55} = 1.61818 \approx 1.618$

   d) $\dfrac{8}{5} = 1.6 \approx 1.600$ e) $\dfrac{5}{3} = 1.\overline{6} \approx 1.667$ f) $\dfrac{21}{13} = 1.61538 \approx 1.615$

3. a) Golden number $= \dfrac{\sqrt{5}+1}{2}$

   b) 1.618 = golden ratio   When a line segment AB is divided at a point C, such that the ratio of the whole, AB, to the larger part, AC, is equal to the ratio of the larger part, AC, to the smaller part, CB, then each

   of the ratios $\dfrac{AB}{AC}$ and $\dfrac{AC}{CB}$ is known as the golden ratio.

   c) The golden proportion is: $\dfrac{AB}{AC} = \dfrac{AC}{CB}$

   d) The golden rectangle: $\dfrac{L}{W} = \dfrac{a+b}{a} = \dfrac{a}{b} = \dfrac{\sqrt{5}+1}{2} =$ golden number

4. All involve the same number, Φ.

6. a) Petals on daisies   b) Parthenon in Athens

5. a) Flowering head of a sunflower b) Great Pyramid

7. a) $\dfrac{\sqrt{5}+1}{2} = 1.618033989$ b) $\dfrac{\sqrt{5}-1}{2} = .618033989$

   c) Differ by 1

8. 89, $\dfrac{1}{89} = .0112359551$, part of Fibonacci sequence

9. 1/1 = 1, 2/1 = 2, 3/2 = 1.5, 5/3 = 1.6, 8/5 = 1.6, 13/8 = 1.625, 21/13 = 1.6154, 34/21 = 1.619, 55/34 = 1.6176 89/55 = 1.61818. The consecutive ratios alternate increasing then decreasing about the golden ratio.

10. The ratio of the second to the first and the fourth to the third estimates the golden ratio.

11. If the first ten are selected; $\dfrac{1+1+2+3+5+8+13+21+34+55}{11} = \dfrac{143}{11} = 13$

12.

Fib. No.	prime factors	Fib. No.	prime factors
1	-------	34	$2 \bullet 17$
1	-------	55	$5 \bullet 11$
2	prime	89	prime
3	prime	144	$2^4 \bullet 3^2$
5	prime	233	prime
8	2^3	377	$13 \bullet 29$
13	prime	610	$2 \bullet 5 \bullet 61$

13. If 2, 3, 5, and 8 are selected the result is $5^2 - 3^2 = 2 \cdot 8 \quad \rightarrow \quad 25 - 9 = 16 \quad \rightarrow \quad 16 = 16$

14. If 5 is selected the result is $2(5) - 8 = 10 - 8 = 2$ which is the second number preceding 5.

15. Answers will vary.   16. $6/4 = 1.5$ which is a little < 1.6.   17. Answers will vary.
18. Answers will vary.   19. Answers will vary.   20. Answers will vary.
21. Answers will vary.   22. Answers will vary.

23. Not Fibonacci type; it is not true that each term is the sum of the two preceding terms.
24. Fibonacci type Each term is not the sum of the two preceding terms. $11 + 18 = 29$, $18 + 29 = 47$
25. Fibonacci type: $1 + 2 = 3$, $2 + 3 = 5$ Each term is the sum of the two preceding terms.
26. Not Fibonacci; it is not true that each term is the sum of the two preceding terms.
27. Fibonacci type; $40 + 65 = 105$; $65 + 105 = 170$

    28. Fibonacci type; $1\frac{1}{4} + 2 = 3\frac{1}{4}$; $2 + 3\frac{1}{4} = 5\frac{1}{4}$

29. Fibonacci type; $-1 + 0 = -1$; $0 + (-1) = -1$ 30. Fibonacci type; $7 + 13 = 20$; $13 + 20 = 33$

31. a) If 6 and 10 are selected the sequence is 6, 10, 16, 26, 42, 68, 110, …
    b) $10/6 = 1.666$, $16/10 = 1.600$, $26/16 = 1.625$, $42/26 = 1.615$, $68/42 = 1.619$, $110/68 = 1.618$, …

32. a) If 5 and 7 are selected the sequence is 5, 7, 12, 19, 31, 50, 81, …
    b) $7/5 = 1.4$, $12/7 = 1.714$, $19/12 = 1.583$, $31/19 = 1.623$, $50/31 = 1.613$, $81/50 = 1.62$, …

33. a) If 5, 8, and 13 are selected the result is $8^2 - (5)(13) = 64 - 65 = -1$.

    b) If 21, 34, and 55 are selected the result is $34^2 - (21)(55) = 1156 - 1155 = 1$.

    c) The square of the middle term of three consecutive terms in a Fibonacci sequence differs from the product of the 1st and 2nd term by 1.

34. The sum of the numbers along the diagonals parallel to the one shown is a Fibonacci number.

35. a) Lucas sequence: 1, 3, 4, 7, 11, 18, 29, 47, …   b) $8 + 21 = 29$; $13 + 34 = 47$
    c) The first column is a Fibonacci-type sequence.

36. $-10, x, -10 + x, -10 + 2x, -20 + 3x, -30 + 5x, -50 + 8x, -80 + 13x, -130 + 21x, -210 + 34x$
    a) $-10, 4, -6, -2, -8, -10, -18, -28, -46, -74$
    b) $-10, 5, -5, 0, -5, -5, -10, -15, -25, -40$
    c) $-10, 6, -4, 2, -2, 0, -2, -2, -4, -6$
    d) $-10, 7, -3, 4, 1, 5, 6, 11, 17, 28$
    e) $-10, 8, -2, 6, 4, 10, 14, 24, 38, 62$
    f) Yes, because each multiple causes the x term to be greater than the number term.

37. $\dfrac{5}{x} = \dfrac{x}{5-x}$ $\qquad 5(5-x) = x^2 \qquad 25 - 5x = x^2 \qquad x^2 + 5x - 25 = 0$

Solve for x using the quadratic formula,

$$x = \frac{-b \pm \sqrt{b^2 - 4ac}}{2a} = \frac{-5 \pm \sqrt{25 - 4(1)(-25)}}{2(1)} = \frac{-5 \pm \sqrt{125}}{2} = 5\left(\frac{\sqrt{5}-1}{2}\right) \text{ since we want an}$$

answer between 0 and 5.

38. $\dfrac{(a+b)}{a} = \dfrac{a}{b}$ $\quad$ Let $x = \dfrac{a}{b}$ $\quad \dfrac{b}{a} = \dfrac{1}{x}$ $\quad 1 + \dfrac{b}{a} = \dfrac{a}{b}$ $\quad 1 + \dfrac{1}{x} = x$ $\quad$ multiply by x $\quad x\left(1 + \dfrac{1}{x}\right) = x(x)$

$x + 1 = x^2 \qquad x^2 - x - 1 = 0$

Solve for x using the quadratic formula, $\quad x = \dfrac{-b \pm \sqrt{b^2 - 4ac}}{2a} = \dfrac{1 \pm \sqrt{1 - 4(1)(-1)}}{2(1)} = \dfrac{1 \pm \sqrt{5}}{2}$

39. Answers will vary. $\{5, 12, 13\}$ $\qquad \{16, 30, 34\}$ $\qquad \{105, 208, 233\}$ $\qquad \{272, 546, 610\}$

40. a) 3 reflections, 5 paths $\qquad$ b) 4 reflections, 8 paths $\qquad$ c) 5 reflections, 13 paths

Review Exercises

1. Use the divisibility rules in section 5.1.

   158,340 is divisible by 2, 3, 4, 5, 6, and 10.

2. Use the divisibility rules in section 5.1.

   400,644 is divisible by 2, 3, 4, 6, and 9

3.
```
2 | 540
2 | 270
3 | 135
3 | 45
3 | 15
    5
```
$540 = 2^2 \cdot 3^3 \cdot 5$

4.
```
3 | 693
3 | 231
7 | 77
    11
```
$693 = 3^2 \cdot 7 \cdot 11$

5.
```
2 | 840
2 | 420
2 | 210
5 | 105
3 | 21
    7
```
$840 = 2^3 \cdot 3 \cdot 5 \cdot 7$

6.
```
2 | 882
3 | 441
3 | 147
7 | 49
    7
```
$882 = 2 \cdot 3^2 \cdot 7^2$

7.
```
2  | 1452
2  | 726
3  | 363
11 | 121
     11
```
$1452 = 2^2 \cdot 3 \cdot 11^2$

8. $30 = 2 \cdot 3 \cdot 5$, $105 = 3 \cdot 5 \cdot 7$

   gcd = 15 $\quad$ lcm = 210

9. $63 = 3 \cdot 3 \cdot 5$, $108 = 3 \cdot 4 \cdot 9$

   gcd = 9; $\quad$ lcm = 756

10. $45 = 3^2 \cdot 5$, $250 = 2 \cdot 5^3$; gcd = 5; lcm = $2 \cdot 3^2 \cdot 5^3 = 2250$

11. $90 = 2 \cdot 3^2 \cdot 5$, $300 = 2^2 \cdot 3 \cdot 5^2$; gcd = $2 \cdot 3 \cdot 5 = 30$; lcm = $2^2 \cdot 3^2 \cdot 5^2 = 900$

12. $60 = 2^2 \cdot 3 \cdot 5$, $40 = 2^3 \cdot 5$, $96 = 2^5 \cdot 3$; $\gcd = 2^2 = 4$; $\text{lcm} = 2^5 \cdot 3 \cdot 5 = 480$

13. $36 = 2^2 \cdot 3^2$, $108 = 2^2 \cdot 3^3$, $144 = 2^4 \cdot 3^2$; $\gcd = 2^2 \cdot 3^2 = 36$; $\text{lcm} = 2^4 \cdot 3^3 = 432$

14. $15 = 3 \cdot 5$, $9 = 3^2$; $\text{lcm} = 3^2 \cdot 5 = 45$. In 45 days the train stopped in both cities.

15. $4 + (-7) = -3$

16. $-2 + 5 = 3$

17. $(-2) + (-4) = -6$

18. $4 - 8 = 4 + (-8) = -4$

19. $-5 - 4 = -5 + (-4) = -9$

20. $-3 - (-6) = -3 + 6 = 3$

21. $(-3 + 7) - 4 = 4 + (-4) = 0$

22. $-1 + (9 - 4) = -1 + 5 = 4$

23. $-5 \cdot 3 = -15$

24. $(-2)(-12) = 24$

25. $14(-4) = -56$

26. $-35/-7 = 5$

27. $12/-6 = -2$

28. $[8 \div (-4)](-3) = (-2)(-3) = 6$

29. $-20 \div (-4 - 1) = -20 \div (-5) = 4$

30. $[-30 \div (10)] \div (-1) = -3 \div (-1) = 3$

31. $3/10 = 0.3$

32. $11/25 = 0.44$

33. $15/40 = 3/8 = 0.375$

34. $13/4 = 3.25$

35. $6/7 = 0.\overline{857142}$

36. $7/12 = 0.58\overline{3}$

37. $3/8 = 0.375$

38. $11/16 = 0.6875$

39. $5/7 = 0.\overline{714285}$

40. $0.225 = \dfrac{225}{1000} = \dfrac{45}{200} = \dfrac{9}{40}$

41. $1.4 = \dfrac{14}{10} = \dfrac{7}{5}$

42. $0.6666\ldots \qquad 10n = 6.6666\ldots$

$10n = 6.\overline{6} \qquad\qquad \dfrac{9n}{9} = \dfrac{6}{9}$

$\underline{-\ n = 0.\overline{6}} \qquad\qquad n = \dfrac{2}{3}$

$9n = 6.0$

43. $0.5151\ldots \qquad 100n = 51.5151\ldots$

$100n = 51.\overline{51} \qquad \dfrac{99n}{99} = \dfrac{51}{99}$

$\underline{-\ n =\ \ 0.\overline{51}} \qquad n = \dfrac{51}{99} = \dfrac{17}{33}$

$99n = 51$

44. $0.083 = \dfrac{83}{1000}$

45. $0.0073 = \dfrac{73}{10{,}000}$

46. $2.344444\ldots \qquad 100n = 234.444444\ldots$

$100n = 234.\overline{4}$

$\underline{-10n =\ \ 23.\overline{4}} \qquad \dfrac{90n}{90} = \dfrac{211}{90} = n$

$90n = 211.00$

47. $1\dfrac{3}{4} = \dfrac{(1)(4) + 3}{4} = \dfrac{7}{4}$

48. $4\dfrac{1}{6} = \dfrac{(4)(6) + 1}{6} = \dfrac{25}{6}$

49. $-3\frac{1}{4} = \dfrac{((-3)(4)) - 1}{4} = \dfrac{-13}{4}$

50. $-35\frac{3}{8} = \dfrac{((-35)(8)) - 3}{8} = \dfrac{-283}{8}$

51. $\dfrac{11}{5} = \dfrac{2 \cdot 5 + 1}{5} = 2\dfrac{1}{5}$

52. $\dfrac{75}{8} = \dfrac{9 \cdot 8 + 3}{8} = 9\dfrac{3}{8}$

53. $\dfrac{-12}{7} = \dfrac{(-1)(7) - 5}{7} = -1\frac{5}{7}$

54. $\dfrac{-136}{5} = \dfrac{(-27)(5) - 1}{5} = -27\frac{1}{5}$

55. $\dfrac{1}{3}+\dfrac{3}{4}=\dfrac{1}{3}\cdot\dfrac{4}{4}+\dfrac{3}{4}\cdot\dfrac{3}{3}=\dfrac{4}{12}+\dfrac{9}{12}=\dfrac{13}{12}$

56. $\dfrac{11}{12}-\dfrac{2}{3}=\dfrac{11}{12}-\dfrac{2}{3}\cdot\dfrac{4}{4}=\dfrac{11}{12}-\dfrac{8}{12}=\dfrac{3}{12}=\dfrac{1}{4}$

57. $\dfrac{1}{6}+\dfrac{5}{4}=\dfrac{1}{6}\cdot\dfrac{2}{2}+\dfrac{5}{4}\cdot\dfrac{3}{3}=\dfrac{2}{12}+\dfrac{15}{12}=\dfrac{17}{12}$

58. $\dfrac{7}{16}\cdot\dfrac{12}{21}=\dfrac{84}{336}=\dfrac{84}{4\cdot84}=\dfrac{1}{4}$

59. $\dfrac{5}{9}\div\dfrac{6}{7}=\dfrac{5}{9}\div\dfrac{7}{6}=\dfrac{35}{54}$

60. $\left(\dfrac{4}{5}+\dfrac{5}{7}\right)\div\dfrac{4}{5}=\dfrac{28+25}{35}\cdot\dfrac{5}{4}=\dfrac{53}{35}\cdot\dfrac{5}{4}=\dfrac{53}{28}$

61. $\left(\dfrac{2}{3}\cdot\dfrac{1}{7}\right)\div\dfrac{4}{7}=\dfrac{2}{21}\cdot\dfrac{7}{4}=\dfrac{1}{6}$

62. $\left(\dfrac{1}{5}+\dfrac{2}{3}\right)\cdot\dfrac{3}{8}=\dfrac{3+10}{15}\cdot\dfrac{3}{8}=\dfrac{13}{15}\cdot\dfrac{3}{8}=\dfrac{13}{40}$

63. $\left(\dfrac{1}{5}\right)\left(\dfrac{2}{3}\right)+\left(\dfrac{1}{5}\div\dfrac{1}{2}\right)=\dfrac{2}{15}+\left(\dfrac{1}{5}\right)\left(\dfrac{2}{1}\right)=\dfrac{2}{15}+\dfrac{2}{5}$
$=\dfrac{2}{15}+\dfrac{6}{15}=\dfrac{8}{15}$

64. $\left(\dfrac{1}{8}\right)(17\tfrac{3}{4})=\left(\dfrac{1}{8}\right)\left(\dfrac{71}{4}\right)=\dfrac{71}{32}=2\tfrac{7}{32}$ teaspoons

65. $45=\sqrt{9\cdot5}=\sqrt{9}\cdot\sqrt{5}=3\sqrt{5}$

66. $\sqrt{200}=\sqrt{100\cdot2}=\sqrt{100}\cdot\sqrt{2}=10\sqrt{2}$

67. $\sqrt{5}+7\sqrt{5}=8\sqrt{5}$

68. $\sqrt{2}-4\sqrt{2}=(1-4)\sqrt{2}=-3\sqrt{2}$

69. $\sqrt{8}+6\sqrt{2}=2\sqrt{2}+6\sqrt{2}=8\sqrt{2}$

70. $\sqrt{3}-7\sqrt{27}=\sqrt{3}-21\sqrt{3}=-20\sqrt{3}$

71. $\sqrt{28}+\sqrt{63}=2\sqrt{7}+3\sqrt{7}=5\sqrt{7}$

72. $\sqrt{3}\cdot\sqrt{6}=\sqrt{18}=\sqrt{9\cdot2}=\sqrt{9}\cdot\sqrt{2}=3\sqrt{2}$

73. $\sqrt{8}\cdot\sqrt{6}=\sqrt{48}=\sqrt{16\cdot3}=\sqrt{16}\cdot\sqrt{3}=4\sqrt{3}$

74. $\dfrac{\sqrt{300}}{\sqrt{3}}=\sqrt{\dfrac{300}{3}}=\sqrt{100}=10$

75. $\dfrac{\sqrt{56}}{\sqrt{2}}=\sqrt{\dfrac{56}{2}}=\sqrt{28}=2\sqrt{7}$

76. $\dfrac{4}{\sqrt{3}}\cdot\dfrac{\sqrt{3}}{\sqrt{3}}=\dfrac{4\sqrt{3}}{3}$

77. $\dfrac{\sqrt{7}}{\sqrt{5}}\cdot\dfrac{\sqrt{5}}{\sqrt{5}}=\dfrac{\sqrt{35}}{5}$

78. $3(2+\sqrt{7})=6+3\sqrt{7}$

79. $\sqrt{3}(4+\sqrt{6})=4\sqrt{3}+\sqrt{18}=4\sqrt{3}+3\sqrt{2}$

80. $\sqrt{3}(\sqrt{6}+\sqrt{15})=\sqrt{18}+\sqrt{45}=3\sqrt{2}+3\sqrt{5}$

81. $x+2=2+x$ Commutative property of addition

82. $5\cdot m=m\cdot5$ Commutative property of multiplication

83. Associative property of addition

84. Distributive property

85. Associative property of addition

86. Commutative property of addition

87. Associative property of multiplication

88. Commutative property of multiplication

89. Distributive property

90. Commutative property of multiplication

91. Natural numbers – not closed for subtraction
$2 - 3 = -1$ and -1 is not a natural number.

92. Whole numbers – closed for multiplication

93. Not closed; $1 \div 2$ is not an integer

94. Closed

95. Not closed; $\sqrt{2} \cdot \sqrt{2} = 2$ is not irrational

96. Not closed; $1 \div 0$ is undefined

97. $5^2 = 5 \bullet 5 = 25$

98. $5^{-2} = \dfrac{1}{5^2} = \dfrac{1}{5 \bullet 5} = \dfrac{1}{25}$

99. $\dfrac{9^5}{9^3} = 9^{5-3} = 9^2 = 81$

100. $5^2 \bullet 5^1 = 5^3 = 125$

101. $7^0 = 1$

102. $4^{-3} = \dfrac{1}{4^3} = \dfrac{1}{64}$

103. $(2^3)^2 = 2^{3 \bullet 2} = 2^6 = 64$

104. $(3^2)^2 = 3^{2 \bullet 2} = 3^4 = 81$

105. $8,200,000,000 = 8.2 \times 10^9$

106. $0.0000158 = 1.58 \times 10^{-5}$

107. $0.02309 = 2.309 \times 10^{-2}$

108. $4,950,000 = 4.95 \times 10^6$

109. $2.8 \times 10^5 = 280,000$

110. $1.39 \times 10^{-4} = 0.000139$

111. $1.75 \times 10^{-4} = 0.000175$

112. $1 \times 10^7 = 10,000,000$

113. a) $(3 \times 10^4)(2 \times 10^{-9}) =$
$6 \times 10^{4-9} = 6 \times 10^{-5}$

114. a) $(5 \times 10^6)(7.5 \times 10^5) =$
$(5)(7.5) \times (10^{6+5}) =$
$37.5 \times 10^{11} = 3.75 \times 10^{12}$

115. $\dfrac{8.4 \times 10^3}{4 \times 10^2} = \dfrac{8.4}{4} \times \dfrac{10^3}{10^2} = 2.1 \times 10^1$

116. $\dfrac{1.5 \times 10^{-3}}{5 \times 10^{-4}} = \dfrac{1.5}{5} \times \dfrac{10^{-3}}{10^{-4}} = 0.3 \times 10^1 = 3.0 \times 10^0$

117. a) $(550,000)(2,000,000) = (5.5 \times 10^5)(2 \times 10^6)$
$= (5.5)(2) \times 10^{5+6} = 11 \times 10^{11}$
$= 1,100,000,000,000$

118. a) $(35,000)(0.00002) = (3.5 \times 10^4)(2.0 \times 10^{-5})$
$= (3.5)(2) \times 10^4 \bullet 10^{-5} = 7.0 \times 10^{-1} = 0.7$

119. $\dfrac{8,400,000}{70,000} = \dfrac{8.4 \times 10^6}{7 \times 10^4} = 1.2 \times 10^2 = 120$

120. $\dfrac{0.000002}{0.0000004} = \dfrac{2 \times 10^{-6}}{4 \times 10^{-7}} = 0.5 \times 10^1 = 5.0$

121. $\dfrac{1.49 \times 10^{11}}{3.84 \times 10^8} = .3880208333 \times 10^3 \approx 388.02$
388 times

122. $\dfrac{20,000,000}{3,600} = \dfrac{2.0 \times 10^7}{3.6 \times 10^3}$
$\approx 0.555556 \times 10^4 = \$5,555.56$

123. Arithmetic   17, 21

124. Geometric   8, 16

125. Arithmetic $-15, -18$

126. Geometric   1/32, 1/64

127. Arithmetic   16, 19

128. Geometric $\dfrac{1}{2}, -\dfrac{1}{2}$

129. $a_1 = 2,\ d = 5$ $a_6 = 2 + (6-1)(5) = 27$

130. $a_1 = -6,\ d = 2$ $a_9 = -6 + (9-1)2 = 10$

131. $a_{10} = -20 + 9(5) = -20 + 45 = 25$

132. 3, 6, 12, 24, 48 $a_4 = 48$

133. $a_5 = 4(1/2)^{5-1} = 4(1/2)^4 = 4(1/16) = 1/4$

134. $a_4 = -6(2)^{4-1} = -6(2)^3 = -6(8) = -48$

135. $s_{50} = \dfrac{50(3+150)}{2} = (25)(153) = 3825$

136. $s_8 = \dfrac{8(-4+(-2\frac{1}{4}))}{2} = \dfrac{(8)(-6\frac{1}{4})}{2} = -25$

137. $s_8 = \dfrac{8(100+58)}{2} = \dfrac{(8)(158)}{2} = 632$

138. $s_{20} = \dfrac{20(0.5+5.25)}{2} = \dfrac{(20)(5.75)}{2} = 57.5$

139. $s_5 = \dfrac{2(1-4^5)}{1-4} = \dfrac{(2)(-1023)}{-3} = 682$

140. $s_4 = \dfrac{3(1-2^4)}{1-2} = \dfrac{(3)(-15)}{-1} = 45$

141. $s_5 = \dfrac{3(1-(-2)^5)}{1-(-2)} = \dfrac{(3)(1+32)}{3} = \dfrac{(3)(33)}{3} = 33$

142. $s_6 = \dfrac{1(1-(-2)^6)}{1-(-2)} = \dfrac{(1)(1-64)}{3} = \dfrac{(1)(-63)}{3} = -21$

143. Arithmetic: $a_n = 3n$

144. Arithmetic: $a_n = 1 + (n-1)3 = 1 + 3n - 3 = 3n - 2$

145. Arithmetic: $a_n = -(3/2)n + (11/2)$

146. Geometric: $a_n = 3(2)^{n-1}$

147. Geometric: $a_n = 2(-1)^{n-1}$

148. Geometric: $a_n = 5(1/3)^{n-1}$

149. No; 13, 21

150. Yes; −8, −13

151. No

152. No

Chapter Test

1. 48,395 is divisible by: 5

2.
$$2\,|\,\underline{414}$$
$$3\,|\,\underline{207}$$
$$3\,|\,\underline{69}$$
$$23$$
$$414 = 2 \cdot 3^2 \cdot 23$$

3. $[(-3)+7] - (-4) = [4] + 4 = 8$

4. $-7 - 13 = -20$

5. $[(-70)(-5)] \div (8-10) = 350 \div [8 + (-10)]$
   $= 350 \div (-2) = -175$

6. $4\frac{5}{8} = \dfrac{(8)(4)+5}{8} = \dfrac{32+5}{8} = \dfrac{37}{8}$

7. $\dfrac{176}{9} = \dfrac{(19)(9)+5}{9} = 19\frac{5}{9}$

8. $\dfrac{5}{8} = 0.625$

9. $6.45 = \dfrac{645}{100} = \dfrac{129}{20}$

10. $\left(\dfrac{5}{16} \div 3\right) + \left(\dfrac{4}{5} \cdot \dfrac{1}{2}\right) = \left(\dfrac{5}{16} \cdot \dfrac{1}{3}\right) + \dfrac{4}{10}$
    $= \dfrac{5}{48} + \dfrac{4}{10} = \dfrac{50}{480} + \dfrac{192}{480} = \dfrac{242}{480} = \dfrac{121}{240}$

11. $\dfrac{17}{24}-\dfrac{7}{12}=\dfrac{17}{24}-\left(\dfrac{7}{12}\right)\left(\dfrac{2}{2}\right)=\dfrac{17}{24}-\dfrac{14}{24}=\dfrac{3}{24}=\dfrac{1}{8}$

12. $\sqrt{75}+\sqrt{48}=\sqrt{25}\sqrt{3}+\sqrt{16}\sqrt{3}=5\sqrt{3}+4\sqrt{3}=9\sqrt{3}$

13. $\dfrac{\sqrt{2}}{\sqrt{7}}=\dfrac{\sqrt{2}}{\sqrt{7}}\cdot\dfrac{\sqrt{7}}{\sqrt{7}}=\dfrac{\sqrt{14}}{\sqrt{49}}=\dfrac{\sqrt{14}}{7}$

14. The integers are closed under multiplication since the product of two integers is always an integer.

15. Associative property of addition

16. Distributive property

17. $\dfrac{4^5}{4^2}=4^{5-2}=4^3=64$

18. $4^3\bullet 4^2=4^5=4\cdot4\cdot4\cdot4\cdot4=1024$

19. $3^{-4}=\dfrac{1}{3^4}=\dfrac{1}{81}$

20. $\dfrac{7.2\times10^6}{9.0\times10^{-6}}=0.8\times10^{12}=8.0\times10^{11}$

21. $a_n=-4n+2$

22. $\dfrac{11\left[-2+(-32)\right]}{2}=\dfrac{11(-34)}{2}=-187$

23. $a_6=2\cdot3^{6-1}=2\cdot243=486$

24. $s_8=\dfrac{(-2)\left(1-2^8\right)}{1-2}=\dfrac{(-2)(-255)}{-1}=-510$

25. $a_n=3\bullet(2)^{n-1}$

26. 1, 1, 2, 3, 5, 8, 13, 21, 34, 55

Group Projects

1. In this exercise, you may obtain different answers depending upon how you work the problem.
   1) a) 2 servings Rice: 2/3 cup, Salt: 1/4 tsp., Butter: 1 tsp.
      b) 1 serving   Rice: 1/3 cup, Salt: 1/8 tsp., Butter: 1/2 tsp.
      c) 29 servings Rice: 9 2/3 cup, Salt: 4 5/8 tsp., Butter: 14 1/2 tsp.

2. a) Area of triangle 1 = $A_1=\dfrac{1}{2}bh=\dfrac{1}{2}(5)\left(2\sqrt{5}\right)=5\sqrt{5}$

   Area of triangle 2 = $A_1=\dfrac{1}{2}bh=\dfrac{1}{2}(6)\left(2\sqrt{5}\right)=6\sqrt{5}$

   Area of rectangle = $A_R=bh=(10)\left(2\sqrt{5}\right)=20\sqrt{5}$

   Area of trapezoid = $A_T=5\sqrt{5}+6\sqrt{5}+20\sqrt{5}=31\sqrt{5}$

   b) Area of trapezoid = $A_r=\dfrac{1}{2}h\left(b_1+b_2\right)=\dfrac{1}{2}\left(2\sqrt{5}\right)(10+21)=31\sqrt{5}$

   c) Yes, same

3. Co-pay for prescriptions = 50%   Co-pay for office visits = $10   Co-pay for medical tests = 20%
   01/10: $10 + .50 ($44) = $32.00
   02/27: $10 + .20 (188) = $47.60
   04/19: $10 + .20 (348) + .50 (76) = $117.60
   a) Total = $197.20
   b) .50 (44) + .80 (188) + .80 (348) + .50 (76) +3(40) = $608.80
   c) $500.00 – 197.20 = $302.80

4. a) 1 branch   b) 5 branches   c) 233 branches   d) Produces the same sequence.

CHAPTER SIX

ALGEBRA, GRAPHS, AND FUNCTIONS

Exercise Set 6.1

1. **Variables** are letters of the alphabet used to represent numbers.
2. A symbol that represents a specific quantity is called a **constant**.
3. The **solution** to an equation is the number or numbers that replace the variable to make the equation a true statement.
4. An **algebraic expression** is a collection of variables, numbers, parentheses, and operation symbols. An example is $5x^2y - 11$.
5. a) Base: 4, exponent: 5   b) Multiply 4 by itself 5 times.
6. First: Perform all operations within parentheses or other grouping symbols. Next: Perform all exponential operations. Next: Perform all multiplication and division from left to right. Finally: Perform all addition and subtraction from left to right.
7. a) $8 + 16 \div 4 = 8 + 4 = 12$ b) $9 + 6 \times 3 = 9 + 18 = 27$
8. a) If $x \neq 0$, then $x^2 > 0$ and thus $-x^2 < 0$.   b) If $x \neq 0$, then $-x \neq 0$ and so $(-x)^2 > 0$.

9. $x = -5, \ x^2 = (-5)^2 = 25$

10. $x = 6, \ x^2 = 6^2 = 36$

11. $x = -2, -x^2 = -(-2)^2 = -4$

12. $x = -3, -x^2 = -(-3)^2 = -9$

13. $x = -7, -2x^3 = -2(-7)^3 = -2(-343) = 686$

14. $x = -4, -x^3 = -(-4)^3 = -(-64) = 64$

15. $x = 4, x - 7 = 4 - 7 = -3$

16. $x = \dfrac{5}{2}, 8x - 3 = 8\left(\dfrac{5}{2}\right) - 3 = 20 - 3 = 17$

17. $x = -2, \ -4x + 4 = -4(-2) + 4 = 8 + 4 = 12$

18. $x = 5, \ x^2 - 3x + 8 = (5)^2 - 3(5) + 8 = 25 - 15 + 8 = 18$

19. $x = -2, \ -x^2 + 3x - 10 = -(-2)^2 + 3(-2) - 10$
$$= -4 - 6 - 10 = -20$$

20. $x = -1, 7x^2 + 5x - 11 = 7(-1)^2 + 5(-1) - 11$
$$= 7 - 5 - 11 = -9$$

21. $x = \dfrac{2}{3}, \dfrac{1}{2}x^2 - 5x + 2 = \dfrac{1}{2}\left(\dfrac{2}{3}\right)^2 - 5\left(\dfrac{2}{3}\right) + 2$
$$= \dfrac{1}{2}\left(\dfrac{4}{9}\right) - \dfrac{10}{3} + 2$$
$$= \dfrac{4}{18} - \dfrac{60}{18} + \dfrac{36}{18} = -\dfrac{20}{18} = -\dfrac{10}{9}$$

22. $x = \dfrac{1}{2}, \ \dfrac{2}{3}x^2 + x - 1 = \dfrac{2}{3}\left(\dfrac{1}{2}\right)^2 + \dfrac{1}{2} - 1$
$$= \dfrac{2}{3}\left(\dfrac{1}{4}\right) + \dfrac{1}{2} - 1$$
$$= \dfrac{2}{12} + \dfrac{1}{2} - 1$$
$$= \dfrac{2}{12} + \dfrac{6}{12} - \dfrac{12}{12} = -\dfrac{4}{12} = -\dfrac{1}{3}$$

23. $x = \frac{1}{2}, 8x^3 - 4x^2 + 7 = 8\left(\frac{1}{2}\right)^3 - 4\left(\frac{1}{2}\right)^2 + 7$

$$= 8\left(\frac{1}{8}\right) - 4\left(\frac{1}{4}\right) + 7$$

$$= 1 - 1 + 7 = 7$$

24. $x = 2, y = -3, -x^2 + 5xy = -(2)^2 + 5(2)(-3)$

$$= -4 - 30 = -34$$

25. $x = -2, \ y = 1, \ 2x^2 + xy + 3y^2$

$= 2(-2)^2 + (-2)(1) + 3(1)^2 = 8 - 2 + 3 = 9$

26. $x = 2, \ y = 5, \ 3x^2 + \frac{2}{5}xy - \frac{1}{5}y^2$

$$= 3(2)^2 + \frac{2}{5}(2)(5) - \frac{1}{5}(5)^2$$

$$= 12 + 4 - 5 = 11$$

27. $x = 2, \ y = -1, \ 4x^2 - 10xy + 3y^2$

$= 4(2)^2 - 10(2)(-1) + 3(-1)^2 = 16 + 20 + 3 = 39$

28. $x = 4, y = -2, (x - 2y)^2 = \left[4 - 2(-2)\right]^2$

$$= 8^2 = 64$$

29. $8x + 3 = 23, \ x = 3$

$8(3) + 3 = 24 + 3 = 27$

$27 \neq 23, x = 3$ is not a solution.

30. $5x - 7 = -27, \ x = -4$

$6(-4) - 7 = -24 - 7 = -31$

$-31 = -31, x = -4$ is a solution.

31. $x - 3y = 0, \ x = 6, \ y = 3$

$6 - 3(3) = 6 - 9 = -3$

$-3 \neq 0, x = 6, y = 3$ is not a solution.

32. $4x + 2y = -2, \ x = -2, \ y = 3$

$4(-2) + 2(3) = -8 + 6 = -2$

$-2 = -2, x = -2, y = 3$ is a solution.

33. $x^2 - 3x + 6 = 5, x = 2$

$(2)^2 - 3(2) + 6 = 4 - 6 + 6 = 4$

$4 \neq 5, x = 2$ is not a solution.

34. $-2x^2 + x + 5 = 0, x = 3$

$-2(3)^2 + 3 + 5 = -2(9) + 3 + 5 = -10$

$-10 \neq 20, x = 3$ is not a solution.

35. $2x^2 + x = 28, x = -4$

$2(-4)^2 + (-4) = 2(16) - 4 = 32 - 4 = 28$

$28 = 28, x = -4$ is a solution.

36. $y = x^2 + 4x - 5, x = -1, y = -8$

$(-1)^2 + 4(-1) - 5 = 1 - 4 - 5 = -8$

$-8 = -8, x = 1, y = -8$ is a solution.

37. $y = -x^2 + 3x - 1, \ x = 3, \ y = -1$

$-(3)^2 + 3(3) - 1 = -9 + 9 - 1 = -1$

$-1 = -1, x = 3, y = -1$ is a solution.

38. $y = x^3 - 3x^2 + 1, x = 2, y = -3$

$(2)^3 - 3(2)^2 + 1 = 8 - 12 + 1 = -3$

$-3 = -3, x = 2, y = -3$ is a solution.

39. $d = \$899, 0.07d = 0.07(\$899) = \$62.93$

40. $n = 8,000,000,000,000$

$0.000002n = 0.000002(8,000,000,000,000)$

$$= 16,000,000 \text{ sec}$$

41. 2010 is 10 years since 2000.

$6.2(10) + 34.8 = 96.8; 96.8$ million

42. $x = 75, 220 + 2.75x = 220 + 2.75(75)$

$$= 220 + 206.25 = \$426.25$$

43. $2(0.60)^2 + 80(0.60) + 40 = 0.72 + 48 + 40 = 88.72;$

88.72 min

44. $s = 72$

$0.08s^2 + 0.24s - 7.10 = 0.08(72)^2 + 0.014(72) - 7.10$

$$= 0.08(5184) + 17.28 - 7.10$$

$$= 414.72 + 17.28 - 7.10$$

$$= 424.9 \text{ ft}$$

45. $R = 2, T = 70, 0.2R^2 + 0.003RT + 0.0001T^2 = 0.2(2)^2 + 0.003(2)(70) + 0.0001(70)^2 = 0.8 + 0.42 + 0.49 = 1.71$ in.

46. $(-1)^n = 1$ for any even number, n, since there will be an even number of factors of (-1), and when these are multiplied, the product will always be 1.

47.

x	y	$(x+y)^2$	$x^2 + y^2$
2	3	$5^2 = 25$	$4+9=13$
-2	-3	$(-5)^2 = 25$	$4+9=13$
-2	3	$1^2 = 1$	$4+9=13$
2	-3	$(-1)^2 = 1$	$4+9=13$

The two expressions are not equal.

48. $1^n = 1$ for all natural numbers since 1 multiplied by itself any number of times will always be 1.

Exercise Set 6.2

1. The parts that are added or subtracted in an algebraic expression are called **terms**.
   In $3x - 2y$, the $3x$ and $-2y$ are terms.

2. **Like terms** are terms that have the same variables with the same exponents on the variables.
   $3x^2$ and $4x^2$ are like terms.

3. The numerical part of a term is called its **numerical coefficient.**
   For the term $3x$, 3 is the numerical coefficient.

4. A **linear equation** is one in which the exponent on the variable is 1. Example: $4x + 6 = 10$

5. To **simplify** an expression means to combine like terms by using the commutative, associative, and distributive properties. Example: $12 + x + 7 - 3x = x - 3x + 12 + 7 = -2x + 19$

6. If $a = b$, then $a + c = b + c$ for all real numbers a, b, and c. Example: If $x - 5 = 2$, then $x - 5 + 5 = 2 + 5$.

7. If $a = b$, then $a \cdot c = b \cdot c$ for all real numbers a, b, and c, where $c \neq 0$. Example: If $\dfrac{x}{3} = 2$, then $3\left(\dfrac{x}{3}\right) = 3(2)$.

8. If $a = b$, then $a - c = b - c$ for all real numbers a, b, and c. Example: If $2x + 3 = 5$, then $2x + 3 - 3 = 5 - 3$.

9. If $a = b$, then $\dfrac{a}{c} = \dfrac{b}{c}$ for all real numbers a, b, and c, where $c \neq 0$. Example: If $4x = 8$ then $\dfrac{4x}{4} = \dfrac{8}{4}$.

10. An **algorithm** is a general procedure for accomplishing a task.

11. A **ratio** is a quotient of two quantities. Example: $\dfrac{7}{9}$

12. A **proportion** is a statement of equality between two ratios. Example: $\dfrac{3}{7} = \dfrac{x}{10}$

13. Yes. They have the same variable and the same exponent on the variable.

14. No. They do not have the same variable.

15. $4x + 6x = 10x$

16. $-7x - 5x = -12x$

17. $5x - 3x + 12 = 2x + 12$

18. $9x - 6x + 21 = 3x + 21$

19. $7x + 3y - 4x + 8y = 3x + 11y$

20. $x - 4x + 3 = -3x + 3$

21. $-3x + 2 - 5x = -8x + 2$

22. $-3x + 4x - 2 + 5 = x + 3$

23. $2 - 3x - 2x + 1 = -5x + 3$

24. $-0.2x + 1.7x - 4 = 1.5x - 4$

25. $6.2x - 8.3 + 7.1x = 13.3x - 8.3$

26. $\dfrac{2}{3}x + \dfrac{1}{6}x - 5 = \dfrac{4}{6}x + \dfrac{1}{6}x - 5 = \dfrac{5}{6}x - 5$

27. $\dfrac{1}{5}x - \dfrac{1}{3}x - 4 = \dfrac{3}{15}x - \dfrac{5}{15}x - 4 = -\dfrac{2}{15}x - 4$

28. $7s + 4t + 9 - 2t - 2s - 15 = 7s - 2s + 4t - 2t + 9 - 15$
$= 5s + 2t - 6$

29. $6x - 4y - 5y + 4x + 3 = 6x + 4x - 4y - 5y + 3$
$$= 10x - 9y + 3$$

30. $2p - 4q - 3p + 4q - 15 = 2p - 3p - 4q + 4q - 15$
$$= -p - 15$$

31.

$$2(s + 3) + 6(s - 4) + 1 = 2s + 6 + 6s - 24 + 1 = 8s - 17$$

32. $6(r - 3) - 2(r + 5) + 10 = 6r - 18 - 2r - 10 + 10$
$$= 4r - 18$$

33. $0.2(x + 4) + 1.2(x - 3) = 0.2x + 0.8 + 1.2x - 3.6$
$$= 1.4x - 2.8$$

34. $\dfrac{3}{5}(x + 1) - \dfrac{3}{10}x = \dfrac{3}{5}x - \dfrac{3}{10}x + \dfrac{3}{5} = \dfrac{3}{10}x + \dfrac{3}{5}$

35. $\dfrac{1}{4}x + \dfrac{4}{5} - \dfrac{2}{3}x = \dfrac{3}{12}x - \dfrac{8}{12}x + \dfrac{4}{5} = -\dfrac{5}{12}x + \dfrac{4}{5}$

36. $n - \dfrac{3}{4} + \dfrac{5}{9}n - \dfrac{1}{6} = \dfrac{9}{9}n + \dfrac{5}{9}n - \dfrac{9}{12} - \dfrac{2}{12} = \dfrac{14}{9}n - \dfrac{11}{12}$

37.

$$0.5(2.6x - 4) + 2.3(1.4x - 5) = 1.3x - 2 + 3.22 - 11.5$$

$$= 4.52x - 13.5$$

38. $\dfrac{2}{3}(3x + 9) - \dfrac{1}{4}(2x + 5) = 2x + 6 - \dfrac{1}{2}x - \dfrac{5}{4}$
$$= \dfrac{4}{2}x - \dfrac{1}{2}x + \dfrac{24}{4} - \dfrac{5}{4} = \dfrac{3}{2}x + \dfrac{19}{4}$$

39.
$$y - 7 = 10$$
$$y - 7 + 7 = 10 + 7 \qquad \text{Add 7 to both sides of the equation.}$$
$$y = 17$$

40.
$$3y + 6 = 24$$
$$3y + 6 - 6 = 24 - 6 \qquad \text{Subtract 6 from both sides of the equation.}$$
$$3y = 18$$
$$\dfrac{3y}{3} = \dfrac{18}{3} \qquad \text{Divide both sides of the equation by 3.}$$
$$y = 6$$

41.
$$15 = 9 - 6$$
$$6 = -6x \qquad \text{Subtract 9 from both sides of the equation.}$$
$$\dfrac{-3}{-6} = \dfrac{-6x}{-6} \qquad \text{Divide both sides of the equation by } -6.$$
$$-1 = x$$

42.
$$18 = 8 + 2x$$
$$18 - 8 = 8 - 8 + 2x \qquad \text{Subtract 8 from both sides of the equation.}$$
$$10 = 2x$$
$$\dfrac{10}{2} = \dfrac{2x}{2} \qquad \text{Divide both sides of the equation by 2.}$$
$$5 = x$$

43.
$$\dfrac{3}{x} = \dfrac{7}{8}$$
$$3(8) = 7x \qquad \text{Cross multiplication}$$
$$24 = 7x$$
$$\dfrac{24}{7} = \dfrac{7x}{7} \qquad \text{Divide both sides of the equation by 7.}$$
$$\dfrac{24}{7} = x$$

44.
$$\frac{x-1}{5} = \frac{x+5}{15}$$

$15(x-1) = 5(x+5)$ Cross multiplication

$15x - 15 = 5x + 25$ Distributive Property

$15x - 5x - 15 = 5x - 5x + 25$ Subtract $5x$ from both sides of the equation.

$10x - 15 = 25$

$10x - 15 + 15 = 25 + 15$ Add 15 to both sides of the equation.

$10x = 40$

$$\frac{10x}{10} = \frac{40}{10}$$ Divide both sides of the equation by 10.

$x = 4$

45.
$$\frac{1}{2}x + \frac{1}{3} = \frac{2}{3}$$

$$6\left(\frac{1}{2}x + \frac{1}{3}\right) = 6\left(\frac{2}{3}\right)$$ Multiply both sides of the equation by the LCD.

$3x + 2 = 4$ Distributive Property

$3x + 2 - 2 = 4 - 2$ Subtract 2 from both sides of the equation.

$3x = 2$

$$\frac{3x}{3} = \frac{2}{3}$$ Divide both sides of the equation by 3.

$$x = \frac{2}{3}$$

46.
$$\frac{1}{2}y + \frac{1}{3} = \frac{1}{4}$$

$$12\left(\frac{1}{2}y + \frac{1}{3}\right) = 12\left(\frac{1}{4}\right)$$ Multiply both sides of the equation by the LCD.

$6y + 4 = 3$ Distributive Property

$6y + 4 - 4 = 3 - 4$ Subtract 4 from both sides of the equation.

$6y = -1$

$$\frac{6y}{6} = \frac{-1}{6}$$ Divide both sides of the equation by 6.

$$y = -\frac{1}{6}$$

47.
$0.9x - 1.2 = 2.4$

$0.9x + 1.2 - 1.2 = 2.4 + 1.2$ Add 1.2 to both sides of the equation.

$0.9x = 3.6$

$$\frac{0.9x}{0.9} = \frac{3.6}{0.9}$$ Divide both sides of the equation by 0.9.

$x = 4$

48.
$$5x + 0.050 = -0.732$$
$$5x + 0.050 - 0.050 = -0.732 - 0.050 \quad \text{Subtract 0.050 from both sides of the equation.}$$
$$5x = -0.782$$
$$\frac{5x}{5} = \frac{-0.782}{5} \quad \text{Divide both sides of the equation by 5.}$$
$$x = -0.1564$$

49.
$$6t - 8 = 4t - 2$$
$$6t - 4t - 8 = 4t - 4t - 2 \quad \text{Subtract } 4t \text{ from both sides of the equation.}$$
$$2t - 8 = -2$$
$$2t - 8 + 8 = -2 + 8 \quad \text{Add 8 to both sides of the equation.}$$
$$2t = 6$$
$$\frac{2t}{2} = \frac{6}{2} \quad \text{Divide both sides of the equation by 2.}$$
$$t = 3$$

50.
$$\frac{x}{4} + 2x = \frac{1}{3}$$
$$12\left(\frac{x}{4} + 2x\right) = 12\left(\frac{1}{3}\right) \quad \text{Mulitply both sides of the equation by the LCD.}$$
$$3x + 24x = 4 \quad \text{Distributive Property}$$
$$27x = 4$$
$$\frac{27x}{27} = \frac{4}{27} \quad \text{Divide both sides of the equation by 27.}$$
$$x = \frac{4}{27}$$

51.
$$\frac{x-3}{2} = \frac{x+4}{3}$$
$$3(x-3) = 2(x+4) \quad \text{Cross multiplication}$$
$$3x - 9 = 2x + 8 \quad \text{Distributive Property}$$
$$3x - 2x - 9 = 2x - 2x + 8 \quad \text{Subtract } 2x \text{ from both sides of the equation.}$$
$$x - 9 = 8$$
$$x - 9 + 9 = 8 + 9 \quad \text{Add 9 to both sides of the equation.}$$
$$x = 17$$

52.
$$\frac{x-5}{4} = \frac{x-9}{3}$$
$$3(x-5) = 4(x-9) \quad \text{Cross multiplication}$$
$$3x - 15 = 4x - 36 \quad \text{Distributive Property}$$
$$3x - 3x - 15 = 4x - 3x - 36 \quad \text{Subtract } 3x \text{ from both sides of the equation.}$$
$$-15 = x - 36$$
$$-15 + 36 = x - 36 + 36 \quad \text{Add 36 to both sides of the equation.}$$
$$21 = x$$

53.
$$6t - 7 = 8t + 9$$
$$6t - 6t - 7 = 8t - 6t + 9$$ Subtract $6t$ from both sides of the equation.
$$-7 = 2t + 9$$
$$-7 - 9 = 2t + 9 - 9$$ Subtract 9 from both sides of the equation.
$$-16 = 2t$$
$$\frac{-16}{2} = \frac{2t}{2}$$ Divide both sides of the equation by 2.
$$-8 = t$$

54.
$$12x - 1.2 = 3x + 1.5$$
$$12x - 3x - 1.2 = 3x - 3x + 1.5$$ Subtract $3x$ from both sides of the equation.
$$9x - 1.2 = 1.5$$
$$9x - 1.2 + 1.2 = 1.5 + 1.2$$ Add 1.2 to both sides of the equation.
$$9x = 2.7$$
$$\frac{9x}{9} = \frac{2.7}{9}$$ Divide both sides of the equation by 9.
$$x = 0.3$$

55.
$$2(x + 3) - 4 = 2(x - 4)$$
$$2x + 6 - 4 = 2x - 8$$ Distributive Property
$$2x + 2 = 2x - 8$$
$$2x - 2x + 2 = 2x - 2x - 8$$ Subtract $2x$ from both sides of the equation.
$$2 = -8$$ False
No solution

56.
$$3(x + 2) + 2(x - 1) = 5x - 7$$
$$3x + 6 + 2x - 2 = 5x - 7$$ Distributive Property
$$5x + 4 = 5x - 7$$
$$5x - 5x + 4 = 5x - 5x - 7$$ Subtract $5x$ from both sides of the equation.
$$4 = -7$$ False
No solution

57.
$$4(x - 4) + 12 = 4(x - 1)$$
$$4x - 16 + 12 = 4x - 4$$ Distributive Property
$$4x - 4 = 4x - 4$$

This equation is an identity. Therefore, the solution is all real numbers.

58.
$$6(t + 2) - 14 = 6t - 2$$
$$6t + 12 - 14 = 6t - 2$$ Distributive Property
$$6t - 2 = 6t - 2$$ Combine like terms.

This equation is an identity. Therefore, the solution is all real numbers

59.

$$\frac{1}{3}(x+3) = \frac{2}{5}(x+2)$$

$$15\left(\frac{1}{3}\right)(x+3) = 15\left(\frac{2}{5}\right)(x+2)$$ Multiply both sides of the equation by the LCD.

$$5(x+3) = 6(x+2)$$

$$5x+15 = 6x+12$$ Distributive Property

$$5x-5x+15 = 6x-5x+12$$ Subtract $5x$ from both sides of the equation.

$$15 = x+12$$

$$15-12 = x+12-12$$ Subtract 12 from both sides of the equation.

$$3 = x$$

60.

$$\frac{2}{3}(x-4) = \frac{1}{4}(x+1)$$

$$12\left(\frac{2}{3}\right)(x-4) = 12\left(\frac{1}{4}\right)(x+1)$$ Multiply both sides of the equation by the LCD.

$$8(x-4) = 3(x+1)$$

$$8x-32 = 3x+3$$ Distributive Property

$$8x-3x-32 = 3x-3x+3$$ Subtract $3x$ from both sides of the equation.

$$5x-32 = 3$$

$$5x-32+32 = 3+32$$ Add 32 to both sides of the equation.

$$5x = 35$$

$$\frac{5x}{5} = \frac{35}{5}$$ Divide both sides of the equation by 5.

$$x = 7$$

61.

$$3x+2-6x = -x-15+8-5x$$

$$-3x+2 = -6x-7$$

$$-3x+6x+2 = -6x+6x-7$$ Add $6x$ to both sides of the equation.

$$3x+2 = -7$$

$$3x+2-2 = -7-2$$ Subtract 2 from both sides of the equation.

$$3x = -9$$

$$\frac{3x}{3} = \frac{-9}{3}$$ Divide both sides of the equation by 3.

$$x = -3$$

62.

$$6x+8-22x = 28+14x-10+12x$$

$$-16x+8 = 26x+18$$

$$-16x-26x+8 = 26x-26x+18$$ Subtract $26x$ from both sides of the equation.

$$-42x+8 = 18$$

$$-42x+8-8 = 18-8$$ Subtract 8 from both sides of the equation.

$$-42x = 10$$

$$\frac{-42x}{-42} = \frac{10}{-42}$$ Divide both sides of the equation by -42.

$$x = -\frac{10}{42} = -\frac{5}{21}$$

63.
$$4(t-3)+8=4(2t-6)$$
$$4t-12+8=8t-24 \qquad \text{Distributive Property}$$
$$4t-4=8t-24$$
$$4t-4t-4=8t-4t-24 \qquad \text{Subtract } 4t \text{ from both sides of the equation.}$$
$$-4=4t-24$$
$$-4+24=4t-24+24 \qquad \text{Add 24 to both sides of the equation.}$$
$$20=4t$$
$$\frac{20}{4}=\frac{4t}{4} \qquad \text{Divide both sides of the equation by 4.}$$
$$5=t$$

64.
$$8.3y-3.1(y-4)=29.04$$
$$8.3y-3.1y+12.4=29.04 \qquad \text{Distributive Property}$$
$$5.2y+12.4=29.04$$
$$5.2y+12.4-12.4=29.04-12.4 \qquad \text{Subtract 12.4 from both sides of the equation.}$$
$$5.2y=16.64$$
$$\frac{5.2y}{5.2}=\frac{16.64}{5.2} \qquad \text{Divide both sides of the equation by 5.2.}$$
$$y=3.2$$

65.
$$\frac{7.75}{1000}=\frac{x}{27,000}$$
$$7.75(27,000)=1000x$$
$$\frac{7.75(27,000)}{1000}=\frac{1000x}{1000}$$
$$7.75(27)=x$$
$$x=\$209.95$$

66.
$$\frac{7.75}{1000}=\frac{200}{x}$$
$$7.75x=(200)(1000)$$
$$\frac{7.75x}{7.75}=\frac{200,000}{7.75}$$
$$x\approx 25,806 \text{ gal}$$

67.
$$\frac{x}{1440}=\frac{1}{360}$$
$$360x=1440$$
$$\frac{360x}{360}=\frac{1440}{360}$$
$$x=4 \text{ gallons}$$

68. a)
$$\frac{6}{9}=\frac{16}{x}$$
$$6x=9(16)$$
$$6x=144$$
$$\frac{6x}{6}=\frac{144}{6}$$
$$x=24 \text{ oz}$$

b)
$$\frac{x}{32}=\frac{6}{16}$$
$$16x=32(6)$$
$$16x=192$$
$$\frac{16x}{16}=\frac{192}{16}$$
$$x=12 \text{ servings}$$

69.
$$\frac{1}{1,102,000} = \frac{14.4}{x}$$
$$x = 1,102,000(14.4)$$
$$x = 15,868,800 \text{ households}$$

70. a)
$$\frac{40}{12} = \frac{x}{480}$$
$$40(480) = 12x$$
$$\frac{40(480)}{12} = \frac{12x}{12}$$
$$x = 1600 \text{ lb}$$

b)
$$\frac{480}{12} = 40 \text{ bags}$$

71. a)
$$\frac{50}{80} = \frac{1}{x}$$
$$50x = 80$$
$$\frac{50x}{50} = \frac{80}{50}$$
$$x = 1.6 \text{ kph}$$

b)
$$\frac{50}{80} = \frac{x}{90}$$
$$80x = 50(90)$$
$$80x = 4500$$
$$\frac{80x}{80} = \frac{4500}{80}$$
$$x = 56.25 \text{ mph}$$

72.
$$\frac{40}{0.6} = \frac{250}{x}$$
$$40x = 0.6(250)$$
$$40x = 150$$
$$\frac{40x}{40} = \frac{150}{40}$$
$$x = 3.75 \text{ m}\ell$$

73.
$$\frac{40}{1} = \frac{15}{x}$$
$$40x = 15$$
$$\frac{40x}{40} = \frac{15}{40}$$
$$x = 0.375 \text{ cc}$$

74.
$$\frac{40}{1} = \frac{35}{x}$$
$$40x = 35$$
$$\frac{40x}{40} = \frac{35}{40}$$
$$x = 0.875 \text{ cc}$$

75. a) Answers will vary.

b)

$$2(x+3) = 4x + 3 - 5x$$

$2x + 6 = -x + 3$	Distributive Property
$2x + x + 6 = -x + x + 3$	Add x to both sides of the equation.
$3x + 6 = 3$	
$3x + 6 - 6 = 3 - 6$	Subtract 6 from both sides of the equation.
$3x = -3$	
$\dfrac{3x}{3} = \dfrac{-3}{3}$	Divide both sides of the equation by 3.
$x = -1$	

76. a) An **identity** is an equation that has an infinite number of solutions.

b) When solving an equation, if you have the same expressions on both sides of the equal sign, the equation is an identity.

77. a) An **inconsistent equation** is an equation that has no solution.

    b) When solving an equation, if you obtain a false statement, then the equation is inconsistent.

78. a) $P = 14.70 + 0.43x$

$148 = 14.70 + 0.43x$ Given $P = 148$, find x.

$148 - 14.70 = 14.70 - 14.70 + 0.43x$ Subtract 14.70 from both sides of the equation.

$133.3 = 0.43x$

$\dfrac{133.3}{0.43} = \dfrac{0.43x}{0.43}$ Divide both sides of the equation by 0.43.

$x = 310$ ft

    b) $P = 14.70 + 0.43x$

$128.65 = 14.70 + 0.43x$ Given $P = 128.65$, find x.

$128.65 - 14.70 = 14.70 - 14.70 + 0.43x$ Subtract 14.70 from both sides of the equation.

$113.95 = 0.43x$

$\dfrac{113.95}{0.43} = \dfrac{0.43x}{0.43}$ Divide both sides of the equation by 0.43.

$x = 265$ ft down

79. a) 2:5; There are $2x$ males and a total of $2x + 3x = 5x$ students.

    b) $m : m + n$

80. a) Yes (multiply the first equation on both sides by 18, and you get the second equation).

    b) Yes (multiply the second equation by 4 on both sides and you get the first equation).

Exercise Set 6.3

1. A **formula** is an equation that typically has a real-life application.
2. To **evaluate a formula**, substitute the given values for their respective variables, then evaluate.
3. **Subscripts** are numbers (or letters) placed below and to the right of variables. They are used to help clarify a formula.
4. $i = prt$
5. An **exponential equation** is of the form $y = a^x, a > 0, a \neq 1$.
6. a) $a > 0, a \neq 1$

    b) P_0 represents the original amount present.

7. $A = lw = 4(14) = 56$ 8. $P = a + b + c = 25 + 53 + 32 = 110$

9. $P = 2l + 2w$ 10. $F = ma$

    $P = 2(12) + 2(16) = 24 + 32 = 56$ $40 = m(5)$

                                                 $\dfrac{40}{5} = \dfrac{5m}{5}$

                                                   $8 = m$

11. $K = \dfrac{1}{2}mv^2$

$4500 = \dfrac{1}{2}m(30)^2$

$4500 = 450m$

$\dfrac{4500}{450} = \dfrac{450m}{450}$

$10 = m$

12. $p = i^2r$

$62{,}500 = (5)^2\, r$

$62{,}500 = 25r$

$\dfrac{62{,}500}{25} = \dfrac{25r}{25}$

$2500 = r$

13. $S = \pi r(r+h)$

$S = 3.14(8)(8+2)$

$S = 3.14(8)(10)$

$S = 3.14(80)$

$S = 251.2$

14. $B = \dfrac{703w}{h^2}$

$B = \dfrac{703(130)}{(67)^2}$

$B = \dfrac{91{,}390}{4489} = 20.35865449 \approx 20.36$

15. $z = \dfrac{x-\mu}{\sigma}$

$\dfrac{2.5}{1} = \dfrac{42.1-\mu}{2}$

$2.5(2) = 42.1-\mu$

$5 = 42.1-\mu$

$5 - 42.1 = 42.1 - 42.1 - \mu$

$-37.1 = -\mu$

$\dfrac{-37.1}{-1} = \dfrac{-\mu}{-1}$

$37.1 = \mu$

16. $S = 2hw + 2lw + 2lh$

$122 = 2(4)(3) + 2l(3) + 2l(4)$

$122 = 24 + 14l$

$122 - 24 = 24 - 24 + 14l$

$98 = 14l$

$\dfrac{98}{14} = \dfrac{14l}{14}$

$7 = l$

17. $T = \dfrac{PV}{k}$

$\dfrac{80}{1} = \dfrac{P(20)}{0.5}$

$80(0.5) = 20P$

$40 = 20P$

$\dfrac{40}{20} = \dfrac{20P}{20}$

$2 = P$

18. $m = \dfrac{a+b+c}{3}$

$70 = \dfrac{a+60+90}{3}$

$\dfrac{70}{1} = \dfrac{a+150}{3}$

$70(3) = a+150$

$210 = a+150$

$210 - 150 = a + 150 - 150$

$60 = a$

19. $A = P(1+rt)$

$3600 = P(1+0.04(5))$

$3600 = P(1+0.2)$

$3600 = 1.2P$

$\dfrac{3600}{1.2} = \dfrac{1.2P}{1.2}$

$3000 = P$

20. $m = \dfrac{a+b}{2}$

$70 = \dfrac{a+77}{2}$

$70(2) = a+77$

$140 = a+77$

$140 - 77 = a + 77 - 77$

$63 = a$

21.
$$V = \frac{1}{2}at^2$$
$$576 = \frac{1}{2}a(12)^2$$
$$\frac{576}{1} = \frac{144a}{2}$$
$$576(2) = 144a$$
$$1152 = 144a$$
$$\frac{1152}{144} = \frac{144a}{144}$$
$$8 = a$$

22.
$$F = \frac{9}{5}C + 32$$
$$F = \frac{9}{5}(7) + 32$$
$$F = \frac{63}{5} + 32 = 12.6 + 32 = 44.6$$

23.
$$C = \frac{5}{9}(F - 32)$$
$$C = \frac{5}{9}(77 - 32)$$
$$C = \frac{5}{9}(45) = 25$$

24.
$$K = \frac{F - 32}{1.8} + 273.1$$
$$K = \frac{100 - 32}{1.8} + 273.1$$
$$K = \frac{68}{1.8} + 273.1$$
$$K = 37.\overline{7} + 273.1 = 310.8\overline{7} \approx 310.88$$

25.
$$m = \frac{y_2 - y_1}{x_2 - x_1}$$
$$m = \frac{8 - (-4)}{-3 - (-5)}$$
$$m = \frac{8 + 4}{-3 + 5} = \frac{12}{2} = 6$$

26.
$$z = \frac{\overline{x} - \mu}{\frac{\sigma}{\sqrt{n}}}$$
$$z = \frac{66 - 60}{\frac{15}{\sqrt{25}}}$$
$$z = \frac{6}{\frac{15}{5}} = \frac{6}{3} = 2$$

27.
$$S = R - rR$$
$$186 = 1R - 0.07R$$
$$186 = 0.93R$$
$$\frac{186}{0.93} = \frac{0.93R}{0.93}$$
$$200 = R$$

28.
$$S = C + rC$$
$$115 = 1C + 0.15C$$
$$115 = 1.15C$$
$$\frac{115}{1.15} = \frac{1.15C}{1.15}$$
$$100 = C$$

29.
$$E = a_1p_1 + a_2p_2 + a_3p_3$$
$$E = 5(0.2) + 7(0.6) + 10(0.2)$$
$$E = 1 + 4.2 + 2 = 7.2$$

30.
$$x = \frac{-b + \sqrt{b^2 - 4ac}}{2a}$$
$$x = \frac{-(-5) + \sqrt{(-5)^2 - 4(2)(-12)}}{2(2)}$$
$$x = \frac{5 + \sqrt{25 + 96}}{4}$$
$$x = \frac{5 + \sqrt{121}}{4} = \frac{5 + 11}{4} = \frac{16}{4} = 4$$

31.
$$s = -16t^2 + v_0t + s_0$$
$$s = -16(4)^2 + 30(4) + 150$$
$$s = -16(16) + 120 + 150$$
$$s = -256 + 120 + 150 = 14$$

32.
$$R = O + (V - D)r$$
$$670 = O + (100 - 10)(4)$$
$$670 = O + 360$$
$$670 - 360 = O + 360 - 360$$
$$310 = O$$

33.
$$P = \frac{f}{1+i}$$
$$3000 = \frac{f}{1+0.08}$$
$$\frac{3000}{1} = \frac{f}{1.08}$$
$$3000(1.08) = f$$
$$3240 = f$$

34.
$$Q_w = m_w c_w (T_f - T_w)$$
$$Q_w = (0.5)(4186)(22 - 19)$$
$$Q_w = (0.5)(4186)(3)$$
$$Q_w = 6279$$

35.
$$R_T = \frac{R_1 R_2}{R_1 + R_2}$$
$$R_T = \frac{(100)(200)}{100 + 200}$$
$$R_T = \frac{20,000}{300}$$
$$R_T = 66.67$$

36.
$$P = \frac{nRT}{V}$$
$$12 = \frac{(10)(60)(8)}{V}$$
$$\frac{12}{1} = \frac{4800}{V}$$
$$12V = 4800$$
$$\frac{12V}{12} = \frac{4800}{12}$$
$$V = 400$$

37.
$$a_n = a_1 + (n-1)d$$
$$a_n = 15 + (4-1)(8)$$
$$a_n = 15 + 24$$
$$a_n = 39$$

38.
$$A = P\left(1 + \frac{r}{n}\right)^{nt}$$
$$A = 100\left(1 + \frac{0.06}{1}\right)^{1(3)}$$
$$A = 100(1 + 0.06)^3$$
$$A = 100(1.06)^3$$
$$A = 100(1.191016)$$
$$A = 119.1016 \approx 119.10$$

39.
$$P = P_0 e^{kt}$$
$$P = 5000 e^{(0.06)(7)}$$
$$P = 5000 e^{0.42}$$
$$P \approx 7609.81$$

40.
$$S = S_0 e^{-0.028t}$$
$$S = 1000 e^{-0.028(35)}$$
$$S = 1000 e^{-0.98}$$
$$S \approx 375.31$$

41.
$$4x - 9y = 14$$
$$4x - 4x - 9y = -4x + 14 \qquad \text{Subtract } 4x \text{ from both sides of the equation.}$$
$$-9y = -4x + 4$$
$$\frac{-9y}{-9} = \frac{-4x + 14}{-9} \qquad \text{Divide both sides of the equation by } -9.$$
$$y = \frac{-4x + 14}{-9} = \frac{-(-4x + 14)}{9}$$
$$= \frac{4x - 14}{9} = \frac{4}{9}x - \frac{14}{9}$$

42. $11x - 15y = 23$

$11x - 11x - 15y = -11x + 23$ Subtract $11x$ from both sides of the equation.

$-15y = -11x + 23$

$\dfrac{-15y}{-15} = \dfrac{-11x + 23}{-15}$ Divide both sides of the equation by -15.

$y = \dfrac{-11x + 23}{-15} = \dfrac{11}{15}x - \dfrac{23}{15}$

43. $8x + 7y = 21$

$-8x + 8x + 7y = -8x + 21$ Subtract $8x$ from both sides of the equation.

$7y = -8x + 21$

$\dfrac{7y}{7} = \dfrac{-8x + 21}{7}$ Divide both sides of the equation by 7.

$y = \dfrac{-8x + 21}{7} = \dfrac{-8x}{7} + \dfrac{21}{7} = -\dfrac{8}{7}x + 3$

44. $-9x + 4y = 11$

$-9x + 9x + 4y = 9x + 11$ Add $9x$ to both sides of the equation.

$4y = 9x + 11$

$\dfrac{4y}{4} = \dfrac{9x + 11}{4}$ Divide both sides of the equation by 4.

$y = \dfrac{9x + 11}{4} = \dfrac{9x}{4} + \dfrac{11}{4} = \dfrac{9}{4}x + \dfrac{11}{4}$

45. $2x - 3y + 6 = 0$

$2x - 3y + 6 - 6 = 0 - 6$ Subtract 6 from both sides of the equation.

$2x - 3y = -6$

$-2x + 2x - 3y = -2x - 6$ Subtract $2x$ from both sides of the equation.

$-3y = -2x - 6$

$\dfrac{-3y}{-3} = \dfrac{-2x - 6}{-3}$ Divide both sides of the equation by -3.

$y = \dfrac{-2x - 6}{-3} = \dfrac{-(-2x - 6)}{3} = \dfrac{2x + 6}{3} = \dfrac{2x}{3} + \dfrac{6}{3} = \dfrac{2}{3}x + 2$

46. $3x + 4y = 0$

$-3x + 3x + 4y = -3x + 0$ Subtract $3x$ from boths sides of the equation.

$4y = -3x$

$\dfrac{4y}{4} = \dfrac{-3x}{4}$ Divide both sides of the equation by 4.

$y = -\dfrac{3}{4}x$

47.

$$-2x+3y+z=15$$

$$-2x+2x+3y+z=2x+15$$ Add $2x$ to both sides of the equation.

$$3y+z=2x+15$$

$$3y+z-z=2x-z+15$$ Subtract z from both sides of the equation.

$$3y=2x-z+15$$

$$\frac{3y}{3}=\frac{2x-z+15}{3}$$ Divide both sides of the equation by 3.

$$y=\frac{2x-z+15}{3}=\frac{2}{3}x-\frac{1}{3}z+5$$

48.

$$5x+3y-2z=22$$

$$5x-5x+3y-2z=-5x+22$$ Subtract $5x$ from both sides of the equation.

$$3y-2z=-5x+22$$

$$3y-2z+2z=-5x+2z+22$$ Add $2z$ to both sides of the equation.

$$3y=-5x+2z+22$$

$$\frac{3y}{3}=\frac{-5x+2z+22}{3}$$ Divide both sides of the equation by 3.

$$y=\frac{-5x+2z+22}{3}=-\frac{5}{3}x+\frac{2}{3}z+\frac{22}{3}$$

49.

$$9x+4z=7+8y$$

$$9x+4z-7=7-7+8y$$ Subtract 7 from both sides of the equation.

$$9x+4z-7=8y$$

$$\frac{9x+4z-7}{8}=\frac{8y}{8}$$ Divide both sides of the equation by 8.

$$y=\frac{9x+4z-7}{8}=\frac{9}{8}x+\frac{1}{2}z-\frac{7}{8}$$

50.

$$2x-3y+5z=0$$

$$2x-3y+3y+5z=0+3y$$ Add $3y$ to both sides of the equation.

$$2x+5z=3y$$

$$\frac{2x+5z}{3}=\frac{3y}{3}$$ Divide both sides of the equation by 3.

$$y=\frac{2x+5z}{3}=\frac{2}{3}x+\frac{5}{3}z$$

51.

$$d=rt$$

$$\frac{d}{t}=\frac{rt}{t}$$ Divide both sides of the equation by t.

$$r=\frac{d}{t}$$

52.

$$V=lwh$$

$$\frac{V}{lh}=\frac{lwh}{lh}$$ Divide both sides of the equation by lh.

$$w=\frac{V}{lh}$$

53.
$$p = a + b + c$$
$$p - b = a + b - b + c$$ Subtract b from both sides of the equation.
$$p - b = a + c$$
$$p - b - c = a + c - c$$ Subtract c from both sides of the equation.
$$a = p - b - c$$

54.
$$p = a + b + s_1 + s_2$$
$$p - a = a - a + b + s_1 + s_2$$ Subtract a from both sides of the equation.
$$p - a = b + s_1 + s_2$$
$$p - a - b = b - b + s_1 + s_2$$ Subtract b from both sides of the equation.
$$p - a - b = s_1 + s_2$$
$$p - a - b - s_2 = s_1 + s_2 - s_2$$ Subtract s_2 from both sides of the equation.
$$s_1 = p - a - b - s_2$$

55.
$$V = \frac{1}{3} Bh$$
$$3V = 3\left(\frac{1}{3} Bh\right)$$ Multiply both sides of the equation by 3.
$$3V = Bh$$
$$\frac{3V}{h} = \frac{Bh}{h}$$ Divide both sides of the equation by h.
$$B = \frac{3V}{h}$$

56.
$$V = \pi r^2 h$$
$$\frac{V}{\pi} = \frac{\pi r^2 h}{\pi}$$ Divide both sides of the equation by π.
$$\frac{V}{\pi} = r^2 h$$
$$\frac{V}{\pi r^2} = \frac{r^2 h}{r^2}$$ Divide both sides of the equation by r^2.
$$h = \frac{V}{\pi r^2}$$

57.
$$C = 2\pi r$$
$$\frac{C}{2} = \frac{2\pi r}{2}$$ Divide both sides of the equation by 2.
$$\frac{C}{2} = \pi r$$
$$\frac{C}{2\pi} = \frac{\pi r}{\pi}$$ Divide both sides of the equation by π.
$$r = \frac{C}{2\pi}$$

58.
$$y = mx + b$$
$$y - b = mx + b - b \qquad \text{Subtract } b \text{ from both sides of the equation.}$$
$$y - b = mx$$
$$\frac{y - b}{x} = \frac{mx}{x} \qquad \text{Divide both sides of the equation by } x.$$
$$m = \frac{y - b}{x}$$

59.
$$y = mx + b$$
$$y - mx = mx - mx + b \qquad \text{Subtract } mx \text{ from both sides of the equation.}$$
$$b = y - mx$$

60.
$$V = \frac{1}{3}\pi r^2 h$$
$$\frac{V}{\frac{1}{3}\pi r^2} = \frac{\frac{1}{3}\pi r^2 h}{\frac{1}{3}\pi r^2} \qquad \text{Divide both sides of the equation by } \frac{1}{3}\pi r^2.$$
$$h = \frac{3V}{\pi r^2}$$

61.
$$P = 2l + 2w$$
$$P - 2l = 2l - 2l + 2w \qquad \text{Subtract } 2l \text{ from both sides of the equation.}$$
$$P - 2l = 2w$$
$$\frac{P - 2l}{2} = \frac{2w}{2} \qquad \text{Divide both sides of the equation by } 2.$$
$$w = \frac{P - 2l}{2}$$

62.
$$A = \frac{d_1 d_2}{2}$$
$$2A = 2\left(\frac{d_1 d_2}{2}\right) \qquad \text{Multiply both sides of the equation by } 2.$$
$$2A = d_1 d_2$$
$$\frac{2A}{d_1} = \frac{d_1 d_2}{d_1} \qquad \text{Divide both sides of the equation by } d_1.$$
$$d_2 = \frac{2A}{d_1}$$

63.
$$A = \frac{a + b + c}{3}$$
$$3A = 3\left(\frac{a + b + c}{3}\right) \qquad \text{Multiply both sides of the equation by } 3.$$
$$3A = a + b + c$$
$$3A - a = a - a + b + c \qquad \text{Subtract } a \text{ from both sides of the equation.}$$
$$3A - a = b + c$$
$$3A - a - b = b - b + c \qquad \text{Subtract } b \text{ from both sides of the equation.}$$
$$c = 3A - a - b$$

64. $$\frac{w_1}{w_2} = \frac{f_2 - f}{f - f_1}$$

$$w_1 = \frac{w_2(f_2 - f)}{f - f_1}$$ Multiply both sides of the equation by w_2.

65. $$P = \frac{KT}{V}$$

$$PV = \left(\frac{KT}{V}\right)V$$ Multiply both sides of the equation by V.

$$PV = KT$$

$$\frac{PV}{K} = \frac{KT}{K}$$ Divide both sides of the equation by K.

$$T = \frac{PV}{K}$$

66. $$\frac{P_1V_1}{T_1} = \frac{P_2V_2}{T_2}$$

$$P_1V_1T_2 = P_2V_2T_1$$ Cross multiplication

$$\frac{P_1V_1T_2}{T_1} = \frac{P_2V_2T_1}{T_1}$$ Divide both sides of the equation by T_1.

$$\frac{P_1V_1T_2}{T_1} = P_2V_2$$

$$\frac{P_1V_1T_2}{T_1P_2} = \frac{P_2V_2}{P_2}$$ Divide both sides of the equation by P_2.

$$V_2 = \frac{P_1V_1T_2}{T_1P_2}$$

67. $$F = \frac{9}{5}C + 32$$

$$F - 32 = \frac{9}{5}C + 32 - 32$$ Subtract 32 from both sides of the equation.

$$F - 32 = \frac{9}{5}C$$

$$\frac{5}{9}(F - 32) = \frac{5}{9}\left(\frac{9}{5}C\right)$$ Multiply both sides of the equation by $\frac{5}{9}$.

$$C = \frac{5}{9}(F - 32)$$

68. $$C = \frac{5}{9}(F - 32)$$

$$\frac{9}{5}C = \frac{9}{5}\left(\frac{5}{9}\right)(F - 32)$$ Multiply both sides of the equation by $\frac{9}{5}$.

$$\frac{9}{5}C = F - 32$$

$$\frac{9}{5}C + 32 = F - 32 + 32$$ Add 32 to both sides of the equation.

$$F = \frac{9}{5}C + 32$$

69.
$$S = 2\pi rh + 2\pi r^2$$
$$S - 2\pi r^2 = 2\pi rh + 2\pi r^2 - 2\pi r^2 \qquad \text{Subtract } 2\pi r^2 \text{ from both sides of the equation.}$$
$$S - 2\pi r^2 = 2\pi rh$$
$$\frac{S - 2\pi r^2}{2\pi r} = \frac{2\pi rh}{2\pi r} \qquad \text{Divide both sides of the equation by } 2\pi r.$$
$$\frac{S - 2\pi r^2}{2\pi r} = h$$

70.
$$A = \frac{1}{2}h(b_1 + b_2)$$
$$2A = 2\left[\frac{1}{2}h(b_1 + b_2)\right] \qquad \text{Multiply both sides of the equation by 2.}$$
$$2A = h(b_1 + b_2)$$
$$\frac{2A}{h} = \frac{h(b_1 + b_2)}{h} \qquad \text{Divide both sides of the equation by } h.$$
$$\frac{2A}{h} = b_1 + b_2$$
$$\frac{2A}{h} - b_1 = b_1 - b_1 + b_2 \qquad \text{Subtract } b_1 \text{ from both sides of the equation.}$$
$$b_2 = \frac{2A}{h} - b_1$$

71. a) $i = prt$
$$i = 4500(0.025)(1) = \$112.50$$
  b) $\$4500 + \$112.50 = \$4612.50$

72.
$$i = prt$$
$$128 = 800(r)(2)$$
$$128 = 1600r$$
$$\frac{128}{1600} = \frac{1600r}{1600}$$
$$r = 0.08 = 8\%$$

73. Radius $= 1$ in.

$$V = \frac{1}{3}\pi r^2 h$$

$$V = \frac{1}{3}\pi(1)^2(4)$$

$$V = \frac{1}{3}\pi(4)$$

$$V \approx 4.19 \text{ in.}^3$$

74. a) $6 \text{ ft} = 6(12) = 72$ in.

$$B = \frac{703w}{h^2}$$

$$B = \frac{703(200)}{(72)^2}$$

$$B = \frac{140,600}{5184} = 27.12191358 \approx 27.12$$

b)

$$B = \frac{703w}{h^2}$$

$$26 = \frac{703w}{(72)^2}$$

$$26 = \frac{703w}{5184}$$

$$134,784 = 703w$$

$$\frac{134,784}{703} = \frac{703w}{703}$$

$$w = 191.7268848 \text{ lb}$$

He would have to lose $200 - 191.7268848$

$$= 8.2731152 \approx 8.27 \text{ lb}$$

75. $y = 2000(3)^x$

$y = 2000(3)^5$

$y = 2000(243)$

$y = 486,000$ bacteria

76. $P_n = P(1+r)^n$

$P_n = 8(1+0.03)^{10}$

$P_n = 8(1.03)^{10}$

$P_n = 8(1.343916379)$

$P_n = \$10.75133103 \approx \$10.75$

77. $V = 24e^{0.08t}$

$V = 24e^{0.08(382)}$

$V = 24e^{30.56}$

$V \approx \$4.49 \times 10^{14}$

78. $R = R_0 e^{-0.000428t}$

$R = 10e^{-0.000428(1000)}$

$R \approx 6.52$ g

79. $V = lwh - \pi r^2 h$

$V = 12(8)(12) - \pi(2)^2(8)$

$V = 1152 - 100.5309649$

$V = 1051.469035 \text{ in.}^3 \approx 1051.47 \text{ in.}^3$

Exercise Set 6.4

1. A **mathematical expression** is a collection of variables, numbers, parentheses, and operation symbols. An **equation** is two algebraic expressions joined by an equal sign.

2. Expression: $2x + 3y$; equation: $2x + 3y = 16$

3. $x + 4$: 4 more than x

4. $x - 7$: 7 less than x

5. $2x - 3$: 2 times x, decreased by 3

6. $3x + 5$: 5 more than 3 times x

7. $8 + x$

8. $y - 5$

9. $3 + 2z$

10. $5x - 8$

11. $6w + 9$

12. $2x + 4$

13. $4x + 6$

14. $8 + 5x$

15. $\dfrac{18 - s}{4}$

16. $\dfrac{8 + t}{2}$

17. $3(x + 7)$

18. $\dfrac{8}{y} - 3x$

19. Let $x =$ the number

$x + 5 = 5$ more than the number

$x + 5 = 11$

$x + 5 - 5 = 11 - 5$

$x = 6$

20. Let $x =$ the number

$x - 4 =$ the number decreased by 4

$x - 4 = 9$

$x - 4 + 4 = 9 + 4$

$x = 13$

21. Let $x =$ the number

$x - 4 =$ the difference between the number and 4

$x - 4 = 20$

$x - 4 + 4 = 20 + 4$

$x = 24$

22. Let $x =$ the number

$7x =$ the number multiplied by 7

$7x = 56$

$\dfrac{7x}{7} = \dfrac{56}{7}$

$x = 8$

23. Let $x =$ the number

$4x - 10 = 4$ times the number decreased by 10

$4x - 10 = 42$

$4x - 10 + 10 = 42 + 10$

$4x = 52$

$\dfrac{4x}{4} = \dfrac{52}{4}$

$x = 13$

24. Let $x =$ the number

$8x + 16 = 16$ more than 8 times the number

$8x + 16 = 88$

$8x + 16 - 16 = 88 - 16$

$8x = 72$

$\dfrac{8x}{8} = \dfrac{72}{8}$

$x = 9$

25.   Let $x =$ the number
$$4x + 12 = 12 \text{ more than 4 times the number}$$
$$4x + 12 = 32$$
$$4x + 12 - 12 = 32 - 12$$
$$4x = 20$$
$$\frac{4x}{4} = \frac{20}{4}$$
$$x = 5$$

26.   Let $x =$ the number
$$3x - 8 = 8 \text{ less than 3 times the number}$$
$$6x + 10 = 6 \text{ times the number increased by 10}$$
$$3x - 8 = 6x + 10$$
$$3x - 3x - 8 = 6x - 3x + 10$$
$$-8 = 3x + 10$$
$$-8 - 10 = 3x + 10 - 10$$
$$-18 = 3x$$
$$\frac{-18}{3} = \frac{3x}{3}$$
$$-6 = x$$

27.   Let $x =$ the number
$$x + 6 = \text{the number increased by 6}$$
$$2x - 3 = 3 \text{ less than twice the number}$$
$$x + 6 = 2x - 3$$
$$x - x + 6 = 2x - x - 3$$
$$6 = x - 3$$
$$6 + 3 = x - 3 + 3$$
$$9 = x$$

28.   Let $x =$ the number
$$\frac{x}{3} = \text{the number divided by 3}$$
$$x - 4 = 4 \text{ less than the number}$$
$$\frac{x}{3} = x - 4$$
$$3\left(\frac{x}{3}\right) = 3(x - 4)$$
$$x = 3x - 12$$
$$x - 3x = 3x - 3x - 12$$
$$-2x = -12$$
$$\frac{-2x}{-2} = \frac{-12}{-2}$$
$$x = 6$$

29.   Let $x =$ the number
$$x + 10 = \text{the number increased by 10}$$
$$2(x + 3) = 2 \text{ times the sum of the number and 3}$$
$$x + 10 = 2(x + 3)$$
$$x + 10 = 2x + 6$$
$$x - x + 10 = 2x - x + 6$$
$$10 = x + 6$$
$$10 - 6 = x + 6 - 6$$
$$4 = x$$

30.   Let $x =$ the number
$$2x = \text{twice a number}$$
$$2x - 3 = \text{twice a number,}$$
$$\text{decreased by 3}$$
$$x + 4 = 4 \text{ more than the number}$$
$$2x - 3 = x + 4$$
$$2x - x - 3 = x - x + 4$$
$$x - 3 = 4$$
$$x - 3 + 3 = 4 + 3$$
$$x = 7$$

31. Let x = the number of miles driven

$0.42x$ = reimbursement for mileage

$150 + 0.42x = 207.54$

$0.42x = 57.54$

$\dfrac{0.42x}{0.42} = \dfrac{57.54}{0.42}$

$x = 137$

137 miles

32. Let x = Tito's dollar sales

$0.06x$ = the amount Tito made

on commission

$400 + 0.06x = 790$

$400 - 400 + 0.06x = 790 - 400$

$0.06x = 390$

$\dfrac{0.06x}{0.06} = \dfrac{390}{0.06}$

$x = \$6500$

33. Let x = the original cost before tax

$0.05x$ = the amount of tax

$x + 0.05x = 42$

$1.05x = 42$

$\dfrac{1.05x}{1.05} = \dfrac{42}{1.05}$

$x = 40; \$40$ per half hour

34. Let x = the original price before tax

$0.10x$ = the amount saved on

spending x dollars

$x - 0.10x = 15.72$

$0.9x = 15.72$

$\dfrac{0.9x}{0.9} = \dfrac{15.72}{0.9}$

$x = 17.4\overline{6} \approx \$17.47$

35. Let x = the number of copies Ronnie

must make

$0.08x$ = the amount spent on x copies

$0.08x = 250$

$\dfrac{0.08x}{0.08} = \dfrac{250}{0.08}$

$x = 3125$ copies

36. Let x = the number of compact discs

for Samantha

$3x$ = the number of compact discs

for Josie

$x + 3x = 12$

$4x = 12$

$\dfrac{4x}{4} = \dfrac{12}{4}$

$x = 3$ compact discs for Samantha

$3x = 3(3) = 9$ compact discs for Josie

37. Let x = the amount donated for Business

$3x$ = the amount donated for

Liberal Arts

$x + 3x = 1000$

$4x = 1000$

$\dfrac{4x}{4} = \dfrac{1000}{4}$

$x = \$250$ for Business

$3x = 3(250) = \$750$ for Liberal Arts

38. Let x = the amount charged

to each homeowner

$50x$ = the total amount charged

to homeowners

$2000 + 50x$ = the total cost for

the repairs

$2000 + 50x = 13,350$

$2000 - 2000 + 50x = 13,350 - 2000$

$50x = 11,350$

$\dfrac{50x}{50} = \dfrac{11,350}{50}$

$x = \$227$

39.
$$\text{Let } w = \text{the width}$$
$$w + 3 = \text{the length}$$
$$2w + 2(w + 3) = P$$
$$2w + 2(w + 3) = 54$$
$$2w + 2w + 6 = 54$$
$$4w + 6 = 54$$
$$4w + 6 - 6 = 54 - 6$$
$$4w = 48$$
$$\frac{4w}{4} = \frac{48}{4}$$
$$\text{width} = 12 \text{ ft}, \text{ length} = w + 3 = 12 + 3 = 15 \text{ ft}$$

41.
$$\text{Let } x = \text{the number of wild mustangs}$$
$$\text{in Utah}$$
$$6x + 2515 = \text{the the number of wild mustangs}$$
$$\text{in Nevada}$$
$$x + 6x + 2515 = 21,730$$
$$7x = 19215$$
$$x = 2745; \text{ Utah: } 2745 \text{ mustangs}$$
$$\text{Nevada: } 21,730 - 2745$$
$$= 18,985 \text{ mustangs}$$

43.
$$\text{Let } x = \text{the typical number of tornados}$$
$$\text{in December}$$
$$14x + 11 = \text{the typical number of tornados}$$
$$\text{in May}$$
$$x + 14x + 11 = 341$$
$$15x + 11 = 330$$
$$x = 22; \text{ December, } 22 \text{ tornados}$$
$$\text{May, } (14)(22) + 11$$
$$= 319 \text{ tornados}$$

45.
$$\text{Let } w = \text{width}$$
$$2w = \text{length of entire enclosed region}$$
$$3w + 2(2w) = \text{total amount of fencing}$$
$$3w + 2(2w) = 140$$
$$3w + 4w = 140$$
$$7w = 140$$
$$\frac{7w}{7} = \frac{140}{7}$$
$$\text{width} = 20 \text{ ft}$$
$$\text{length} = 2w = 2(20) = 40 \text{ ft}$$

40. a)
$$\text{Let } x = \text{area of smaller ones}$$
$$3x = \text{area of largest one}$$
$$x + x + 3x = 45,000$$
$$5x = 45,000$$
$$\frac{5x}{5} = \frac{45,000}{5}$$
$$x = 9000 \text{ ft}^2 \text{ for the two smaller barns}$$
$$3x = 3(9000)$$
$$= 27,000 \text{ ft}^2 \text{ for the largest barn}$$

b) Yes

42.
$$\text{Let } x = \text{the number of steps to burn off}$$
$$\text{a 12-oz soda}$$
$$2x + 690 = \text{the number of steps to burn off}$$
$$\text{a cheeseburger}$$
$$x + 2x + 690 = 11,040$$
$$3x + 690 = 11,040$$
$$3x = 10350$$
$$x = 3450; \text{ soda, } 3540 \text{ steps}$$
$$\text{cheesburger, } 11,040 - 3540$$
$$= 7590 \text{ steps}$$

44.
$$\text{Let } x = \text{the cost of the car before tax}$$
$$0.05x = 5\% \text{ of the cost of the car (tax)}$$
$$x + 0.05x = 14,512$$
$$1.05x = 14,512$$
$$\frac{1.05x}{1.05} = \frac{14,512}{1.05}$$
$$x = \$13,820.95238 \approx \$13,820.95$$

46.
$$\text{Let } l = \text{length of a shelf}$$
$$l + 2 = \text{height of the bookcase}$$
$$4l + 2(l + 2) = \text{total amount of wood}$$
$$4l + 2(l + 2) = 32$$
$$4l + 2l + 4 = 32$$
$$6l + 4 = 32$$
$$6l + 4 - 4 = 32 - 4$$
$$6l = 28$$
$$\frac{6l}{6} = \frac{28}{6}$$
$$\text{length} = 4\frac{4}{6} = 4\frac{2}{3} \text{ ft} = 4 \text{ ft 8 in.}$$
$$\text{height} = l + 2 = 4 \text{ ft 8 in.} + 2 \text{ ft} = 6 \text{ ft 8 in.}$$

47. Let $x =$ the number of months

$70x =$ cost of laundry for x months

$70x = 760$

$$\frac{70x}{70} = \frac{760}{70}$$

$x = 10.85714286$ months ≈ 11 months

48. Let $x =$ the number rentals under

the single option

$3.50x = 28$

$x = 8$; for 8 DVDs the two plans

have equal cost.

49. Let $r =$ regular fare

$\dfrac{r}{2} =$ half off regular fare

$0.07r =$ tax on regular fare

$$\frac{r}{2} + 0.07r = 257$$

$$2\left(\frac{r}{2} + 0.07r\right) = 2(257)$$

$r + 0.14r = 514$

$1.14r = 514$

$$\frac{1.14r}{1.14} = \frac{514}{1.14}$$

$r = \$450.877193$

$\approx \$450.88$

50. Let $x =$ the number of miles in one day

$35 + 0.20x =$ U-Haul charge per day

$25 + 0.32x =$ Ryder charge per day

$35 + 0.20x = 25 + 0.32x$

$35 + 0.20x - 25 = 25 - 25 + 0.32x$

$10 + 0.20x = 0.32x$

$10 + 0.20x - 0.20x = 0.32x - 0.20x$

$10 = 0.12x$

$$\frac{10}{0.12} = \frac{0.12x}{0.12}$$

$x = 83.\overline{3}$ mi $= 83\dfrac{1}{3}$ mi

51. Let $x =$ amount of tax reduction to be

deducted from Mr. McAdam's

income

$3640 - x =$ amount of tax reduction to be

deducted from Mrs. McAdam's

income

$24,200 - x = 26,400 - (3640 - x)$

$24,200 - x = 26,400 - 3640 + x$

$24,200 - x = 22,760 + x$

$24,200 - x + x = 22,760 + x + x$

$24,200 = 22,760 + 2x$

$24,200 - 22,760 = 22,760 - 22,760 + 2x$

$1440 = 2x$

$$\frac{1440}{2} = \frac{2x}{2}$$

$x = \$720$ deducted from

Mr. McAdam's income

$3640 - x = 3640 - 720 = \$2920$ deducted

from Mrs. McAdam's income

52. a) A number increased by 3 is 13.

b) 3 times a number increased by 5 is 8.

c) 3 times a number decreased by 8 is 7.

53.   Let $x =$ the first integer

$x + 1 =$ the second integer

$x + 2 =$ the third integer (the largest)

$$x + (x+1) + (x+2) = 3(x+2) - 3$$
$$3x + 3 = 3x + 6 - 3$$
$$3x + 3 = 3x + 3$$

54. a)   Let $x =$ the number of months for the amount

saved to equal the price of the course

$$0.10(100) = \$10 \text{ saved per year}$$
$$10x = 45$$
$$x = 4.5 \; = 4\frac{1}{2} \text{ months}$$

b) $25 - 18 = 7$ years

$7(12)(10) = \$840$ saved before paying for course

$\$840 - \$45 = \$795$ total savings

55. $F = \dfrac{9}{5}C + 32$

The thermometers will read the same when $F = C$.

Substitute C for F in the above equation.

$$C = \frac{9}{5}C + 32$$
$$5C = 5\left(\frac{9}{5}C + 32\right)$$
$$5C = 9C + 160$$
$$5C - 9C = 9C - 9C + 160$$
$$-4C = 160$$
$$\frac{-4C}{-4} = \frac{160}{-4}$$
$$C = -40°$$

Exercise Set 6.5

1. **Direct variation** — y varies directly with x if $y = kx$.

2. **Inverse variation** — y varies inversely with x if $y = \frac{k}{x}$.

3. **Joint variation** — One quantity varies directly as the product of two or more other quantities.

4. **Combined variation** uses the two forms of variation.

5. Direct	6. Inverse	7. Inverse	8. Direct
9. Direct	10. Direct	11. Inverse	12. Direct
13. Inverse	14. Direct	15. Inverse	16. Direct
17. Direct	18. Inverse	19. Direct	20. Inverse

21. Answers will vary.

23. a) $y = kx$

    b) $y = 8(15) = 120$

22. Answers will vary.

24. a) $x = \dfrac{k}{y}$

    b) $x = \dfrac{14}{7} = 2$

25. a) $m = \dfrac{k}{n^2}$

    b) $m = \dfrac{16}{(8)^2} = \dfrac{16}{64} = 0.25$

26. a) $r = ks^2$

    b) $r = 13(2)^2 = 13(4) = 52$

27. a) $A = \dfrac{kB}{C}$

    b) $A = \dfrac{(5)5}{10} = 2.5$

28. a) $M = \dfrac{kJ}{C}$

    b) $M = \dfrac{(8)10}{20} = 4$

29. a) $F = kDE$

    b) $F = 7(3)(10) = 210$

30. a) $A = \dfrac{kR_1R_2}{L^2}$

    b) $A = \dfrac{\frac{3}{2}(120)(8)}{(5)^2} = \dfrac{(1.5)(120)(8)}{25} = \dfrac{1440}{25} = 57.6$

31. a) $t = \dfrac{kd^2}{f}$

    b) $192 = \dfrac{k(8)^2}{4}$

    $192 = \dfrac{64k}{4}$

    $768 = 64k$

    $\dfrac{768}{64} = \dfrac{64k}{64}$

    $k = 12$

    $t = \dfrac{12d^2}{f}$

    $t = \dfrac{12(10)^2}{6} = \dfrac{12(100)}{6} = \dfrac{1200}{6} = 200$

32. a) $y = \dfrac{k\sqrt{t}}{s}$

    b) $12 = \dfrac{k\sqrt{36}}{2}$

    $12 = \dfrac{6k}{2}$

    $24 = 6k$

    $\dfrac{24}{6} = \dfrac{6k}{6}$

    $k = 4$

    $y = \dfrac{4\sqrt{t}}{s}$

    $y = \dfrac{4\sqrt{81}}{4} = \dfrac{4(9)}{4} = \dfrac{36}{4} = 9$

33. a) $Z = kWY$

    b) $12 = k(9)(4)$

    $12 = 36k$

    $\dfrac{12}{36} = \dfrac{36k}{36}$

    $k = \dfrac{1}{3}$

    $Z = \dfrac{1}{3}WY$

    $Z = \dfrac{1}{3}(50)(6) = \dfrac{300}{3} = 100$

34. a) $y = kR^2$

    b) $4 = k(4)^2$

    $4 = 16k$

    $\dfrac{4}{16} = \dfrac{16k}{16}$

    $k = 0.25$

    $y = 0.25R^2$

    $y = 0.25(8)^2 = 0.25(64) = 16$

35. a) $H = kL$

   b) $15 = k(50)$

     $\dfrac{15}{50} = \dfrac{50k}{50}$

      $k = 0.3$

     $H = 0.3L$

     $H = 0.3(10) = 3$

36. a) $C = \dfrac{k}{J}$

   b) $7 = \dfrac{k}{0.7}$

      $k = 7(0.7) = 4.9$

     $C = \dfrac{4.9}{J}$

     $C = \dfrac{4.9}{12} = 0.408\overline{3} \approx 0.41$

37. a) $A = kB^2$

   b) $245 = k(7)^2$

      $245 = 49k$

     $\dfrac{245}{49} = \dfrac{49k}{49}$

       $k = 5$

      $A = 5B^2$

      $A = 5(12)^2 = 5(144) = 720$

38. a) $F = \dfrac{kM_1M_2}{d^2}$

   b) $20 = \dfrac{k(5)(10)}{(0.2)^2}$

      $20 = \dfrac{50k}{0.04}$

     $50k = 0.8$

       $k = \dfrac{0.8}{50} = 0.016$

       $F = \dfrac{0.016M_1M_2}{d^2}$

       $F = \dfrac{0.016(10)(20)}{(0.4)^2} = \dfrac{3.2}{0.16} = 20$

39. a) $F = \dfrac{kq_1q_2}{d^2}$

   b) $80 = \dfrac{k(4)(16)}{(0.4)^2}$

      $80 = \dfrac{64k}{0.16}$

       $k = 0.2$

       $F = \dfrac{0.2q_1q_2}{d^2}$

       $F = \dfrac{0.2(12)(20)}{(0.2)^2} = \dfrac{48}{0.04} = 1200$

40. a) $S = kIT^2$

   b) $4 = k(10)(4)^2$

      $4 = 160k$

      $k = \dfrac{4}{160} = 0.025$

      $S = 0.025IT^2$

      $S = 0.025(4)(6)^2 = 0.025(4)(36) = 3.6$

41. a) $t = kv$

   b) $2100 = k(140,000)$

    $\dfrac{2100}{140,000} = \dfrac{140,000k}{140,000}$

       $k = 0.015$

       $t = 0.015v$

       $t = 0.015(180,000) = \$2700$

42. a) $R = kL$

   b) $0.24 = k(30)$

    $\dfrac{0.24}{30} = \dfrac{30k}{30}$

       $k = 0.008$

      $R = 0.008L$

      $R = 0.008(40) = 0.32 \text{ ohm}$

43. a) $l = \dfrac{k}{d^2}$

     b) $20 = \dfrac{k}{(6)^2}$

         $k = 20(36) = 720$

         $l = \dfrac{720}{d^2}$

         $l = \dfrac{720}{(3)^2} = \dfrac{720}{9} = 80 \text{ dB}$

44. a) $t = \dfrac{k}{T}$

     b) $2 = \dfrac{k}{75}$

         $k = 75(2) = 150$

         $t = \dfrac{150}{T}$

         $t = \dfrac{150}{80} = 1.875 \text{ minutes}$

45. a) $R = \dfrac{kA}{P}$

     b) $4800 = \dfrac{k(600)}{3}$

         $600k = 14,400$

         $k = \dfrac{14,400}{600} = 24$

         $R = \dfrac{24A}{P}$

         $R = \dfrac{24(700)}{3.50} = \dfrac{16,800}{3.50} = 4800 \text{ tapes}$

46. a) $d = ks^2$

     b) $80 = k(40)^2$

         $80 = 1600k$

         $k = \dfrac{80}{1600} = 0.05$

         $d = 0.05s^2$

         $d = 0.05(65)^2 = 0.05(4225)$

         $= 211.25 \text{ feet}$

47. a) $v = \dfrac{k\sqrt{t}}{l}$

     b) $5 = \dfrac{k\sqrt{225}}{0.60}$

         $k = \dfrac{5(0.60)}{\sqrt{225}} = \dfrac{3}{15} = 0.2$

         $v = \dfrac{0.2\sqrt{t}}{l}$

         $v = \dfrac{0.2\sqrt{196}}{0.70} = \dfrac{0.2(14)}{0.70}$

         $= 4 \text{ vibrations per second}$

48. a) $R = \dfrac{kL}{A}$

     b) $0.2 = \dfrac{k(200)}{0.05}$

         $200k = 0.01$

         $k = \dfrac{0.01}{200} = 0.00005$

         $R = \dfrac{0.00005L}{A}$

         $R = \dfrac{0.00005(5000)}{0.01} = \dfrac{0.25}{0.01} = 25 \text{ ohms}$

49. a) $N = \dfrac{kp_1 p_2}{d}$

b) $100,000 = \dfrac{k(60,000)(200,000)}{300}$

$12,000,000,000k = 30,000,000$

$k = \dfrac{30,000,000}{12,000,000,000} = 0.0025$

$N = \dfrac{0.0025 p_1 p_2}{d}$

$N = \dfrac{0.0025(125,000)(175,000)}{450}$

$N = \dfrac{54,687,500}{450}$

$= 121,527.7778 \approx 121,528 \text{ calls}$

50. a) $y = kx$

$y = 2x$

$\dfrac{y}{2} = \dfrac{2x}{2}$

$x = \dfrac{y}{2} = 0.5y$

Directly

b) $k = 0.5$

51. a) $y = \dfrac{k}{x}$

$y = \dfrac{0.3}{x}$

$xy = 0.3$

$\dfrac{xy}{y} = \dfrac{0.3}{y}$

$x = \dfrac{0.3}{y}$

Inversely

b) k stays 0.3

52. $I = \dfrac{k}{d^2}$

$\dfrac{1}{16} = \dfrac{k}{(4)^2}$

$\dfrac{1}{16} = \dfrac{k}{16}$

$k = 1$

$I = \dfrac{1}{d^2}$

$I = \dfrac{1}{(3)^2} = \dfrac{1}{9}$

53. $W = \dfrac{kTA\sqrt{F}}{R}$

$72 = \dfrac{k(78)(1000)\sqrt{4}}{5.6}$

$156,000k = 403.2$

$k = \dfrac{403.2}{156,000} = 0.0025846154$

$W = \dfrac{0.0025846154 TA\sqrt{F}}{R}$

$W = \dfrac{0.0025846154(78)(1500)\sqrt{6}}{5.6}$

$W = \dfrac{740.7256982}{5.6} = 132.2724461 \approx \$132.27$

Exercise Set 6.6

1. $a < b$ means that a is less than b, $a \leq b$ means that a is less than or equal to b, $a > b$ means that a is greater than b, $a \geq b$ means that a is greater than or equal to b.

2. a) An **inequality** consists of two (or more) expressions joined by an inequality sign.
   b) $2 < 7, 3 > -1, 5x + 2 \geq 9$

3. When both sides of an inequality are multiplied or divided by a negative number, the direction of the inequality symbol must be reversed.

4. Yes, the inequality symbol points to the x in both cases.

5. Yes, the inequality symbol points to the -3 in both cases.

6. You should use an open circle if the solution does not include the number. You should use a closed circle if the solution includes the number.

7. a) An inequality of the form $a < x < b$ is called a compound inequality.
   b) $-7 < x < 3$

8. a) $x \geq 4$
   b) $x > 4$

9. $x \geq 4$

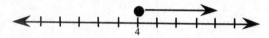

10. $x < 7$

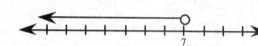

11. $\quad x - 8 \geq 3$
$x - 8 + 8 \geq 3 + 8$
$\quad x \geq 11$

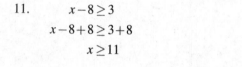

12. $\quad x + 5 > -2$
$x + 5 - 5 > -2 - 5$
$\quad x > -7$

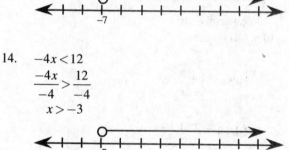

13. $-3x \leq 18$
$\dfrac{-3x}{-3} \geq \dfrac{18}{-3}$
$\quad x \geq -6$

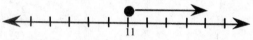

14. $-4x < 12$
$\dfrac{-4x}{-4} > \dfrac{12}{-4}$
$\quad x > -3$

15. $\dfrac{x}{5} < 4$
$5\left(\dfrac{x}{5}\right) < 5(4)$
$\quad x < 20$

16. $\dfrac{x}{6} > 2$
$6\left(\dfrac{x}{6}\right) > 6(2)$
$\quad x > 12$

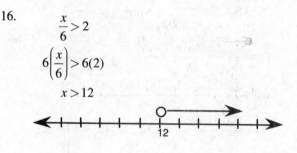

17.
$$\frac{-x}{3} \geq 3$$
$$-3\left(\frac{-x}{3}\right) \leq -3(3)$$
$$x \leq -9$$

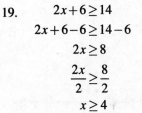

18.
$$\frac{x}{2} \geq -4$$
$$2\left(\frac{x}{2}\right) \geq 2(-4)$$
$$x \geq -8$$

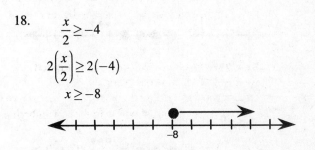

19.
$$2x + 6 \geq 14$$
$$2x + 6 - 6 \geq 14 - 6$$
$$2x \geq 8$$
$$\frac{2x}{2} \geq \frac{8}{2}$$
$$x \geq 4$$

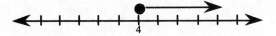

20.
$$3x + 12 < 5x + 14$$
$$3x - 5x + 12 < 5x - 5x + 14$$
$$-2x + 12 < 14$$
$$-2x + 12 - 12 < 14 - 12$$
$$-2x < 2$$
$$\frac{-2x}{-2} > \frac{2}{-2}$$
$$x > -1$$

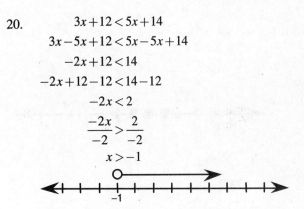

21.
$$4(2x - 1) < 2(4x - 3)$$
$$8x - 4 < 8x - 6$$
$$-4 < -6$$
False, no solution

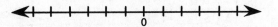

22.
$$-2(x - 3) \leq 4x + 6$$
$$-2x + 6 \leq 4x + 6$$
$$-2x \leq 4x$$
$$0 \leq 6x$$
$$0 \leq x$$

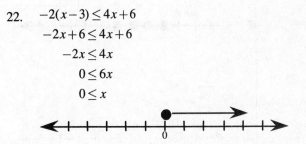

23. $-1 \leq x \leq 3$

24. $-4 < x \leq 1$

25.
$$3 < x - 7 \leq 6$$
$$3 + 7 < x - 7 + 7 \leq 6 + 7$$
$$10 < x \leq 13$$

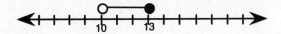

26.
$$\frac{1}{2} < \frac{x + 4}{2} \leq 4$$
$$2\left(\frac{1}{2}\right) < 2\left(\frac{x + 4}{2}\right) \leq 2(4)$$
$$1 < x + 4 \leq 8$$
$$1 - 4 < x + 4 - 4 \leq 8 - 4$$
$$-3 < x \leq 4$$

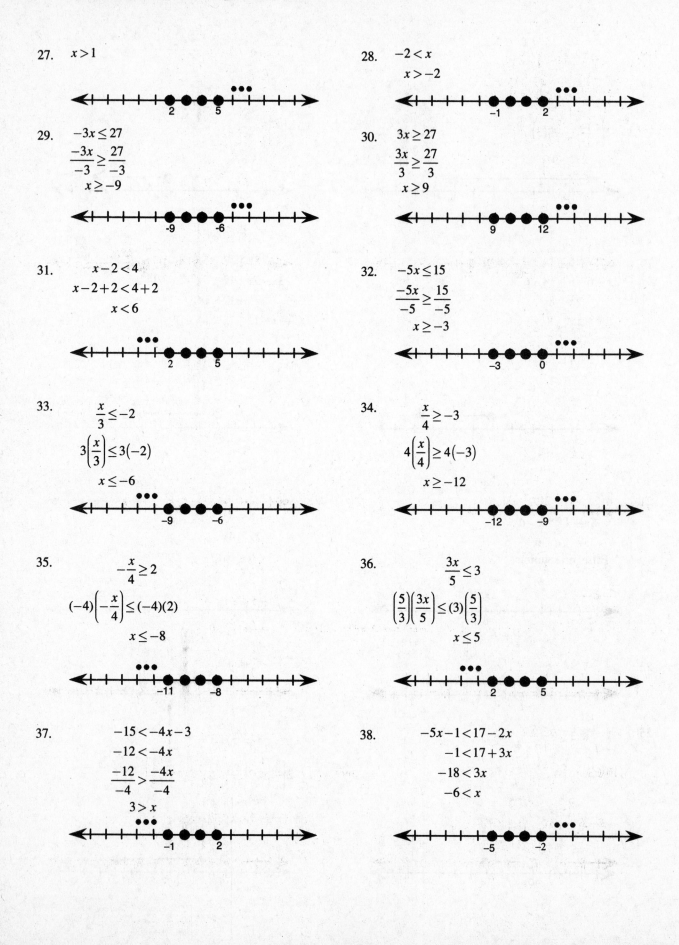

27. $x > 1$

28. $-2 < x$
$x > -2$

29. $-3x \le 27$
$\dfrac{-3x}{-3} \ge \dfrac{27}{-3}$
$x \ge -9$

30. $3x \ge 27$
$\dfrac{3x}{3} \ge \dfrac{27}{3}$
$x \ge 9$

31. $x - 2 < 4$
$x - 2 + 2 < 4 + 2$
$x < 6$

32. $-5x \le 15$
$\dfrac{-5x}{-5} \ge \dfrac{15}{-5}$
$x \ge -3$

33. $\dfrac{x}{3} \le -2$
$3\left(\dfrac{x}{3}\right) \le 3(-2)$
$x \le -6$

34. $\dfrac{x}{4} \ge -3$
$4\left(\dfrac{x}{4}\right) \ge 4(-3)$
$x \ge -12$

35. $-\dfrac{x}{4} \ge 2$
$(-4)\left(-\dfrac{x}{4}\right) \le (-4)(2)$
$x \le -8$

36. $\dfrac{3x}{5} \le 3$
$\left(\dfrac{5}{3}\right)\left(\dfrac{3x}{5}\right) \le (3)\left(\dfrac{5}{3}\right)$
$x \le 5$

37. $-15 < -4x - 3$
$-12 < -4x$
$\dfrac{-12}{-4} > \dfrac{-4x}{-4}$
$3 > x$

38. $-5x - 1 < 17 - 2x$
$-1 < 17 + 3x$
$-18 < 3x$
$-6 < x$

39.
$$3(x+4) \geq 4x+13$$
$$3x+12 \geq 4x+13$$
$$3x-4x+12 \geq 4x-4x+13$$
$$-x+12 \geq 13$$
$$-x+12-12 \geq 13-12$$
$$-x \geq 1$$
$$\frac{-x}{-1} \leq \frac{1}{-1}$$
$$x \leq -1$$

40.
$$-2(x-1) < 3(x-4)+5$$
$$-2x+2 < 3x-12+5$$
$$-2x+2 < 3x-7$$
$$-2x-3x+2 < 3x-3x-7$$
$$-5x+2 < -7$$
$$-5x+2-2 < -7-2$$
$$-5x < -9$$
$$\frac{-5x}{-5} > \frac{-9}{-5}$$
$$x > \frac{9}{5}$$

41.
$$5(x+4)-6 \leq 2x+8$$
$$5x+20-6 \leq 2x+8$$
$$5x+14 \leq 2x+8$$
$$5x-2x+14 \leq 2x-2x+8$$
$$3x+14 \leq 8$$
$$3x+14-14 \leq 8-14$$
$$3x \leq -6$$
$$\frac{3x}{3} \leq \frac{-6}{3}$$
$$x \leq -2$$

42. $-3 \leq x < 5$

43.
$$1 > -x > -5$$
$$\frac{1}{-1} < \frac{-x}{-1} < \frac{-5}{-1}$$
$$-1 < x < 5$$

44.
$$-2 < 2x+3 < 6$$
$$-2-3 < 2x+3-3 < 6-3$$
$$-5 < 2x < 3$$
$$\frac{-5}{2} < \frac{2x}{2} < \frac{3}{2}$$
$$-\frac{5}{2} < x < \frac{3}{2}$$

45.
$$0.3 \leq \frac{x+2}{10} \leq 0.5$$
$$10(0.3) \leq 10\left(\frac{x+2}{10}\right) \leq 10(0.5)$$
$$3 \leq x+2 \leq 5$$
$$3-2 \leq x+2-2 \leq 5-2$$
$$1 \leq x \leq 3$$

46.
$$-\frac{1}{3} < \frac{x-2}{12} \leq \frac{1}{4}$$
$$12\left(-\frac{1}{3}\right) < 12\left(\frac{x-2}{12}\right) \leq 12\left(\frac{1}{4}\right)$$
$$-4 < x-2 \leq 3$$
$$-4+2 < x-2+2 \leq 3+2$$
$$-2 < x \leq 5$$

47. a) 2009 through 2015
    b) 2005 through 2008
    c) 2006 through 2015
    d) 2005 and 2006

48. a) 1999, 2002, 2003, 2004
    b) 2000
    c) 1999 through 2004
    d) 2000 and 2001

49. Let $x =$ the number of videos

No Fee Plan cost: $2.99x$

Annual Fee Plan: $30 + 1.49x$

$$2.99x < 30 + 1.49x$$
$$2.99x - 1.49x < 30 + 1.49x - 1.49x$$
$$1.50x < 30$$
$$\frac{1.50x}{1.50} < \frac{30}{1.50}$$
$$x < 20$$

The maximum number of videos that can be rented for the No Fee Plan to cost less than the Annual Fee Plan is 19.

50. Let $x =$ the dollar amount of weekly sales

Plan A: $500 + 0.06x$

Plan B: $400 + 0.08x$

$$400 + 0.08x > 500 + 0.06x$$
$$400 + 0.08x - 0.06x > 500 + 0.06x - 0.06x$$
$$400 + 0.02x > 500$$
$$400 - 400 + 0.02x > 500 - 400$$
$$0.02x > 100$$
$$\frac{0.02x}{0.02} > \frac{100}{0.02}$$
$$x > 5000$$

The dollar amount of weekly sales that would result in Bobby earning more by **Plan B** than by **Plan A** is more than $5000.

51. Let $x =$ the number hours she works as cashier

$$725 + 6.50x \le 3000$$
$$6.50x \le 2275$$
$$\frac{6.50x}{6.50} \le \frac{2275}{6.50}$$
$$x \le 350$$

The maximum number of hours that Samantha can work as a cashier is 350 hours.

52. a) Let $x =$ the number of boxes of books

$60x =$ the weight of x boxes of books

$$180 + 60x \le 1200$$

b) $$180 - 180 + 60x \le 1200 - 180$$
$$60x \le 1020$$
$$\frac{60x}{60} \le \frac{1020}{60}$$
$$x \le 17$$

The maximum number of boxes is 17.

53. Let $x =$ the length of time Tom can park.

$$1.75 + 0.50(x - 1) \le 4.25$$
$$1.75 + 0.50x - 0.50 \le 4.25$$
$$0.50x \le 3$$
$$\frac{0.50x}{0.50} \le \frac{3}{0.50}$$
$$x \le 6$$

He can park for at most 6 hours.

54. $$12x > 2x + 2000$$
$$12x - 2x > 2x - 2x + 2000$$
$$10x > 2000$$
$$\frac{10x}{10} > \frac{2000}{10}$$
$$x > 200$$

More than 200 books must be sold weekly to make a profit.

55. $$36 < 84 - 32t < 68$$
$$36 - 84 < 84 - 84 - 32t < 68 - 84$$
$$-48 < -32t < -16$$
$$\frac{-48}{-32} > \frac{-32t}{-32} > \frac{-16}{-32}$$
$$1.5 > t > 0.5$$
$$0.5 < t < 1.5$$

The velocity will be between $36\dfrac{\text{ft}}{\text{sec}}$ and $68\dfrac{\text{ft}}{\text{sec}}$ when t is between $0.5\,\text{sec}$ and $1.5\,\text{sec}$.

56. Let $x =$ the number of miles

distance = rate $\times$ time

$$40(4) \le x \le 55(4)$$
$$160 \le x \le 220$$

57. Let $x =$ Devon's grade on the fifth test

$$80 \leq \frac{78+64+88+76+x}{5} < 90$$

$$80 \leq \frac{306+x}{5} < 90$$

$$5(80) \leq 5\left(\frac{306+x}{5}\right) < 5(90)$$

$$400 \leq 306+x < 450$$

$$400-306 \leq 306-306+x < 450-306$$

$$94 \leq x < 144$$

Devon must have a score of $94 \leq x \leq 100$, assuming 100 is the highest grade possible.

58. Let $x =$ the number of tents rented

$$950 \leq 325+125x \leq 1200$$

$$950-325 \leq 325-325+125x \leq 1200-325$$

$$625 \leq 125x \leq 875$$

$$\frac{625}{125} \leq \frac{125x}{125} \leq \frac{875}{125}$$

$$5 \leq x \leq 7$$

Minimum: 5   Maximum: 7

59. Let $x =$ the number of gallons

$$250x = 2750 \text{ and } 400x = 2750$$

$$x = \frac{2750}{250}, \ x = \frac{2750}{400}$$

$$x = 11, \ x = 6.875$$

$$6.875 \leq x \leq 11$$

60. Let $x =$ the final exam grade

The semester average $= \dfrac{86+74+68+96+72}{5} = \dfrac{396}{5} = 79.2$

The final grade is found by taking $\dfrac{2}{3}$ of the semester average and adding this to $\dfrac{1}{3}$ of the final exam. The final

grade is $\dfrac{2}{3}(79.2) + \dfrac{1}{3}x = 52.8 + \dfrac{1}{3}x$. In order for Teresa to receive a final grade of B in the course, she must have an

average greater than or equal to 80 and less than 90.

$$80 \leq 52.8 + \frac{1}{3}x < 90$$

$$80-52.8 \leq 52.8-52.8 + \frac{1}{3}x < 90-52.8$$

$$27.2 \leq \frac{1}{3}x < 37.2$$

$$3(27.2) \leq 3\left(\frac{1}{3}x\right) < 3(37.2)$$

$$81.6 \leq x < 111.6$$

Thus, Teresa must receive $81.6 \leq x \leq 100$, assuming that 100 is the highest grade possible.

61. Student's answer: $-\dfrac{1}{3}x \le 4$

$$-3\left(-\dfrac{1}{3}x\right) \le -3(4)$$

$$x \le -12$$

Correct answer: $-\dfrac{1}{3}x \le 4$

$$-3\left(-\dfrac{1}{3}x\right) \ge -3(4)$$

$$x \ge -12$$

Yes, -12 is in both solution sets.

Exercise Set 6.7

1. A **graph** is an illustration of all the points whose coordinates satisfy an equation.

2. To find the **x-intercept**, set $y = 0$ and solve the equation for x.

3. To find the **y-intercept**, set $x = 0$ and solve the equation for y.

4. The **slope of a line** is a ratio of the vertical change to the horizontal change for any two points on the line.

5. a) Divide the difference between the y-coordinates by the difference between the x-coordinates.

   b) $m = \dfrac{5-2}{-3-6} = \dfrac{3}{-9} = -\dfrac{1}{3}$

6. Plotting points, using intercepts, and using the slope and y-intercept

7. a) First
   b) Third

8. Two

9. - 16.   17. - 24.

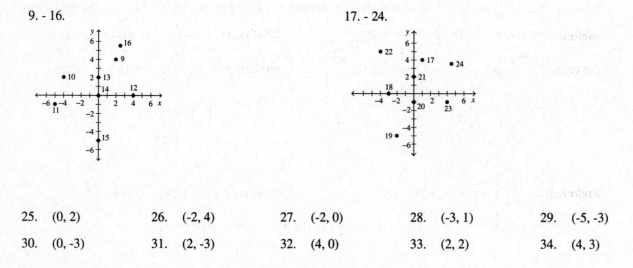

25. (0, 2)   26. (-2, 4)   27. (-2, 0)   28. (-3, 1)   29. (-5, -3)

30. (0, -3)   31. (2, -3)   32. (4, 0)   33. (2, 2)   34. (4, 3)

35. Substituting (5, 2) into $x+2y=9$, we have
$$5+2(2)=9$$
$$5+4=9$$
$$9=9$$
Therefore, (5, 2) satisfies $x+2y=9$.

Substituting (1, 4) into $x+2y=9$, we have
$$1+2(4)=9$$
$$1+8=9$$
$$9=9$$
Therefore, (1, 4) satisfies $x+2y=9$.

Substituting (0, 5) into $x+2y=9$, we have
$$0+2(5)=9$$
$$10 \neq 9$$

Therefore, (0, 5) does not satisfy $x+2y=9$.

36. Substituting (0, –4) into $4x-y=4$, we have
$$4(0)-(-4)=4$$
$$0+4=4$$
$$4=4$$
Therefore, (0, –4) satisfies $4x-y=4$.

Substituting (1, 0) into $4x-y=4$, we have
$$4(1)-0=4$$
$$4-0=4$$
$$4=4$$
Therefore, (1, 0) satisfies $4x-y=4$.

Substituting (2, –3) into $4x-y=4$, we have
$$4(2)-(-3)=4$$
$$8+3=4$$
$$11 \neq 4$$
Therefore, (2, –3) does not satisfy $4x-y=4$.

37. Substituting (8, 2) into $2x-3y=10$, we have
$$2(8)-3(2)=10$$
$$16-6=10$$
$$10=10$$
Therefore, (8, 2) satisfies $2x-3y=10$.

Substituting (–1, 4) into $2x-3y=10$, we have
$$2(-1)-3(4)=10$$
$$-2-12=10$$
$$-14 \neq 10$$
Therefore, (–1, 4) does not satisfy $2x-3y=10$.

Substituting $\left(0, -\dfrac{10}{3}\right)$ into $2x-3y=10$, we have
$$2(0)-3\left(-\frac{10}{3}\right)=10$$
$$0+10=10$$
$$10=10$$
Therefore, $\left(0, -\dfrac{10}{3}\right)$ satisfies $2x-3y=10$.

38. Substituting (2, 1) into $3y=4x+2$, we have
$$3(1)=4(2)+2$$
$$3=8+2$$
$$3 \neq 10$$
Therefore, (2, 1) does not satisfy $3y=4x+2$.

Substituting (1, 2) into $3y=4x+2$, we have
$$3(2)=4(1)+2$$
$$6=4+2$$
$$6=6$$
Therefore, (1, 2) satisfies $3y=4x+2$.

Substituting $\left(0, \dfrac{2}{3}\right)$ into $3y=4x+2$, we have
$$3\left(\frac{2}{3}\right)=4(0)+2$$
$$2=0+2$$
$$2=2$$
Therefore, $\left(0, \dfrac{2}{3}\right)$ satisfies $3y=4x+2$.

39. Substituting $(1, -1)$ into $7y = 3x - 5$, we have
$$7(-1) = 3(1) - 5$$
$$-7 = 3 - 5$$
$$-7 \neq -2$$
Therefore, $(1, -1)$ does not satisfy $7y = 3x - 5$.

Substituting $(-3, -2)$ into $7y = 3x - 5$, we have
$$7(-2) = 3(-3) - 5$$
$$-14 = -9 - 5$$
$$-14 = -14$$
Therefore, $(-3, -2)$ satisfies $7y = 3x - 5$.

Substituting $(2, 5)$ into $7y = 3x - 5$, we have
$$7(5) = 3(2) - 5$$
$$35 = 6 - 5$$
$$35 \neq 1$$
Therefore, $(2, 5)$ does not satisfy $7y = 3x - 5$.

40. Substituting $(1, 3)$ into $3x - 5y = -12$, we have
$$3(1) - 5(3) = -12$$
$$3 - 15 = -12$$
$$-12 = -12$$
Therefore, $(1, 3)$ satisfies $3x - 5y = -12$.

Substituting $(-1, 2)$ into $3x - 5y = -12$, we have
$$3(-1) - 5(2) = -12$$
$$-3 - 10 = -12$$
$$-13 \neq -12$$
Therefore, $(-1, 2)$ does not satisfy $3x - 5y = -12$.

Substituting $(-4, 0)$ into $3x - 5y = -12$, we have
$$3(-4) - 5(0) = -12$$
$$-12 - 0 = -12$$
$$-12 = -12$$
Therefore, $(-4, 0)$ satisfies $3x - 5y = -12$.

41. Substituting $(8, 0)$ into $\dfrac{x}{4} + \dfrac{2y}{3} = 2$, we have
$$\frac{8}{4} + \frac{2(0)}{3} = 2$$
$$2 + 0 = 2$$
$$2 = 2$$
Therefore, $(8, 0)$ satisfies $\dfrac{x}{4} + \dfrac{2y}{3} = 2$.

Substituting $\left(1, \dfrac{1}{2}\right)$ into $\dfrac{x}{4} + \dfrac{2y}{3} = 2$, we have
$$\frac{1}{4} + \frac{2}{3}\left(\frac{1}{2}\right) = 2$$
$$\frac{7}{12} \neq 2$$
Therefore, $\left(1, \dfrac{1}{2}\right)$ does not satisfy $\dfrac{x}{4} + \dfrac{2y}{3} = 2$.

Substituting $(0, 3)$ into $\dfrac{x}{4} + \dfrac{2y}{3} = 2$, we have
$$\frac{0}{4} + \frac{3(2)}{3} = 2$$
$$2 = 2$$
Therefore, $(0, 3)$ satisfies $\dfrac{x}{4} + \dfrac{2y}{3} = 2$.

42. Substituting $\left(0, \dfrac{4}{3}\right)$ into $\dfrac{x}{2} + 3y = 4$, we have
$$\frac{0}{2} + 3\left(\frac{4}{3}\right) = 4$$
$$0 + 4 = 4$$
$$4 = 4$$
Therefore, $\left(0, \dfrac{4}{3}\right)$ satisfies $\dfrac{x}{2} + 3y = 4$.

Substituting $(8, 0)$ into $\dfrac{x}{2} + 3y = 4$, we have
$$\frac{8}{2} + 3(0) = 4$$
$$4 + 0 = 4$$
$$4 = 4$$
Therefore, $(8, 0)$ satisfies $\dfrac{x}{2} + 3y = 4$.

Substituting $(10, -2)$ into $\dfrac{x}{2} + 3y = 4$, we have
$$\frac{10}{2} + 3(-2) = 4$$
$$5 - 6 = 4$$
$$-1 \neq 4$$
Therefore, $(10, -2)$ does not satisfy $\dfrac{x}{2} + 3y = 4$.

43.   Since the line is vertical, its slope is undefined.

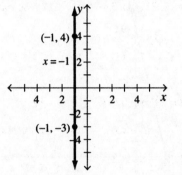

44.   Since the line is vertical, its slope is undefined.

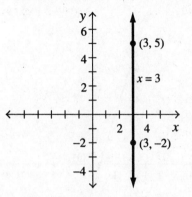

45.   Since the line is horizontal, its slope is 0.

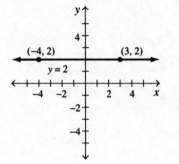

46.   Since the line is horizontal, its slope is 0.

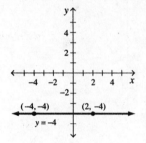

47.

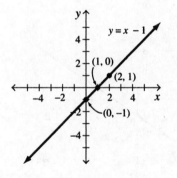

48.

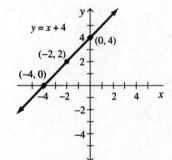

49.

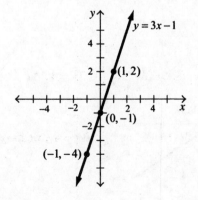

50.

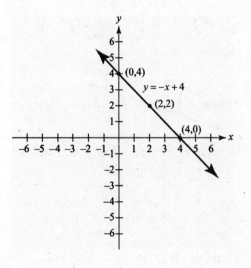

51.

52.

53.

54.

55.

56.

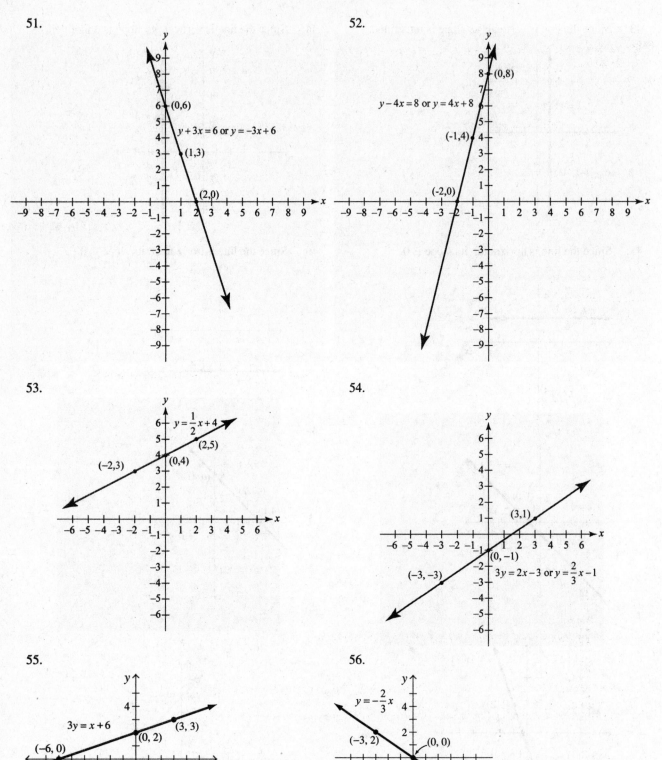

57.

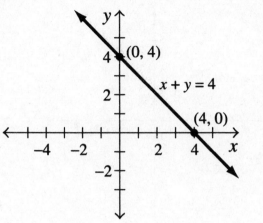

58.

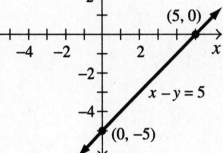

59.

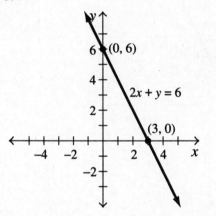

60.

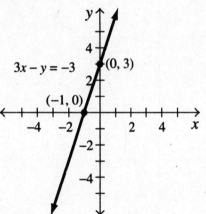

61.

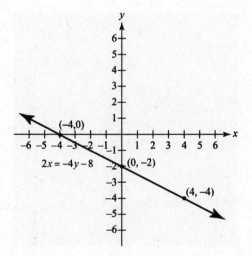

62.

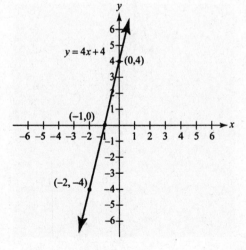

63.

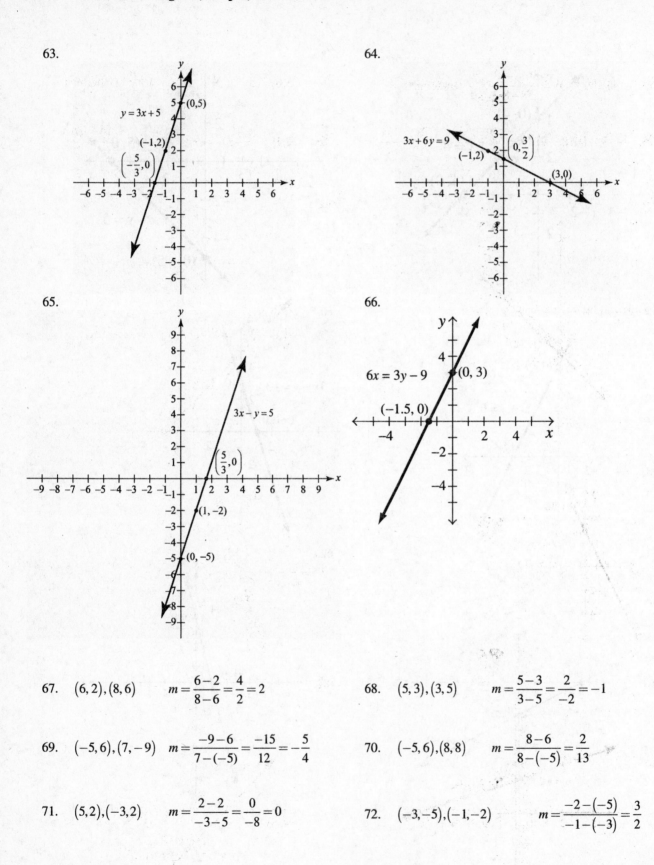

64.

65.

66.

67. $(6,2),(8,6)$ $m=\dfrac{6-2}{8-6}=\dfrac{4}{2}=2$

68. $(5,3),(3,5)$ $m=\dfrac{5-3}{3-5}=\dfrac{2}{-2}=-1$

69. $(-5,6),(7,-9)$ $m=\dfrac{-9-6}{7-(-5)}=\dfrac{-15}{12}=-\dfrac{5}{4}$

70. $(-5,6),(8,8)$ $m=\dfrac{8-6}{8-(-5)}=\dfrac{2}{13}$

71. $(5,2),(-3,2)$ $m=\dfrac{2-2}{-3-5}=\dfrac{0}{-8}=0$

72. $(-3,-5),(-1,-2)$ $m=\dfrac{-2-(-5)}{-1-(-3)}=\dfrac{3}{2}$

73. $(8,-3),(8,3)$ $m = \dfrac{3-(-3)}{8-8} = \dfrac{6}{0}$ **Undefined**

74. $(2,6),(2,-3)$ $m = \dfrac{-3-6}{2-2} = \dfrac{-9}{0}$ **Undefined**

75. $(-3,-1),(8,-9)$ $m = \dfrac{-9-(-1)}{8-(-3)} = \dfrac{-8}{11} = -\dfrac{8}{11}$

76. $(2,1),(-5,-9)$ $m = \dfrac{-9-1}{-5-2} = \dfrac{-10}{-7} = \dfrac{10}{7}$

77.

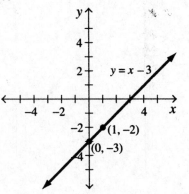

78.

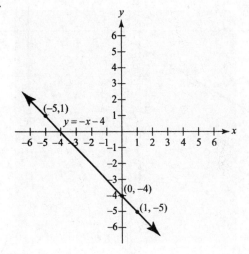

79.

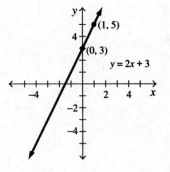

80.

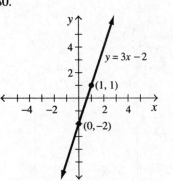

81.

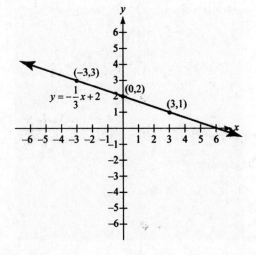

82.

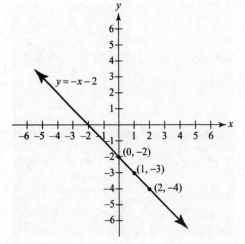

83.

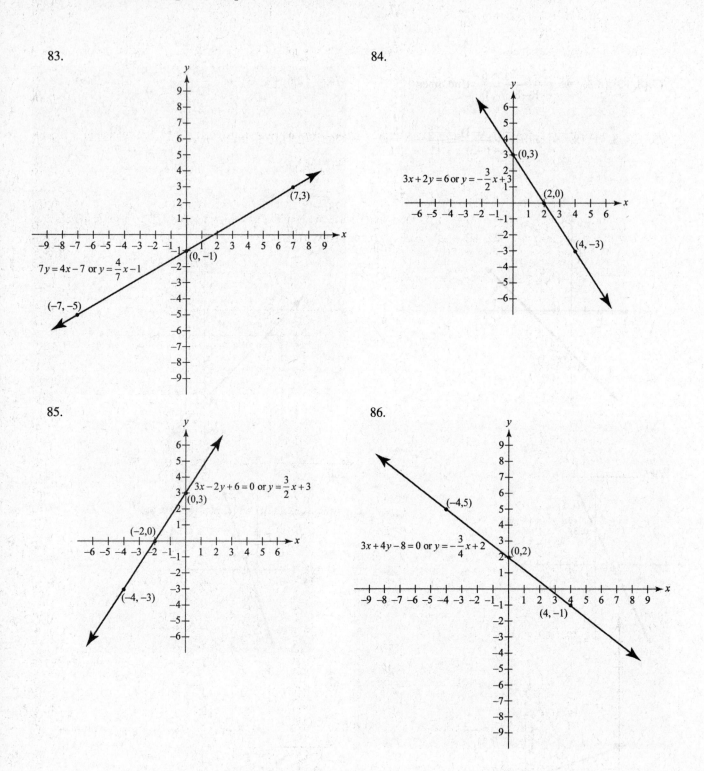

84.

85.

86.

87. The y-intercept is 4; thus $b = 4$. The slope is negative since the graph falls from left to right. The change in y is 4, while the change in x is 2. Thus m, the slope, is $-\dfrac{4}{2} = -2$. The equation is $y = -2x + 4$.

88. The y-intercept is 2; thus $b=2$. The slope is positive since the graph rises from left to right. The change in y is 2, while the change in x is 3. Thus m, the slope, is $\dfrac{2}{3}$. The equation is $y=\dfrac{2}{3}x+2$.

89. The y-intercept is 2; thus $b=2$. The slope is positive since the graph rises from left to right. The change in y is 3, while the change in x is 1. Thus m, the slope, is $\dfrac{3}{1}=3$. The equation is $y=3x+2$.

90. The y-intercept is 1; thus $b=1$. The slope is negative since the graph falls from left to right. The change in y is 2, while the change in x is 1. Thus m, the slope, is -2. The equation is $y=-2x+1$.

91. a)

92. a)

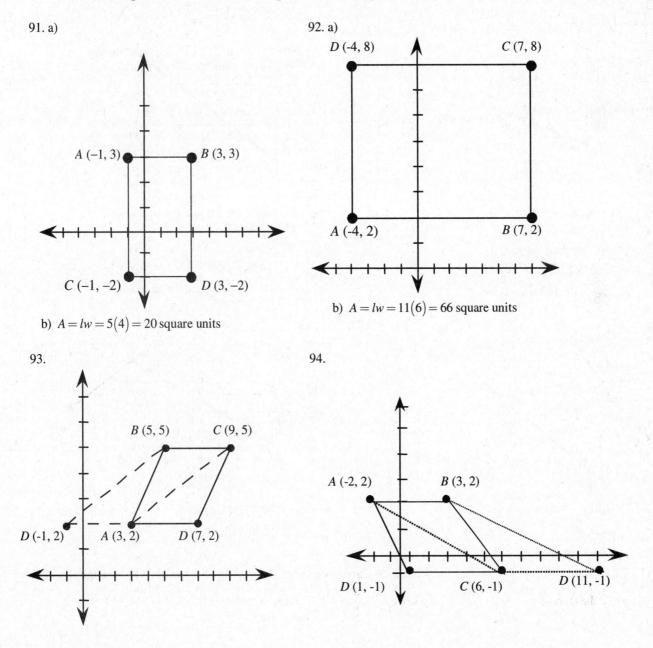

b) $A=lw=5(4)=20$ square units

b) $A=lw=11(6)=66$ square units

93.

94.

95. For the line joining points P and Q to be parallel to the x-axis, both ordered pairs must have the same y-value. Thus, $b = -3$.

96. For the line joining points P and Q to be parallel to the y-axis, both ordered pairs must have the same x-value. Thus, $b = 4$.

97. For the line joining points P and Q to be parallel to the x-axis, both ordered pairs must have the same y-value.
$$2b + 1 = 7$$
$$2b + 1 - 1 = 7 - 1$$
$$2b = 6$$
$$b = 3$$

98. For the line joining points P and Q to be parallel to the x-axis, both ordered pairs must have the same y-value.
$$2b + 3 = -1$$
$$2b + 3 - 3 = -1 - 3$$
$$2b = -4$$
$$b = -2$$

99. a)

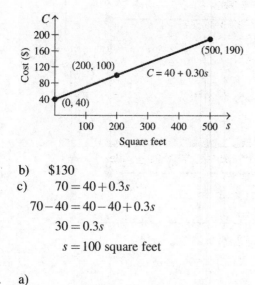

   b) $130
   c) $70 = 40 + 0.3s$
   $$70 - 40 = 40 - 40 + 0.3s$$
   $$30 = 0.3s$$
   $$s = 100 \text{ square feet}$$

100. a)

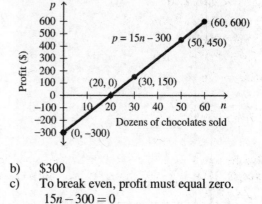

   b) $300
   c)   To break even, profit must equal zero.
   $$15n - 300 = 0$$
   $$15n - 300 + 300 = 0 + 300$$
   $$15n = 300$$
   $$n = 20 \text{ dozens of chocolates}$$

101. a)

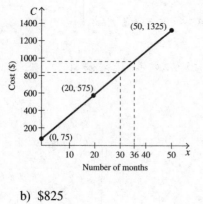

   b) $825
   c) 36 months

102. a)

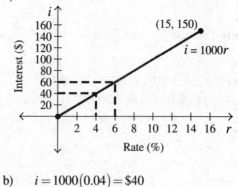

   b) $i = 1000(0.04) = \$40$
   c) $i = 1000(0.06) = \$60$

103. a) $m = \dfrac{19-9}{5-0} = \dfrac{10}{5} = 2$

    b) $y = 2x + 9$

    c) $y = 2(3) + 9 = 6 + 9 = 15$ defects

    d) $17 = 2x + 9$

        $17 - 9 = 2x + 9 - 9$

            $8 = 2x$

            $x = 4$ workers

104. a) $m = \dfrac{96-53}{4-0} = \dfrac{43}{4} = 10.75$

    b) $y = 10.75x + 53$

    c) $y = 10.75(3) + 53 = 32.25 + 53 = 85.25$

    d) $80 = 10.75x + 53$

        $27 = 10.75x$

        $x = 2.511627907 \approx 2.5$ hours

105. a) slope $\approx \dfrac{2.41-2.60}{2004-2000} = \dfrac{-0.19}{4} \approx -0.05$

    b) $y = -0.05x + 2.60$

    c) $y = -0.05x + 2.60$

        $y = -0.05(2) + 2.60 = 2.50$

        $2.50 billion

    d) $2.4 = -0.05x + 2.60$

      $-0.20 = -0.05x$

         $4 = x$

        4 years after 2000, or in 2004

106. a) slope $\approx \dfrac{1.38-1.15}{2004-2001} = \dfrac{0.23}{3} \approx 0.08$

    b) $y = 0.08x + 1.15$

    c) $y = 0.08x + 1.15$

        $y = 0.08(2) + 1.15 = 1.31$

        1.31 million passengers

    d) $1.55 = 0.08x + 1.15$

      $-0.40 = -0.08x$

         $5 = x$

        5 years after 2001, or in 2006

107. a) Solve the equations for y to put them in slope-intercept form. Then compare the slopes and y-intercepts. If the slopes are equal but the y-intercepts are different, then the lines are parallel.

    b) $2x - 3y = 6$ $4x = 6y + 6$

        $2x - 2x - 3y = -2x + 6$ $4x - 6 = 6y + 6 - 6$

               $-3y = -2x + 6$ $4x - 6 = 6y$

             $\dfrac{-3y}{-3} = \dfrac{-2x}{-3} + \dfrac{6}{-3}$ $\dfrac{4x}{6} - \dfrac{6}{6} = \dfrac{6y}{6}$

                 $y = \dfrac{2}{3}x - 2$ $\dfrac{2}{3}x - 1 = y$

    Since the two equations have the same slope, $m = \dfrac{2}{3}$, the graphs of the equations are parallel lines.

108. Quadrants 1, 2, and 4. The graph of the line $x + y = 1$ is in quadrants 1, 2, and 4; therefore, the set of points that satisfy the equation is in these quadrants.

Exercise Set 6.8

1. (1) Mentally substitute the equal sign for the inequality sign and plot points as if you were graphing the equation. (2) If the inequality is < or >, draw a dashed line through the points. If the inequality is ≤ or ≥, draw a solid line through the points. (3) Select a test point not on the line and substitute the x- and y- coordinates into the inequality. If the substitution results in a true statement, shade in the area on the same side of the line as the test point. If the substitution results in a false statement, shade in the area on the opposite side of the line as the test point.

2. To indicate that the line is part of the solution set, we draw a solid line. To indicate that the line is not part of the solution set, we draw a dashed line.

3. A half-plane is the set of all the points in a plane on one side of a line.

4. a) The shading of the solution set is on opposite sides of the line.

    b) The solution set of $y > x + 3$ is a half-plane. The solution set of $y \geq x + 3$ is a half-plane and the line representing the solution of $y = x + 3$.

5. a) $2x + 3y < 11$

    $2(1) + 3(3) < 11$

    $2 + 9 < 11$

    $11 < 11$ False

    No

    b) $2x + 3y \leq 11$

    $2(1) + 3(3) \leq 11$

    $2 + 9 \leq 11$

    $11 \leq 11$ True

    Yes

    c) $2x + 3y \geq 11$

    $2(1) + 3(3) \geq 11$

    $2 + 9 \geq 11$

    $11 \geq 11$ True

    Yes

    d) $2x + 3y > 11$

    $2(1) + 3(3) > 11$

    $2 + 9 > 11$

    $11 > 11$ False

    No

6. a) $4x - 2y < -10$

    $4(-2) - 2(4) < -10$

    $-8 - 8 < -10$

    $-16 < -10$ True

    Yes

    b) $4x - 2y \leq -10$

    $4(-2) - 2(4) \leq -10$

    $-8 - 8 \leq -10$

    $-16 \leq -10$ True

    Yes

    c) $4x - 2y > -10$

    $4(-2) - 2(4) > -10$

    $-8 - 8 > -10$

    $-16 > -10$ False

    No

    d) $4x - 2y \geq -10$

    $4(-2) - 2(4) \geq -10$

    $-8 - 8 \geq -10$

    $-16 \geq -10$ False

    No

7. Graph $x = 3$. Since the original statement is less than or equal to, a solid line is drawn.
    Since the point (0, 0) satisfies the inequality $x \le 3$, all points on the line and in the half-plane to the left of the line $x = 3$ are in the solution set.

    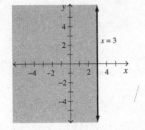

8. Graph $y = -3$. Since the original statement is greater than or equal to, a solid line is drawn.
    Since the point (0, 0) satisfies the inequality $y \ge -3$, all points on the line and in the half-plane above the line $y = -3$ are in the solution set.

    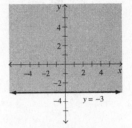

9. Graph $y = x - 4$. Since the original statement is greater than, a dashed line is drawn.
    Since the point (0, 0) satisfies the inequality $y > x - 4$, all points in the half-plane above the line $y = x - 4$ are in the solution set.

    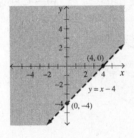

10. Graph $y = x + 1$. Since the original statement is less than, a dashed line is drawn.
    Since the point (0, 0) satisfies the inequality $y < x + 1$, all points in the half-plane below the line $y = x + 1$ are in the solution set.

    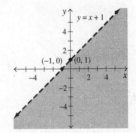

11. Graph $y = 2x - 6$. Since the original statement is greater than or equal to, a solid line is drawn.
    Since the point (0, 0) satisfies the inequality $y \ge 2x - 6$, all points on the line and in the half-plane above the line $y = 2x - 6$ are in the solution set.

    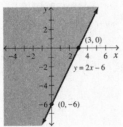

12. Graph $y = -2x + 2$. Since the original statement is strictly less than, a dashed line is drawn. Since the point (0, 0) satisfies the inequality $y < -2x + 2$, all points in the half-plane below the line $y = -2x + 2$ are in the solution set.

    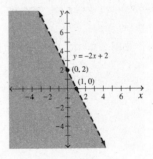

13.   Graph $3x - 4y = 12$. Since the original statement is strictly greater than, a dashed line is drawn. Since the point (0, 0) does not satisfy the inequality $3x - 4y > 12$, all points in the half-plane below the line $3x - 4y = 12$ are in the solution set.

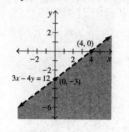

14.   Graph $x + 2y = 4$. Since the original statement is   strictly greater than, a dashed line is drawn. Since   the point (0, 0) does not satisfy the inequality

   $x + 2y > 4$, all points in the half-plane above the line $x + 2y = 4$ are in the solution set.

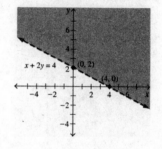

15.   Graph $3x - 4y = 9$. Since the original statement is less than or equal to, a solid line is drawn. Since the point (0, 0) satisfies the inequality $3x - 4y \leq 9$, all points on the line and in the half-plane above the line $3x - 4y = 9$ are in the solution set.

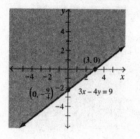

16.   Graph $4y - 3x = 9$. Since the original statement is   greater than or equal to, a solid line is drawn.   Since the point (0, 0) does not satisfy the inequality $4y - 3x \geq 9$, all points on the line and in the half-   plane above the line $4y - 3x = 9$ are in the solution   set.

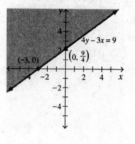

17. Graph $3x + 2y = 6$. Since the original statement is strictly less than, a dashed line is drawn. Since the point $(0, 0)$ satisfies the inequality $3x + 2y < 6$, all points in the half-plane to the left of the line $3x + 2y = 6$ are in the solution set.

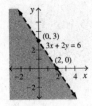

18. Graph $-x + 2y = 2$. Since the original statement is strictly less than, a dashed line is drawn. Since the point $(0, 0)$ satisfies the inequality $-x + 2y < 2$, all points in the half-plane below the line $-x + 2y = 2$ are in the solution set.

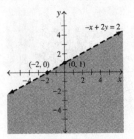

19. Graph $x + y = 0$. Since the original statement is strictly greater than, a dashed line is drawn. Since the point $(1, 1)$ satisfies the inequality $x + y > 0$, all points in the half-plane above the line $x + y = 0$ are in the solution set.

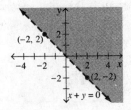

20. Graph $x + 2y = 0$. Since the original statement is less than or equal to, a solid line is drawn. Since the point $(1, 1)$ does not satisfy the inequality $x + 2y \leq 0$, all points on the line $x + 2y = 0$ and in the half-plane below the line are in the solution set.

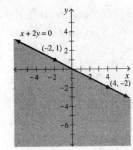

21.   Graph $5x + 2y = 10$. Since the original statement is greater than or equal to, a solid line is drawn. Since the point (0, 0) does not satisfy the inequality $5x + 2y \geq 10$, all points on the line and in the half-plane above the line $5x + 2y = 10$ are in the solution set.

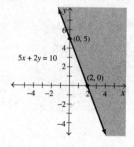

22.   Graph $y = -2x + 1$. Since the original statement is greater than or equal to, a solid line is drawn. Since the point (0, 0) does not satisfy the inequality $y \geq -2x + 1$, all points on the line and in the half-plane above the line $y = -2x + 1$ are in the solution set.

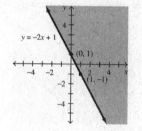

23.   Graph $3x - 2y = 12$. Since the original statement is strictly less than, a dashed line is drawn. Since the point (0, 0) satisfies the inequality $3x - 2y < 12$, all points in the half-plane above the line $3x - 2y = 12$ are in the solution set.

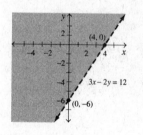

24.   Graph $y = 3x - 4$. Since the original statement is less than or equal to, a solid line is drawn. Since the point (0, 0) does not satisfy the inequality $y \leq 3x - 4$, all points on the line and in the half-plane below the line $y = 3x - 4$ are in the solution set.

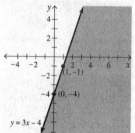

25. Graph $\frac{2}{5}x - \frac{1}{2}y = 1$. Since the original statement is less than or equal to, a solid line is drawn. Since the point (0, 0) satisfies the inequality $\frac{2}{5}x - \frac{1}{2}y \le 1$, all points on the line and in the half-plane above the line $\frac{2}{5}x - \frac{1}{2}y = 1$ are in the solution set.

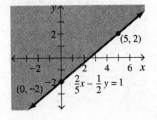

26. Graph $\frac{1}{2}x + \frac{2}{3}y = 1$. Since the original statement is greater than or equal to, a solid line is drawn. Since the point (0, 0) does not satisfy the inequality $\frac{1}{2}x + \frac{2}{3}y \ge 1$, all points on the line and in the half-plane above the line $\frac{1}{2}x + \frac{2}{3}y = 1$ are in the solution set.

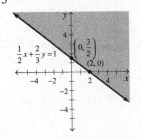

27. Graph $0.1x + 0.3y = 0.4$. Since the original statement is less than or equal to, a solid line is drawn. Since the point (0, 0) satisfies the inequality $0.1x + 0.3y \le 0.4$, all points on the line and in the half-plane below the line $0.1x + 0.3y = 0.4$ are in the solution set.

28. Graph $0.2x + 0.5y = 0.3$. Since the original statement is less than or equal to, a solid line is drawn. Since the point (0, 0) satisfies the inequality $0.2x + 0.5y \le 0.3$, all points on the line and in the half-plane below the line $0.2x + 0.5y = 0.3$ are in the solution set.

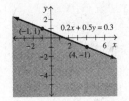

29. a) $x+y \leq 300$

b)

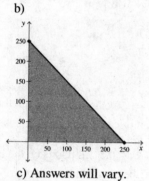

30.   a) $20x+10y \leq 100$

b)

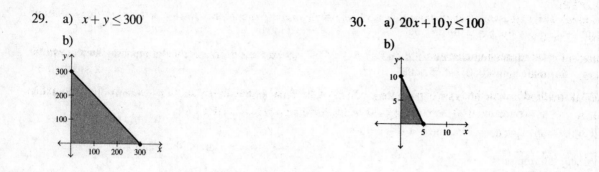

31. a) No, you cannot have a negative number of shirts.

b)

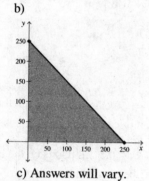

c) Answers will vary.

32. a)
$$2x - y < 8$$
$$2x - 2x - y < -2x + 8$$
$$-y < -2x + 8$$
$$\frac{-y}{-1} > \frac{-2x}{-1} + \frac{2}{-1}$$
$$y > 2x - 8$$

b)
$$-2x + y > -8$$
$$-2x + 2x + y > 2x - 8$$
$$y > 2x - 8$$

c)
$$2x - 4y < 16$$
$$2x - 2x - 4y < -2x + 16$$
$$-4y < -2x + 16$$
$$\frac{-4y}{-4} > \frac{-2x}{-4} + \frac{16}{-4}$$
$$y > \frac{1}{2}x - 4$$

d) $y > 2x - 8$

a, b, and d are equivalent to the same inequality.

Exercise Set 6.9

1. A **binomial** is an expression that contains two terms in which each exponent that appears on the variable is a whole number. Examples: $2x+3$, $x-7$, x^2-9

2. A **trinomial** is an expression containing three terms in which each exponent that appears on the variable is a whole number. Examples: $x+y+2, 2x+y+1, x^2-y^4-1$

3. The **FOIL method** is a method that obtains the products of the First, Outer, Inner, and Last terms of the binomials.

4. If the product of two factors is 0, then one or both of the factors must have a value of 0.

5. $ax^2+bx+c=0, \ a \neq 0$

6. $x = \dfrac{-b \pm \sqrt{b^2-4ac}}{2a}$

7. $x^2+8x+15=(x+5)(x+3)$ 8. $x^2+9x+14=(x+7)(x+2)$

9. $x^2-x-2=(x-2)(x+1)$ 10. $x^2+3x-4=(x+4)(x-1)$

11. $x^2+2x-24=(x+6)(x-4)$ 12. $x^2-6x+8=(x-4)(x-2)$

13. $x^2-2x-3=(x+1)(x-3)$ 14. $x^2-5x-6=(x-6)(x+1)$

15. $x^2-10x+21=(x-7)(x-3)$ 16. $x^2-x-20=(x-5)(x+4)$

17. $x^2-49=(x-7)(x+7)$ 18. $x^2-64=(x-8)(x+8)$

19. $x^2+3x-28=(x+7)(x-4)$ 20. $x^2+4x-32=(x-4)(x+8)$

21. $x^2+2x-63=(x+9)(x-7)$ 22. $x^2-2x-48=(x+6)(x-8)$

23. $2x^2-x-6=(2x+3)(x-2)$ 24. $3x^2-7x-6=(3x+2)(x-3)$

25. $5x^2+16x+3=(5x+1)(x+3)$ 26. $2x^2+3x-20=(2x-5)(x+4)$

27. $5x^2+12x+4=(5x+2)(x+2)$ 28. $2x^2-9x+10=(2x-5)(x-2)$

29. $4x^2+11x+6=(4x+3)(x+2)$ 30. $4x^2+20x+21=(2x+7)(2x+3)$

31. $4x^2-11x+6=(4x-3)(x-2)$ 32. $6x^2-11x+4=(3x-4)(2x-1)$

33. $8x^2-10x-3=(4x+1)(2x-3)$ 34. $6x^2-19x+3=(6x-1)(x-3)$

35. $(x-3)(x+6)=0$

$x-3=0 \quad$ or $\quad x+6=0$

$x=3 \qquad\qquad x=-6$

36. $(2x+1)(x-5)=0$

$2x+1=0 \quad$ or $\quad x-5=0$

$2x=-1 \qquad\qquad x=5$

$x=-\dfrac{1}{2}$

37. $(3x+4)(2x-1)=0$

$3x+4=0 \quad$ or $\quad 2x-1=0$

$3x=-4 \qquad\qquad 2x=1$

$x=-\dfrac{4}{3} \qquad\qquad x=\dfrac{1}{2}$

38. $(x-6)(5x-4)=0$

$x-6=0 \ $ or $\ 5x-4=0$

$x=6 \qquad 5x=4$

$x=\dfrac{4}{5}$

39. $x^2 + 7x + 10 = 0$

$(x+5)(x+2) = 0$

$x+5 = 0 \quad \text{or} \quad x+2 = 0$

$x = -5 \qquad\qquad x = -2$

40. $x^2 + x - 12 = 0$

$(x+4)(x-13) = 0$

$x+4 = 0 \quad \text{or} \quad x-3 = 0$

$x = -4 \qquad\qquad x = 3$

41. $x^2 - 7x + 6 = 0$

$(x-6)(x-1) = 0$

$x-6 = 0 \quad \text{or} \quad x-1 = 0$

$x = 6 \qquad\qquad x = 1$

42. $x^2 - 10x + 21 = 0$

$(x-7)(x-3) = 0$

$x-7 = 0 \quad \text{or} \quad x-3 = 0$

$x = 7 \qquad\qquad x = 3$

43. $x^2 - 15 = 2x$

$x^2 - 2x - 15 = 0$

$(x-5)(x+3) = 0$

$x-5 = 0 \text{ or } x+3 = 0$

$x = 5 \qquad x = -3$

44. $x^2 - 7x = -6$

$x^2 - 7x + 6 = 0$

$(x-6)(x-1) = 0$

$x-6 = 0 \text{ or } x-1 = 0$

$x = 6 \qquad x = 1$

45. $x^2 = 4x - 3$

$x^2 - 4x + 3 = 0$

$(x-3)(x-1) = 0$

$x-3 = 0 \text{ or } x-1 = 0$

$x = 3 \qquad x = 1$

46. $x^2 - 13x + 40 = 0$

$(x-5)(x-8) = 0$

$x-5 = 0 \text{ or } x-8 = 0$

$x = 5 \qquad x = 8$

47. $x^2 - 81 = 0$

$(x-9)(x+9) = 0$

$x-9 = 0 \text{ or } x+9 = 0$

$x = 9 \qquad x = -9$

48. $x^2 - 64 = 0$

$(x-8)(x+8) = 0$

$x-8 = 0 \text{ or } x+8 = 0$

$x = 8 \qquad x = -8$

49. $x^2 + 5x - 36 = 0$

$(x+9)(x-4) = 0$

$x+9 = 0 \text{ or } x-4 = 0$

$x = -9 \qquad x = 4$

50. $x^2 + 12x + 20 = 0$

$(x+10)(x+2) = 0$

$x+10 = 0 \text{ or } x+2 = 0$

$x = -10 \qquad\qquad x = -2$

51. $3x^2 + 10x = 8$

$3x^2 + 10x - 8 = 0$

$(3x-2)(x+4) = 0$

$3x-2 = 0 \quad \text{or} \quad x+4 = 0$

$3x = 2 \qquad\qquad x = -4$

$x = \dfrac{2}{3}$

52. $3x^2 - 5x = 2$

$3x^2 - 5x - 2 = 0$

$(3x+1)(x-2) = 0$

$3x+1 = 0 \quad \text{or} \quad x-2 = 0$

$3x = -1 \qquad\qquad x = 2$

$x = -\dfrac{1}{3}$

53. $5x^2 + 11x = -2$
$5x^2 + 11x + 2 = 0$
$(5x+1)(x+2) = 0$
$5x + 1 = 0 \text{ or } x + 2 = 0$
$5x = -1 \qquad x = -2$
$x = -\dfrac{1}{5}$

54. $2x^2 = -5x + 3$
$2x^2 + 5x - 3 = 0$
$(2x-1)(x+3) = 0$
$2x - 1 = 0 \text{ or } x + 3 = 0$
$2x = 1 \qquad x = -3$
$x = \dfrac{1}{2}$

55. $3x^2 - 4x = -1$
$3x^2 - 4x + 1 = 0$
$(3x-1)(x-1) = 0$
$3x - 1 = 0 \text{ or } x - 1 = 0$
$3x = 1 \qquad x = 1$
$x = \dfrac{1}{3}$

56. $5x^2 + 16x + 12 = 0$
$(5x+6)(x+2) = 0$
$5x + 6 = 0 \text{ or } x + 2 = 0$
$5x = -6 \qquad x = -2$
$x = -\dfrac{6}{5}$

57. $6x^2 - 11x + 3 = 0$
$(3x-1)(2x-3) = 0$
$3x - 1 = 0 \text{ or } 2x - 3 = 0$
$3x = 1 \qquad 2x = 3$
$x = \dfrac{1}{3} \qquad x = \dfrac{3}{2}$

58. $4x^2 + 11x - 3 = 0$
$(4x-1)(x+3) = 0$
$4x - 1 = 0 \text{ or } x + 3 = 0$
$4x = 1 \qquad x = -3$
$x = \dfrac{1}{4}$

59. $x^2 + 2x - 15 = 0$
$a = 1, \; b = 2, \; c = -15$

$$x = \frac{-2 \pm \sqrt{(2)^2 - 4(1)(-15)}}{2(1)}$$

$$x = \frac{-2 \pm \sqrt{4+60}}{2} = \frac{-2 \pm \sqrt{64}}{2} = \frac{-2 \pm 8}{2}$$

$$x = \frac{6}{2} = 3 \text{ or } x = \frac{-10}{2} = -5$$

60. $x^2 + 12x + 27 = 0$
$a = 1, \; b = 12, \; c = 27$

$$x = \frac{-12 \pm \sqrt{(12)^2 - 4(1)(27)}}{2(1)}$$

$$x = \frac{-12 \pm \sqrt{144-108}}{2} = \frac{-12 \pm \sqrt{36}}{2} = \frac{-12 \pm 6}{2}$$

$$x = \frac{-6}{2} = -3 \text{ or } x = \frac{-18}{2} = -9$$

61. $x^2 - 3x - 18 = 0$
$a = 1, \; b = -3, \; c = -18$

$$x = \frac{-(-3) \pm \sqrt{(-3)^2 - 4(1)(-18)}}{2(1)}$$

$$x = \frac{3 \pm \sqrt{9+72}}{2} = \frac{3 \pm \sqrt{81}}{2} = \frac{3 \pm 9}{2}$$

$$x = \frac{12}{2} = 6 \text{ or } x = \frac{-6}{2} = -3$$

62. $x^2 - 6x - 16 = 0$
$a = 1, \; b = -6, \; c = -16$

$$x = \frac{-(-6) \pm \sqrt{(-6)^2 - 4(1)(-16)}}{2(1)}$$

$$x = \frac{6 \pm \sqrt{36+64}}{2} = \frac{6 \pm \sqrt{100}}{2} = \frac{6 \pm 10}{2}$$

$$x = \frac{16}{2} = 8 \text{ or } x = \frac{-4}{2} = -2$$

63. $x^2 - 8x = 9$

$x^2 - 8x - 9 = 0$

$a = 1, b = -8, c = -9$

$x = \dfrac{-(-8) \pm \sqrt{(-8)^2 - 4(1)(-9)}}{2(1)}$

$x = \dfrac{8 \pm \sqrt{64 + 36}}{2} = \dfrac{8 \pm \sqrt{100}}{2} = \dfrac{8 \pm 10}{2}$

$x = \dfrac{18}{2} = 9$ or $x = \dfrac{-2}{2} = -1$

64. $x^2 = -8x + 15$

$x^2 + 8x - 15 = 0$

$a = 1, b = 8, c = -15$

$x = \dfrac{-8 \pm \sqrt{(8)^2 - 4(1)(-15)}}{2(1)}$

$x = \dfrac{-8 \pm \sqrt{64 + 60}}{2} = \dfrac{-8 \pm \sqrt{124}}{2} = \dfrac{-8 \pm 2\sqrt{31}}{2}$

$x = -4 \pm \sqrt{31}$

65. $x^2 - 2x + 3 = 0$

$a = 1, b = -2, c = 3$

$x = \dfrac{-(-2) \pm \sqrt{(-2)^2 - 4(1)(3)}}{2(1)}$

$x = \dfrac{2 \pm \sqrt{4 - 12}}{2} = \dfrac{2 \pm \sqrt{-8}}{2}$

No real solution

66. $2x^2 - x - 3 = 0$

$a = 2, b = -1, c = -3$

$x = \dfrac{-(-1) \pm \sqrt{(-1)^2 - 4(2)(-3)}}{2(2)}$

$x = \dfrac{1 \pm \sqrt{1 + 24}}{4} = \dfrac{1 \pm \sqrt{25}}{4} = \dfrac{1 \pm 5}{4}$

$x = \dfrac{6}{4} = \dfrac{3}{2}$ or $x = \dfrac{-4}{4} = -1$

67. $x^2 - 4x + 2 = 0$

$a = 1, b = -4, c = 2$

$x = \dfrac{-(-4) \pm \sqrt{(-4)^2 - 4(1)(2)}}{2(1)}$

$x = \dfrac{4 \pm \sqrt{16 - 8}}{2} = \dfrac{4 \pm \sqrt{8}}{2} = \dfrac{4 \pm 2\sqrt{2}}{2}$

$x = 2 \pm \sqrt{2}$

68. $2x^2 - 5x - 2 = 0$

$a = 2, b = -5, c = -2$

$x = \dfrac{-(-5) \pm \sqrt{(-5)^2 - 4(2)(-2)}}{2(2)}$

$x = \dfrac{5 \pm \sqrt{25 + 16}}{4} = \dfrac{5 \pm \sqrt{41}}{4}$

69. $3x^2 - 8x + 1 = 0$

$a = 3, \ b = -8, \ c = 1$

$x = \dfrac{-(-8) \pm \sqrt{(-8)^2 - 4(3)(1)}}{2(3)}$

$x = \dfrac{8 \pm \sqrt{64 - 12}}{6} = \dfrac{8 \pm \sqrt{52}}{6} = \dfrac{8 \pm 2\sqrt{13}}{6}$

$x = \dfrac{4 \pm \sqrt{13}}{3}$

70. $2x^2 + 4x + 1 = 0$

$a = 2, \ b = 4, \ c = 1$

$x = \dfrac{-4 \pm \sqrt{(4)^2 - 4(2)(1)}}{2(2)}$

$x = \dfrac{-4 \pm \sqrt{16 - 8}}{4} = \dfrac{-4 \pm \sqrt{8}}{4} = \dfrac{-4 \pm 2\sqrt{2}}{4}$

$x = \dfrac{-2 \pm \sqrt{2}}{2}$

71. $3x^2 - 6x - 5 = 0$

$a = 3, b = -6, c = -5$

$$x = \frac{-(-6) \pm \sqrt{(-6)^2 - 4(3)(-5)}}{2(3)}$$

$$x = \frac{6 \pm \sqrt{96}}{6} = \frac{6 \pm 4\sqrt{6}}{6} = \frac{3 \pm 2\sqrt{6}}{3}$$

72. $4x^2 - 5x - 3 = 0$

$a = 4, b = -5, c = -3$

$$x = \frac{-(-5) \pm \sqrt{(-5)^2 - 4(4)(-3)}}{2(4)}$$

$$x = \frac{5 \pm \sqrt{25 + 48}}{8} = \frac{5 \pm \sqrt{73}}{8}$$

73. $2x^2 + 7x + 5 = 0$

$a = 2, b = 7, c = 5$

$$x = \frac{-7 \pm \sqrt{(7)^2 - 4(2)(5)}}{2(2)}$$

$$x = \frac{-7 \pm \sqrt{49 - 40}}{4} = \frac{-7 \pm \sqrt{9}}{4} = \frac{-7 \pm 3}{4}$$

$$x = \frac{-4}{4} = -1 \text{ or } x = \frac{-10}{4} = -\frac{5}{2}$$

74. $3x^2 = 9x - 5$

$3x^2 - 9x + 5 = 0$

$a = 3, b = -9, c = 5$

$$x = \frac{-(-9) \pm \sqrt{(-9)^2 - 4(3)(5)}}{2(3)}$$

$$x = \frac{9 \pm \sqrt{81 - 60}}{6} = \frac{9 \pm \sqrt{21}}{6}$$

75. $3x^2 - 10x + 7 = 0$

$a = 3, b = -10, c = 7$

$$x = \frac{-(-10) \pm \sqrt{(-10)^2 - 4(3)(7)}}{2(3)}$$

$$x = \frac{10 \pm \sqrt{100 - 84}}{6} = \frac{10 \pm \sqrt{16}}{6} = \frac{10 \pm 4}{6}$$

$$x = \frac{14}{6} = \frac{7}{3} \text{ or } x = \frac{6}{6} = 1$$

76. $4x^2 + 7x - 1 = 0$

$a = 4, b = 7, c = -1$

$$x = \frac{-7 \pm \sqrt{(7)^2 - 4(4)(-1)}}{2(4)}$$

$$x = \frac{-7 \pm \sqrt{49 + 16}}{8} = \frac{-7 \pm \sqrt{65}}{8}$$

77. $4x^2 + 6x + 5 = 0$

$a = 4, b = 6, c = 5$

$$x = \frac{-6 \pm \sqrt{6^2 - 4(4)(5)}}{2(4)}$$

$$x = \frac{-6 \pm \sqrt{36 - 80}}{8} = \frac{6 \pm \sqrt{-44}}{8}$$

No real solution

78. $5x^2 - 4x + 2 = 0$

$a = 5, b = -4, c = 2$

$$x = \frac{-(-4) \pm \sqrt{(-4)^2 - 4(5)(2)}}{2(5)}$$

$$x = \frac{4 \pm \sqrt{16 - 40}}{10} = \frac{4 \pm \sqrt{-24}}{10}$$

No real solution

79. Area of backyard $= lw = 30(20) = 600 \text{ m}^2$

Let $x =$ width of grass around all sides of the flower garden

Width of flower garden $= 20 - 2x$

Length of flower garden $= 30 - 2x$

Area of flower garden $= lw = (30 - 2x)(20 - 2x)$

Area of grass $= 600 - (30 - 2x)(20 - 2x)$

$600 - (30 - 2x)(20 - 2x) = 336$

$600 - (600 - 100x + 4x^2) = 336$

$600 - 600 + 100x - 4x^2 = 336$

$-4x^2 + 100x = 336$

$4x^2 - 100x + 336 = 0$

$x^2 - 25x + 84 = 0$

$(x - 21)(x - 4) = 0$

$x - 21 = 0 \quad \text{or} \quad x - 4 = 0$

$x = 21 \qquad\qquad x = 4$

$x \neq 21$ since the width of the backyard is 20 m.

Width of grass $= 4$ m

Width of flower garden

$= 20 - 2x = 20 - 2(4) = 20 - 8 = 12$ m

Length of flower garden

$= 30 - 2x = 30 - 2(4) = 30 - 8 = 22$ m

80. $1090 = x^2 + 40x - 110$

$x^2 + 40x - 1200 = 0$

$(x + 60)(x - 20) = 0$

$x + 60 = 0 \quad \text{or} \quad x - 20 = 0$

$x = -60 \qquad\qquad x = 20$

Cannot mow a negative number of lawns. Thus, 20 lawns for maximum profit.

81. a) Since the equation is equal to 6 and not 0, the zero-factor property cannot be used.

b) $(x - 4)(x - 7) = 6$

$x^2 - 11x + 28 = 6$

$x^2 - 11x + 22 = 0$

$a = 1, b = -11, c = 22$

$x = \dfrac{-(-11) \pm \sqrt{(-11)^2 - 4(1)(22)}}{2(1)}$

$x = \dfrac{11 \pm \sqrt{121 - 88}}{2} = \dfrac{11 \pm \sqrt{33}}{2}$

$x \approx 8.37 \ \text{or} \ x \approx 2.63$

82. $x = \dfrac{-b \pm \sqrt{b^2 - 4ac}}{2a}$

The $b^2 - 4ac$ is the radicand in the quadratic formula, the part under the square root sign.

a) If $b^2 - 4ac > 0$, then you are taking the square root of a positive number and there are two solutions.

These solutions are $x = \dfrac{-b + \sqrt{b^2 - 4ac}}{2a}$ and $x = \dfrac{-b - \sqrt{b^2 - 4ac}}{2a}$.

b) If $b^2 - 4ac = 0$, then you are taking the square root of zero and there is one solution. This solution is $x = \dfrac{-b \pm \sqrt{0}}{2a} = \dfrac{-b}{2a}$.

c) If $b^2 - 4ac < 0$, then you are taking the square root of a negative number and there is no real solution.

83. $(x + 1)(x - 3) = 0$

   $x^2 - 2x - 3 = 0$

Exercise Set 6.10

1. A **function** is a special type of relation where each value of the independent variable corresponds to a unique value of the dependent variable.

2. A **relation** is any set of ordered pairs.

3. The **domain** of a function is the set of values that can be used for the independent variable.

4. The **range** of a function is the set of values obtained for the dependent variable.

5. The vertical line test can be used to determine if a graph represents a function. If a vertical line can be drawn so that it intersects the graph at more than one point, then each value of x does not have a unique value of y and the graph does not represent a function. If a vertical line cannot be made to intersect the graph in at least two different places, then the graph represents a function.

6. The area of a square is a function of the length of a side, the average stopping distance of a car is a function of its speed, the cost of apples is a function of the number of apples.

7. $x = -\dfrac{b}{2a}$

8. A parabola opens upward when the coefficient of the squared term is greater than 0. A parabola opens downward when the coefficient of the squared term is less than 0.

9. Not a function since $x = 2$ is not paired with a unique value of y.

10. Function since each value of x is paired with a unique value of y.
    D: $x = -2, -1, 1, 2, 3$ R: $y = -1, 1, 2, 3$

11. Function since each vertical line intersects the graph at only one point.
    D: all real numbers   R: all real numbers

12. Function since each vertical line intersects the graph at only one point.
    D: all real numbers   R: all real numbers

13. Not a function since $x = -1$ is not paired with a unique value of y.

14. Function since each vertical line intersects the graph at only one point.
    D: all real numbers   R: $y = 2$

15. Function since each vertical line intersects the graph at only one point.
    D: all real numbers   R: $y \geq -4$

16. Function since each vertical line intersects the graph at only one point.
    D: all real numbers   R: $y \leq 10$

17. Not a function since it is possible to draw a vertical line that intersects the graph at more than one point.

18. Function since each vertical line intersects the graph at only one point.

    D: $0 \le x \le 8$ R: $-1 \le y \le 1$

19. Function since each vertical line intersects the graph at only one point.

    D: $0 \le x < 12$ R: $y = 1, 2, 3$

20. Function since each vertical line intersects the graph at only one point.

    D: all real numbers   R: all real numbers

21. Not a function since it is possible to draw a vertical line that intersects the graph at more than one point.

22. Function since each vertical line intersects the graph at only one point.

    D: all real numbers   R: all real numbers

23. Function since each vertical line intersects the graph at only one point.

    D: all real numbers   R: $y > 0$

24. Function since each vertical line intersects the graph at only one point.

    D: $0 \le x \le 10$ R: $-1 \le y \le 3$

25. Not a function since it is possible to draw a vertical line that intersects the graph at more than one point.

26. Function since each vertical line intersects the graph at only one point.

    D: all real numbers   R: $y \ge 0$

27. Function since each value of x is paired with a unique value of y.

28. Function since each value of x is paired with a unique value of y.

29. Not a function since $x = 6$ is paired with two different values of y.

30. Not a function since $x = 4$ is paired with three different values of y.

31. Function since each value of x is paired with a unique value of y.

32. Not a function since $x = 1$ is paired with three different values of y.

33. $f(x) = x + 5, \quad x = 3$

    $f(3) = 3 + 5 = 8$

34. $f(x) = 2x + 4, \quad x = 1$

    $f(1) = 2(1) + 4 = 6$

35. $f(x) = -2x - 7, \quad x = -4$

    $f(-4) = -2(-4) - 7 = 8 - 7 = 1$

36. $f(x) = -5x + 3, \quad x = -1$

    $f(-1) = -5(-1) + 3 = 5 + 3 = 8$

37. $f(x) = 10x - 6, \quad x = 0$

    $f(0) = 10(0) - 6 = 0 - 6 = -6$

38. $f(x) = 7x - 6, \quad x = 4$

    $f(4) = 7(4) - 6 = 28 - 6 = 22$

39. $f(x) = x^2 - 3x + 1, \quad x = 4$

    $f(4) = (4)^2 - 3(4) + 1 = 16 - 12 + 1 = 5$

40. $f(x) = x^2 - 5, \quad x = 7$

    $f(7) = (7)^2 - 5 = 49 - 5 = 44$

41. $f(x) = -x^2 - 2x + 1, \quad x = 4$

    $f(4) = -(4)^2 - 2(4) + 1 = -16 - 8 + 1 = -23$

42. $f(x) = 2x^2 + 3x - 1, \quad x = 3$

    $f(3) = 2(3)^2 + 3(3) - 1 = 18 + 9 - 1 = 26$

43. $f(x) = 4x^2 - 6x - 9, \quad x = -3$

    $f(-3) = 4(-3)^2 - 6(-3) - 9 = 36 + 18 - 9 = 45$

44. $f(x) = 3x^2 + 2x - 5, \quad x = -4$

    $f(-4) = 3(-4)^2 + 2(-4) - 5 = 48 - 8 - 5 = 35$

45. $f(x) = -5x^2 + 3x - 9, \quad x = -1$

$f(-1) = -5(-1)^2 + 3(-1) - 9 = -5 - 3 - 9 = -17$

46. $f(x) = -3x^2 - 6x + 10, \quad x = -2$

$f(-2) = -3(-2)^2 - 6(-2) + 10 = -12 + 12 + 10 = 10$

47.

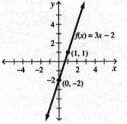

48.

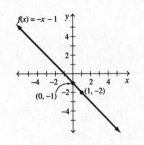

49.

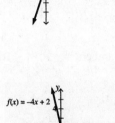

50.

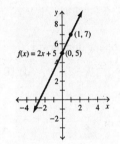

51.

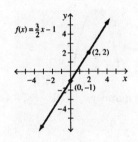

52.

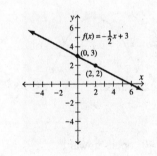

53. $y = x^2 - 9$

a) $a = 1 > 0$, opens upward

b) $x = 0$ c) $(0, -9)$ d) $(0, -9)$

e) $(3, 0), (-3, 0)$

f)

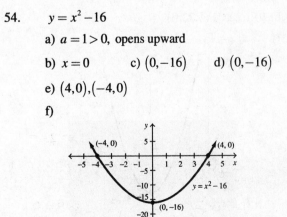

g) D: all real numbers   R: $y \geq -9$

54. $y = x^2 - 16$

a) $a = 1 > 0$, opens upward

b) $x = 0$ c) $(0, -16)$ d) $(0, -16)$

e) $(4, 0), (-4, 0)$

f)

g) D: all real numbers   R: $y \geq -16$

55. $y = -x^2 + 4$

a) $a = -1 < 0$, opens downward

b) $x = 0$ c) $(0, 4)$ d) $(0, 4)$

e) $(-2, 0), (2, 0)$

f)

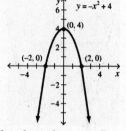

g) D: all real numbers   R: $y \leq 4$

56. $y = -x^2 + 16$

a) $a = -1 < 0$, opens downward

b) $x = 0$ c) $(0, 16)$ d) $(0, 16)$

e) $(-4, 0), (4, 0)$

f)

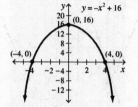

g) D: all real numbers   R: $y \leq 16$

57. $y = -2x^2 - 8$

a) $a = -2 < 0$, opens downward

b) $x = 0$ c) $(0, -8)$ d) $(0, -8)$

e) no x-intercepts

f)

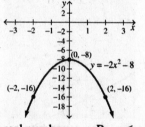

g) D: all real numbers   R: $y \leq -8$

58. $f(x) = -x^2 - 4$

a) $a = -1 < 0$, opens downward

b) $x = 0$ c) $(0, -4)$ d) $(0, -4)$

e) no x-intercepts

f)

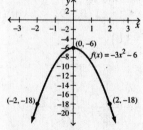

g) D: all real numbers   R: $y \leq -4$

59. $y = 2x^2 - 3$

a) $a = 2 > 0$, opens upward

b) $x = 0$ c) $(0, -3)$ d) $(0, -3)$

e) $(-1.22, 0), (1.22, 0)$

f)

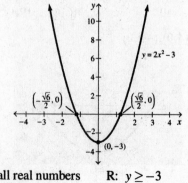

g) D: all real numbers   R: $y \geq -3$

60. $f(x) = -3x^2 - 6$

a) $a = -3 < 0$, opens downward

b) $x = 0$ c) $(0, -6)$ d) $(0, -6)$

e) no x-intercepts

f)

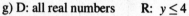

g) D: all real numbers   R: $y \leq -6$

61. $f(x) = x^2 + 2x + 6$

a) $a = 1 > 0$, opens upward

b) $x = -1$ c) $(-1, 5)$ d) $(0, 6)$

e) no x-intercepts

f)

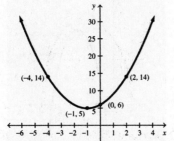

g) D: all real numbers   R: $y \geq 5$

62. $y = x^2 - 8x + 1$

a) $a = 1 > 0$, opens upward

b) $x = 4$ c) $(4, -15)$ d) $(0, 1)$

e) $(7.87, 0), (0.13, 0)$

f)

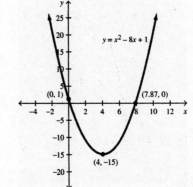

g) D: all real numbers   R: $y \geq -15$

63. $y = x^2 + 5x + 6$

a) $a = 1 > 0$, opens upward

b) $x = -\dfrac{5}{2}$ c) $(-2.5, -0.25)$ d) $(0, 6)$

e) $(-3, 0), (-2, 0)$

f)

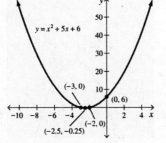

g) D: all real numbers   R: $y \geq -0.25$

64. $y = x^2 - 7x - 8$

a) $a = 1 > 0$, opens upward

b) $x = \dfrac{7}{2}$ c) $\left(\dfrac{7}{2}, -\dfrac{81}{4}\right)$ d) $(0, -8)$

e) $(-1, 0), (8, 0)$

f)

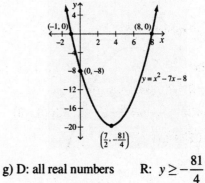

g) D: all real numbers   R: $y \geq -\dfrac{81}{4}$

65. $y = -x^2 + 4x - 6$

a) $a = -1 < 0$, opens downward

b) $x = 2$ c) $(2, -2)$ d) $(0, -6)$

e) no x-intercepts

f)

g) D: all real numbers   R: $y \leq -2$

66. $y = -x^2 + 8x - 8$

a) $a = -1 < 0$, opens downward

b) $x = 4$ c) $(4, 8)$ d) $(0, -8)$

e) $(1.17, 0), (6.83, 0)$

f)

g) D: all real numbers   R: $y \leq 8$

67. $y = -2x^2 + 3x - 2$

a) $a = -2 < 0$, opens downward

b) $x = \dfrac{3}{4}$ c) $\left(\dfrac{3}{4}, -\dfrac{7}{8}\right)$ d) $(0, -2)$

e) None

f)

g) D: all real numbers   R: $y \leq -\dfrac{7}{8}$

68. $y = -4x^2 - 6x + 4$

a) $a = -4 < 0$, opens downward

b) $x = -\dfrac{3}{4}$ c) $\left(-\dfrac{3}{4}, \dfrac{25}{4}\right)$ d) $(0, 4)$

e) $(-2, 0), \left(\dfrac{1}{2}, 0\right)$

f)

g) D: all real numbers   R: $y \leq \dfrac{25}{4}$

69.

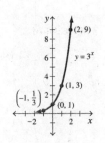

D: all real numbers   R: $y > 0$

70.

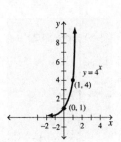

D: all real numbers   R: $y > 0$

71.

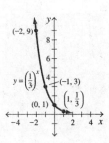

D: all real numbers   R: $y > 0$

72.

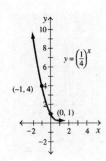

D: all real numbers   R: $y > 0$

73.

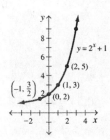

D: all real numbers   R: $y > 1$

74.

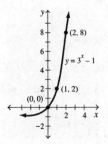

D: all real numbers   R: $y > -1$

75.

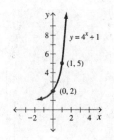

D: all real numbers   R: $y > 1$

76.

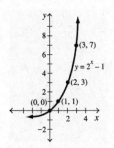

D: all real numbers   R: $y > -1$

77.

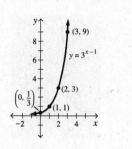

D: all real numbers   R: $y > 0$

78.

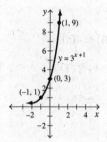

D: all real numbers   R: $y > 0$

79.

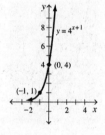

D: all real numbers   R: $y > 0$

80.

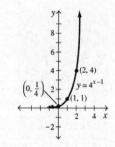

D: all real numbers   R: $y > 0$

81. $p(x) = 0.3x - 4000$

$p(150,000) = 0.3(150,000) - 4000$

$= 45,000 - 4000 = \$41,000$

82. $d(t) = 60t$

a) $t = 3, \ d(3) = 60(3) = 180$ mi

b) $t = 7, \ d(7) = 60(7) = 420$ mi

83. a) $2004 \rightarrow x = 74$

$f(74) = 0.005(74)^2 - 0.36(74) + 11.8$

$= 12.54 \approx 13\%$

b) 1970

c) $x = -\dfrac{b}{2a} = -\dfrac{-0.36}{2(0.005)} = 36$

$f(36) = 0.005(36)^2 - 0.36(36) + 11.8$

$\approx 5.32 \approx 5\%$

84. a) 6 A.M. $\rightarrow x = 6$

$t(6) = -1.11(6^2) + 6.60(6) + 51.28$

$= 50.92 \approx 51°$

b) 2 A.M., 3 A.M.

c) $x = -\dfrac{b}{2a} = -\dfrac{6.60}{2(-1.11)} \approx 2.973$

≈ 3

$t(3) = -1.11(3^2) + 6.60(3) + 51.28$

$= 61.09 \approx 61°$

85. $P(x) = 4000(1.3)^{0.1x}$

 a) $x = 10$, $P(10) = 4000(1.3)^{0.1(10)}$

  $= 4000(1.3) = 5200$ people

 b) $x = 50$, $P(50) = 4000(1.3)^{0.1(50)}$

  $= 4000(3.71293)$

  $= 14{,}851.72 \approx 14{,}852$ people

86. $S = S_0 e^{-0.028t}$

 $P = 1000e^{-0.028(40)}$

 $= 1000e^{-1.12}$

 $\approx 1000(0.326)$

 $= 326\,\text{g}$

87. a) Yes

 b) $\approx \$59$

88. a) Yes

 b) $\approx 180{,}000$ subscribers

89. $d = (21.9)(2)^{(20-x)/12}$

 a) $x = 19$, $d = (21.9)(2)^{(20-19)/12}$

  $= (21.9)(1.059463094) \approx 23.2\,\text{cm}$

 b) $x = 4$, $d = (21.9)(2)^{(20-4)/12}$

  $= (21.9)(2.519842099) \approx 55.2\,\text{cm}$

 c) $x = 0$, $d = (21.9)(2)^{(20-0)/12}$

  $= (21.9)(3.174802105) \approx 69.5\,\text{cm}$

90. $f(n) = 150{,}000(1.04)^n$

 a) $f(8) = 150{,}000(1.04)^8$

  $= 150{,}000(1.36856905) \approx 205{,}285$;

  The value of the house after 8 years is about $\$205{,}285$.

 b) 14 years since $f(13) \approx \$249{,}800$ and

  $f(14) \approx \$259{,}800$

91. $f(x) = -0.85x + 187$

 a) $f(20) = -0.85(20) + 187 = 170$ beats per minute

 b) $f(30) = -0.85(30) + 187 = 161.5 \approx 162$ beats per minute

 c) $f(50) = -0.85(50) + 187 = 144.5 \approx 145$ beats per minute

 d) $f(60) = -0.85(60) + 187 = 136$ beats per minute

 e) $-0.85x + 187 = 85$

  $-0.85x = -102$

  $x = 120$ years of age

92. $d(t) = 186{,}000t$

 a) $t = 1.3$, $d(1.3) = 186{,}000(1.3) = 241{,}800\,\text{mi}$

 b) $186{,}000\,\dfrac{\text{m}}{\text{sec}} \times 60\,\dfrac{\text{sec}}{\text{min}} = 11{,}160{,}000\,\dfrac{\text{m}}{\text{min}}$

  $d(t) = 11{,}160{,}000t$

 c) $d(8.3) = 11{,}160{,}000(8.3) = 92{,}628{,}000\,\text{mi}$

Review Exercises

1. $x = 2, \quad x^2 + 15 = (2)^2 + 15 = 4 + 15 = 19$

2. $x = -1, \quad -x^2 - 7 = -(-1)^2 - 7 = -1 - 7 = -8$

3. $x = 2, 4x^2 - 2x + 5 = 4(2)^2 - 2(2) + 5$
   $= 16 - 4 + 5 = 17$

4. $x = \dfrac{1}{2}, \; -x^2 + 7x - 3 = -\left(\dfrac{1}{2}\right)^2 + 7\left(\dfrac{1}{2}\right) - 3$
   $$= -\dfrac{1}{4} + \dfrac{14}{4} - \dfrac{12}{4} = \dfrac{1}{4}$$

5. $x = -1, 4x^3 - 7x^2 + 3x + 1$
   $= 4(-1)^3 - 7(-1)^2 + 3(-1) + 1$
   $= -4 - 7 - 3 + 1 = -13$

6. $x = 1, y = -2, \; 3x^2 - xy + 2y^2$
   $= 3(1)^2 - 1(-2) + 2(-2)^2$
   $= 3 + 2 + 8 = 13$

7. $3x - 2 + x + 7 = 4x + 5$

8. $2x + 5(x - 2) + 8x = 3x + 5x - 10 + 8x = 15x - 10$

9. $4(x - 1) + \dfrac{1}{3}(9x + 3) = 4x - 4 + 3x + 1 = 7x - 3$

10. $\quad\;\; 4s + 10 = -30$
    $4s + 10 - 10 = -30 - 10$
    $\quad\qquad 4s = -40$
    $\quad\qquad \dfrac{4s}{4} = \dfrac{-40}{4}$
    $\quad\qquad\; s = -10$

11. $\quad\;\; 3t + 14 = -6t - 13$
    $3t - 3t + 14 = -6t - 3t - 13$
    $\quad\qquad 14 = -9t - 13$
    $\quad 14 + 13 = -9t - 13 + 13$
    $\quad\qquad 27 = -9t$
    $\quad\qquad \dfrac{27}{-9} = \dfrac{-9t}{-9}$
    $\quad\qquad -3 = t$

12. $\quad\;\; \dfrac{x + 5}{2} = \dfrac{x - 3}{4}$
    $\quad 4(x + 5) = 2(x - 3)$
    $\quad\; 4x + 20 = 2x - 6$
    $4x - 2x + 20 = 2x - 2x - 6$
    $\quad\; 2x + 20 = -6$
    $2x + 20 - 20 = -6 - 20$
    $\quad\qquad 2x = -26$
    $\quad\qquad \dfrac{2x}{2} = \dfrac{-26}{2}$
    $\quad\qquad\; x = -13$

13. $\quad\; 4(x - 2) = 3 + 5(x + 4)$
    $\quad\; 4x - 8 = 3 + 5x + 20$
    $\quad\; 4x - 8 = 5x + 23$
    $4x - 4x - 8 = 5x - 4x + 23$
    $\quad\qquad -8 = x + 23$
    $\quad -8 - 23 = x + 23 - 23$
    $\quad\qquad -31 = x$

14. $\quad\qquad \dfrac{x}{4} + \dfrac{3}{5} = 7$
    $20\left(\dfrac{x}{4} + \dfrac{3}{5}\right) = 20(7)$
    $\quad\quad 5x + 12 = 140$
    $\; 5x + 12 - 12 = 140 - 12$
    $\quad\qquad 5x = 128$
    $\quad\qquad \dfrac{5x}{5} = \dfrac{128}{5}$
    $\quad\qquad\;\; x = \dfrac{128}{5}$

15.
$$\frac{2}{\frac{1}{3}} = \frac{3}{x}$$

$$2x = 3\left(\frac{1}{3}\right)$$

$$2x = 1$$

$$\frac{2x}{2} = \frac{1}{2}$$

$$x = \frac{1}{2} \text{ cup}$$

16. 1 hr 40 min = 60 min + 40 min = 100 min

$$\frac{120}{100} = \frac{300}{x}$$

$$120x = 100(300)$$

$$120x = 30,000$$

$$\frac{120x}{120} = \frac{30,000}{120}$$

$$x = 250 \text{ min, or 4 hr 10 min}$$

17. $A = bh$

$A = 12(4) = 48$

18. $V = 2\pi R^2 r^2$

$V = 2(3.14)(3)^2(1.75)^2$

$V = 2(3.14)(9)(3.0625)$

$V = 173.0925 \approx 173.1$

19.
$$z = \frac{\bar{x} - \mu}{\frac{\sigma}{\sqrt{n}}}$$

$$2 = \frac{\bar{x} - 100}{\frac{3}{\sqrt{16}}}$$

$$\frac{2}{1} = \frac{\bar{x} - 100}{\frac{3}{4}}$$

$$2\left(\frac{3}{4}\right) = 1(\bar{x} - 100)$$

$$\frac{3}{2} = \bar{x} - 100$$

$$\frac{3}{2} + 100 = \bar{x} - 100 + 100$$

$$\frac{3}{2} + \frac{200}{2} = \bar{x}$$

$$\frac{203}{2} = \bar{x}$$

$$101.5 = \bar{x}$$

20. $E = mc^2$

$$400 = m(4)^2$$

$$400 = 16m$$

$$\frac{400}{16} = \frac{16m}{16}$$

$$25 = m$$

21.
$$8x - 4y = 24$$

$$8x - 8x - 4y = -8x + 24$$

$$-4y = -8x + 24$$

$$\frac{-4y}{-4} = \frac{-8x + 24}{-4}$$

$$y = 2x - 6$$

22.
$$2x + 7y = 15$$

$$2x - 2x + 7y = -2x + 15$$

$$7y = -2x + 15$$

$$\frac{7y}{7} = \frac{-2x + 15}{7} = -\frac{2}{7}x + \frac{15}{7}$$

23.

$$2x - 3y + 52 = 30$$
$$2x - 2x - 3y + 52 = -2x + 30$$
$$-3y + 52 = -2x + 30$$
$$-3y + 52 - 52 = -2x + 30 - 52$$
$$-3y = -2x - 22$$
$$\frac{-3y}{-3} = \frac{-2x - 22}{-3}$$
$$y = \frac{-2x - 22}{-3} = \frac{2x + 22}{3} = \frac{2}{3}x + \frac{22}{3}$$

24.

$$-3x - 4y + 5z = 4$$
$$-3x + 3x - 4y + 5z = 3x + 4$$
$$-4y + 5z = 3x + 4$$
$$-4y + 5z - 5z = 3x - 5z + 4$$
$$-4y = 3x - 5z + 4$$
$$\frac{-4y}{-4} = \frac{3x - 5z + 4}{-4}$$
$$y = \frac{3x - 5z + 4}{-4}$$
$$= \frac{-(3x - 5z + 4)}{4}$$
$$= \frac{-3x + 5z - 4}{4}$$
$$= -\frac{3}{4}x + \frac{5}{4}z - 1$$

25.

$$A = lw$$
$$\frac{A}{l} = \frac{lw}{l}$$
$$\frac{A}{l} = w$$

26.

$$P = 2l + 2w$$
$$P - 2l = 2l - 2l + 2w$$
$$P - 2l = 2w$$
$$\frac{P - 2l}{2} = \frac{2w}{2}$$
$$\frac{P - 2l}{2} = w$$

27.

$$L = 2(wh + lh)$$
$$L = 2wh + 2lh$$
$$L - 2wh = 2wh - 2wh + 2lh$$
$$L - 2wh = 2lh$$
$$\frac{L - 2wh}{2h} = \frac{2lh}{2h}$$
$$\frac{L - 2wh}{2h} = l \text{ or } l = \frac{L}{2h} - \frac{2wh}{2h} = \frac{L}{2h} - w$$

28.

$$a_n = a_1 + (n-1)d$$
$$a_n - a_1 = a_1 - a_1 + (n-1)d$$
$$a_n - a_1 = (n-1)d$$
$$\frac{a_n - a_1}{n-1} = \frac{(n-1)d}{n-1}$$
$$\frac{a_n - a_1}{n-1} = d$$

29. $7 - 4x$

30. $2y + 7$

31. $10 + 3r$

32. $\dfrac{9}{q} - 15$

33.

$$\text{Let } x = \text{the number}$$
$$7x = 7 \text{ times the number}$$
$$3 + 7x = 3 \text{ increased by } 7 \text{ times the number}$$
$$3 + 7x = 17$$
$$3 - 3 + 7x = 17 - 3$$
$$7x = 14$$
$$\frac{7x}{7} = \frac{14}{7}$$
$$x = 2$$

34. Let $x =$ the number

$$3x = \text{the product of } 3 \text{ and a number}$$
$$3x + 8 = \text{the product of } 3 \text{ and a number}$$
$$\text{increased by } 8$$
$$x - 6 = 6 \text{ less than the number}$$
$$3x + 8 = x - 6$$
$$3x - x + 8 = x - x - 6$$
$$2x + 8 = -6$$
$$2x + 8 - 8 = -6 - 8$$
$$2x = -14$$
$$\frac{2x}{2} = \frac{-14}{2}$$
$$x = -7$$

35. Let $x =$ the number

$$x - 4 = \text{the difference of a number and } 4$$
$$5(x - 4) = 5 \text{ times the difference of a number}$$
$$\text{and } 4$$
$$5(x - 4) = 45$$
$$5x - 20 = 45$$
$$5x - 20 + 20 = 45 + 20$$
$$5x = 65$$
$$\frac{5x}{5} = \frac{65}{5}$$
$$x = 13$$

36. Let $x =$ the number

$$10x = 10 \text{ times a number}$$
$$10x + 14 = 14 \text{ more than } 10 \text{ times a number}$$
$$x + 12 = \text{the sum of a number and } 12$$
$$8(x + 12) = 8 \text{ times the sum of a number and } 12$$
$$10x + 14 = 8(x + 12)$$
$$10x + 14 = 8x + 96$$
$$10x - 8x + 14 = 8x - 8x + 96$$
$$2x + 14 = 96$$
$$2x + 14 - 14 = 96 - 14$$
$$2x = 82$$
$$\frac{2x}{2} = \frac{82}{2}$$
$$x = 41$$

37.

$$\text{Let } x = \text{the amount invested in bonds}$$
$$2x = \text{the amount invested in mutual funds}$$
$$x + 2x = 15,000$$
$$3x = 15,000$$
$$\frac{3x}{3} = \frac{15,000}{3}$$
$$x = \$5000 \text{ in bonds}$$
$$2x = 2(5000) = \$10,000 \text{ in mutual funds}$$

38. Let $x =$ number of lawn chairs

$$9.50x = \text{variable cost per lawn chair}$$
$$9.50x + 15,000 = 95,000$$
$$9.50x + 15,000 - 15,000 = 95,000 - 15,000$$
$$9.50x = 80,000$$
$$\frac{9.50x}{9.50} = \frac{80,000}{9.50}$$
$$x \approx 8421.05 \approx 8421 \text{ lawn chairs}$$

39.

Let $x =$ the number of species
of threatened mammals

$6x + 2 =$ the number of species
of endangered mammals

$6x + 2 + x = 79$

$7x + 2 = 79$

$7x + 2 - 2 = 79 - 2$

$7x = 77$

$\dfrac{7x}{7} = \dfrac{77}{7}$

$x = 11$ species of
threatened mammals

$6x + 2 = 6(11) + 2$

$= 68$ species of
endangered mammals

40. Let $x =$ profit at restaurant B

$x + 12,000 =$ profit at restaurant A

$x + (x + 12,000) = 68,000$

$2x + 12,000 = 68,000$

$2x + 12,000 - 12,000 = 68,000 - 12,000$

$2x = 56,000$

$\dfrac{2x}{2} = \dfrac{56,000}{2}$

$x = \$28,000$ for restaurant B

$x + 12,000 = 28,000 + 12,000 = \$40,000$ for restaurant A

41.

$s = kt$

$40 = k(5)$

$k = \dfrac{40}{5} = 8$

$s = 8t$

$s = 8(8)$

$s = 64$

42.

$J = \dfrac{k}{A^2}$

$8 = \dfrac{k}{3^2}$

$k = 3^2(8)$

$k = 72$

$J = \dfrac{72}{A^2}$

$J = \dfrac{72}{6^2}$

$J = \dfrac{72}{36} = 2$

43.

$W = \dfrac{kL}{A}$

$80 = \dfrac{k(100)}{20}$

$100k = 1600$

$\dfrac{100k}{100} = \dfrac{1600}{100}$

$k = 16$

$W = \dfrac{16L}{A}$

$W = \dfrac{16(50)}{40} = \dfrac{800}{40} = 20$

44.

$z = \dfrac{kxy}{r^2}$

$12 = \dfrac{k(20)(8)}{(8)^2}$

$160k = 768$

$\dfrac{160k}{160} = \dfrac{768}{160}$

$k = 4.8$

$z = \dfrac{4.8xy}{r^2}$

$z = \dfrac{4.8(10)(80)}{(3)^2} = \dfrac{3840}{9} = 426.\overline{6} \approx 426.7$

45. a)
$$\frac{30 \text{ lb}}{2500 \text{ ft}^2} = \frac{x \text{ lb}}{12,500 \text{ ft}^2}$$
$$30(12,500) = 2500x$$
$$375,000 = 2500x$$
$$\frac{375,000}{2500} = \frac{2500x}{2500}$$
$$x = 150 \text{ lb}$$

b) $\dfrac{150}{30} = 5$ bags

46.
$$\frac{1 \text{ in.}}{30 \text{ mi}} = \frac{x \text{ in.}}{120 \text{ mi}}$$
$$30x = 120$$
$$\frac{30x}{30} = \frac{120}{30}$$
$$x = 4 \text{ in.}$$

47.
$$\frac{1 \text{ } kWh}{\$0.162} = \frac{740 \text{ } kWh}{x}$$
$$x = \$119.88$$

48.
$$S = kw$$
$$4.2 = k(60)$$
$$\frac{4.2}{60} = \frac{60k}{60}$$
$$k = 0.07$$
$$S = 0.07w$$
$$S = 0.07(25)$$
$$S = 1.75 \text{ in.}$$

49.
$$8 + 7x \le 5x - 4$$
$$8 - 8 + 7x \le 5x - 4 - 8$$
$$7x \le 5x - 12$$
$$7x - 5x \le 5x - 5x - 12$$
$$2x \le -12$$
$$\frac{2x}{2} \le \frac{-12}{2}$$
$$x \le -6$$

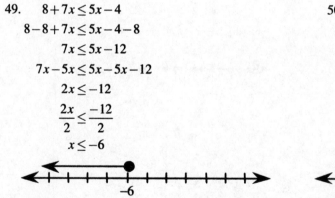

50.
$$2x + 8 \ge 5x + 11$$
$$2x - 5x + 8 \ge 5x - 5x + 11$$
$$-3x + 8 \ge 11$$
$$-3x + 8 - 8 \ge 11 - 8$$
$$-3x \ge 3$$
$$\frac{-3x}{-3} \le \frac{3}{-3}$$
$$x \le -1$$

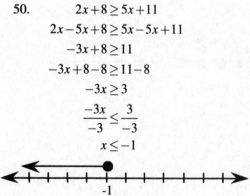

51. $3(x+9) \le 4x+11$

$3x+27 \le 4x+11$

$3x-4x+27 \le 4x-4x+11$

$-x+27 \le 11$

$-x+27-27 \le 11-27$

$-x \le -16$

$\dfrac{-x}{-1} \ge \dfrac{-16}{-1}$

$x \ge 16$

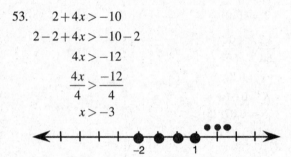

52. $-3 \le x+1 < 7$

$-3-1 \le x+1-1 < 7-1$

$-4 \le x < 6$

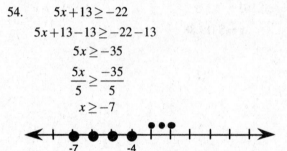

53. $2+4x > -10$

$2-2+4x > -10-2$

$4x > -12$

$\dfrac{4x}{4} > \dfrac{-12}{4}$

$x > -3$

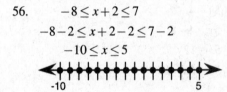

54. $5x+13 \ge -22$

$5x+13-13 \ge -22-13$

$5x \ge -35$

$\dfrac{5x}{5} \ge \dfrac{-35}{5}$

$x \ge -7$

55. $-1 < x \le 9$

56. $-8 \le x+2 \le 7$

$-8-2 \le x+2-2 \le 7-2$

$-10 \le x \le 5$

57. - 60.

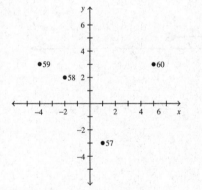

61.

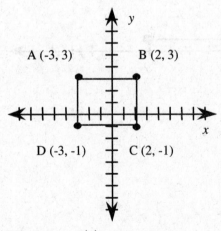

A (-3, 3)   B (2, 3)

D (-3, -1)   C (2, -1)

Area $= lw = 5(4) = 20$ square units

62.

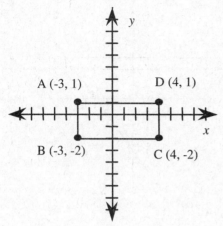

A (-3, 1)   D (4, 1)

B (-3, -2)   C (4, -2)

Area $= lw = 7(3) = 21$ square units

63.

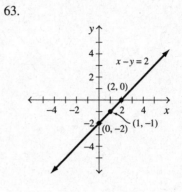

64.

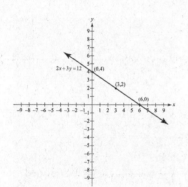

65.

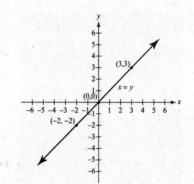

66.

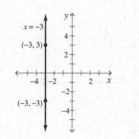

67.

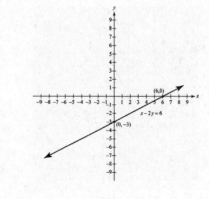

68.

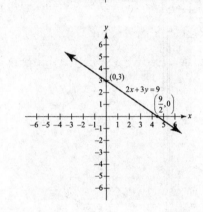

69.

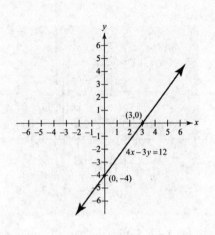

70.

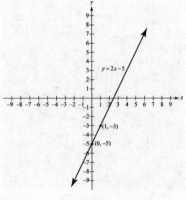

71. $m = \dfrac{5-3}{6-1} = \dfrac{2}{5}$

72. $m = \dfrac{-4-(-1)}{5-3} = \dfrac{-4+1}{5-3} = -\dfrac{3}{2}$

73. $m = \dfrac{3-(-4)}{2-(-1)} = \dfrac{3+4}{2+1} = \dfrac{7}{3}$

74. $m = \dfrac{-2-2}{6-6} = \dfrac{-4}{0}$ Undefined

75.

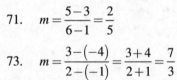

76.

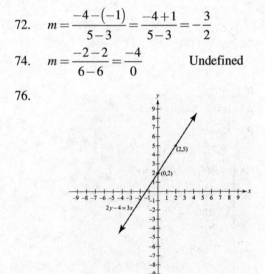

77.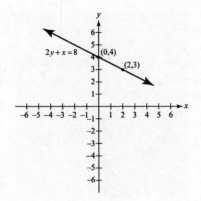

78.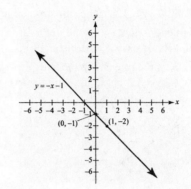

79. The *y*-intercept is 4, thus $b = 4$. Since the graph rises from left to right, the slope is positive. The change in *y* is 4 units while the change in *x* is 2. Thus, *m*, the slope is $\frac{4}{2}$ or 2. The equation is $y = 2x + 4$.

80. The *y*-intercept is 1, thus $b = 1$. Since the graph falls from left to right, the slope is negative. The change in *y* is 3 units while the change in *x* is 3. Thus, *m*, the slope is $\frac{-3}{3}$ or -1. The equation is $y = -x + 1$.

81. a)

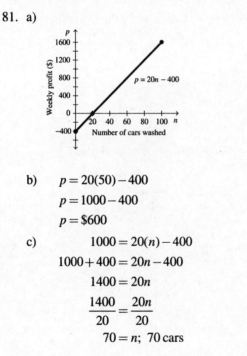

b) $p = 20(50) - 400$

   $p = 1000 - 400$

   $p = \$600$

c) $1000 = 20(n) - 400$

   $1000 + 400 = 20n - 400$

   $1400 = 20n$

   $\dfrac{1400}{20} = \dfrac{20n}{20}$

   $70 = n; \ 70 \text{ cars}$

82. a)

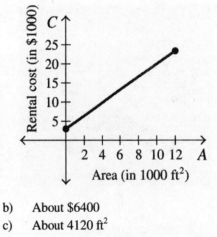

b) About $6400

c) About 4120 ft^2

83. Graph $2x + 3y = 12$. Since the original inequality is less than or equal to, a solid line is drawn. Since the point (0, 0) satisfies the inequality $2x + 3y \leq 12$, all points on the line and in the half-plane below the line $2x + 3y = 12$ are in the solution set.

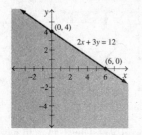

84. Graph $4x + 2y = 12$. Since the original inequality is greater than or equal to, a solid line is drawn. Since the point (0, 0) does not satisfy the inequality $4x + 2y \geq 12$, all points on the line and in the half plane above the line $4x + 2y = 12$ are in the solution set.

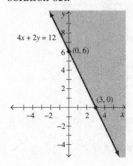

85. Graph $2x - 3y = 12$. Since the original inequality is strictly greater than, a dashed line is drawn. Since the point (0, 0) does not satisfy the inequality $2x - 3y > 12$, all points in the half-plane below the line $2x - 3y = 12$ are in the solution set.

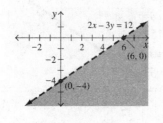

86. Graph $-7x - 2y = 14$. Since the original inequality is strictly less than, a dashed line is drawn. Since the point (0, 0) satisfies the inequality $-7x - 2y < 14$, all points in the half-plane to the right of the line $-7x - 2y = 14$ are in the solution set.

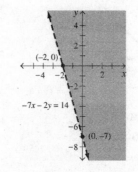

87. $x^2 + 11x + 18 = (x + 2)(x + 9)$

88. $x^2 + x - 30 = (x + 6)(x - 5)$

89. $x^2 - 10x + 24 = (x - 6)(x - 4)$

90. $x^2 - 9x + 20 = (x - 5)(x - 4)$

91. $6x^2 + 7x - 3 = (3x - 1)(2x + 3)$

92. $2x^2 + 13x - 7 = (2x - 1)(x + 7)$

93. $x^2 + 4x + 3 = 0$
$(x + 1)(x + 3) = 0$
$x + 1 = 0$ or $x + 3 = 0$
$x = -1 \qquad x = -3$

94. $x^2 + 3x = 18$
$x^2 + 3x - 18 = 0$
$(x + 6)(x - 3) = 0$
$x + 6 = 0$ or $x - 3 = 0$
$x = -6 \qquad x = 3$

95. $3x^2 - 17x + 10 = 0$

    $(3x - 2)(x - 5) = 0$

    $3x - 2 = 0$ or $x - 5 = 0$

    $3x = 2$ $x = 5$

    $x = \dfrac{2}{3}$

96. $3x^2 = -7x - 2$

    $3x^2 + 7x + 2 = 0$

    $(x + 2)(3x + 1) = 0$

    $x + 2 = 0$ or $3x + 1 = 0$

    $x = -2$ $3x = -1$

    $x = -\dfrac{1}{3}$

97. $x^2 - 4x - 1 = 0$

    $a = 1, \; b = -4, \; c = -1$

    $x = \dfrac{-(-4) \pm \sqrt{(-4)^2 - 4(1)(-1)}}{2(1)}$

    $x = \dfrac{4 \pm \sqrt{16 + 4}}{2} = \dfrac{4 \pm \sqrt{20}}{2} = \dfrac{4 \pm 2\sqrt{5}}{2} = 2 \pm \sqrt{5}$

98. $x^2 - 6x - 16 = 0$

    $a = 1, b = -6, c = -6$

    $x = \dfrac{-(-6) \pm \sqrt{(-6)^2 - 4(1)(-16)}}{2(1)}$

    $x = \dfrac{6 \pm \sqrt{36 + 64}}{2} = \dfrac{6 \pm \sqrt{100}}{2} = \dfrac{6 \pm 10}{2}$

    $x = \dfrac{16}{2} = 8$ or $x = \dfrac{-4}{2} = -2$

99. $2x^2 - 3x + 4 = 0$

    $a = 2, b = -3, c = 4$

    $x = \dfrac{-(-3) \pm \sqrt{(-3)^2 - 4(2)(4)}}{2(2)}$

    $x = \dfrac{3 \pm \sqrt{9 - 32}}{4} = \dfrac{3 \pm \sqrt{-23}}{4}$

    No real solution

100. $2x^2 - x - 3 = 0$

    $a = 2, b = -1, c = -3$

    $x = \dfrac{-(-1) \pm \sqrt{(-1)^2 - 4(2)(-3)}}{2(2)}$

    $x = \dfrac{1 \pm \sqrt{1 + 24}}{4} = \dfrac{1 \pm \sqrt{25}}{4} = \dfrac{1 \pm 5}{4}$

    $x = \dfrac{6}{4} = \dfrac{3}{2}$ or $x = \dfrac{-4}{4} = -1$

101. Function since each value of x is paired with a unique value of y.

    D: $x = -2, -1, 2, 3$ R: $y = -1, 0, 2$

102. Not a function since it is possible to draw a vertical line that intersects the graph at more than one point.

103. Not a function since it is possible to draw a vertical line that intersects the graph at more than one point.

104. Function since each vertical line intersects the graph at only one point.

    D: all real numbers   R: all real numbers

105. $f(x) = 3x - 7, \; x = 4$

    $f(4) = 3(4) - 7 = 12 - 7 = 5$

106. $f(x) = -2x + 9, \; x = -3$

    $f(-3) = -2(-3) + 9 = 6 + 9 = 15$

107. $f(x) = 2x^2 - 3x + 4, \; x = 5$

    $f(5) = 2(5)^2 - 3(5) + 4 = 50 - 15 + 4 = 39$

108. $f(x) = -4x^2 + 7x + 9, \; x = -2$

    $f(-2) = -4(-2)^2 + 7(-2) + 9 = -16 - 14 + 9 = -21$

109. $y = -x^2 - 4x + 21$

a) $a = -1 < 0$, opens downward

b) $x = -2$ c) $(-2, 25)$ d) $(0, 21)$

e) $(-7, 0), (3, 0)$

f)

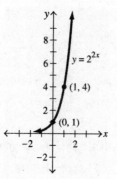

g) D: all real numbers R: $y \leq 25$

110. $f(x) = 2x^2 + 8x + 6$

a) $a = 2 > 0$, opens upward

b) $x = -\dfrac{8}{2(2)} = -2$ c) $(-2, -2)$ d) $(0, 6)$

e) $(-3, 0), (-1, 0)$

f)

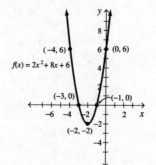

g) D: all real numbers R: $y \geq -2$

111.

D: all real numbers R: $y > 0$

112.

D: all real numbers R: $y > 0$

113. $m = 30 - 0.002n^2$, $n = 60$

$m = 30 - 0.002(60)^2 = 30 - 0.002(3600)$

$\quad = 30 - 7.2 = 22.8$ mpg

114. $n = 2a^2 - 80a + 5000$

a) $a = 18$

$\quad n = 2(18)^2 - 80(18) + 5000$

$\quad\quad = 648 - 1440 + 5000 = 4208$

b) $a = 25$

$\quad n = 2(25)^2 - 80(25) + 5000$

$\quad\quad = 1250 - 2000 + 5000 = 4250$

115. $P = 100(0.92)^x$, $x = 4.5$

$P = 100(0.92)^{4.5}$

$\quad = 100(0.6871399881) = 68.71399881 \approx 68.7\%$

Chapter Test

1. $4x^2 + 3x - 1, \quad x = -2$

    $4(-2)^2 + 3(-2) - 1 = 16 - 6 - 1 = 9$

2. $3x + 5 = 2(4x - 7)$

    $3x + 5 = 8x - 14$

    $3x - 8x + 5 = 8x - 8x - 14$

    $-5x + 5 = -14$

    $-5x + 5 - 5 = -14 - 5$

    $-5x = -19$

    $\dfrac{-5x}{-5} = \dfrac{-19}{-5}$

    $x = \dfrac{19}{5}$

3. $-2(x - 3) + 6x = 2x + 3(x - 4)$

    $-2x + 6 + 6x = 2x + 3x - 12$

    $4x + 6 = 5x - 12$

    $4x - 5x + 6 = 5x - 5x - 12$

    $-x + 6 = -12$

    $-x + 6 - 6 = -12 - 6$

    $-x = -18$

    $\dfrac{-x}{-1} = \dfrac{-18}{-1}$

    $x = 18$

4. Let $x =$ the number

    $3x =$ the product of the number and 3

    $3x + 5 =$ the product of the number and 3, increased by 5

    $3x + 5 = 17$

    $3x + 5 - 5 = 17 - 5$

    $3x = 12$

    $\dfrac{3x}{3} = \dfrac{12}{3}$

    $x = 4$

5. Let $x =$ Mary's weekly sales

    $0.06x =$ the amount of commission

    $350 + 0.06x = 710$

    $0.06x = 360$

    $\dfrac{0.06x}{0.06} = \dfrac{360}{0.06}$

    $x = \$6000$

6. $L = ah + bh + ch; \ a = 3, \ b = 4, \ c = 5, \ h = 7$

    $L = 2(7) + 5(7) + 4(7)$

    $= 14 + 35 + 28 = 77$

7. $3x + 5y = 11$

    $3x - 3x + 5y = -3x + 11$

    $5y = -3x + 11$

    $\dfrac{5y}{5} = \dfrac{-3x + 11}{5}$

    $y = \dfrac{-3x + 11}{5} = -\dfrac{3}{5}x + \dfrac{11}{5}$

8. $L = \dfrac{kMN}{P}$

    $12 = \dfrac{k(8)(3)}{2}$

    $24k = 24$

    $k = \dfrac{24}{24} = 1$

    $L = \dfrac{(1)MN}{P}$

    $L = \dfrac{(1)(10)(5)}{15} = \dfrac{50}{15} = 3.\overline{3} = 3\dfrac{1}{3}$

9.　$l = \dfrac{k}{w}$

$15 = \dfrac{k}{9}$

$k = 15(9) = 135$

$l = \dfrac{135}{w}$

$l = \dfrac{135}{20} = 6.75 \text{ ft}$

10.　　$-3x + 11 \le 5x + 35$

$-3x - 5x + 11 \le 5x - 5x + 35$

$-8x + 11 \le 35$

$-8x + 11 - 11 \le 35 - 11$

$-8x \le 24$

$\dfrac{-8x}{-8} \ge \dfrac{24}{-8}$

$x \ge -3$

11.　$m = \dfrac{14 - 8}{1 - (-2)} = \dfrac{6}{3} = 2$

12.

13.

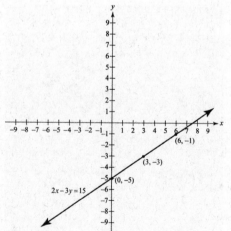

14.　Graph $3y = 5x - 12$. Since the original statement is greater than or equal to, a solid line is drawn. Since the point (0, 0) satisfies the inequality $3y \ge 5x - 12$, all points on the line and in the half-plane above the line $3y = 5x - 12$ are in the solution set.

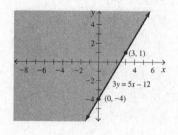

15. $x^2 + 5x = -4$

$x^2 + 5x + 4 = 0$

$(x+4)(x+1) = 0$

$x + 4 = 0$ or $x + 1 = 0$

$x = -4 \qquad x = -1$

16. $3x^2 + 2x = 8$

$3x^2 + 2x - 8 = 0$

$a = 3, b = 2, c = -8$

$x = \dfrac{-2 \pm \sqrt{(2)^2 - 4(3)(-8)}}{2(3)}$

$x = \dfrac{-2 \pm \sqrt{4 + 96}}{6} = \dfrac{-2 \pm \sqrt{100}}{6} = \dfrac{-2 \pm 10}{6}$

$x = \dfrac{8}{6} = \dfrac{4}{3}$ or $x = \dfrac{-12}{6} = -2$

17. Function since each vertical line intersects the graph at only one point.

18. $f(x) = -3x^2 - 12x + 5, \; x = -2$

$f(-2) = -3(-2)^2 - 12(-2) + 5$

$\qquad = -12 + 24 + 5 = 17$

19. $y = x^2 - 2x + 4$

a) $a = 1 > 0$, opens upward

b) $x = 1$ c) $(1, 3)$ d) $(0, 4)$

e) no x-intercepts

f)

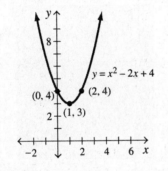

g) D: all real numbers   R: $y \geq 3$

Group Projects

1. a) - b) Answers will vary.

    c) $h = 3.14H + 64.98 = 3.14(29.42) + 64.98 = 157.3588$ cm. ≈ 157.36 cm.

    Yes

    d) $h = 2.53T + 72.57$
       $167.64 = 2.53T + 72.57$
       $95.07 = 2.53T$
       $T = 37.5770751$ cm. ≈ 37.58 cm.

    e) i) $h = 3.14H + 64.98$
          $168 = 3.14H + 64.98$
          $103.02 = 3.14H$
          $H = 32.8089172 \approx 32.81$ cm.

       ii) $H = 32.81 - 0.06(30) = 32.81 - 1.8 = 31.01$ cm.

    f) Answers will vary.

2. a) - e) Answers will vary.

CHAPTER SEVEN

SYSTEMS OF LINEAR EQUATIONS AND INEQUALITIES

Exercise Set 7.1

1. Two or more linear equations form a system of linear equations.
2. A solution to a system of linear equations is the ordered pair or pairs that satisfy all equations in the system.
3. An inconsistent system of equations is a system that has no solution.
4. A consistent system of equations is a system that has a solution.
5. A dependent system of equations is a system that has an infinite number of solutions.
6. a) Graph each equation on the same axes. The point(s) of intersection of the graphs is (are) the solution(s) to the system.

   b) You may not be able to obtain an exact solution by graphing.
7. The graphs of the system of equations are parallel and do not intersect.
8. The graphs of the system of equations intersect at one point.
9. The graphs of the system of equations are in fact the same line.
10. No. If no solution, the graphs are parallel; if they intersect, there is one; or they are the same line.

11. $(3, 5)$ $y = 3x - 4$ $y = -x + 8$

    $5 = 3(3) - 4$ $5 = -(3) + 8$

    $5 = 9 - 4$ $5 = 5$

    $5 = 5$

Therefore, $(3, 5)$ is a solution.

12. $(-2, 4)$ $x + 2y = 6$ $x - y = -6$

    $(-2) + 2(4) = 6$ $(-2) - (4) = -6$

    $-2 + 8 = 6$ $-6 = -6$

    $6 = 6$

Therefore, $(-2, 4)$ is a solution.

13.

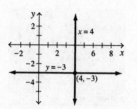

14.

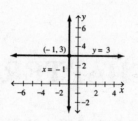

15.

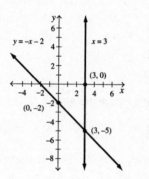

16.

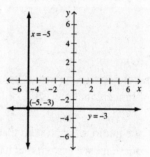

17.

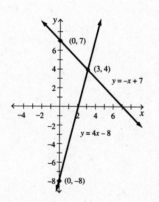

18.

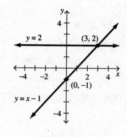

19.

20.

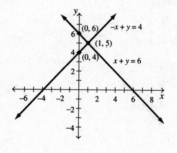

21.

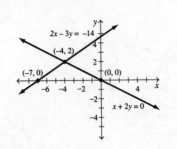

22.

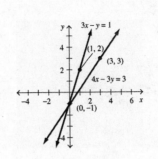

23.

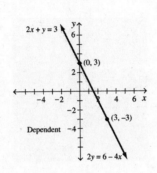

24.

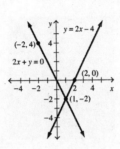

25.

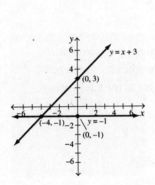

26.

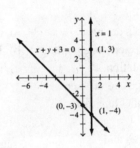

27.

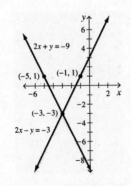

28.

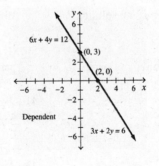

29.

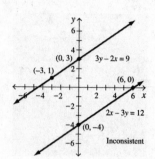

$3y - 2x = 9$

$(0, 3)$

$(-3, 1)$

$(6, 0)$

$2x - 3y = 12$

$(0, -4)$

Inconsistent

30.

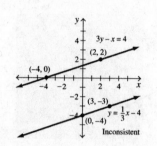

$3y - x = 4$

$(2, 2)$

$(-4, 0)$

$(3, -3)$

$y = \frac{1}{3}x - 4$

$(0, -4)$

Inconsistent

31.

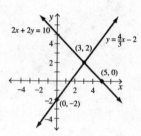

$2x + 2y = 10$

$(3, 2)$

$y = \frac{4}{3}x - 2$

$(5, 0)$

$(0, -2)$

32.

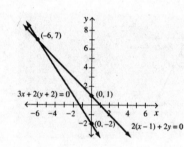

$(-6, 7)$

$3x + 2(y + 2) = 0$

$(0, 1)$

$(0, -2)$

$2(x - 1) + 2y = 0$

33. a) Two lines with different slopes are not parallel, and therefore have exactly one point of intersection giving one solution.

b) Two lines with the same slope and different y-intercepts are distinct parallel lines and have no solution.

c) Two lines with the same slopes and y-intercepts have infinitely many solutions, each point on the line.

34. a) Consistent; the system has one solution.

b) Inconsistent; the system has no solution.

c) Dependent; the system has infinitely many solutions.

35. $3x + y = 9$ $y = -3x + 9$

same slope, same y-intercept;
infinite number of solutions

36. $4x + 3y = 8$ $6y = -8x + 4$

same slopes, diff. y-intercepts; no solution

37. $3x + y = -6$ $4x - 2y = -8$

different slopes, one solution

38. $x - 3y - 8$ $3x - y = 6$

different slopes, one solution

39. $3x + y = 7$ $y = -3x + 9$

same slope, diff. y-intercepts; no solution

40. $x + 4y = 12$ $x = 4y + 3$

different slopes, one solution

41. $2x - 3y = 6$ $x - (3/2)y = 3$

same slopes, same y-intercepts;
infinite number of solutions

42. $x - 2y = 6$ $x + 2y = 4$

different slopes, one solution

43. $3x = 6y + 5$ $y = (1/2)x - 3$

same slope, diff. y-intercepts; no solution

44. $3y = 6x + 4$ $-2x + y = 4/3$
    same slopes, same y-intercepts;
    infinite number of solutions

45. $4x + 7y = 2$ $4x = 6 + 7y$
    different slopes, one solution

46. $12x - 5y = 4$ $3x + 4y = 6$
    different slopes, one solution

47. $4y - 2x = 15$ $3y - 5x = 9$
    slopes are not negative reciprocals,
    not perpendicular

48. $4y - x = 6$ $y = x + 8$
    slopes are not negative reciprocals, not
    perpendicular

49. $2x + y = 3$ $2y - x = 5$
    slopes are negative reciprocals,
    perpendicular

50. $6x + 5y = 3$ $-10x = 2 + 12y$
    slopes are not negative reciprocals, not
    perpendicular

51. a)
Let x equal the number of years, C equal cost

Cost (annual cost plus repair): $C_{\text{fix}} = 375x + 250$

Cost (annual cost plus

replacement): $C_{\text{rep}} = 225x + 700$

   b)

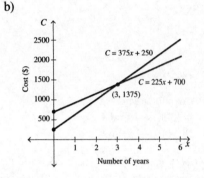

   c) $375x + 250 = 225x + 700$

   $375x - 225x + 250 = 225x - 225x + 700$

   $150x + 250 = 700$

   $150x + 250 - 250 = 700 - 250$

   $150x = 450$

   $\dfrac{150x}{150} = \dfrac{450}{450}$

   $x = 3$

   3 years

52. a) Let h = rate per hour
         y = cost
   Cost for Tom's $y_{\text{T}} = 60h + 200$
   Cost for Lawn Perfect $y_{\text{LP}} = 25h + 305$

   b)

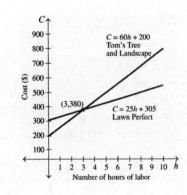

   c) $60h + 200 = 25h + 305$
       $\underline{-25h - 200 \quad -25h - 200}$
       $35h \qquad = \qquad 105$
       $\dfrac{35h}{35} = \dfrac{105}{35}$ so $h = 3$ hours

53. a) Let C = cost , R = revenue

$C(x) = 15x + 400$

$R(x) = 25x$

b)

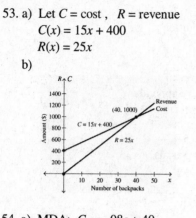

53. c) The cost and revenue graphs intersect when $x = 40$ so 40 is the number of backpacks Benjamin's must sell to break even.

d) $P = R(x) - C(x) = 25x - (15x + 400)$

$P = 10x - 400$

e) $P = 10(30) - 400 = 300 - 400 = -\$100$ (loss)

f) $1000 = 10x - 400 \quad \rightarrow \quad 10x = 1400$

$x = 140$ BPs

54. a) MDA: $C_M = .08s + 40$

AHA: $C_A = .18s + 15$

c) $.08s + 40 = .18s + 15$

$\underline{-.08x - 15 \quad -.08x - 15}$

$25 \qquad = .10x$

$\dfrac{.10x}{.10} = \dfrac{25}{.10} \quad$ so $\quad x = 250$ shares

d) For 300 shares, MDA would be less expensive. $\quad C_M = .08(300) + 40 = 64$

$C_A = .18(300) + 15 = 69$

54. b)

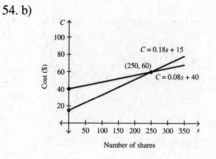

55. a) Let $C(x)$ = cost , $R(x)$ = revenue

$C(x) = 230x + 8400$

$R(x) = 300x$

b)

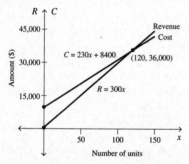

55. c) The cost and revenue graphs intersect when $x = 120$ so 120 is the number of units the manufacturer must sell to break even.

d) $P = R(x) - C(x) = 300x - (230x + 8400)$

$P = 70x - 8400$

e) $P = 70(100) - 8400 = 7000 - 8400$

$= -\$1400$ (loss)

f) $1260 = 70x - 8400 \quad \rightarrow \quad 70x = 9660$

$x = 138$ units

56. Two systems are: consistent if they have different slopes; dependent if they have the same slopes and same y-intercepts; and inconsistent if they have same slopes and different y-intercepts.

57. a) $s_1 = .15x + 500$
    $s_2 = 650$

 b)

 c) $.15x + 500 = 650$
    $\underline{\quad -500 \quad -300}$
    $.15x \qquad = 150$

    $\dfrac{.15x}{.15} = \dfrac{150}{.15}$ so $x = \$1000$

58. a) Let $x =$ number of minutes
     ATT: $y_A = .07x + 3.95$
     SNAP: $y_S = .05x + 8.95$

 b)

 c) $.07x + 3.95 = .05x + 8.95$
    $\underline{-.05x - 3.95 \quad -.05x - 3.95}$
    $.02x \qquad = \qquad 5.00$
    $\dfrac{.02x}{.02} = \dfrac{5.00}{.02}$ so $x = 250$ minutes

59. a) 1 point b) 3 pts. c) 6 pts.
    d) 10 pts.
    e) For n lines, the maximum number of intersections
       is $\dfrac{n(n-1)}{2}$; for six lines,
       there are 15 points.

60.

Exercise Set 7.2

1. Solve one of the equations for one of the variables in terms of the other variable. Then substitute that expression into the other equation and solve for the variable. Substitute the value found into one of the original equations and solve for the other variable.
2. Write the equations with the variables on one side and the constants on the other side. If necessary multiply one or both equations by a constant(s) so that when the equations are added one of the variables will be eliminated. Solve for the remaining variable and then substitute that value into one of the original equations to solve for the other variable.
3. The system is dependent if the result is of the form a = a.
4. The system is inconsistent if the result is a false statement.

5. Solve one equation for the variable that is most readily manipulated, then substitute into the other equation.

$x + 3y = 3$

$\underline{\quad -3y \ -3y \quad}$ → $3(3-3y) + 4y = 9$

$x = 3 - 3y$

6. Manipulate the coefficient of one variable to equate it with the negative coefficient of the same variable in the other equation, then add; here multiply the first equation by -3.

7. $y = x + 8$

$y = -x + 4$

Substitute $(x + 8)$ in place of y in the second equation.

$x + 8 = -x + 4$ (solve for x)

$\underline{+x \qquad +x \qquad\qquad}$

$2x + 8 = 4$

$\underline{\quad -8 \ -8}$

$2x \quad = -4$

$\dfrac{2x}{2} = \dfrac{-4}{2}$ $x = -2$

Now substitute -2 for x in an equation

$y = x + 8$

$y = (-2) + 8 = 6$

The solution is $(-2, 6)$. Consistent

8. $y = 4x - 3$

$y = 3x - 1$

Substitute $(4x - 3)$ in place of y in the second equation

$4x - 3 = 3x - 1$ (solve for x)

$\underline{-3x +7 \ \ -43 +3}$

$x \quad = \quad 2$

Now substitute 2 for x in an equation

$y = 4(2) - 3$

$y = 8 - 3 = 5$

The solution is $(2, 5)$. Consistent

9. $6x + 5y = 1$

$x - 3y = 4$ → $x = 3y + 4$

Substitute $(3y + 4)$ in place of x in the first equation.

$6(3y + 4) + 5y = 1$ (solve for y)

$18y + 24 + 5y = 1$

$23y = -23$ $y = -1$

Now substitute -1 for y in the 1st equation

$6x + 5(-1) = 1$

$6x = 6$ $x = 1$

The solution is $(1, -1)$. Consistent

10. $4x - y = 3$ → $y = 4x - 3$

$3x - y = 1$

Substitute $(4x - 3)$ in place of y in the second equation.

$3x - (4x - 3) = 1$ (solve for x)

$3x - 4x + 3 = 1$

$-x = -2$ $x = 2$

Now substitute 2 for x in the 1st equation

$4(2) - y = 3$

$8 - y = 3$

$y = 5$

The solution is $(2, 5)$. Consistent

11. $y - x = 4$

$x - y = 3$

Solve the first equation for y.

$y - x + x = x + 4$

$y = x + 4$

Substitute $(x + 4)$ for y in the second equation.

$x - (x + 4) = 3$ (combine like terms)

$-4 \quad 3 \quad$ False

Since -4 does not equal 3, there is no solution to this system. The equations are inconsistent.

12. $x + y = 3$

$y + x = 5$

Solve the second equation for y.

$y + x - x = -x + 5$

$y = -x + 5$

Substitute $(-x + 5)$ for y in the first equation.

$x + (-x + 5) = 3$

$5 \quad 3 \quad$ False

Since 5 does not equal 3, there is no solution to this system. The equations are inconsistent.

13. $3y + 2x = 4$

$y = 6 - x$

Solve the second equation for x.

$3y = 6 - x$

$3y - 6 = 6 - 6 - x$

$3y - 6 = -x$

$-3y + 6 \qquad = x$

Now substitute $(-3y + 6)$ for x in the 1st eq'n.

$3y + 2(6 - 3y) = 4$ (solve for y)

$3y + 12 - 6y = 4$

$-3y = -8$ (div. by -3) $y = 8/3$

Substitute 8/3 for y in the 2nd eq'n.

$3(8/3) n = 6 - x$

$8 = 6 - x \qquad x = -2$

The solution is $(-2, 8/3)$.   Consistent

14. $x = 5y - 12$

$x - y = 0$

Substitute $(5y - 12)$ for x in the second equation.

$5y - 12 - y = 0$ (solve for y)

$4y - 12 \qquad\quad = 0$

$4y = 12$ (div. by 4) $y = 3$

Now substitute 3 for y in the second equation.

$x - 3 = 0$

$x = 3$

The solution is $(3,3)$.   Consistent

15. $y - 2x = 3$

$2y = 4x + 6$

Solve the first equation for y.

$y - 2x + 2x = 2x + 3$

$y = 2x + 3$

Now substitute $(2x + 3)$ for y in the 2nd eq'n.

$2(2x + 3) = 4x + 6$

$4x + 6 = 4x + 6$

$4x - 4x + 6 = 4x - 4x + 6$

$6 = 6$

This statement is true for all values of x.

The system is dependent.

16. $y = 2$

$y + x + 3 = 0$

Substitute 2 in place of y in the second equation.

$2 + x + 3 = 0$

$x + 5 = 0$

$x + 5 - 5 = 0 - 5 \qquad x = -5$

The solution is $(-5,2)$.   Consistent

17. $x = y + 3$

$x = -3$

Substitute -3 in place of x in the first equation.

$-3 = y + 3$

$-3 - 3 = y + 3 - 3$

$-6 = y$

The solution is $(-3, -6)$.   Consistent

18. $x + 2y = 6$

$y = 2x + 3$

Substitute $(2x + 3)$ for y in the first equation.

$x + 2(2x + 3) = 6$

$x + 4x + 6 = 6$

$5x + 6 - 6 = 6 - 6$

$5x = 0$

$\dfrac{5x}{5} = \dfrac{0}{5} \qquad x = 0$

Now substitute 0 for x in the second equation.

$y = 2(0) + 3 = 0 + 3 = 3$

The solution is $(0,3)$.   Consistent

19. $y + 3x - 4 = 0$
$2x - y = 7$
Solve the first equation for y.
$y + 3x - 4 = 0$
$y = 4 - 3x$
Substitute $4 - 3x$ for y in the second eq.
$2x - (4 - 3x) = 7$ (solve for x)
$2x - 4 + 3x = 7$
$5x = 11$ $x = 11/5$
Substitute 11/5 for x in the second eq'n.
$2(11/5) - y = 7$ (solve for y)
$22/5 - y = 7$
$-y = 13/5$ $y = -13/5$
The solution is (11/5, −13/5).   Consistent

20. $x + 4y = 7$
$2x + 3y = 5$
Solve the first equation for x.
$x = 7 - 4y$
Substitute $(7 - 4y)$ for x in the second equation.
$2(7 - 4y) + 3y = 5$ (solve for y)
$14 - 8y + 3y = 5$
$-5y = -9$ $y = 9/5$
Now substitute (9/5) for y in the eq'n. $x + 4y = 7$.
$x + 4(9/5) = 7$
$x + 36/5 = 35/5$ $x = -1/5$
The solution is (−1/5, 9/5).   Consistent

21. $x = 2y + 3$
$y = 3x - 1$
Substitute $(3x - 1)$ for y in the first equation.
$x = 2(3x - 1) + 3$
$x = 6x - 2 + 3$
$x = 6x + 1$
$x - 6x = 6x - 6x + 1$
$-5x = 1$
$$\frac{-5x}{-5} = \frac{1}{-5} \qquad x = -1/5$$
Substitute −1/5 for x in the second equation.
$y = 3(-1/5) - 1 = -3/5 - 5/5 = -8/5$
The solution is (−1/5, −8/5).   Consistent

22. $x + 4y = 9$
$2x - y - 6 = 0$
Solve the first equation for x.
$x + 4y - 4y = 9 - 4y$
$x = 9 - 4y$
Substitute $(9 - 4y)$ for x in the second equation.
$2(9 - 4y) - y - 6 = 0$
$18 - 8y - y - 6 = 0$
$12 - 9y = 0$
$12 - 9y + 9y = 0 + 9y$
$12 = 9y$ $12/9 = y$
Substitute $(12/9) = (4/3)$ for y in the equation.
$x = 9 - 4y$
$x = 9 - 4(4/3) = 27/3 - 16/3 = 11/3$
The solution is (11/3, 4/3).   Consistent

23. $y = -2x + 3$
$4x + 2y = 12$
Substitute $-2x + 3$ for y in the 2nd equation.
$4x + 2(-2x + 3) = 12$
$4x - 4x + 6 = 12$

6   12   False

Since 6 does not equal 12, there is no solution.
The equations are inconsistent.

24. $2x + y = 12$
$x = (-1/2)y + 6$
Substitute $(-1/2)x + 6$ for x in the 1st equation.
$2(-1/2y + 6) + y = 12$
$-y + 12 + y = 12$
$12 = 12$
This statement is true for all values of x.
The system is dependent.

25. $3x + y = 9$
$2x - y = 6$
Add the equations to eliminate y.
$5x = 15$ $x = 3$
Substitute 3 for x in either eq'n.
$3(3) + y = 9$ (solve for y)
$9 + y = 9$ $y = 0$
The solution is (3, 0)   Consistent

26. $x + 3y = 9$
$x - 3y = -3$
Add the equations to eliminate y.
$2x = 6$ $x = 3$
Substitute 3 for x in either eq'n.
$(3) + 3y = 9$
$3y = 6$ $y = 2$
The solution is (3, 2)   Consistent

27. $x + y = 12$
$x - 2y = -3$
Multiply the 1st eq'n. by 2, then add the eq'ns.
To eliminate y.
$2x + 2y = 24$
$x - 2y = -3$
$3x = 21$ $x = 7$
Substitute 7 for x in either eq'n.
$(7) + y = 12$ (solve for y) $y = 5$

The solution is (7, 5)   Consistent

28. $2x + y = 10$
$-2x + 2y = -16$
Add the equations to eliminate x.
$3y = -6$ $y = -2$
Substitute -2 for y in either eq'n.
$2x + (-2) = 10$ (solve for x)
$2x = 12$ $x = 6$

The solution is (6, -2)   Consistent

29. $2x - y = -4$
$-3x - y = 6$
Multiply the second equation by -1,
$2x - y = -4$
$3x + y = -6$ add the equations to eliminate y
$5x = -10$ $x = -2$
Substitute -2 in place of x in the first equation.
$2(-2) - y = -4$
$-4 - y = -4$
$-y = 0$ $y = 0$

The solution is $(-2, 0)$.   Consistent

30. $x + y = 6$
$-2x + y = -3$
Multiply the second equation by -1,
$x + y = 6$
$2x - y = 3$ add the equations to eliminate y
$3x = 9$ $x = 3$
Substitute 3 for x in the first equation.
$3 + y = 6$ $y = 3$

The solution is (3, 3).   Consistent

1. $4x + 3y = -1$
$2x - y = -13$
Multiply the second equation by 3,
$4x + 3y = -1$
$6x - 3y = -39$ add the equations to eliminate y
$10x = -40$ $x = -4$
Substitute -4 for x in the 2nd equation.
$2(-4) - y = -13$
$-8 - y = -13$ $y = 5$
The solution is $(-4, 5)$.   Consistent

32. $2x + y = 6$
$3x + y = 5$
Multiply the first equation by -1,
$-2x - y = -6$
$3x + y = 5$ add the equations to eliminate y
$x = -1$
Substitute -1 in place of x in the first equation.
$2(-1) + y = 6$
$-2 + y = 6$ $y = 8$
The solution is $(-1, 8)$.   Consistent

33. $2x + y = 11$
$x + 3y = 18$
Multiply the second equation by -2,
$2x + y = 11$
$-2x - 6y = -36$ add the equations to elim. x
$-5y = -25$ $y = 5$
Substitute 5 for y in the 2nd equation.
$x + 3(5) = 18$
$x + 15 = 18$ $x = 3$
The solution is (3, 5).

34. $5x - 2y = 11$
$-3x + 2y = 1$ add the equations to eliminate y
$2x = 12$ $x = 6$
Substitute 6 for x in the second equation.
$-3(6) + 2y = 1$
$-18 + 2y = 1$
$2y = 19$ $y = 19/2$
The solution is (6, 19/2).

35. $3x - 4y = 11$

    $3x + 5y = -7$

    Multiply the first equation by (– 1),

    $-3x + 4y = -11$

    $3x + 5y = -7$ add the equations to elim. x

    $9y = -18$ $y = -2$

    Substitute – 2 for y in the first equation.

    $3x - 4(-2) = 11$

    $3x = 3$ $x = 1$

    The solution is $(1, -2)$.   Consistent

36. $4x - 2y = 6$

    $4y = 8x - 12$ or $8x - 4y = 12$

    Multiply the first equation by (– 2),

    $-8x + 4y = -12$

    $8x - 4y = -12$ add the equations to elim. y

    $0 = 0$ True

    This statement is true for all values of x.

    This system is dependent.

37. $4x + y = 6$

    $-8x - 2y = 13$

    Multiply the first equation by 2,

    $8x + 2y = 12$

    $-8x - 2y = 13$ add the equations to elim. y

    $0 \quad 25$ False

    Since this statement is not true for any values of x and y, the equations are inconsistent.

38. $2x + 3y = 6$

    $5x - 4y = -8$

    Multiply the first equation by 5, and the second equation by (– 2),

    $10x + 15y = 30$

    $-10x + 8y = 16$ add the equations to elim. x

    $23y = 46$ $y = 2$

    Substitute 2 for y in the first equation.

    $2x + 3(2) = 6$

    $2x = 0$ $x = 0$

    The solution is $(0, 2)$.   Consistent

39. $3x - 4y = 2$

    $4x + 3y = 11$

    Multiply the first equation by 3, and the second equation by 4,

    $9x - 12y = 6$

    $16x + 12y = 44$ add the equations to elim. y

    $25x = 50$ $x = 2$

    Substitute 2 for x in the second equation.

    $4(2) + 3y = 11$

    $8 + 3y = 11$

    $3y = 3$ $y = 1$

    The solution is $(2, 1)$.   Consistent

40. $6x + 6y = 1$

    $4x + 9y = 4$

    Multiply the first equation by 2, and the second equation by -3,

    $12x + 12y = 2$

    $-12x - 27y = -12$ add the equations to elim. x

    $-15y = -10$ $y = 2/3$

    Substitute 2/3 for y in the 1st equation.

    $6x + 6(2/3) = 1$

    $6x + 4 = 1$

    $6x = -3$ $x = -1/2$

    The solution is $(-1/2, 2/3)$.   Consistent

41. $S_1 = .15p + 12000$
    $S_2 = .05p + 27000$

    $.15p + 12000 = .05p + 27000$
    $-.05p \; -12000 \quad -.05p \; -12000$
    $.10p = 15000$
    $p = \$ 150,000.00$

42. Let x = amount invested at 6%, y = amount invested at 4.5%.

    $0.06x + 0.045y = 1380$
    $\qquad\qquad x + y = 25,000 \rightarrow x = 25,000 - y$
    Substitute $25,000 - y$ for x in the first equation.
    $0.06(25,000 - y) + 0.045y = 1380$
    $1500 - 0.06y + 0.045y = 1380$
    $-0.015y = -1200$
    $\qquad\quad y = 8000$
    Substitute 8000 for y in the second equation.
    $x + 8000 = 25,000$
    $x = 17,000$
    He invested \$17,000 in the 6% bond and \$8000 in the 4.5% bond.

43. Let x = # of medium pizzas
    $50 - x$ = # of large pizzas

    $10.95x + 14.95(50-x) = 663.50$
    $10.95x + 747.50 - 14.95x = 663.50$
    $-4.00x = -84.00 \qquad x = 21$
    Substitute 21 for x in 2nd let statement
    $50 - x = 50 - (21) = 29$

    21 medium pizzas and 29 large pizzas

44. Let x = no. of 2-pointers
    $\quad\;\; y$ = no. of 3-pointers
    $x + y = 45 \qquad y = -x + 45$
    $2x + 3y = 101$
    Substitute $-x + 45$ for y in 2nd eq'n.
    $2x + 3(-x + 45) = 101$
    $2x - 3x + 135 = 101$
    $-x = -34 \qquad x = 34$
    Substitute 34 for x in 1st eq'n.
    $34 + y = 45 \qquad y = -34 + 45 = 11$
    34 two pointers and 11 three pointers

45. Let x = # of liters at 25%
    $10 - x$ = # of liters at 50%

    $.25x + .50(10 - x) = .40(10)$
    $.25x + 5 - .50x = 4$
    $-.25x = -1 \qquad x = 4$
    Substitute 4 for x in 2nd let statement
    $10 - x = 10 - (4) = 6$

    4 liters of 25% solution and
    6 liters of 50% solution

46. Let x = number of \$30 sets she purchased
    $\quad\;\; y$ = number of \$40 sets she purchased

    $x + y = 100 \rightarrow y = 100 - x$
    $30x + 40y = 3200$
    Substitute $100 - x$ for y in the second equation
    $30x + 40(100 - x) = 3200$
    $-10x + 4000 = 3200$
    $-10x = -8000$
    $x = 80$
    Substitute 80 for x in the first equation.
    $80 + y = 100$
    $y = 20$
    Thus, she purchased 80 of the \$30 sets and 20 of the \$40 sets.

47. Let c = monthly cost
    x = number of copies

    Eco. Sales: c = 18 + 0.02x
    Office Sup.: c = 24 + 0.015x   set eq'ns.
    equal
    18 + 0.02x = 24 + 0.015x
    0.005x = 6   x = 1200

    1200 copies per month

48. HD cost = 2.65x + 468.75
    HG cost = 3.10x + 412.50
    where x is the number of square feet installed

    a) 2.65x + 468.75 = 3.10x + 412.50
       -2.65x – 412.50 -2.65x -412.50
       _____
            56.25   =   0.45x
       $$\frac{6.25}{0.45} = \frac{0.45x}{0.45}$$
            125 = x
    The costs are equal when Roberto has
    125 square feet of flooring installed.

    b) 195 square feet is 70 square feet more than
        125 square feet. The costs are equal for
        125 square feet, and since Home Depot has
        the smaller cost per square foot, the
        additional 70 square will cast less with
        Home Depot

49. Let x = no. of pounds of nuts
      y = no. of pounds of pretzels
    x + y = 20   y = -x + 20
    3x + 1y = 30
    Substitute (20 – x) for y in the 2nd equation.
    3x + (20 – x) = 30
    3x + 20 – x = 30
    2x = 10   x = 5   Solve for y
    y = 20 – 5 = 15

    Mix 5 lbs. of nuts with 15 lbs. of pretzels

50. Let a = number of grams of Mix A
      b = number of grams of Mix B
    Protein: 0.10a + 0.20b = 20
    Carbohydrates: 0.06a + 0.02b = 6
    Multiply the 2nd equation by (– 10),
    – 0.60a – 0.20b = – 60
    0.10a + 0.20b= 20   add to eliminate b
    – 0.50a = – 40   a = 80
    Substitute 80 for a in the first equation.
    0.10(80) + 0.20b = 20
    8 + 0.20b = 20
    0.20b = 12   b = 60
    a = 80 grams of Mix A
    b = 60 grams of Mix B

51. Let x = no. of inside tickets
      y = no. of lawn tickets
    x + y = 4600   x = 4600 - y
    27x + 14y = 104,700
    Substitute (4600 - y) for x in the 2nd
    equation.
    27(4600 - y) + 14y = 104,700
    124,200 – 27y + 14y = 104,700
    -13y = -19,500   y = 1500
    Substitute 1500 for y in the 1st eq'n.
    x + (1500) = 4600   x = 3100

    3100 inside tickets and 1500 lawn tickets

52. Let c = total cost
      r = no. of rounds of golf.
    Oakwood: O = 3000 + 18r
    Pinecrest: P = 2500 + 20r
    a) 3000 + 18r = 2500 + 20r
        500 = 2r   250= r
    A golfer must play 250 rounds for the cost to be
    the same at both clubs.

    b) Oakwood: O = 3000 + 18(30) = $3540
       Pinecrest: P = 2500 + 20(30) = $3100
    Tamika can play 30 rounds cheaper at
    Pinecrest.

53. $y_{GM} = -0.83x + 28.33$
    $y_T = 0.89x + 9.11$

    $-0.83x + 28.33 = 0.89x + 9.11$
    $\underline{0.83x \quad -9.11 \quad 0.83x - 9.11}$
    $19.22 = 1.72x$
    $\dfrac{19.22}{1.72} = \dfrac{1.72x}{1.72}$
    $x = 11.17... \approx 11.2$

    11.2 years after 2000, or in 2011

54. $y_T = -2.3x + 29.9$
    $y_D = 1.5x + 0.4$

    $-2.3x + 29.9 = 1.5x + 0.4$
    $\underline{2.3x \quad -0.4 \quad 2.3x - 0.4}$
    $29.5 = 3.8x$
    $\dfrac{29.5}{3.8} = \dfrac{3.8x}{3.8}$
    $x = 7.76 \approx 7.8$

    7.8 years after 2000, or in 2007

55. $(1/u) + (2/v) = 8$
    $(3/u) - (1/v) = 3$

    Substitute x for $\dfrac{1}{u}$ and y for $\dfrac{1}{v}$.

    (1) $x + 2y = 8$
    (2) $3x - y = 3$
    Multiply eq'n. (2) by 2,
    $x + 2y = 8$
    $6x - 2y = 6$ add to eliminate y
    $7x = 14$ x= 2, thus u = ½
    Substitute 2 for x in eq. (1).
    $(2) + 2y = 8$
    $2y = 6$ y = 3, thus v = 1/3

    Answer: (1/2, 1/3)

56. Determine the equations of two lines that pass
    through (6,5) and another point.
    Example: $y = 5$
    $\qquad\qquad y = (5/6)x$

57. a) $(2) + (1) + (4) = 7$ $(2) - (1) + 2(4) = 9$
    $\qquad 7 = 7$ $\qquad 9 = 9$
    $\qquad -(2) + 2(1) + (4) = 4$
    $\qquad 4 = 4$ (2,1,4) is a solution.

    b) Add eq'ns. 1 and 2 to yield eq'n. 4
    Multiply eq'n. 2 by 2, then add eq'ns. 2 and 3
    to yield eq'n. 5
    Combine eq'ns. 4 and 5 to find one variable.
    Substitute back into various equations to find
    the other 2 variables.

58. $y = 2x - 7$
    $y = 2x + 5$
    The system of equations has no solution
    because the slopes of the corresponding lines
    are equal ($m = 2$) but the y-intercepts are
    different.

59. $y = 3x + 3$
    $(1/3)y = x + 1$
    If we multiply the 2nd eq'n. by 3, we get the eq'n.
    $y = 3x + 1$, the same as eq'n. # 1.
    2 lines that lie on top of one another have an
    infinite number of solutions.

60. When solving a system of equations, if you
obtain a true statement such as 0 = 0, the system is
dependent and has an infinite number of solutions.

61. a) (0, 0)   b) (1, 0)   c) (0, 1)   d) (1, 1)

Exercise Set 7.3
1. A matrix is a rectangular array of elements.
2. The dimensions of a matrix are determined by the number of rows and columns.
3. A square matrix contains the same number of rows as columns.
4. A 3 x 2 matrix has 2 columns.
5. A 4 x 3 matrix has 4 rows.
6. They must have the same dimensions (the number of rows must be the same and the number of columns
   must be the same).

7. a) Add numbers in the same positions to produce an entry in that position.

b) $\begin{bmatrix} 5 & 4 & -1 \\ 3 & 9 & 5 \end{bmatrix} + \begin{bmatrix} 2 & 5 & -6 \\ -1 & 7 & 4 \end{bmatrix} = \begin{bmatrix} 5+2 & 4+5 & -1+(-6) \\ 3+(-1) & 9+7 & 5+4 \end{bmatrix} = \begin{bmatrix} 7 & 9 & -7 \\ 2 & 16 & 9 \end{bmatrix}$

8. a) Subtract the entry in each position in the 2nd matrix from the # in the same position in the 1st matrix.

b) $\begin{bmatrix} 3 & -5 & 6 \\ -2 & 3 & 4 \end{bmatrix} - \begin{bmatrix} 8 & 4 & 2 \\ 0 & -2 & 4 \end{bmatrix} = \begin{bmatrix} 3-8 & -5-4 & 6-2 \\ -2-0 & 3-(-2) & 4-4 \end{bmatrix} = \begin{bmatrix} -5 & -9 & 4 \\ -2 & 5 & 0 \end{bmatrix}$

9. a) The number of columns of the first matrix must be the same as the number of rows of the second matrix.

   b) The dimensions of the resulting matrix will have the same number of rows as the first matrix and the same number of columns as the second matrix. The product of a 2 x 2 with a 2 x 3 matrix will yield a 2 x 3 matrix.

10. a) The numbers in the first row of the first matrix are multiplied by the numbers in the first column of the second matrix and the results are added together to produce the first entry of the result. Continue this procedure with each row of the first matrix and each column of the second matrix to obtain all the entries in the result matrix.

b) $\begin{bmatrix} 8 & -1 \\ 6 & 0 \end{bmatrix}\begin{bmatrix} 2 & -3 \\ 5 & -4 \end{bmatrix} = \begin{bmatrix} 8(2)+(-1)(5) & 8(-3)+(-1)(-4) \\ 6(2)+0(5) & 6(-3)+0(-4) \end{bmatrix} = \begin{bmatrix} 11 & -20 \\ 12 & -18 \end{bmatrix}$

11. a) Identity matrix for 2x2 $\begin{bmatrix} 1 & 0 \\ 0 & 1 \end{bmatrix}$ b) Identity matrix for 3x3 $\begin{bmatrix} 1 & 0 & 0 \\ 0 & 1 & 0 \\ 0 & 0 & 1 \end{bmatrix}$

12. $\begin{matrix} E \\ W \\ C \end{matrix}\begin{bmatrix} 110 & 232 & 103 & 190 & 212 \\ 107 & 250 & 135 & 203 & 189 \\ 115 & 218 & 122 & 192 & 210 \end{bmatrix}$

13. $A = \begin{bmatrix} 1 & 8 \\ 2 & 7 \end{bmatrix}$ $B = \begin{bmatrix} -4 & 1 \\ 7 & 2 \end{bmatrix}$ $A+B = \begin{bmatrix} 1+(-4) & 8+1 \\ 2+7 & 7+2 \end{bmatrix} = \begin{bmatrix} -3 & 9 \\ 9 & 9 \end{bmatrix}$

14. $A+B = \begin{bmatrix} 5 & 6 & -7 \\ 0 & 1 & -1 \end{bmatrix} + \begin{bmatrix} -4 & 2 & -8 \\ 7 & -3 & 0 \end{bmatrix} = \begin{bmatrix} 5+(-4) & 6+2 & -7+(-8) \\ 0+7 & 1+(-3) & -1+0 \end{bmatrix} = \begin{bmatrix} 1 & 8 & -15 \\ 7 & -2 & -1 \end{bmatrix}$

15. $A+B = \begin{bmatrix} 2 & 1 \\ -1 & 4 \\ 6 & 0 \end{bmatrix} + \begin{bmatrix} -3 & 3 \\ -4 & 0 \\ 1 & 6 \end{bmatrix} = \begin{bmatrix} 2+(-3) & 1+3 \\ -1+(-4) & 4+0 \\ 6+1 & 0+6 \end{bmatrix} = \begin{bmatrix} -1 & 4 \\ -5 & 4 \\ 7 & 6 \end{bmatrix}$

16. $A+B = \begin{bmatrix} 2 & 6 & 3 \\ -1 & -6 & 4 \\ 3 & 0 & 5 \end{bmatrix} + \begin{bmatrix} -1 & 3 & 1 \\ 7 & -2 & 1 \\ 2 & 3 & 8 \end{bmatrix} = \begin{bmatrix} 2+(-1) & 6+3 & 3+1 \\ -1+7 & -6+(-2) & 4+1 \\ 3+2 & 0+3 & 5+8 \end{bmatrix} = \begin{bmatrix} 1 & 9 & 4 \\ 6 & -8 & 5 \\ 5 & 3 & 13 \end{bmatrix}$

17. $A-B = \begin{bmatrix} 4 & -2 \\ -3 & 5 \end{bmatrix} - \begin{bmatrix} -2 & 5 \\ 9 & 1 \end{bmatrix} = \begin{bmatrix} 4-(-2) & -2-(-5) \\ -3-(9) & 5-1 \end{bmatrix} = \begin{bmatrix} 6 & -7 \\ -12 & 4 \end{bmatrix}$

18. $A - B = \begin{bmatrix} 10 & 1 \\ 12 & 2 \\ -3 & -9 \end{bmatrix} - \begin{bmatrix} -3 & 3 \\ 4 & 7 \\ -2 & 6 \end{bmatrix} = \begin{bmatrix} 10-(-3) & 1-3 \\ 12-4 & 2-7 \\ -3-(-2) & -9-(6) \end{bmatrix} = \begin{bmatrix} 13 & -2 \\ 8 & -5 \\ -1 & -15 \end{bmatrix}$

19. $A - B = \begin{bmatrix} -5 & 1 \\ 8 & 6 \\ 1 & -5 \end{bmatrix} - \begin{bmatrix} -6 & -8 \\ -10 & -11 \\ 3 & -7 \end{bmatrix} = \begin{bmatrix} -5+6 & 1+8 \\ 8+10 & 6+11 \\ 1-3 & -5+7 \end{bmatrix} = \begin{bmatrix} 1 & 9 \\ 18 & 17 \\ -2 & 2 \end{bmatrix}$

20. $A - B = \begin{bmatrix} 5 & 3 & -1 \\ 7 & 4 & 2 \\ 6 & -1 & -5 \end{bmatrix} - \begin{bmatrix} 4 & 3 & 6 \\ -2 & -4 & 9 \\ 0 & -2 & 4 \end{bmatrix} = \begin{bmatrix} 5-4 & 3-3 & -1-6 \\ 7+2 & 4+4 & 2-9 \\ 6-0 & -1+2 & -5-4 \end{bmatrix} = \begin{bmatrix} 1 & 0 & -7 \\ 9 & 8 & -7 \\ 6 & 1 & -9 \end{bmatrix}$

21. $2B = 2\begin{bmatrix} 3 & 2 \\ 5 & 0 \end{bmatrix} = \begin{bmatrix} 2(3) & 2(2) \\ 2(5) & 2(0) \end{bmatrix} = \begin{bmatrix} 6 & 4 \\ 10 & 0 \end{bmatrix}$

22. $3B = $
$-3\begin{bmatrix} 3 & 2 \\ 5 & 0 \end{bmatrix} = \begin{bmatrix} -3(3) & -3(2) \\ -3(5) & -3(0) \end{bmatrix} = \begin{bmatrix} -9 & -6 \\ -15 & 0 \end{bmatrix}$

23. $2B + 4C = 2\begin{bmatrix} 3 & 2 \\ 5 & 0 \end{bmatrix} + 4\begin{bmatrix} -2 & 3 \\ 4 & 0 \end{bmatrix} = \begin{bmatrix} 6 & 4 \\ 10 & 0 \end{bmatrix} + \begin{bmatrix} -8 & 12 \\ 16 & 0 \end{bmatrix} = \begin{bmatrix} 6-8 & 4+12 \\ 10+16 & 0+0 \end{bmatrix} = \begin{bmatrix} -2 & 16 \\ 26 & 0 \end{bmatrix}$

24. $2B + 3A = 2\begin{bmatrix} 3 & 2 \\ 5 & 0 \end{bmatrix} + 3\begin{bmatrix} 1 & 2 \\ 0 & 5 \end{bmatrix} = \begin{bmatrix} 6 & 4 \\ 10 & 0 \end{bmatrix} + \begin{bmatrix} 3 & 6 \\ 0 & 15 \end{bmatrix} = \begin{bmatrix} 6+3 & 4+6 \\ 10+0 & 0+15 \end{bmatrix} = \begin{bmatrix} 9 & 10 \\ 10 & 15 \end{bmatrix}$

25. $4B - 2C = 4\begin{bmatrix} 3 & 2 \\ 5 & 0 \end{bmatrix} - 2\begin{bmatrix} -2 & 3 \\ 4 & 0 \end{bmatrix} = \begin{bmatrix} 12 & 8 \\ 20 & 0 \end{bmatrix} - \begin{bmatrix} -4 & 6 \\ 8 & 0 \end{bmatrix} = \begin{bmatrix} 12+4 & 8-6 \\ 20-8 & 0-0 \end{bmatrix} = \begin{bmatrix} 16 & 2 \\ 12 & 0 \end{bmatrix}$

26. $3C - 2A = 3\begin{bmatrix} -2 & 3 \\ 4 & 0 \end{bmatrix} - 2\begin{bmatrix} 1 & 2 \\ 0 & 5 \end{bmatrix} = \begin{bmatrix} -6 & 9 \\ 12 & 0 \end{bmatrix} - \begin{bmatrix} 2 & 4 \\ 0 & 10 \end{bmatrix} = \begin{bmatrix} -6-(2) & 9-(4) \\ 12-(0) & 0-(10) \end{bmatrix} = \begin{bmatrix} -8 & 5 \\ 12 & -10 \end{bmatrix}$

27. $A \times B = \begin{bmatrix} 1 & 3 \\ 0 & 6 \end{bmatrix}\begin{bmatrix} 2 & 6 \\ 8 & 4 \end{bmatrix} = \begin{bmatrix} 1(2)+3(8) & 1(6)+3(4) \\ 0(2)+6(8) & 0(6)+6(4) \end{bmatrix} = \begin{bmatrix} 26 & 18 \\ 48 & 24 \end{bmatrix}$

28. $A \times B = \begin{bmatrix} 1 & -1 \\ 2 & 6 \end{bmatrix}\begin{bmatrix} 4 & -2 \\ -3 & -2 \end{bmatrix} = \begin{bmatrix} 1(4)+(-1)(-3) & 1(-2)+(-1)(-2) \\ 2(4)+6(-3) & 2(-2)+6(-2) \end{bmatrix} = \begin{bmatrix} 7 & 0 \\ -10 & -16 \end{bmatrix}$

29. $A \times B = \begin{bmatrix} 2 & 3 & -1 \\ 0 & 4 & 6 \end{bmatrix}\begin{bmatrix} 2 \\ 4 \\ 1 \end{bmatrix} = \begin{bmatrix} 2(2)+3(4)-1(1) \\ 0(2)+4(4)+6(1) \end{bmatrix} = \begin{bmatrix} 15 \\ 22 \end{bmatrix}$

30. $A \times B = \begin{bmatrix} 1 & 1 \\ 1 & 1 \end{bmatrix}\begin{bmatrix} 1 & -1 \\ -1 & 2 \end{bmatrix} = \begin{bmatrix} 1(1)+1(-1) & 1(-1)+1(2) \\ 1(1)+1(-1) & 1(-1)+1(2) \end{bmatrix} = \begin{bmatrix} 0 & 1 \\ 0 & 1 \end{bmatrix}$

31. $A \times B = \begin{bmatrix} 4 & 7 & 6 \\ -2 & 3 & 1 \\ 5 & 1 & 2 \end{bmatrix}\begin{bmatrix} 1 & 0 & 0 \\ 0 & 1 & 0 \\ 0 & 0 & 1 \end{bmatrix} = \begin{bmatrix} 4+0+0 & 0+7+0 & 0+0+6 \\ -2+0+0 & 0+3+0 & 0+0+1 \\ 5+0+0 & 0+1+0 & 0+0+2 \end{bmatrix} = \begin{bmatrix} 4 & 7 & 6 \\ -2 & 3 & 1 \\ 5 & 1 & 2 \end{bmatrix}$

32. $A \times B = \begin{bmatrix} 1 & -3 \\ 7 & 2 \end{bmatrix} \begin{bmatrix} 0 & 4 \\ 6 & 1 \end{bmatrix} = \begin{bmatrix} 1(0)+(-3)(6) & 1(4)+(-3)(1) \\ 7(0)+2(6) & 7(4)+2(1) \end{bmatrix} = \begin{bmatrix} -18 & 1 \\ 12 & 30 \end{bmatrix}$

33. $A + B = \begin{bmatrix} 2 & 3 & 5 \\ 4 & 0 & 3 \end{bmatrix} + \begin{bmatrix} 7 & -2 & 3 \\ 2 & -1 & 1 \end{bmatrix} = \begin{bmatrix} 2+7 & 3+(-2) & 5+3 \\ 4+2 & 0+(-1) & 3+1 \end{bmatrix} = \begin{bmatrix} 9 & 1 & 8 \\ 6 & -1 & 4 \end{bmatrix}$

$A \times B = \begin{bmatrix} 2 & 3 & 5 \\ 4 & 0 & 3 \end{bmatrix} \times \begin{bmatrix} 7 & -2 & 3 \\ 2 & -1 & 1 \end{bmatrix}$

Operation cannot be performed because number of columns of A is not equal to number of rows of B.

34. $A = \begin{bmatrix} 6 & 4 & -1 \\ 2 & 3 & 4 \end{bmatrix} \quad B = \begin{bmatrix} 1 & 0 \\ 4 & -1 \end{bmatrix}$

A + B cannot be performed because A and B have different dimensions.

A×B cannot be performed because the number of columns of A is not equal to number of rows of B.

35. Matrices A and B cannot be added because they do not have the same dimensions.

$A \times B = \begin{bmatrix} 4 & 5 & 3 \\ 6 & 2 & 1 \end{bmatrix} \times \begin{bmatrix} 3 & 2 \\ 4 & 6 \\ -2 & 0 \end{bmatrix} = \begin{bmatrix} 4(3)+5(4)+3(-2) & 4(2)+5(6)+3(0) \\ 6(3)+2(4)+1(-2) & 6(2)+2(6)+1(0) \end{bmatrix} = \begin{bmatrix} 26 & 38 \\ 24 & 24 \end{bmatrix}$

36. $A + B = \begin{bmatrix} 6 & 5 \\ 4 & 3 \\ 2 & 1 \end{bmatrix} + \begin{bmatrix} 6 & 5 \\ 4 & 3 \\ 2 & 1 \end{bmatrix} = \begin{bmatrix} 6+6 & 5+5 \\ 4+4 & 3+3 \\ 2+2 & 1+1 \end{bmatrix} = \begin{bmatrix} 12 & 10 \\ 8 & 6 \\ 4 & 2 \end{bmatrix}$

A and B cannot be multiplied because the # of columns in A is not equal to the number of rows in B.

37. A and B cannot be added because they do not have the same dimensions.

$A \times B = \begin{bmatrix} 1 & 2 \\ 3 & 4 \end{bmatrix} \begin{bmatrix} -3 \\ 2 \end{bmatrix} = \begin{bmatrix} 1(-3)+2(2) \\ 3(-3)+4(2) \end{bmatrix} = \begin{bmatrix} 1 \\ -1 \end{bmatrix}$

38. $A + B = \begin{bmatrix} 5 & -1 \\ 6 & -2 \end{bmatrix} + \begin{bmatrix} 1 & 2 \\ 3 & 4 \end{bmatrix} = \begin{bmatrix} 5+1 & -1+2 \\ 6+3 & -2+4 \end{bmatrix} = \begin{bmatrix} 6 & 1 \\ 9 & 2 \end{bmatrix}$

$A \times B = \begin{bmatrix} 5 & -1 \\ 6 & -2 \end{bmatrix} \times \begin{bmatrix} 1 & 2 \\ 3 & 4 \end{bmatrix} = \begin{bmatrix} 5(1)+(-1)(3) & 5(2)+(-1)(4) \\ 6(1)+(-2)(3) & 6(2)+(-2)(4) \end{bmatrix} = \begin{bmatrix} 2 & 6 \\ 0 & 4 \end{bmatrix}$

39. $A + B = \begin{bmatrix} 3 & 5 \\ -2 & -3 \end{bmatrix} + \begin{bmatrix} 4 & 5 \\ 6 & 7 \end{bmatrix} = \begin{bmatrix} 3+4 & 5+5 \\ -2+6 & -3+7 \end{bmatrix} = \begin{bmatrix} 7 & 10 \\ 4 & 4 \end{bmatrix}$

$B + A = \begin{bmatrix} 4 & 5 \\ 6 & 7 \end{bmatrix} + \begin{bmatrix} 3 & 5 \\ -2 & -3 \end{bmatrix} = \begin{bmatrix} 4+3 & 5+5 \\ 6+(-2) & 7+(-3) \end{bmatrix} = \begin{bmatrix} 7 & 10 \\ 4 & 4 \end{bmatrix}$ Thus A + B = B + A.

40. $A + B = \begin{bmatrix} 9 & 4 \\ 1 & 7 \end{bmatrix} + \begin{bmatrix} 2 & 0 \\ -1 & 6 \end{bmatrix} = \begin{bmatrix} 9+2 & 4+0 \\ 1+(-1) & 7+6 \end{bmatrix} = \begin{bmatrix} 11 & 4 \\ 0 & 13 \end{bmatrix}$

$B + A = \begin{bmatrix} 2 & 0 \\ -1 & 6 \end{bmatrix} + \begin{bmatrix} 9 & 4 \\ 1 & 7 \end{bmatrix} = \begin{bmatrix} 2+9 & 0+4 \\ -1+1 & 6+7 \end{bmatrix} = \begin{bmatrix} 11 & 4 \\ 0 & 13 \end{bmatrix}$ Thus $A + B = B + A$.

41. $A + B = \begin{bmatrix} 0 & -1 \\ 3 & -4 \end{bmatrix} + \begin{bmatrix} 8 & 1 \\ 3 & -4 \end{bmatrix} = \begin{bmatrix} 0+8 & -1+1 \\ 3+3 & -4+(-4) \end{bmatrix} = \begin{bmatrix} 8 & 0 \\ 6 & -8 \end{bmatrix}$

$B + A = \begin{bmatrix} 8 & 1 \\ 3 & -4 \end{bmatrix} + \begin{bmatrix} 0 & -1 \\ 3 & -4 \end{bmatrix} = \begin{bmatrix} 8+0 & 1+(-1) \\ 3+3 & -4+(-4) \end{bmatrix} = \begin{bmatrix} 8 & 0 \\ 6 & -8 \end{bmatrix}$ Thus $A + B = B + A$.

42. $A + B = \begin{bmatrix} 1 & 2 \\ 3 & 2 \end{bmatrix} + \begin{bmatrix} 5 & 6 \\ 6 & 5 \end{bmatrix} = \begin{bmatrix} 1+5 & 2+6 \\ 3+6 & 2+5 \end{bmatrix} = \begin{bmatrix} 6 & 8 \\ 9 & 7 \end{bmatrix}$

$B + A = \begin{bmatrix} 5 & 6 \\ 6 & 5 \end{bmatrix} + \begin{bmatrix} 1 & 2 \\ 3 & 2 \end{bmatrix} = \begin{bmatrix} 5+1 & 6+2 \\ 6+3 & 5+2 \end{bmatrix} = \begin{bmatrix} 6 & 8 \\ 9 & 7 \end{bmatrix}$ Thus $A + B = B + A$.

43. $(A + B) + C = \left(\begin{bmatrix} 5 & 2 \\ 3 & 6 \end{bmatrix} + \begin{bmatrix} 3 & 4 \\ -2 & 7 \end{bmatrix} \right) + \begin{bmatrix} -1 & 4 \\ 5 & 0 \end{bmatrix} = \begin{bmatrix} 8 & 6 \\ 1 & 13 \end{bmatrix} + \begin{bmatrix} -1 & 4 \\ 5 & 0 \end{bmatrix} = \begin{bmatrix} 7 & 10 \\ 6 & 13 \end{bmatrix}$

$A + (B + C) = \begin{bmatrix} 5 & 2 \\ 3 & 6 \end{bmatrix} + \left(\begin{bmatrix} 3 & 4 \\ -2 & 7 \end{bmatrix} + \begin{bmatrix} -1 & 4 \\ 5 & 0 \end{bmatrix} \right) = \begin{bmatrix} 5 & 2 \\ 3 & 6 \end{bmatrix} + \begin{bmatrix} 2 & 8 \\ 3 & 7 \end{bmatrix} = \begin{bmatrix} 7 & 10 \\ 6 & 13 \end{bmatrix}$

Thus, $(A + B) + C = A + (B + C)$.

44. $(A + B) + C = \left(\begin{bmatrix} 4 & 1 \\ 6 & 7 \end{bmatrix} + \begin{bmatrix} -9 & 1 \\ -7 & 2 \end{bmatrix} \right) + \begin{bmatrix} -6 & -3 \\ 3 & 6 \end{bmatrix} = \begin{bmatrix} -5 & 2 \\ -1 & 9 \end{bmatrix} + \begin{bmatrix} -6 & -3 \\ 3 & 6 \end{bmatrix} = \begin{bmatrix} -11 & -1 \\ 2 & 15 \end{bmatrix}$

$A + (B + C) = \begin{bmatrix} 4 & 1 \\ 6 & 7 \end{bmatrix} + \left(\begin{bmatrix} -9 & 1 \\ -7 & 2 \end{bmatrix} + \begin{bmatrix} -6 & -3 \\ 3 & 6 \end{bmatrix} \right) = \begin{bmatrix} 4 & 1 \\ 6 & 7 \end{bmatrix} + \begin{bmatrix} -15 & -2 \\ -4 & 8 \end{bmatrix} = \begin{bmatrix} -11 & -1 \\ 2 & 15 \end{bmatrix}$

Thus, $(A + B) + C = A + (B + C)$.

45. $(A + B) + C = \left(\begin{bmatrix} 7 & 4 \\ 9 & -36 \end{bmatrix} + \begin{bmatrix} 5 & 6 \\ -1 & -4 \end{bmatrix} \right) + \begin{bmatrix} -7 & -5 \\ -1 & 3 \end{bmatrix} = \begin{bmatrix} 12 & 10 \\ 8 & -40 \end{bmatrix} + \begin{bmatrix} -7 & -5 \\ -1 & 3 \end{bmatrix} = \begin{bmatrix} 5 & 5 \\ 7 & -37 \end{bmatrix}$

$A + (B + C) = \begin{bmatrix} 7 & 4 \\ 9 & -36 \end{bmatrix} + \left(\begin{bmatrix} 5 & 6 \\ -1 & -4 \end{bmatrix} + \begin{bmatrix} -7 & -5 \\ -1 & 3 \end{bmatrix} \right) = \begin{bmatrix} 7 & 4 \\ 9 & -36 \end{bmatrix} + \begin{bmatrix} -2 & 1 \\ -2 & -1 \end{bmatrix} = \begin{bmatrix} 5 & 5 \\ 7 & -37 \end{bmatrix}$

Thus, $(A + B) + C = A + (B + C)$.

46. $A = \begin{bmatrix} 1 \\ 1 \end{bmatrix}$, $B = \begin{bmatrix} 2 \\ 0 \end{bmatrix}$ $C = \begin{bmatrix} 3 \\ 3 \end{bmatrix}$ (Your choices may be different)

$(A + B) + C = \left(\begin{bmatrix} 1 \\ 1 \end{bmatrix} + \begin{bmatrix} 2 \\ 0 \end{bmatrix} \right) + \begin{bmatrix} 3 \\ 3 \end{bmatrix} = \begin{bmatrix} 3 \\ 1 \end{bmatrix} + \begin{bmatrix} 3 \\ 3 \end{bmatrix} = \begin{bmatrix} 6 \\ 4 \end{bmatrix}$

$A + (B + C) = \begin{bmatrix} 1 \\ 1 \end{bmatrix} + \left(\begin{bmatrix} 2 \\ 0 \end{bmatrix} + \begin{bmatrix} 3 \\ 3 \end{bmatrix} \right) = \begin{bmatrix} 1 \\ 1 \end{bmatrix} + \begin{bmatrix} 5 \\ 3 \end{bmatrix} = \begin{bmatrix} 6 \\ 4 \end{bmatrix}$ Thus, $(A+B) + C = A + (B+C)$.

47. $A \times B = \begin{bmatrix} 1 & -2 \\ 4 & -3 \end{bmatrix}\begin{bmatrix} -1 & -3 \\ 2 & 4 \end{bmatrix} = \begin{bmatrix} 1(-1)-2(2) & 1(-3)-2(4) \\ 4(-1)+(-3)(2) & 4(-3)+(-3)(4) \end{bmatrix} = \begin{bmatrix} -5 & -11 \\ -10 & -24 \end{bmatrix}$

$B \times A = \begin{bmatrix} -1 & -3 \\ 2 & 4 \end{bmatrix}\begin{bmatrix} 1 & -2 \\ 4 & -3 \end{bmatrix} = \begin{bmatrix} -1(1)+(-3)4 & -1(-2)+(-3)(-3) \\ 2(1)+4(4) & 2(-2)+4(-3) \end{bmatrix} = \begin{bmatrix} -13 & 11 \\ 18 & -16 \end{bmatrix}$

Thus, $A \times B \neq B \times A$.

48. $A \times B = \begin{bmatrix} 3 & 1 \\ 6 & 6 \end{bmatrix}\begin{bmatrix} 1 & 0 \\ 0 & 1 \end{bmatrix} = \begin{bmatrix} 3(1)+1(0) & 3(0)+1(1) \\ 6(1)+6(0) & 6(0)+6(1) \end{bmatrix} = \begin{bmatrix} 3 & 1 \\ 6 & 6 \end{bmatrix}$

$B \times A = \begin{bmatrix} 1 & 0 \\ 0 & 1 \end{bmatrix}\begin{bmatrix} 3 & 1 \\ 6 & 6 \end{bmatrix} = \begin{bmatrix} 1(3)+0(6) & 0(3)+1(1) \\ 1(6)+0(6) & 0(6)+1(6) \end{bmatrix} = \begin{bmatrix} 3 & 1 \\ 6 & 6 \end{bmatrix}$ Thus, $A \times B = B \times A$.

49. $A \times B = \begin{bmatrix} 4 & 2 \\ 1 & -3 \end{bmatrix}\begin{bmatrix} 2 & 4 \\ -3 & 1 \end{bmatrix} = \begin{bmatrix} 4(2)+2(-3) & 4(4)+2(1) \\ 1(2)+(-3)(-3) & 1(4)+(-3)(1) \end{bmatrix} = \begin{bmatrix} 2 & 18 \\ 11 & 1 \end{bmatrix}$

$B \times A = \begin{bmatrix} 2 & 4 \\ -3 & 1 \end{bmatrix}\begin{bmatrix} 4 & 2 \\ 1 & -3 \end{bmatrix} = \begin{bmatrix} 2(4)+4(1) & 2(2)+4(-3) \\ -3(4)+1(1) & -3(2)+1(-3) \end{bmatrix} = \begin{bmatrix} 12 & -8 \\ -11 & -9 \end{bmatrix}$ Thus, $A \times B \neq B \times A$.

50. $A \times B = \begin{bmatrix} -3 & 2 \\ 6 & -5 \end{bmatrix}\begin{bmatrix} -5/3 & -2/3 \\ -2 & -1 \end{bmatrix} = \begin{bmatrix} -3(-5/3)+2(-2) & -3(-2/3)+2(-1) \\ 6(-5/3)-5(-2) & 6(-2/3)-5(-1) \end{bmatrix} = \begin{bmatrix} 1 & 0 \\ 0 & 1 \end{bmatrix}$

$B \times A = \begin{bmatrix} -5/3 & -2/3 \\ -2 & -1 \end{bmatrix}\begin{bmatrix} -3 & 2 \\ 6 & -5 \end{bmatrix} = \begin{bmatrix} (-5/3)(-3)-(2/3)(6) & -(5/3)(2)-(2/3)(5) \\ -2(-3)-1(6) & -2(2)-1(-5) \end{bmatrix} = \begin{bmatrix} 1 & 0 \\ 0 & 1 \end{bmatrix}$

Thus, $A \times B = B \times A$

51. Since $B = I$, (the identity matrix), and $A \times I = I \times A = A$, we can conclude that $A \times B = B \times A$.

52. $A = \begin{bmatrix} 1 & 1 \\ 0 & 2 \end{bmatrix}$, $B = \begin{bmatrix} 2 & 3 \\ 2 & 3 \end{bmatrix}$ (Your choices may be different)

$A \times B = \begin{bmatrix} 1 & 1 \\ 0 & 2 \end{bmatrix}\begin{bmatrix} 2 & 3 \\ 2 & 3 \end{bmatrix} = \begin{bmatrix} 1(2)+1(2) & 1(3)+1(3) \\ 0(2)+2(2) & 0(3)+2(3) \end{bmatrix} = \begin{bmatrix} 4 & 6 \\ 4 & 6 \end{bmatrix}$

$B \times A = \begin{bmatrix} 2 & 3 \\ 2 & 3 \end{bmatrix}\begin{bmatrix} 1 & 1 \\ 0 & 2 \end{bmatrix} = \begin{bmatrix} 2(1)+3(0) & 2(1)+3(2) \\ 2(1)+3(0) & 2(1)+3(2) \end{bmatrix} = \begin{bmatrix} 2 & 8 \\ 2 & 8 \end{bmatrix}$ Thus, $A \times B \neq B \times A$.

53. $(A \times B) \times C = \left(\begin{bmatrix} 1 & 3 \\ 4 & 0 \end{bmatrix}\begin{bmatrix} 4 & 2 \\ 3 & 1 \end{bmatrix}\right)\begin{bmatrix} 2 & 1 \\ 3 & 0 \end{bmatrix} = \begin{bmatrix} 13 & 5 \\ 16 & 8 \end{bmatrix}\begin{bmatrix} 2 & 1 \\ 3 & 0 \end{bmatrix} = \begin{bmatrix} 41 & 13 \\ 56 & 16 \end{bmatrix}$

$A \times (B \times C) = \begin{bmatrix} 1 & 3 \\ 4 & 0 \end{bmatrix}\left(\begin{bmatrix} 4 & 2 \\ 3 & 1 \end{bmatrix}\begin{bmatrix} 2 & 1 \\ 3 & 0 \end{bmatrix}\right) = \begin{bmatrix} 1 & 3 \\ 4 & 0 \end{bmatrix}\begin{bmatrix} 14 & 4 \\ 9 & 3 \end{bmatrix} = \begin{bmatrix} 41 & 13 \\ 56 & 16 \end{bmatrix}$ Thus, $(A \times B) \times C = A \times (B \times C)$.

54. $(A \times B) \times C = \left(\begin{bmatrix} -2 & 3 \\ 0 & 4 \end{bmatrix} \begin{bmatrix} 4 & 0 \\ 3 & 5 \end{bmatrix} \right) \begin{bmatrix} 3 & 4 \\ -2 & 5 \end{bmatrix} = \begin{bmatrix} 1 & 15 \\ 12 & 20 \end{bmatrix} \begin{bmatrix} 3 & 4 \\ -2 & 5 \end{bmatrix} = \begin{bmatrix} -27 & 79 \\ -4 & 148 \end{bmatrix}$

$A \times (B \times C) = \begin{bmatrix} -2 & 3 \\ 0 & 4 \end{bmatrix} \left(\begin{bmatrix} 4 & 0 \\ 3 & 5 \end{bmatrix} \begin{bmatrix} 3 & 4 \\ -2 & 5 \end{bmatrix} \right) = \begin{bmatrix} -2 & 3 \\ 0 & 4 \end{bmatrix} \begin{bmatrix} 12 & 16 \\ -1 & 37 \end{bmatrix} = \begin{bmatrix} -27 & 79 \\ -4 & 148 \end{bmatrix}$

Thus, $(A \times B) \times C = A \times (B \times C)$.

55. $(A \times B) \times C = \left(\begin{bmatrix} 4 & 3 \\ -6 & 2 \end{bmatrix} \begin{bmatrix} 1 & 2 \\ 0 & 1 \end{bmatrix} \right) \begin{bmatrix} 4 & 3 \\ 0 & -2 \end{bmatrix} = \begin{bmatrix} 4 & 11 \\ -6 & -10 \end{bmatrix} \begin{bmatrix} 4 & 3 \\ 0 & -2 \end{bmatrix} = \begin{bmatrix} 16 & -10 \\ -24 & 2 \end{bmatrix}$

$A \times (B \times C) = \begin{bmatrix} 4 & 3 \\ -6 & 2 \end{bmatrix} \left(\begin{bmatrix} 1 & 2 \\ 0 & 1 \end{bmatrix} \begin{bmatrix} 4 & 3 \\ 0 & -2 \end{bmatrix} \right) = \begin{bmatrix} 4 & 3 \\ -6 & 2 \end{bmatrix} \begin{bmatrix} 4 & -1 \\ 0 & -2 \end{bmatrix} = \begin{bmatrix} 16 & -10 \\ -24 & 2 \end{bmatrix}$

Thus, $(A \times B) \times C = A \times (B \times C)$.

56. $(A \times B) \times C = (A \times I) \times C = A \times C$, and $A \times (B \times C) = A \times (I \times C) = A \times C$, thus $(A \times B) \times C = A \times (B \times C)$.

57. $(A \times B) \times C = \left(\begin{bmatrix} 3 & 4 \\ -1 & -2 \end{bmatrix} \begin{bmatrix} 0 & 1 \\ 1 & 0 \end{bmatrix} \right) \begin{bmatrix} 2 & 0 \\ 3 & 0 \end{bmatrix} = \begin{bmatrix} 4 & 3 \\ -2 & -1 \end{bmatrix} \begin{bmatrix} 2 & 0 \\ 3 & 0 \end{bmatrix} = \begin{bmatrix} 17 & 0 \\ -7 & 0 \end{bmatrix}$

$A \times (B \times C) = \begin{bmatrix} 3 & 4 \\ -1 & -2 \end{bmatrix} \left(\begin{bmatrix} 0 & 1 \\ 1 & 0 \end{bmatrix} \begin{bmatrix} 2 & 0 \\ 3 & 0 \end{bmatrix} \right) = \begin{bmatrix} 3 & 4 \\ -1 & -2 \end{bmatrix} \begin{bmatrix} 3 & 0 \\ 2 & 0 \end{bmatrix} = \begin{bmatrix} 17 & 0 \\ -7 & 0 \end{bmatrix}$

Thus, $(A \times B) \times C = A \times (B \times C)$.

58. $(A \times B) \times C = A \times (B \times C)$ for any choices of A, B, and C that can be multiplied.

59. $A + B = \begin{bmatrix} 40 & 22 & 31 \\ 38 & 25 & 34 \end{bmatrix} + \begin{bmatrix} 48 & 36 & 39 \\ 40 & 29 & 37 \end{bmatrix}$

$= \begin{bmatrix} 40+48 & 22+36 & 31+39 \\ 38+40 & 25+29 & 34+37 \end{bmatrix} = \begin{bmatrix} 88 & 58 & 70 \\ 78 & 54 & 71 \end{bmatrix}$

Total weight: $\begin{matrix} \text{T} & \text{O} & \text{C} \\ \begin{bmatrix} 88 & 58 & 70 \\ 78 & 54 & 71 \end{bmatrix} & \begin{matrix} \text{Chase's} \\ \text{Gro-More} \end{matrix} \end{matrix}$

60. $A - B = \begin{bmatrix} 31 & 18 \\ 39 & 16 \\ 41 & 22 \\ 34 & 21 \end{bmatrix} - \begin{bmatrix} 14 & 9 \\ 18 & 9 \\ 19 & 15 \\ 15 & 9 \end{bmatrix} = \begin{bmatrix} 17 & 9 \\ 21 & 7 \\ 22 & 7 \\ 19 & 12 \end{bmatrix}$

Sweatshirts sold: $\begin{matrix} \text{A} & \text{Y} \\ \begin{bmatrix} 17 & 9 \\ 21 & 7 \\ 22 & 7 \\ 19 & 12 \end{bmatrix} & \begin{matrix} \text{Small} \\ \text{Medium} \\ \text{Large} \\ \text{Extra Large} \end{matrix} \end{matrix}$

61. $A \times B = \begin{bmatrix} 7 & 8.5 & 10 \\ 7.5 & 8 & 11 \end{bmatrix} \times \begin{bmatrix} 3 \\ 2 \\ 1.5 \end{bmatrix} = \begin{bmatrix} 7(3)+8.5(2)+10(1.5) \\ 7.5(3)+8(2)+11(1.5) \end{bmatrix} = \begin{bmatrix} 53 \\ 55 \end{bmatrix}$

Total cost: $\begin{bmatrix} 53 \\ 55 \end{bmatrix}$ Java's
Spot

62. $A \times B = \begin{bmatrix} 35 & 28 & 23 \end{bmatrix} \times \begin{bmatrix} 45 & 12 & 8 & 10 \\ 52 & 8 & 6 & 15 \\ 49 & 7 & 9 & 11 \end{bmatrix}$

The four entries going across the one row are:

$35(45)+28(52)+23(49)$, $35(12)+28(8)+23(7)$,

$35(8)+28(6)+23(9)$, and $35(10)+28(15)+23(11)$.

The product is $\begin{bmatrix} 4158 & 805 & 655 & 1023 \end{bmatrix}$.

$$\qquad\qquad M \qquad V \qquad S \qquad D$$

Total cost: $\begin{bmatrix} 4158 & 805 & 655 & 1023 \end{bmatrix}$

63. $A \times B = \begin{bmatrix} 2 & 2 & .5 & 1 \\ 3 & 2 & 1 & 2 \\ 0 & 1 & 0 & 3 \\ .5 & 1 & 0 & 0 \end{bmatrix} \begin{bmatrix} 10 & 12 \\ 5 & 8 \\ 8 & 8 \\ 4 & 6 \end{bmatrix} = \begin{bmatrix} 2 \cdot 10+2 \cdot 5+.5 \cdot 8+1 \cdot 4 & 2 \cdot 12+2 \cdot 8+.5 \cdot 8+1 \cdot 6 \\ 3 \cdot 10+2 \cdot 5+1 \cdot 8+2 \cdot 4 & 3 \cdot 12+2 \cdot 8+1 \cdot 8+2 \cdot 6 \\ 0 \cdot 10+1 \cdot 5+0 \cdot 8+3 \cdot 4 & 0 \cdot 12+1 \cdot 8+0 \cdot 8+3 \cdot 6 \\ .5 \cdot 10+1 \cdot 5+0 \cdot 8+0 \cdot 4 & .5 \cdot 12+1 \cdot 8+0 \cdot 8+0 \cdot 6 \end{bmatrix} = \begin{bmatrix} 38 & 50 \\ 56 & 72 \\ 17 & 26 \\ 10 & 14 \end{bmatrix}$

64. a) Let C = [40 30 12 20].

b) $C \times A = \begin{bmatrix} 40 & 30 & 12 & 20 \end{bmatrix} \begin{bmatrix} 2 & 2 & .5 & 1 \\ 3 & 2 & 1 & 2 \\ 0 & 1 & 0 & 3 \\ .5 & 1 & 0 & 0 \end{bmatrix} = [\underset{\text{sugar}}{180} \quad \underset{\text{flour}}{172} \quad \underset{\text{milk}}{50} \quad \underset{\text{eggs}}{136}]$

65. $C(A \times B) = \begin{bmatrix} 40 & 30 & 12 & 20 \end{bmatrix} \begin{bmatrix} 38 & 50 \\ 56 & 72 \\ 17 & 26 \\ 10 & 14 \end{bmatrix} = [36.04 \quad 47.52]$ cents $\qquad$ small \$36.04, large \$47.52

66. $A \times B = \begin{bmatrix} 52 & 50 & 75 \\ 48 & 43 & 60 \\ 62 & 57 & 81 \end{bmatrix} \begin{bmatrix} .30 & .75 \\ .25 & .50 \\ .15 & .45 \end{bmatrix} = \begin{bmatrix} 39.35 & 97.75 \\ 34.15 & 84.50 \\ 45.00 & 111.45 \end{bmatrix}$

67. a) A must have 3 rows and B must have one column.

b) $A = \begin{bmatrix} 1 & -2 \\ 0 & 1 \\ 1 & 3 \end{bmatrix} \qquad B = \begin{bmatrix} 6 \\ 7 \end{bmatrix} \qquad A \times B = \begin{bmatrix} -8 \\ 7 \\ 27 \end{bmatrix}$

68. a) A must have 4 rows and B must have one column.

b) $A = \begin{bmatrix} 1 & 5 \\ 2 & 6 \\ 3 & 7 \\ 4 & 8 \end{bmatrix} \qquad B = \begin{bmatrix} 2 \\ 5 \end{bmatrix} \qquad A \times B = \begin{bmatrix} 27 \\ 34 \\ 41 \\ 48 \end{bmatrix}$

69. $A \times B = \begin{bmatrix} 5 & -2 \\ -2 & 1 \end{bmatrix}\begin{bmatrix} 1 & 2 \\ 2 & 5 \end{bmatrix} = \begin{bmatrix} 5(1)-2(2) & 5(2)-2(5) \\ -2(1)+1(2) & -2(2)+1(5) \end{bmatrix} = \begin{bmatrix} 1 & 0 \\ 0 & 1 \end{bmatrix}$

$B \times A = \begin{bmatrix} 1 & 2 \\ 2 & 5 \end{bmatrix}\begin{bmatrix} 5 & -2 \\ -2 & 1 \end{bmatrix} = \begin{bmatrix} 1(5)+2(-2) & 1(-2)+2(1) \\ 2(5)+5(-2) & 2(-2)+5(1) \end{bmatrix} = \begin{bmatrix} 1 & 0 \\ 0 & 1 \end{bmatrix}$

Thus, A and B are multiplicative inverses.

70. $A \times B = \begin{bmatrix} 7 & 3 \\ 2 & 1 \end{bmatrix}\begin{bmatrix} 1 & -3 \\ -2 & 7 \end{bmatrix} = \begin{bmatrix} 7(1)+3(-2) & 7(-3)+3(7) \\ 2(1)+1(-2) & 2(-3)+1(7) \end{bmatrix} = \begin{bmatrix} 1 & 0 \\ 0 & 1 \end{bmatrix}$

$B \times A = \begin{bmatrix} 1 & -3 \\ -2 & 7 \end{bmatrix}\begin{bmatrix} 7 & 3 \\ 2 & 1 \end{bmatrix} = \begin{bmatrix} 1(7)-3(2) & 1(3)-3(1) \\ -2(7)+7(2) & -2(3)+7(1) \end{bmatrix} = \begin{bmatrix} 1 & 0 \\ 0 & 1 \end{bmatrix}$

Thus, A and B are multiplicative inverses.

71. False. Let A = [1 3] and B = [2 1]. Then A – B = [-1, 2] and B – A = [1, -2]   A – B ≠ B – A.

72. True. For all scalars a and all matrices B and C, a(B + C) = aB + aC. As an example,
Let a = 2, B = [1 3], and C = [2 1].   Then a(B + C) = 2([1 3] + [2 1]) = 2[3 4] = [6 8],
and   aB + aC = 2[1 3] + 2[2 1] = [2 6] + [4 2] = [6 8] = a(B + C).

73. a) 1.4(14) + 0.7(10) + 0.3(7) = $28.70
    b) 2.7(12) + 2.8(9) + 0.5(5) = $60.10

c) $L \times C = \begin{bmatrix} 28.7 & 24.6 \\ 41.3 & 35.7 \\ 69.3 & 60.1 \end{bmatrix} \begin{matrix} \text{small} \\ \text{medium} \\ \text{large} \end{matrix}$ ☐ Ames Bay (above columns)

This array shows the total cost of each sofa at each plant.

74. $A + B = \begin{bmatrix} 1 & 2 & 3 \\ 3 & 2 & 1 \end{bmatrix} + \begin{bmatrix} 0 & 1 & 2 \\ 4 & 5 & 1 \end{bmatrix} = \begin{bmatrix} 1 & 3 & 5 \\ 7 & 7 & 2 \end{bmatrix}$

A x B cannot be calculated because the # of columns of A ≠ # of rows of B.

75. A + B cannot be calculated because the # of columns of A ≠ # of rows of B and the # of rows of A ≠ # of rows of B.

$A \times B = \begin{bmatrix} 1 & 2 & 3 \\ 3 & 2 & 1 \end{bmatrix}\begin{bmatrix} 0 & 4 \\ 1 & 5 \\ 2 & 1 \end{bmatrix} = \begin{bmatrix} 1(0)+2(1)+3(2) & 1(4)+2(5)+3(1) \\ 3(0)+2(1)+1(2) & 3(4)+2(5)+1(1) \end{bmatrix} = \begin{bmatrix} 8 & 17 \\ 4 & 23 \end{bmatrix}$

76. Answers will vary; an example is $A = \begin{bmatrix} 1 & 0 \\ 0 & 0 \end{bmatrix}$ and $B = \begin{bmatrix} 0 & 0 \\ 0 & 1 \end{bmatrix}$.

Exercise Set 7.4

1. a) An augmented matrix is a matrix formed with the coefficients of the variables and the constants. The coefficients are separated from the constants by a vertical bar.

   b) $\begin{bmatrix} 1 & 3 & | & 7 \\ 2 & -1 & | & 4 \end{bmatrix}$

2. 1) Rows of a matrix can be interchanged.

   2) All values in a row can be multiplied by a nonzero real number.

   3) A multiple of one row may be added to another row.

3. If you obtain an augmented matrix in which a 0 appears across an entire row, the system of equations is dependent.

4. If you obtain an augmented matrix in which one row of numbers on the left side of the vertical line are all zeroes but a zero does not appear in the same row on the other side of the vertical line, the system is inconsistent.

5. 1) Multiply the 2nd row by -1/2; 2) add -3 times the 2nd row to the first row; and 3) identify the values of x and y.

   1) $\begin{bmatrix} 1 & 3 & | & 5 \\ 0 & 1 & | & (-1/2) \end{bmatrix}$ 2) $\begin{bmatrix} 1+0 & 3+(-3) & | & 5+(3/2) \\ 0 & 1 & | & (-1/2) \end{bmatrix} = \begin{bmatrix} 1 & 0 & | & 13/2 \\ 0 & 1 & | & -1/2 \end{bmatrix}$ 3) $(x, y) = \left(\dfrac{13}{2}, \dfrac{-1}{2} \right)$

6. 1) Add 2 times the 2nd row to the 1st row, and 2) identify the values of x and y.

   $\begin{bmatrix} 1 & -2 & | & 1 \\ 0 & 1 & | & 3 \end{bmatrix}$ 1) $\begin{bmatrix} 1+0 & -2+2 & | & 1+6 \\ 0 & 1 & | & 3 \end{bmatrix} = \begin{bmatrix} 1 & 0 & | & 7 \\ 0 & 1 & | & 3 \end{bmatrix}$ 2) $(x, y) = (7, 3)$

7. $x + 3y = 7$ $-x + y = 1$

   $\begin{bmatrix} 1 & 3 & | & 7 \\ -1 & 1 & | & 1 \end{bmatrix} \rightarrow \begin{bmatrix} 1 & 3 & | & 7 \\ -1+1 & 1+3 & | & 7+1 \end{bmatrix} = \begin{bmatrix} 1 & 3 & | & 7 \\ 0 & 4 & | & 8 \end{bmatrix} \rightarrow$

   $\begin{bmatrix} 1 & 3 & | & 7 \\ 0 & 1 & | & 2 \end{bmatrix} \rightarrow \begin{bmatrix} 1+0 & 3+(-3) & | & 7+(-6) \\ 0 & 1 & | & 2 \end{bmatrix} = \begin{bmatrix} 1 & 0 & | & 1 \\ 0 & 1 & | & 2 \end{bmatrix} \rightarrow (1, 2)$

8. $x - y = 2$ $2x - y = 4$

   $\begin{bmatrix} 1 & -1 & | & 2 \\ 2 & -1 & | & 4 \end{bmatrix} \rightarrow \begin{bmatrix} 1 & -1 & | & 2 \\ 2-2 & -1+2 & | & 4-4 \end{bmatrix} = \begin{bmatrix} 1 & -1 & | & 2 \\ 0 & 1 & | & 0 \end{bmatrix} \rightarrow \begin{bmatrix} 1+0 & -1+1 & | & 2+0 \\ 0 & 1 & | & 0 \end{bmatrix} = \begin{bmatrix} 1 & 0 & | & 2 \\ 0 & 1 & | & 0 \end{bmatrix} \rightarrow (2, 0)$

9. $x - 2y = -1$ $2x + y = 8$

   $\begin{bmatrix} 1 & -2 & | & -1 \\ 2 & 1 & | & 8 \end{bmatrix} \rightarrow \begin{bmatrix} 1 & -2 & | & -1 \\ 2-2 & 1+4 & | & 8+2 \end{bmatrix} = \begin{bmatrix} 1 & -2 & | & -1 \\ 0 & 5 & | & 10 \end{bmatrix} \rightarrow \begin{bmatrix} 1+0 & -2+2 & | & -1+4 \\ 0 & 5 & | & 10 \end{bmatrix} \rightarrow$

   $\begin{bmatrix} 1 & 0 & | & 3 \\ 0 & 5 & | & 10 \end{bmatrix} = \begin{bmatrix} 1 & 0 & | & 3 \\ 0 & 1 & | & 2 \end{bmatrix} \rightarrow (3, 2)$

10. $x + y = -1 \qquad 2x + 3y = -5$

$$\begin{bmatrix} 1 & 1 & | & -1 \\ 2 & 3 & | & -5 \end{bmatrix} \rightarrow \begin{bmatrix} 1 & 1 & | & -1 \\ 2-2 & 3-2 & | & -5+2 \end{bmatrix} = \begin{bmatrix} 1 & 1 & | & -1 \\ 0 & 1 & | & -3 \end{bmatrix} \rightarrow \begin{bmatrix} 1+0 & 1-1 & | & -1+3 \\ 0 & 1 & | & -3 \end{bmatrix} = \begin{bmatrix} 1 & 0 & | & 2 \\ 0 & 1 & | & -3 \end{bmatrix} \rightarrow \quad (2, -3)$$

11. $\begin{bmatrix} 2 & -5 & | & -6 \\ -4 & 10 & | & 12 \end{bmatrix} \underset{(r_2 + 2r_1)}{=} \begin{bmatrix} 2 & -5 & | & -6 \\ 0 & 0 & | & 0 \end{bmatrix} \Rightarrow$ Dependent system

The solution is all points on the line $2x - 5y = -6$.

12. $\begin{bmatrix} 1 & 1 & | & 5 \\ 3 & -1 & | & 3 \end{bmatrix} \underset{(r_2 - 3r_1)}{=} \begin{bmatrix} 1 & 1 & | & 5 \\ 0 & -4 & | & -12 \end{bmatrix} \underset{(r_2 \div (-4))}{=} \begin{bmatrix} 1 & 1 & | & 5 \\ 0 & 1 & | & 3 \end{bmatrix} \underset{=}{(r_1 - r_2)} \begin{bmatrix} 1 & 0 & | & 2 \\ 0 & 1 & | & 3 \end{bmatrix}$ The solution is (2, 3).

13. $\begin{bmatrix} 2 & -3 & | & 10 \\ 2 & 2 & | & 5 \end{bmatrix} \underset{(r_2 - 2r_1)}{(r_1 \div 2)} \begin{bmatrix} 1 & -\frac{3}{2} & | & 5 \\ 0 & 5 & | & -5 \end{bmatrix} \underset{=}{(r_2 \div (5))} \begin{bmatrix} 1 & -\frac{3}{2} & | & 5 \\ 0 & 1 & | & -1 \end{bmatrix} \underset{=}{(r_1 + \frac{3}{2}r_2)} \begin{bmatrix} 1 & 0 & | & \frac{7}{2} \\ 0 & 1 & | & -1 \end{bmatrix}$ The solution is (7/2, – 1).

14. $\begin{bmatrix} 1 & 3 & | & 1 \\ -2 & 1 & | & 5 \end{bmatrix} \underset{(r_2 + 2r_1)}{=} \begin{bmatrix} 1 & 3 & | & 1 \\ 0 & 7 & | & 7 \end{bmatrix} \underset{(r_2 \div 7)}{=} \begin{bmatrix} 1 & 3 & | & 1 \\ 0 & 1 & | & 1 \end{bmatrix} \underset{=}{(r_1 - 3r_2)} \begin{bmatrix} 1 & 0 & | & -2 \\ 0 & 1 & | & 1 \end{bmatrix}$ The solution is (– 2, 1).

15. $\begin{bmatrix} 4 & 2 & | & 6 \\ 5 & 4 & | & 9 \end{bmatrix} \underset{=}{(r_1 \div 4)} \begin{bmatrix} 1 & \frac{1}{2} & | & \frac{3}{2} \\ 5 & 4 & | & 9 \end{bmatrix} \underset{(r_2 - 5r_1)}{=} \begin{bmatrix} 1 & \frac{1}{2} & | & \frac{3}{2} \\ 0 & \frac{3}{2} & | & \frac{3}{2} \end{bmatrix} \underset{(\frac{2}{3}r_2)}{=} \begin{bmatrix} 1 & \frac{1}{2} & | & \frac{3}{2} \\ 0 & 1 & | & 1 \end{bmatrix} \underset{=}{(r_1 - \frac{1}{2}r_2)} \begin{bmatrix} 1 & 0 & | & 1 \\ 0 & 1 & | & 1 \end{bmatrix}$

The solution is (1, 1).

16. $\begin{bmatrix} 4 & 2 & | & -10 \\ -2 & 1 & | & -7 \end{bmatrix} \underset{r_2 + \frac{1}{2}r_1}{=} \begin{bmatrix} 4 & 2 & | & -10 \\ 0 & 2 & | & -12 \end{bmatrix} \underset{=}{(r_1 \div 4)} \begin{bmatrix} 1 & 1/2 & | & -10/4 \\ 0 & 2 & | & -12 \end{bmatrix} \underset{(r_2 \div 2)}{=} \begin{bmatrix} 1 & 1/2 & | & -10/4 \\ 0 & 1 & | & -6 \end{bmatrix}$

$\begin{bmatrix} 1 & 1/2 & | & -10/4 \\ 0 & 1 & | & -6 \end{bmatrix} \underset{=}{(r_1 - \frac{1}{2}r_2)} \begin{bmatrix} 1 & 0 & | & 1/2 \\ 0 & 1 & | & -6 \end{bmatrix}$ The solution is (1/2, -6).

17. $\begin{bmatrix} -3 & 6 & | & 5 \\ 2 & -4 & | & 8 \end{bmatrix} \underset{=}{(r_1 \div (-3))} \begin{bmatrix} 1 & -2 & | & \frac{-5}{3} \\ 2 & -4 & | & 8 \end{bmatrix} \underset{(r_2 - 2r_1)}{=} \begin{bmatrix} 1 & -2 & | & \frac{-5}{3} \\ 0 & 0 & | & \frac{34}{3} \end{bmatrix} \Rightarrow$ Inconsistent system   No solution.

18. $\begin{bmatrix} 2 & -5 & | & 10 \\ 3 & 1 & | & 15 \end{bmatrix} = \begin{bmatrix} 1 & \frac{-5}{2} & | & 5 \\ 0 & \frac{15}{2} & | & 0 \end{bmatrix} = \begin{bmatrix} 1 & \frac{-5}{2} & | & 5 \\ 0 & 1 & | & 0 \end{bmatrix} = \begin{bmatrix} 1 & 0 & | & 5 \\ 0 & 1 & | & 0 \end{bmatrix}$ The solution is (5, 0).

19. $\begin{bmatrix} 3 & 1 & | & 13 \\ 1 & 3 & | & 15 \end{bmatrix} \underset{=}{(r_1 \div 3)} \begin{bmatrix} 1 & \frac{1}{3} & | & \frac{13}{3} \\ 1 & 3 & | & 15 \end{bmatrix} \underset{(r_2 - r_1)}{=} \begin{bmatrix} 1 & \frac{1}{3} & | & \frac{13}{3} \\ 0 & \frac{8}{3} & | & \frac{32}{3} \end{bmatrix} \underset{(\frac{3}{8}r_2)}{=} \begin{bmatrix} 1 & \frac{1}{3} & | & \frac{13}{3} \\ 0 & 1 & | & 4 \end{bmatrix} \underset{=}{(r_1 - \frac{1}{3}r_2)} \begin{bmatrix} 1 & 0 & | & 3 \\ 0 & 1 & | & 4 \end{bmatrix}$

The solution is (3, 4).

20. $\begin{bmatrix} 4 & -3 & | & 7 \\ -2 & 5 & | & 14 \end{bmatrix} \underset{=}{(r_1 \div 4)} \begin{bmatrix} 1 & -\frac{3}{4} & | & \frac{7}{4} \\ -2 & 5 & | & 14 \end{bmatrix} \underset{(r_2 + 2r_1)}{=} \begin{bmatrix} 1 & -\frac{3}{4} & | & \frac{7}{4} \\ 0 & \frac{7}{2} & | & \frac{35}{2} \end{bmatrix} \underset{(\frac{2}{7}r_2)}{=} \begin{bmatrix} 1 & -\frac{3}{4} & | & \frac{7}{4} \\ 0 & 1 & | & 5 \end{bmatrix} \underset{=}{(r_1 + \frac{3}{4}r_2)} \begin{bmatrix} 1 & 0 & | & \frac{11}{2} \\ 0 & 1 & | & 5 \end{bmatrix}$

The solution is (11/2, 5).

21. $F + S = 32 \qquad 35F + 25S = 980$

$$\begin{bmatrix} 1 & 1 & | & 32 \\ 35 & 25 & | & 980 \end{bmatrix} \begin{matrix} \\ (r_2 - 35r_1) \end{matrix} \begin{bmatrix} 1 & 1 & | & 32 \\ 0 & -10 & | & -140 \end{bmatrix} \begin{matrix} \\ (r_2 \div -10) \end{matrix} \begin{bmatrix} 1 & 1 & | & 32 \\ 0 & 1 & | & 14 \end{bmatrix} \begin{matrix} (r_1 - r_2) \\ = \end{matrix} \begin{bmatrix} 1 & 0 & | & 18 \\ 0 & 1 & | & 14 \end{bmatrix}$$

The solution is (18, 14); 18 fitted caps and 14 stretch-fit caps.

22. $p = 2H + 2W \qquad 2H + 2W = 124 \qquad H - W = 8$

$$\begin{bmatrix} 2 & 2 & | & 124 \\ 1 & -1 & | & 8 \end{bmatrix} \begin{matrix} (r_1 + 2r_2) \\ = \end{matrix} \begin{bmatrix} 4 & 0 & | & 140 \\ 1 & -1 & | & 8 \end{bmatrix} \begin{matrix} \\ (r_1 \div 4) \end{matrix} \begin{bmatrix} 1 & 0 & | & 35 \\ 1 & -1 & | & 8 \end{bmatrix} \begin{matrix} \\ (r_2 - r_1) \end{matrix} \begin{bmatrix} 1 & 0 & | & 35 \\ 0 & -1 & | & -27 \end{bmatrix} \begin{matrix} (r_2 \cdot -1) \\ = \end{matrix} \begin{bmatrix} 1 & 0 & | & 35 \\ 0 & 1 & | & 27 \end{bmatrix}$$

The solution is (35, 27); 35 inches wide and 27 inches high.

23. Let T = # of hours for truck driver $\qquad$ L = # of hours for laborer

$10T + 8L = 144 \qquad L = T + 2 \quad \rightarrow \quad T = L - 2$

$$\begin{bmatrix} 10 & 8 & | & 144 \\ 1 & -1 & | & -2 \end{bmatrix} \begin{matrix} r_1 + 8r_2 \\ = \end{matrix} \begin{bmatrix} 18 & 0 & | & 128 \\ 1 & -1 & | & -2 \end{bmatrix} \begin{matrix} (r_1 \div 18) \\ = \end{matrix} \begin{bmatrix} 1 & 0 & | & 64/9 \\ 1 & -1 & | & -2 \end{bmatrix} \begin{matrix} \\ (r_2 - r_1) \end{matrix} \begin{bmatrix} 1 & 0 & | & 64/9 \\ 0 & -1 & | & -82/9 \end{bmatrix}$$

$$\begin{bmatrix} 1 & 0 & | & 64/9 \\ 0 & -1 & | & -82/9 \end{bmatrix} \begin{matrix} \\ (r_2 \cdot -1) \end{matrix} \begin{bmatrix} 1 & 0 & | & 64/9 \\ 0 & 1 & | & 82/9 \end{bmatrix} \qquad (64/9, 82/9)$$

7 1/9 hours for the truck driver and 9 1/9 hours for the laborer.

24. Let x = cost per pound of caramel corn $\qquad$ y = cost per pound of mixed nuts

$2x + 3y = 27 \qquad x + 2y = 17$

$$\begin{bmatrix} 2 & 3 & | & 27 \\ 1 & 2 & | & 17 \end{bmatrix} = \begin{bmatrix} 1 & \frac{3}{2} & | & \frac{27}{2} \\ 1 & 2 & | & 17 \end{bmatrix} = \begin{bmatrix} 1 & \frac{3}{2} & | & \frac{27}{2} \\ 0 & \frac{1}{2} & | & \frac{7}{2} \end{bmatrix} = \begin{bmatrix} 1 & \frac{3}{2} & | & \frac{27}{2} \\ 0 & 1 & | & 7 \end{bmatrix} = \begin{bmatrix} 1 & 0 & | & 3 \\ 0 & 1 & | & 7 \end{bmatrix}$$

Caramel corn is $3 per pound and mixed nuts are $7 per pound.

25. Let x = amount of $6/ream paper ordered and y = amount of $7.50/ream paper ordered.

$6x + 7.5y = 1275 \qquad x + y = 200$

$$\begin{bmatrix} 6 & 7.5 & | & 1275 \\ 1 & 1 & | & 200 \end{bmatrix} = \begin{bmatrix} 1 & 1.25 & | & 212.5 \\ 1 & 1 & | & 200 \end{bmatrix} = \begin{bmatrix} 1 & 1.25 & | & 212.5 \\ 0 & -.25 & | & -12.5 \end{bmatrix} = \begin{bmatrix} 1 & 1.25 & | & 212.5 \\ 0 & 1 & | & 50 \end{bmatrix} = \begin{bmatrix} 1 & 0 & | & 150 \\ 0 & 1 & | & 50 \end{bmatrix}$$

The solution is 150 reams at $6/ream and 50 reams at $7.50/ream.

Exercise Set 7.5

1. The solution set of a system of linear inequalities is the set of points that satisfy all inequalities in the system.

2. No, a solution must satisfy both inequalities, and the intersection point satisfies only one of them.

3. Yes; a point of intersection satisfies both inequalities and is therefore a solution.

4. No, a solution must satisfy both inequalities, and the intersection point satisfies neither.

5.

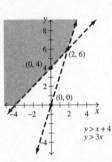

$$y > x + 4$$
$$y > 3x$$

6.

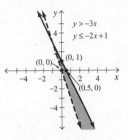

$$y > -3x$$
$$y \le -2x + 1$$

7.

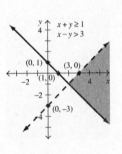

$$x + y \ge 1$$
$$x - y > 3$$

8.

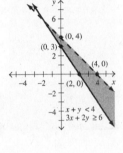

$$x + y < 4$$
$$3x + 2y \ge 6$$

9.

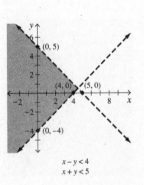

$$x - y < 4$$
$$x + y < 5$$

10.

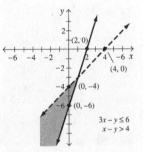

$$3x - y \le 6$$
$$x - y > 4$$

11.

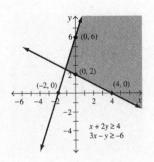

$$x + 2y \ge 4$$
$$3x - y \ge -6$$

12.

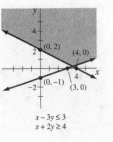

$$x - 3y \le 3$$
$$x + 2y \ge 4$$

13.

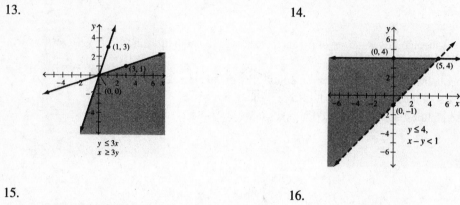

$y \le 3x$
$x \ge 3y$

14.

$y \le 4,$
$x - y < 1$

15.

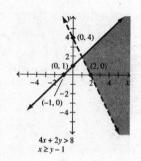

$x \le 0$
$y \le 0$

16.

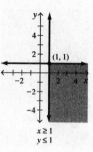

$x \ge 1$
$y \le 1$

17.

$4x + 2y > 8$
$x \ge y - 1$

18.

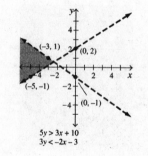

$5y > 3x + 10$
$3y < -2x - 3$

19.

$3x + 2y > 8$
$x < 5y - 5$

20.

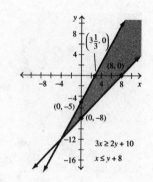

$3x \ge 2y + 10$
$x \le y + 8$

21. a) $20x + 30y \leq 600$, $x \geq 2y$, $x \geq 10$, $y \geq 5$

    b)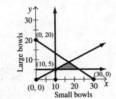

   c) One example is 15 small bowls, 7 large
      bowls.

22. a) $x + y < 500$, $x \geq 150$, $y \geq 150$

    b)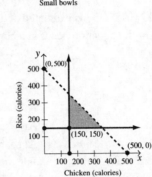

   c) One example is (220, 220).
$$\frac{220}{180}(3) \approx 3.7, \quad \frac{220}{200}(8) = 8.8$$
     3.7 oz of chicken, 8.8 oz of rice

23. $x \leq 0$, $y \geq 0$

24. a) No, if the lines are parallel there may not be a
      solution to the system.

   b) Example: $y \geq x$ $y \leq x - 2$
      This system has no solution.

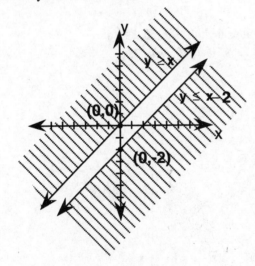

25. Yes. One example is
$x \leq 0$, $y \leq 0$, $x \geq 0$, $y \geq 0$.

26. No. Every line divides the plane into two halves
     only one of which can be part of the solution.
     Therefore, the points in the other half cannot
     satisfy both inequalities and so do not solve
     the system.
     Example: $y \geq x$ $x \geq 2$

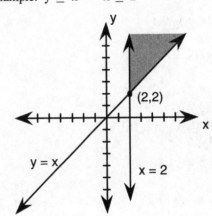

27. $y \leq x$, $y \geq x$, $y \leq 0$, $y \geq 0$

28. $y \leq x$, $y \geq x$

Exercise Set 7.6

1. Constraints are restrictions that are represented as linear inequalities.

2. The feasible region is formed by graphing the system of inequalities.

3. Vertices

4. a) Objective function: $K = Ax + By$
   b) The objective function is the formula for the quantity we want to maximize or minimize.

5. If a linear equation of the form $K = Ax + By$ is evaluated at each point in a closed polygonal region, the maximum and minimum values of the equation occur at a corner.

6. At $(1, 1)$, $P = 4(1) + 6(1) = 10$
   At $(1, 4)$, $P = 4(1) + 6(4) = 28$
   At $(5, 1)$, $P = 4(5) + 6(1) = 26$
   At $(7, 1)$, $P = 4(7) + 6(1) = 34$
   The maximum profit is 34. Determine the value of the profit function at each vertex; the largest profit value is the maximum.

7. At $(0, 0)$, $K = 6(0) + 4(0) = 0$
   At $(0, 4)$, $K = 6(0) + 4(4) = 16$
   At $(2, 3)$, $K = 6(2) + 4(3) = 24$
   At $(5, 0)$, $K = 6(5) + 4(0) = 30$
   The maximum value is 30 at $(5, 0)$; the minimum value is 0 at $(0, 0)$.

8. At $(0, 0)$, $K = 10(0) + 8(0) = 0$
   At $(20, 0)$, $K = 10(20) + 8(0) = 200$
   At $(15, 11)$, $K = 10(15) + 8(11) = 238$
   At $(8, 16)$, $K = 10(8) + 8(16) = 208$
   At $(0, 20)$, $K = 10(0) + 8(20) = 160$

   The maximum value is 238 at $(15, 11)$; the minimum value is 0 at $(0, 0)$.

9. At $(10, 20)$, $K = 2(10) + 3(20) = 80$
   At $(10, 40)$, $K = 2(10) + 3(40) = 140$
   At $(50, 30)$, $K = 2(50) + 3(30) = 190$
   At $(50, 10)$, $K = 2(50) + 3(10) = 130$
   At $(20, 10)$, $K = 2(20) + 3(10) = 70$

   The maximum value is 190 at $(50, 30)$; the minimum value is 70 at $(20, 10)$.

10. At $(1, 1)$, $K = 40(1) + 50(1) = 90$

    At $(4, 1)$, $K = 40(4) + 50(1) = 210$

    At $(5, 2)$, $K = 40(5) + 50(2) = 300$

    At $(4, 3)$, $K = 40(4) + 50(3) = 310$

    At $(2, 5)$, $K = 40(2) + 50(5) = 330$

    The maximum value is 330 at $(2, 5)$; the minimum value is 90 at $(1, 1)$.

11. a)

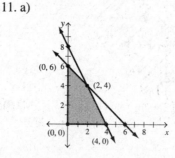

b) $x + y \le 6$ $2x + y \le 8$ $x \ge 0$ $y \ge 0$
    $P = 4x + 5y$
    At $(0,0)$, $P = 4(0) + 5(0) = 0$ min. at $(0, 0)$
    At $(0,4)$, $P = 4(0) + 5(4) = 20$
    At $(2, 4)$, $P = 4(2) + 5(4) = 28$
    At $(0,6)$, $P = 4(0) + 5(6) = 30$ max. at $(0, 6)$

12. a)

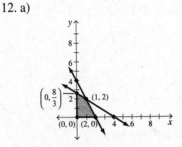

b) P = 2x + 6y

At (0,0), P = 2(0) + 6(0) = 0   min. at (0, 0)

At (1,2), P = 2(1) + 6(2) = 14

At (2,0), P = 2(2) + 6(0) = 4

At (0,8/3), P = 2(0) + 6(8/3) = 16 max. at (0, 8/3)

13. a)

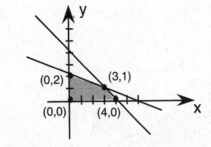

b) P = 7x + 6y

At (0,0), P = 7(0) + 6(0) = 0   min. at (0, 0)

At (0,2), P = 7(0) + 6(2) = 12

At (3,1), P = 7(3) + 6(1) = 27

At (4,0), P = 7(4) + 6(0) = 28   max. at (4, 0)

14. a)

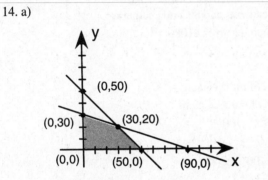

b) P = 20x + 40y

At (0, 0), P = 20(0)+40(0) = 0

At (0,30), P = 20(0+40(30) = 120

At (30,20), P = 20(30)+40(20) = 1400

At (50, 0), P = 20(50)+40(0) = 1000

Minimum of 0 at (0, 0) and Maximum of

1400at (30, 20).

15. a)

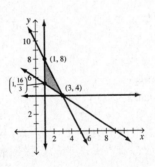

b) P = 2.20x + 1.65y

At (3, 4), P = 2.20(3)+1.65(4) = 13.2

At (1, 8), P = 2.20(1)+1.65(8) = 15.4

At (1, 16/3), P = 2.20(1)+1.65(16/3) = 11

Maximum of 15.4 at (1, 8) and

Minimum of 11 at (1, 16/3)

16. a)

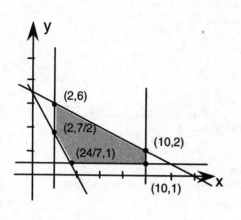

b) P = 15.13x + 9.35y

Max. profit is 170 at (10,2)

Min. profit is 61.22 at (24/7,1)

17. a) $x + y \leq 24$, $x \geq 2y$, $y \geq 4$, $x \geq 0$, $y \geq 0$

b) $P = 40x + 55y$

c)

d) (8, 4), (16, 8), (20, 4)

e) At (8, 4), P = 40(8) + 55(4) = 540

At (16, 8), P = 40(16) + 55(8) = 1080

At (20, 4), P = 40(20) + 55(4) = 1020

16 Kodak cameras and 8 Canon cameras

f) The maximum profit is $1080

18. a) Let x = number of skateboards

y = number of in-line skates

x + y ≤ 20   x ≥ 3   x ≤ 6   y ≥ 2

b) P = 25x + 20y

c)

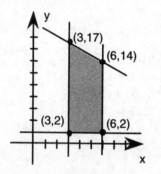

d) (3,2) (3,17) (6,14) (6,2)

e) At (3,2), P = 25(3) + 20(2) = 115

At (3,17), P = 25(3) + 20(17) = 415

At (6,14), P = 25(6) + 20(14) = 430

At (6,2), P = 25(6) + 20(2) = 190

Six skateboards and 14 pairs of in-line skates.

f) Max. profit = $430

19. Let x = gallons of indoor paint

y = gallons of outdoor paint

x ≥ 60   y ≥ 100

(a) 3x + 4y ≥ 60   x ≥ 0

10x + 5y ≥ 100   y ≥ 0

(b) C = 28x + 33y

(c)

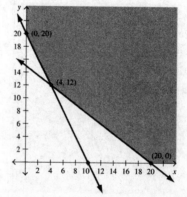

d) At (0, 20), C = 28(0) + 33(20) = 660

At (20, 0), C = 28(20) + 33(0) = 560

At (4, 12), C = 28(4) + 33(12) = 508

e) 4 hours on Mach. 1 and 12 hours on Mach. 2

f) Min. profit = $ 508.00

20. Let x = pounds of all-beef hot dogs
    y = pounds of regular hot dogs
    $x + (1/2)y \leq 200$

    $(1/2)y \leq 150$ $x \geq 0$ $y \geq 0$

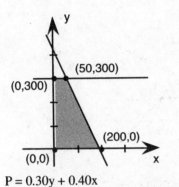

$P = 0.30y + 0.40x$

Maximum profit occurs at (50,300).

Thus the manufacturer should make 50 lb.

of the all-beef hot dogs and 300 lb. of the

regular hot dogs for a profit of $110.

21. Let x = # of car seats
    y = # of strollers
    $x + 3y \leq 24$ $2x + y \leq 16$ $x + y \leq 10$

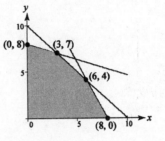

$P = 25x + 35y$

At (0, 8), P = 25(0) + 35(8) = 280

At (3, 7), P = 25(3) + 35(7) = 320

At (6, 4), P = 25(6) + 35(4) = 290

At (8, 0), P = 25(8) + 35(0) = 200

3 car seats and 7 strollers

Max. profit = $ 320.00

22. a) $3x + y \geq 9$, $x + 2y \geq 8$, $x \geq 0$, $y \geq 0$

    b) $C = 0.50x + 0.30y$

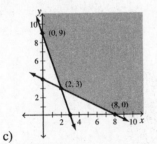

    c)

    d) (0, 9), (2, 3), (8, 0)

    e) At (0, 9), C = 0.50(0) + 0.30(4) = 3.60
       At (2, 3), C = 0.50(2) + 0.30(3) = 1.90
       At (8, 0), C = 0.50(8) + 0.30(0) = 4.00
       2 oz of group A and 3 oz of group B

    f) The minimum cost is $1.90.

Review Exercises

1.

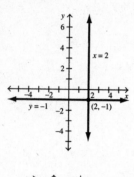

2.

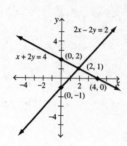

3.

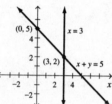

4.

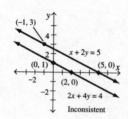

5. $y = (1/3)x + 5$
    $y = (1/3)x + 5$
    Same slope and y-intercept. Infinite # of solutions.

6. $y = -2x + 4$
    $y = -2x + 6$
    Same slope but different y-intercepts. No solution.

7. $6y - 2x = 20$ becomes $y = (1/3)x + 10/3$
    $4y + 2x = 10$ becomes $y = -(1/2)x + 5/2$
    Different slopes. One solution.

8. $y = (1/2)x - 2$
    $y = 2x + 6$
    Different slopes. One solution.

9. (1) $-x + y = -2$
    (2) $\underline{x + 2y = 5}$ (add)
    $3y = 3 y = 1$
    Substitute 1 in place of y in the first equation.
    $-x + 1 = -2$
    $-x = -3 x = 3$
    The solution is (3, 1).

10. $x - 2y = 9$
    $y = 2x - 3$
    Substitute $(2x - 3)$ in place of y in the 1st equation.
    $x - 2(2x - 3) = -11$ (solve for x)
    $x - 4x - 6 = -11$
    $5x - 6 = -1$
    $5x = -5 x = -1$
    Substitute (-1) in place of x in the 2nd equation.
    $y = 2(-1) - 3 = -2 - 3 = -5$
    The solution is (-1, -5).

11. $2x - y = 4 \qquad y = 2x - 4$

$3x - y = 2$

Substitute $2x - 4$ for y in the second equation.

$3x - (2x - 4) = 2$ (solve for x)

$3x - 2x + 4 = 2$

$x + 4 = 2 \qquad x = -2$

Substitute -2 for x in an equation.

$2(-2) - y = 4$

$-4 - y = 4 \qquad y = -8$

The solution is $(-2, -8)$.

12. $3x + y = 1 \qquad y = -3x + 1$

$3y = -9x - 4$

Substitute $-3x + 1$ for y in the second equation.

$3(-3x + 1) = -9x - 4$ (solve for x)

$-9x + 3 = -9x - 4$

$3 \neq 4$ False There is no solution to this system.

The equations are inconsistent.

13. (1) $x - 2y = 8$

(2) $2x + y = 6$

Multiply the second equation by 2.

$x - 2y = 8$

$\underline{4x + 2y = 12}$

$5x \qquad = 20$

$x = 4$

Substitute 4 in place of x in the equation (2).

$2(4) + y = 6$

$y = 6 - 8$

$y = -2$

The solution is $(4, -2)$.

14. (1) $2x + y = 2$

(2) $\underline{-3x - y = 5}$ (add)

$-x = 7 \qquad x = -7$

Substitute (-7) in place of x in the 1st equation.

$2(-7) + y = 2$

$-14 y = 2 \qquad y = 16$

The solution is $(-7, 16)$.

15. (1) $x + y = 2$

(2) $x + 3y = -2$

Multiply the first equation by -1.

$-x - y = -2$

$\underline{x + 3y = -2}$ (add)

$2y = -4 \qquad y = -2$

Substitute (-2) for y in equation (2).

$x + 3(-2) = -2$

$x - 6 = -2 \qquad x = 4$

The solution is $(4, -2)$.

16. (1) $4x - 8y = 16$

(2) $x - 2y = 4 \qquad x = 2y + 4$

Substitute $2y + 4$ for x in the first equation.

$4(2y + 4) - 8y = 16$

$8y + 16 - 8y = 16$

$16 = 16$ True

There are an infinite number of solutions.

The system is dependent.

17. (1) $3x - 4y = 10$

(2) $5x + 3y = 7$

Multiply the first equation by 3, and the 2nd equation by 4.

$9x - 12y = 30$

$\underline{20x + 12y = 28}$ (add)

$29x = 58 \qquad x = 2$

Substitute 2 for x in the second equation.

$5(2) + 3y = 7$

$3y = -3 \qquad y = -1$

The solution is $(2, -1)$.

18. (1) $3x + 4y = 6$

(2) $2x - 3y = 4$

Multiply the first equation by 2, and the second equation by -3.

$6x + 8y = 12$

$\underline{-6x + 9y = -12}$ (add)

$17y = 0 \qquad y = 0$

Substitute 0 for y in the first equation.

$3x + 4(0) = 6$

$3x = 6 \qquad x = 2$

The solution is $(2, 0)$.

19. $A + B = \begin{bmatrix} 1 & -3 \\ 2 & 4 \end{bmatrix} + \begin{bmatrix} -2 & -5 \\ 6 & 3 \end{bmatrix} = \begin{bmatrix} 1+(-2) & -3+(-5) \\ 2+6 & 4+3 \end{bmatrix} = \begin{bmatrix} -1 & -8 \\ 8 & 7 \end{bmatrix}$

20. $A - B = \begin{bmatrix} 1 & -3 \\ 2 & 4 \end{bmatrix} - \begin{bmatrix} -2 & -5 \\ 6 & 3 \end{bmatrix} = \begin{bmatrix} 1-(-2) & -3-(-5) \\ 2-6 & 4-3 \end{bmatrix} = \begin{bmatrix} 3 & 2 \\ -4 & 1 \end{bmatrix}$

21. $2A = 2\begin{bmatrix} 1 & -3 \\ 2 & 4 \end{bmatrix} = \begin{bmatrix} 2(1) & 2(-3) \\ 2(2) & 2(4) \end{bmatrix} = \begin{bmatrix} 2 & -6 \\ 4 & 8 \end{bmatrix}$

22. $2A - 3B = 2\begin{bmatrix} 1 & -3 \\ 2 & 4 \end{bmatrix} - 3\begin{bmatrix} -2 & -5 \\ 6 & 3 \end{bmatrix} = \begin{bmatrix} 2 & -6 \\ 4 & 8 \end{bmatrix} + \begin{bmatrix} 6 & 15 \\ -18 & -9 \end{bmatrix} = \begin{bmatrix} 2+6 & -6+15 \\ 4-18 & 8-9 \end{bmatrix} = \begin{bmatrix} 8 & 9 \\ -14 & -1 \end{bmatrix}$

23. $A \times B = \begin{bmatrix} 1 & -3 \\ 2 & 4 \end{bmatrix} \times \begin{bmatrix} -2 & -5 \\ 6 & 3 \end{bmatrix} = \begin{bmatrix} 1(-2)+(-3)6 & 1(-5)+(-3)3 \\ 2(-2)+4(6) & 2(-5)+4(3) \end{bmatrix} = \begin{bmatrix} -20 & -14 \\ 20 & 2 \end{bmatrix}$

24. $B \times A = \begin{bmatrix} -2 & -5 \\ 6 & 3 \end{bmatrix} \times \begin{bmatrix} 1 & -3 \\ 2 & 4 \end{bmatrix} = \begin{bmatrix} (-2)1+(-5)2 & (-2)(-3)+(-5)4 \\ 6(1)+3(2) & 6(-3)+3(4) \end{bmatrix} = \begin{bmatrix} -12 & -14 \\ 12 & -6 \end{bmatrix}$

25. $\begin{bmatrix} 1 & 3 & | & 8 \\ 1 & 1 & | & 4 \end{bmatrix} \underset{(r_2 - r_1)}{=} \begin{bmatrix} 1 & 3 & | & 8 \\ 0 & -2 & | & -4 \end{bmatrix} \underset{-\frac{1}{2}r_2}{=} \begin{bmatrix} 1 & 3 & | & 8 \\ 0 & 1 & | & 2 \end{bmatrix} \underset{(r_1 - 3r_2)}{=} \begin{bmatrix} 1 & 0 & | & 2 \\ 0 & 1 & | & 2 \end{bmatrix}$ The solution is (2, 2).

26. $\begin{bmatrix} -1 & 1 & | & 4 \\ 1 & 3 & | & 4 \end{bmatrix} = \begin{bmatrix} 1 & -1 & | & 4 \\ 0 & 4 & | & 8 \end{bmatrix} = \begin{bmatrix} -1 & 1 & | & 4 \\ 0 & 1 & | & 2 \end{bmatrix} = \begin{bmatrix} 1 & -1 & | & -4 \\ 0 & 1 & | & 2 \end{bmatrix} = \begin{bmatrix} 1 & 0 & | & -2 \\ 0 & 1 & | & 2 \end{bmatrix}$ The solution is (– 2, 2).

27. $\begin{bmatrix} 2 & 1 & | & 3 \\ 3 & -1 & | & 12 \end{bmatrix} \underset{=}{(r_1 \div 2)} \begin{bmatrix} 1 & \frac{1}{2} & | & \frac{3}{2} \\ 3 & -1 & | & 12 \end{bmatrix} \underset{(r_2 - 3r_1)}{=} \begin{bmatrix} 1 & \frac{1}{2} & | & \frac{3}{2} \\ 0 & -\frac{5}{2} & | & \frac{15}{2} \end{bmatrix} \underset{(-\frac{2}{5}r_2)}{=} \begin{bmatrix} 1 & \frac{1}{2} & | & \frac{3}{2} \\ 0 & 1 & | & -3 \end{bmatrix} \underset{=}{(-\frac{1}{2}r_2 + r_1)} \begin{bmatrix} 1 & 0 & | & 3 \\ 0 & 1 & | & -3 \end{bmatrix}$
The solution is (3,– 3).

28. $\begin{bmatrix} 2 & 3 & | & 2 \\ 4 & -9 & | & 4 \end{bmatrix} = \begin{bmatrix} 1 & \frac{3}{2} & | & 1 \\ 0 & -15 & | & 0 \end{bmatrix} = \begin{bmatrix} 1 & \frac{3}{2} & | & 1 \\ 0 & 1 & | & 0 \end{bmatrix} = \begin{bmatrix} 1 & 0 & | & 1 \\ 0 & 1 & | & 0 \end{bmatrix}$ The solution is (1,0)

29. $\begin{bmatrix} 1 & 3 & | & 3 \\ 3 & -2 & | & 2 \end{bmatrix} = \begin{bmatrix} 1 & 3 & | & 3 \\ 0 & -11 & | & -7 \end{bmatrix} = \begin{bmatrix} 1 & 3 & | & 3 \\ 0 & 1 & | & \frac{7}{11} \end{bmatrix} = \begin{bmatrix} 1 & 0 & | & \frac{12}{11} \\ 0 & 1 & | & \frac{7}{11} \end{bmatrix}$ The solution is $\left(\dfrac{12}{11}, \dfrac{7}{11} \right)$

30. $\begin{bmatrix} 3 & -6 & | & -9 \\ 4 & 5 & | & 14 \end{bmatrix} \begin{matrix} (r_1 \bullet -1) \\ {} \end{matrix} \begin{bmatrix} -3 & 6 & | & 9 \\ 4 & 5 & | & 14 \end{bmatrix} \begin{matrix} (r_2 + r_1) \\ {} \end{matrix} \begin{bmatrix} 1 & 11 & | & 23 \\ 4 & 5 & | & 14 \end{bmatrix} \begin{matrix} (r_1 \bullet -4) \\ (r_2 + r_1) \end{matrix} \begin{bmatrix} 1 & 11 & | & 23 \\ 0 & -39 & | & -78 \end{bmatrix}$

$\begin{bmatrix} 1 & 11 & | & 23 \\ 0 & -39 & | & -78 \end{bmatrix} \begin{matrix} (r_1 \bullet 11/39) \\ (r_2 + r_1) \end{matrix} \begin{bmatrix} 1 & 0 & | & 1 \\ 0 & -39 & | & -78 \end{bmatrix} \begin{matrix} (r_2 \div -2) \\ {} \end{matrix} \begin{bmatrix} 1 & 0 & | & 1 \\ 0 & 1 & | & 2 \end{bmatrix}$ The solution is (1, 2).

31. Let x = amount borrowed at 4%   y = amount borrowed at 6%

.04x + .06y = 29000   x + y = 600000

$$\begin{bmatrix} .04 & .06 & | & 29000 \\ 1 & 1 & | & 600000 \end{bmatrix} (r_2 \bullet 25) \begin{bmatrix} 1 & 1.5 & | & 725000 \\ 1 & 1 & | & 600000 \end{bmatrix} = \begin{bmatrix} 1 & 1.5 & | & 725000 \\ 0 & -0.5 & | & -125000 \end{bmatrix}$$

$$= \begin{bmatrix} 1 & 1.5 & | & 725000 \\ 0 & 1 & | & 250000 \end{bmatrix} (r_1 - 1.5 r_1) \begin{bmatrix} 1 & 0 & | & 350000 \\ 0 & 1 & | & 250000 \end{bmatrix}$$
$(-2 \bullet r_2)$

$350,000 borrowed at 4% and $ 250,000 borrowed at 6%

32. Let s = liters of 80% acid solution
    w = liters of 50% acid solution

s + w = 100

0.80s + 0.50w = 100(0.75)

0.80s + 0.50w = 75

s = 100 – w

0.80(100 – w) + 0.50w = 75

80 – 0.80w + 0.50w = 75

– 0.30w = – 5

w = – 5/(– 0.30) = 16 2/3 liters

s = 100 – 16 2/3 = 83 1/3 liters

Mix 83 1/3 liters of 80% solution with 16 2/3 liters of 50% solution.

33. Let t = price per ton of topsoil
    m = price per ton of mulch

(1) 4t + 3m = 1529

(2) 2t + 5m = 1405

Subtract 2 times eq'n. (2) from eq'n. (1):

-7m = -1281

m = 183

Substitute 183 for m in eq'n. 1.

4t = 1529 – 3(183) = 980 so t = 245

Topsoil costs $245 per ton and mulch costs $183 per ton.

34. Let c = total cost
    x = no. of months to operate

a) model 1600A: $c_A = 950 + 32x$
   model 6070B: $c_B = 1275 + 22x$

   950 + 32x= 1275 + 22x

   10x = 325   x = 32.5 months

   After 32.5 months of operation the total cost of the units will be equal.

b) After 32.5 months or 2.7 years, the most cost effective unit is the unit with the lower per month to operate cost. Thus, model 6070B is the better deal in the long run.

35. a) Let C = total cost for parking
    x = number of additional hours

   All-Day: C = 5 + 0.50x

   Sav-A-Lot: C = 4.25 + 0.75x

   5 + 0.50x= 4.25 + 0.75x

   0.75 = 0.25x   3 = x

   The total cost will be the same after 3 additional hours or 4 hours total.

b) After 5 hours or x = 4 additional hours:

   All-Day: C = 5 + 0.50(4) = $7.00

   Sav-A-Lot: C = 4.25 + 0.75(4) = $7.25

   All-Day would be less expensive.

36.

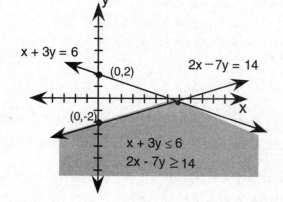

$y \leq 3x - 1$
$y > -2x + 1$

37.

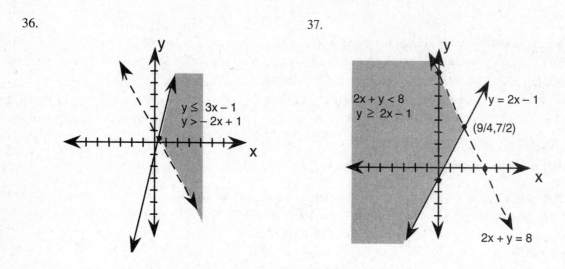

$2x + y < 8$
$y \geq 2x - 1$

$y = 2x - 1$

$(9/4, 7/2)$

$2x + y = 8$

38.

$x + 3y = 6$

$(0,2)$

$2x - 7y = 14$

$(0,-2)$

$x + 3y \leq 6$
$2x - 7y \geq 14$

39.

$(0,6)$

$6x + 5y = 30$

$(5,0)$

$(0,-5)$ $x - y = 5$

40. a)

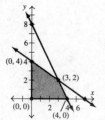

$(0,4)$
$(0,0)$ $(4,0)$
$(3,2)$

b) $P = 5x + 3y$

At $(0, 0)$ $P = 5(0) + 3(0) = 0$

At $(0, 4)$, $P = 5(0) + 3(4) = 12$

At $(3, 2)$, $P = 5(3) + 3(2) = 21$

At $(4, 0)$, $P = 5(4) + 3(0) = 20$

The maximum is 21 at $(3, 2)$ and the
minimum is 0 at $(0, 0)$.

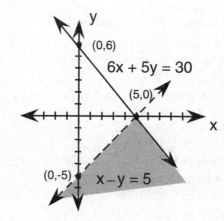

Chapter Test

1. If the lines do not intersect (parallel) the system of equations is inconsistent. The system of equations is consistent if the lines intersect only once. If both equations represent the same line then the system of equations is dependent.

2.

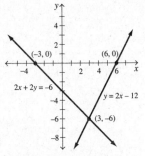

The solution is (3, –6).

3. Write each equation in slope intercept form, then compare slopes and intercepts.

$$4x + 5y = 6 \qquad -3x + 5y = 13$$
$$5y = -4x + 6 \qquad 5y = 3x + 13$$
$$y = -(4/5)x + 6/5$$

$$y = (3/5)x + 13/5$$

The slopes are different so there is only one solution.

4. $x + y = -1 \qquad x = -y - 1$
   $2x + 3y = -5$
   Substitute $(-y - 1)$ for x in the second equation.
   $2(-y - 1) + 3y = -5$ (solve for y)
   $-2y - 2 + 3y = -5$
   $y = -3$
   Substitute (-3) for y in the equation $x = -y - 1$.
   $x = -(-3) - 1 = 2$ \qquad The solution is (2, –3).

5. $y = 3x - 7 \qquad y = 5x - 3$
   Substitute $(3x - 7)$ for y in the second equation.
   $3x - 7 = 5x - 3$ (solve for x)
   $2x = -4 \qquad x = -2$
   Substitute -2 for x in the first equation.
   $y = 3(-2) - 7 = -13$
   The solution is (–2, –13).

6. $x - y = 4$
   $\underline{2x + y = -10}$ (add)
   $3x = -6 \qquad x = -2$
   Substitute -2 for x in the 2nd equation.
   $2(-2) + y = -10$
   $-4 + y = -10 \qquad y = -6$
   The solution is (–2, –6).

7. $4x + 3y = 5$
   $2x + 4y = 10$
   Multiply the second equation by (-2).
   $4x + 3y = 5$
   $\underline{-4x - 8y = -20}$ (add)
   $-5y = -15 \qquad y = 3$
   Substitute 3 for y in the first equation.
   $4x + 3(3) = 5$
   $4x + 9 = 5$
   $4x = -4 \qquad x = -1$
   The solution is (–1,3).

8. $3x + 4y = 6$
   $2x - 3y = 4$
   Multiply the 1st eq'n. by 3 and the 2nd eq'n. by 4.
   $9x + 12y = 18$
   $\underline{8x - 12y = 16}$
   $17x = 34 \qquad x = 2$

Substitute 2 for x in an equation.
$2(2) - 3y = 4$ (solve for y)
$-3y = 0 \qquad y = 0$

The solution is (2, 0).

9. $\begin{bmatrix} 1 & 3 & | & 4 \\ 5 & 7 & | & 4 \end{bmatrix}_{(-5r_1 + r_2)} = \begin{bmatrix} 1 & 3 & | & 4 \\ 0 & -8 & | & -16 \end{bmatrix}_{(r_2 \div (-8))} = \begin{bmatrix} 1 & 3 & | & 4 \\ 0 & 1 & | & 2 \end{bmatrix}_{(r_1 - 3r_2)} \begin{bmatrix} 1 & 0 & | & -2 \\ 0 & 1 & | & 2 \end{bmatrix}$

   The solution is $(-2, 2)$.

10. $A + B = \begin{bmatrix} 2 & -5 \\ 1 & 3 \end{bmatrix} + \begin{bmatrix} -1 & -3 \\ 5 & 2 \end{bmatrix} = \begin{bmatrix} 2 + (-1) & -5 - 3 \\ 1 + 5 & 3 + 2 \end{bmatrix} = \begin{bmatrix} 1 & -8 \\ 6 & 5 \end{bmatrix}$

11. $A - 2B = \begin{bmatrix} 2 & -5 \\ 1 & 3 \end{bmatrix} - 2 \begin{bmatrix} -1 & -3 \\ 5 & 2 \end{bmatrix} = \begin{bmatrix} 2 - 2(-1) & -5 - 2(-3) \\ 1 - 2(5) & 3 - 2(2) \end{bmatrix} = \begin{bmatrix} 4 & 1 \\ -9 & -1 \end{bmatrix}$

12. $A \times B = \begin{bmatrix} 2 & -5 \\ 1 & 3 \end{bmatrix} \begin{bmatrix} -1 & -3 \\ 5 & 2 \end{bmatrix} = \begin{bmatrix} 2(-1) + (-5)(5) & 2(-3) + (-5)(2) \\ 1(-1) + (3)(5) & 1(-3) + 3(2) \end{bmatrix} = \begin{bmatrix} -27 & -16 \\ 14 & 3 \end{bmatrix}$

13. $y < -2x + 2$ $y > 3x + 2$

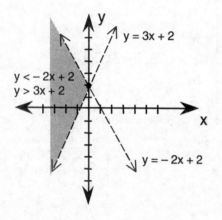

14. Let x = daily fee
    y = mileage charge
    $3x + 150y = 132$
    $2x + 400y = 142$ $x = 71 - 200y$
    Substitute $(71 - 200y)$ for x in the 1st equation.
    $3(71 - 200y) + 150y = 132$
    $213 - 600y + 150y = 132$
    $-450y = -81$
    $y = 0.18$
    Substitute 0.18 for y in the first equation.
    $3x + 150(0.18) = 132$
    $3x + 27 = 132$
    $3x = 105$ so $x = 35$
    The daily fee is \$35 and the mileage charge is 18 cents per mile.

15. (a) Let x = no. of checks written in one month.
    Cost at Union Bank: $6 + .10x$
    Cost at Citrus Bank: $2 + .20x$
    These are equal when:
    $2 + .2x = 6 + .1x$
    $.1x = 4$
    $x = 40$

    (b) Since $14 < 40$, the bank with the lower monthly fee is better, which is Citrus Bank.

16. a)

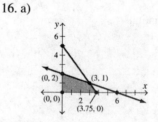

    b) $P = 6x + 4y$
    At $(0, 0)$ $P = 6(0) + 4(0) = 0$
    At $(0, 2)$ $P = 6(0) + 4(2) = 8$
    At $(3, 1)$ $P = 6(3) + 4(1) = 22$
    At $(3.75, 0)$ $P = 6(3.75) + 4(0) = 22.5$
    Max. is 22.5 at $(3.75, 0)$
    and min. is 0 at $(0, 0)$

Group Projects

1. Answers will vary.
2. Let x = # of Model 01 bookcases
     y = # of Model 02 bookcases

   a) $5x + 4y \leq 1000$ $2x + 3y \leq 600$
      $x \geq 40$ $y \geq 50$

   b) $P = 75x + 125y$

   d) Determine the maximum profit.

      At (40,173) $P = 75(40) + 125(173) = \$24,625$

      At (40,50) $P = 75(40) + 125(50) = \$9,250$

      At (160,50) $P = 75(160) + 125(50) = \$18,250$

      At (86,143) $P\ 75(86) + 125(143) = \$24,325$

      Maximum profit occurs at 40 Model 01 bookcases

      and 173 Model 02 bookcases.

   e) Maximum profit = \$24,625

3. Answers will vary.

2. c)

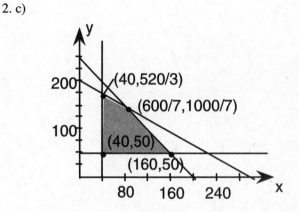

CHAPTER EIGHT

THE METRIC SYSTEM

Exercise Set 8.1

1. The metric system.

2. The U.S. customary system.

3. It is the worldwide accepted standard of measurement. There is only 1 basic unit of measurement for each quantity. It is based on the number 10, which makes many calculations easier.

4. a) meter   b) kilogram   c) liter   d) degree Celsius

5. a) Move the decimal point one place for each change in unit of measure.

   b) $214.6 \text{ cm} = \dfrac{214.6}{10^5} \text{ km} = 214.6 \times 10^{-5} \text{ km} = 0.002146 \text{ km}$

   c) $60.8 \text{ hm} = (60.8)(1000) \text{ dm} = 60800 \text{ dm}$

6. a) mega   b) micro

7.
kilo	1000 times the base unit	k
hecto	100 times the base unit	h
deka	10 times the base unit	da
deci	1/10 times the base unit	d
centi	1/100 times the base unit	c
milli	1/1000 times the base unit	m

8. a) 100 times greater
   b) 1 dam = 100 dm
   c) 1dm = 0.01 dam

9. a) 10,000 times greater
   b) 1 h = 10,000 cm
   c) 1 cm = 0.0001 hm

10. a) 0° C
   b) 100° C
   c) 37° C

11. 1 yard

12. 2 pounds

13. 5 grams

14. 30° C

15. 22° C

16. 2 m.

17. milli   b

18. kilo   d

19. hecto   c

20. deka   e

21. deci   f

22. centi   a

23. a) 100 grams   b) 0.001 gram   c) 1000 grams   d) 0.01 gram   e) 10 grams   f) 0.1 gram

24. a) 10 liters   b) 1/100 liter   c) 1/1000 liter   d) 1/10 liter   e) 1000 liters   f) 100 liters

25. cg   1/100 gm

26. mg   1/1000 gm

27. dg   1/10 gm

28. dag   10 gm

29. hg   100 gm

30. kg   1000 gm

31. Max. mass 320 kg = (320 x 1000) g = 320 000 g

32. Max. mass 320 kg = (320 x 1,000,000) mg
     = 320,000,000 mg

33. 5 m = (5 x 1000) mm = 5000 mm

34. 35.7 hg = (35.7 x 100) g = 3570 g

35. $0.085\ h\ell = (0.085)(0.1)\ k\ell = 0.0085\ k\ell$

36. $8\ dam = (8 \times 10)\ m = 80\ m$

37. $242.6\ cm = (242.6)(0.0001)\ hm = 0.02426\ hm$

38. $1.34\ m\ell = (1.34)(0.001)\ \ell = 0.00134\ \ell$

39. $22435\ mg = (2435)(0.00001)\ hg = 0.02435\ hg$

40. $14.27\ k\ell = (14.27)(1000)\ \ell = 14\ 270\ \ell$

41. $1.34\ hm = (1.34)(10000)\ cm = 13,400\ cm$

42. $0.000062\ kg = (0.000062)(1,000,000)\ mg = 62\ mg$

43. $32.5\ kg = 325\ hg$

44. $7.3\ m = 7300\ mm$

45. $895\ \ell = 895,000\ m\ell$

46. $24\ dm = 0.0024\ km$

47. $140\ cg = 1.40\ g$

48. $6,049\ mm = 6.049\ m$

49. $40,302\ m\ell = 4.0302\ da\ell$

50. $0.034\ m\ell = 0.000034\ \ell$

51. $590\ cm,\ 2.3\ dam,\ 0.47\ km$

52. $680\ m,\ 514\ hm,\ 62\ km$

53. $1.4\ kg,\ 1600\ g,\ 16,300\ dg$

54. $420\ c\ell,\ 4.3\ \ell,\ 0.045\ k\ell$

55. $203,000\ mm,\ 2.6\ km,\ 52.6\ hm$

56. $0.032\ k\ell,\ 460\ d\ell,\ 48,000\ c\ell$

57. Jim, since a meter is longer than a yard.

58. 1 hectometer in 10 min. 1 hm > 1 dm

59. The pump that removes 1 $da\ell$ of water per min.
    1 dekaliter > 1 deciliter

60. The side with the 15 lb. weight would go down.
    $5\ kg = 5(2.2\ lbs.) = 11\ lbs.$

61. a) Perimeter= $2l + 2w = 2(74) + 2(99) = 346\ cm$
    b) $346\ cm = (346 \times 10)\ mm = 3,460\ mm$

62. a) $(2)(250)(7) = 3,500\ mg\ /\ week$
    b) $3,500\ mg\ /\ week = 3.5\ g\ /\ week$

63. a) $1,200\ km\ /\ 187\ \ell = 6.417\ km/\ell$
    b) $1,200,00\ /\ 187\ \ell = 6,417\ m/\ell$

64. $8\ (400)\ m = 3,200\ m;\qquad 3,200\ m = 3.2\ km$

65. a) $6(360)\ ml = 2,160\ m\ell$
    b) $2160(1000) = 2.16\ \ell$
    c) $2.45\ /\ 2.16 = \$1.13$ per liter

66. a) $(6.9)(1000) = 6,900\ gm$
    b) $6,900\ /\ 3 = 2300\ gm\qquad 2300\ gm = 23,000\ dg$

67. a) $(4)(27\ m) = 108\ m$ b) $108\ m = 0.108\ km$
    c) $108\ m = 108\ 000\ mm$

68. $(\$\ 1.63)(37.7\ \ell\ ) = \$61.45$

69. a) $(16950 - 5830)\ km = 11,120\ km$
    b) $11,120,000\ m$

70. $(92 + 100 + 62 + 96 + 128 - 375)\ kg = 103\ kg$

71. 1 gigameter = 1000 megameters

72. 1 nanogram = .001 microgram

73. 1 teraliter = 1×10^{24} picoliters

74. 1 megagram = 1×10^{15} nanogms

75. $0.8/.027 = 29.6 \approx 30$ eggs

76. $0.8/.288 = 2.777... \approx 2.8$ cups

77. $195\ mg = 0.195\ g$
    $0.8/0.195 = 4.1$ cups

78. $1.6\ mg = 0.0016\ g$
    $0.8/0.0016 = 500$
    $500(49) = 24,500\ g$

79. $7000\ cm = 7\ dam$

80. $4000\ mm = 4\ m$

81. $0.00006\ hg = 6\ mg$

82. $3000\ dm = 3\ hm$

83. $0.02\ k\ell = 2\ da\ell$

84. $500\ cm = 5\ m$

85. magr   gram

86. migradec   decigram

87. rteli   liter

88. raktileed   dekaliter

89. terem   meter

90. leritililm   milliliter

91. reketolim   kilometer

92. timenceret   centimeter

93. greseed sulesic   degrees celsius

94. togmeharc   hectogram

Exercise Set 8.2

1. volume
2. length
3. area
4. length
5. volume
6. volume
7. volume
8. volume
9. area
10. volume
11. length
12. area
13. Answers will vary. (AWV)
14. Answers will vary.
15. Answers will vary.
16. Answers will vary.
17. Answers will vary.
18. Answers will vary.
19. 1 cubic decimeter
20. 1000 ℓ = 1 kiloliter
21. 1 cubic centimeter
22. square kilometers
23. area
24. 2.5 acres
25. centimeters
26. kilometers
27. cm or mm
28. centimeters
29. centimeters
30. meters
31. kilometers
32. meters
33. centimeters
34. cm or mm
35. kilometers
36. cm or m
37. c 36 m
38. a 2 cm x 3 cm
39. c 130 km
40. a 160 cm
41. b 4 cm
42. b 8 cm
43. c 375 m
44. b 1000 m
45. mm AWV
46. cm AWV
47. cm or m AWV
48. mm or cm AWV
49. mm or cm AWV
50. mm AWV
51. cm, km
52. km
53. m
54. m
55. cm
56. km
57. sq. cm
58. sq. m
59. sq. cm or sq. m
60. sq. m or hectares
61. sq. m or hectares
62. sq. mm or sq. cm
63. sq. cm
64. sq. km or hectares
65. sq. m
66. sq. km or hectares
67. a 5 cm^2
68. a 800 m^2
69. b 1/8 ha
70. c 930 cm^2
71. a 100 cm^2
72. c 1200 cm^2
73. c 4900 km^2
74. b 2.2 m^2
75. AWV
76. AWV
77. AWV
78. AWV
79. AWV
80. AWV
81. liters
82. milliliters
83. kiloliters
84. liters
85. cubic meters or cubic centimeters
86. cubic meters
87. liters
88. liters or milliliters
89. cubic meters
90. cubic centimeters
91. c 7780 cm^3
92. a 3 mℓ
93. c 55 kℓ
94. b 355 mℓ
95. c 0.04 m^3
96. b 120 mℓ
97. a 30 m^3
98. b 5000 cm^3
99. a) AWV
99. b) 152,561 cm^3

100. a) AWV b) $(2)(1.5)(.25) = 0.75$ m^3

101. a) AWV b) $v \approx (3.14)(0.25)^2(1) = 0.20$ m^3

102. a) AWV b) $v = \pi r^2 h \approx (3.14)(0.20)^2(2) = 0.25$ m^3

103. a) AWV b) $A = lw = (4)(2.2) = 8.8$ cm^2

104. $r \approx 1.2$ cm, $A = \pi r^2 \approx 3.14(1.2^2) \approx 4.52$ cm^2

105. $A = \pi r^2 \approx 3.14(10.2^2) \approx 326.7$ m^3

106. a) $(27)(28) = 1036$ cm^2
 b) $2540 - 1036 = 1504$ cm^2

107. a) $(73)(53) = 3869$ m^2
 b) $3869 - (70)(50) = 3869 - 3500 = 369$ m^2

108. a) $(3.75)(1.4) = 5.25$ km
 b) $(5.25)(100$ ha$) = 525$ ha

109. a) $(62.4)(50.5) = 3151.2$ m^2
 b) $(3151.2)(0.0001)$ ha $= 0.31512$ ha

110. a) $(18)(10)(2.5) = 450$ m^3
 b) 450 m$^3 = 450$ kℓ

111. Total Surface Area of 4 walls = 2lh + 2wh = 2(20)(6) + 2(12)(6) = 384 m^2

Liters for first coat = $(384$ m$^2)\left(\dfrac{1\,\ell}{10\,\text{m}^2}\right) = 38.4$ l   Liters for second coat = $(384$ m$^2)\left(\dfrac{1\,\ell}{15\,\text{m}^2}\right) = 25.6$ l

Total liters = 38.4 + 25.6 = 64 ℓ Total cost = (64)($4.75) = $304

112. $V = \pi r^2 h \approx (3.14)(4.0)^2(12.5) = 628$ cm^3

113. a) $V = lwh = (70)(40)(20) = 56,000$ cm^3 b) $56,000$ cm$^3 = 56,000$ mℓ c) $56\ 000$ m$\ell = \left(\dfrac{56000}{1000}\right)\ell = 56\ \ell$

114. a) radius $= \dfrac{0.56\ m}{2} = 0.28$ m; $V = \pi r^2 h \approx 3.14\left(0.28^2\right)(1.17) \approx 0.29$ m^3

   b) $(0.29)(1000)\ \ell\ = 290\ \ell$

115. $10^2 = 100$ times larger   116. $100^2 = 10,000$ times larger

117. $10^3 = 1000$ times larger   118. $10^3 = 1000$ times larger   119. 100 mm^2

120. $100,000,000$ cm^2 121. 100 hm^2 122. 0.0001 m^2

123. 0.000001 dm^3 124. $1,000,000$ mm^2 125. $1,000,000$ cm^3

126. 1 hm$^3 = 0.001$ km^3 127. 218 cm$^3 = 218$ mℓ 128. 435 cm$^3 = 0.435\ \ell$

129. 76 k$\ell = 76$ m^3 130. $4.2\ \ell = 4,200$ cm^3 131. 60 m$^3 = 60$ kℓ

132. $(600,000)(100) =$ 133. AWV   134. AWV
    $60,000,000$ m$\ell =$
    $60,000,000$ cm^3

135. 6.7 kl $= 6.7$ m$^3 = (6.7 \times 10^3)$ dm$^3 = 6,700$ dm^3 136. 1.4 ha $= 14,000$ m$^2 = (14000 \times 100^2)$ cm$^2 =$
                                                                              $140,000,000$ cm^2

137. a) 1 sq mi $= (1$ mi$^2)(5280)^2\ \dfrac{ft^2}{mi^2} = 27,878,400$ ft^2

    $27,878,400$ ft^2 x $(12)^2\ \dfrac{in^2}{ft^2} = 4,014,489,600$ in^2

   b) It is easier to convert in the metric system
      because it is a base 10 system.

138. a) $(1$ yd$^3) = (36$ in$)^3 = 46,656$ in^3
       $(46,656$ in$^3)(6) = 279,936$ in^3

    b) It is easier to convert in the metric system
       because it is a base 10 system.

139. a) AWV; the average use is 5150.7 liters / day
    b) AWV; the average use is 493.2 liters / day

Exercise Set 8.3

1. kilogram   2. 5 gm   3. 2 lb   4. metric tonne
5. approx. 35° C AWV   6. approx. – 15° C AWV   7. Answers will vary

8. 8.a) Yes; mass is a measure of the amount of matter in an object.
   b) No; weight is a measure of gravitational force.
9. kilograms   10. grams or milligrams   11. grams   12. grams
13. grams   14. metric tonnes   15. kilograms   16. milligrams
17. kilograms   18. grams   19. b   2.26 kg   20. c   4 g
    or metric tonnes
21. b   1.4 kg   22. c   0.45 kg   23. b   2800 kg   24. c   1.6 t
25. AWV   26. AWV   27. AWV   28. AWV

29. c 0° C

30. b 27° C

31. b   Dress warmly and walk.

32. b 5° C

33. c 40° C

34. c   bathing suit

35. c 177° C

36. c 110° C

37. c 40° C

38. b -5° C

39. $F = \dfrac{9}{5}(25) + 32 = 45 + 32 = 77^\circ$ F

40. $F = \dfrac{9}{5}(-5) + 32 = -9 + 32 = 23^\circ$ F

41. $C = \dfrac{5}{9}(92 - 32) = \dfrac{5}{9}(60) = 33.3^\circ$ C

42. $C = \dfrac{5}{9}(-10 - 32) = \dfrac{5}{9}(-42) = -23.3^\circ$ C

43. $C = \dfrac{5}{9}(0 - 32) = \dfrac{5}{9}(-32) \approx -17.8^\circ$ C

44. $C = \dfrac{5}{9}(98 - 32) = \dfrac{5}{9}(66) = 36.7^\circ$ C

45. $F = \dfrac{9}{5}(37) + 32 = 66.6 + 32 = 98.6^\circ$ F

46. $F = \dfrac{9}{5}(-4) + 32 = -7.2 + 32 = 24.8^\circ$ F

47. $C = \dfrac{5}{9}(13 - 32) = \dfrac{5}{9}(-19) = -10.6^\circ$ C

48. $C = \dfrac{5}{9}(75 - 32) = \dfrac{5}{9}(43) = 23.9^\circ$ C

49. $F = \dfrac{9}{5}(0) + 32 = 0 + 32 = 32^\circ$ F

50. $F = \dfrac{9}{5}(50) + 32 = 90 + 32 = 122^\circ$ F

51. $C = \dfrac{5}{9}(-20 - 32) = \dfrac{5}{9}(-52) = -28.9^\circ$ C

52. $C = \dfrac{5}{9}(425 - 32) = \dfrac{5}{9}(393) = 218.3^\circ$ C

53. $C = \dfrac{5}{9}(165 - 32) = \dfrac{5}{9}(133) = 73.9^\circ$ F

54. $F = \dfrac{9}{5}(74) + 32 = 133.2 + 32 = 165.2^\circ$ F

55. $F = \dfrac{9}{5}(22) + 32 = 39.6 + 32 = 71.6^\circ$ F

56. $F = \dfrac{9}{5}(35.1) + 32 = 63.2 + 32 = 95.2^\circ$ F

57. $F = \dfrac{9}{5}(35.1) + 32 = 63.2 + 32 = 95.2^\circ$ F

58. $F = \dfrac{9}{5}(32.3) + 32 = 58.1 + 32 = 90.1^\circ$ F

59. low: $F = \dfrac{9}{5}(17.8) + 32 = 32 + 32 = 64.04^\circ$ F

    high: $F = \dfrac{9}{5}(23.5) + 32 = 42.3 + 32 = 74.3^\circ$ F

    Range = $74.30 - 64.04 = 10.26^\circ$ F

60. low: $F = \dfrac{9}{5}(22) + 32 = 39.6 + 32 = 71.6^\circ$ F

    high: $F = \dfrac{9}{5}(34) + 32 = 61.2 + 32 = 93.2^\circ$ F

    Range = $93.2 - 71.6 = 21.6^\circ$ F

61. cost = (8.1)(2.50) = \$20.25

62. cost = (5.2)(2.60) = \$13.52

63. total mass = 45 g + 29 g + 370 mℓ = 45 g + 29 g + 370 g = 444 g

64. fuel used = (4320)(17) = 73,440 kg

    $73,440 \text{ kg}\left(\dfrac{1 \text{ t}}{1000 \text{ kg}}\right) = 73.44$ t

65. a) V= lwh,   l = 16 m, w = 12 m, h = 12 m

    V = (16)(12)(12) = 2304 m^3

    b) 2304 m^3 = 2304 kℓ

    c) 2304 kℓ = 2304 t

66. a) V = π r^{2}h   r = 50 cm = 0.50 m

    h = 150 cm = 1.5 m

    V = (3.14)(0.50)^2(1.50) = 1.1775 m^3

    b) 1.1775 m^3 = 1.1775 kℓ = 1177.5 ℓ

    c) 1177.5 ℓ = 1177.5 kg

67. Yes, 78° F $= \dfrac{5}{9}(78-32) \approx 25.6^\circ$ C, not 20° C

68. Normal body temperature is 98.6° F or 37° C. Maria's temperature is 38.2° C which is above normal. She should take an aspirin.

69. 4.2 kg $= (4.2 \text{ kg})\left(\dfrac{1 \text{ t}}{1000 \text{ kg}}\right) = 0.0042$ t

70. 9.52 t $= (9.52 \text{ t})\left(\dfrac{1000 \text{ kg}}{1 \text{ t}}\right) = 9520$ kg

71. 17.4 t $= (17.4 \text{ t})\left(\dfrac{1000 \text{ kg}}{1 \text{ t}}\right) = 17,400$ kg $=$ $17,400,000$ g

72. $1,460,000$ mg $= 1.46$ kg $= (1.46 \text{ kg})\left(\dfrac{1 \text{ t}}{1000 \text{ kg}}\right) =$ 0.00146 t

73. $1.2\, \ell = 1200$ mℓ a) 1200 g   b) 1200 cm^3

74. -40° C $= \dfrac{9}{5}(-40) + 32 = -72 + 32 = -40^\circ$ F

75. a) $V = lwh$ $l = 1$ yd $= 3$ ft $w = 15$ in $= 1.25$ ft
           $h = 1.5$ ft
       $V = (3)(1.25)(1.5) = 5.625$ cubic feet

   b) $(5.625 \text{ ft}^3)\left(62.5 \dfrac{\text{lbs}}{\text{ft}^3}\right) = 351.6$ lb

   c) $(351.6 \text{ lb})\left(\dfrac{1 \text{ gal}}{8.3 \text{ lb}}\right) = 42.4$ gal

76. 3 kg _____ x
    (3)(2) = 6 = 4x
    x = 6/4 = 3/2 = 1.5   1.5 kg
    1.5 kg = 1500 g

77. a) -62.11° C $F = \dfrac{9}{5}(-62.11) + 32 = -111.798 + 32 = -79.8^\circ$ F

   b) 2.5° C $F = \dfrac{9}{5}(2.5) + 32 = 4.5 + 32 = 36.5^\circ$ F

   c) $918,000,000^\circ$ F $C = \dfrac{5}{9}(918,000,000 - 32) = \dfrac{5}{9}(917,999,968) = 509,999,982.2 \approx 510,000,000^\circ$ C

Exercise Set 8.4

1. **Dimensional analysis** is a procedure used to convert from one unit of measurement to a different unit of measurement.

2. A **unit fraction** is a fraction in which the numerator and denominator contain different units and the value of the fraction is 1.

3. $\dfrac{60 \text{ seconds}}{1 \text{ minute}}$ or $\dfrac{1 \text{ minute}}{60 \text{ seconds}}$ because 60 seconds $= 1$ minute

4. $\dfrac{3 \text{ ft}}{1 \text{ yd}}$ or $\dfrac{1 \text{ yd}}{3 \text{ ft}}$ because 3 ft $= 1$ yd

5. $\dfrac{1 \text{ lb}}{0.45 \text{ kg}}$ Since we need to eliminate kilograms, kg must appear in the denominator. Since we need to convert to pounds, lb must appear in the numerator.

6. $\dfrac{1 \text{ ft}}{30 \text{ cm}}$ Since we need to eliminate centimeters, cm must appear in the denominator. Since we need to convert to feet, ft must appear in the numerator.

7. $\dfrac{3.8\, \ell}{1 \text{ gal}}$ Since we need to eliminate gallons, gal must appear in the denominator. Since we need to convert to liters, l must appear in the numerator.

8. $\dfrac{0.8\ \text{m}^2}{1\ \text{yd}^2}$ Since we need to eliminate square yards, yd^2 must appear in the denominator. Since we need to convert to square meters, m^2 must appear in the numerator.

9. $62\ \text{in.} = (62\ \text{in.})\left(\dfrac{2.54\ \text{cm}}{1\ \text{in.}}\right) = 157.48\ \text{cm}$

10. $9\ \text{lb} = (9\ \text{lb})\left(\dfrac{0.45\ \text{kg}}{1\ \text{lb}}\right) = 4.05\ \text{kg}$

11. $4.2\ \text{ft} = (4.2\ \text{ft})\left(\dfrac{30\ \text{cm}}{1\ \text{ft}}\right)\left(\dfrac{1\ \text{m}}{100\ \text{cm}}\right) = 1.26\ \text{m}$

12. $427\ \text{g} = (427\ \text{g})\left(\dfrac{1\ \text{oz}}{28\ \text{g}}\right) = 15.25\ \text{oz}$

13. $120\ \text{kg} = (120\ \text{kg})\left(\dfrac{1\ \text{lb}}{0.45\ \text{kg}}\right) = 266.\overline{6} \approx 266.67\ \text{lb}$

14. $20\ \text{yd}^2 = (20\ \text{yd}^2)\left(\dfrac{0.8\ \text{m}^2}{1\ \text{yd}^2}\right) = 16\ \text{m}^2$

15. $39\ \text{mi} = (39\ \text{mi})\left(\dfrac{1.6\ \text{km}}{1\ \text{mi}}\right) = 62.4\ \text{km}$

16. $765\ \text{mm} = (765\ \text{mm})\left(\dfrac{1\ \text{cm}}{10\ \text{mm}}\right)\left(\dfrac{1\ \text{in.}}{2.54\ \text{cm}}\right) = 30.11811024 \approx 30.12\ \text{in.}$

17. $675\ \text{ha} = (675\ \text{ha})\left(\dfrac{1\ \text{acre}}{0.4\ \text{ha}}\right) = 1687.5\ \text{acres}$

18. $192\ \text{oz} = (192\ \text{oz})\left(\dfrac{28\ \text{g}}{1\ \text{oz}}\right) = 5376\ \text{g}$

19. $15.6\ \ell = (15.6\ \ell)\left(\dfrac{1\ \text{pt}}{0.47\ \ell}\right) = 33.19148936 \approx 33.19\ \text{pints}$

20. $4\ \text{T} = (4\ \text{T})\left(\dfrac{0.9\ \text{t}}{1\ \text{T}}\right) = 3.6\ \text{t}$

21. $3.8\ \text{km}^2 = (3.8\ \text{km}^2)\left(\dfrac{1\ \text{mi}^2}{2.6\ \text{km}^2}\right) = 1.4615... \approx 1.46\ \text{mi}^2$

22. $25.6\ \text{m}\ell = (25.6\ \text{m}\ell)\left(\dfrac{1\ \text{fl oz}}{30\ \text{m}\ell}\right) = 0.85\overline{3} \approx 0.85\ \text{fl oz}$

23. $120\ \text{lb} = (120\ \text{lb})\left(\dfrac{0.45\ \text{kg}}{1\ \text{lb}}\right) = 54\ \text{kg}$

24. $6.2\ \text{acres} = (6.2\ \text{acres})\left(\dfrac{0.4\ \text{ha}}{1\ \text{acre}}\right) = 2.48\ \text{ha}$

25. 28 grams
26. 28 grams, 0.45 kilogram
27. 0.45 kilogram

28. $5 \text{ ft} = (5 \text{ ft})\left(\dfrac{12 \text{ in.}}{1 \text{ ft}}\right)\left(\dfrac{2.54 \text{ cm}}{1 \text{ in.}}\right) = 152.4 \text{ cm}$

$2 \text{ in.} = (2 \text{ in.})\left(\dfrac{2.54 \text{ cm}}{1 \text{ in.}}\right) = 5.08 \text{ cm}$

$152.4 \text{ cm} + 5.08 \text{ cm} = 157.48 \text{ centimeters}$

$157.48 \text{ cm} = (157.48 \text{ cm})\left(\dfrac{1 \text{ m}}{100 \text{ cm}}\right) = 1.5748 \approx 1.57 \text{ meters}$

29. 2.54 centimeters, 1.6 kilometers

30. 1.6 kilometers

31. 0.9 meter

32. $10 \text{ yd} = (10 \text{ yd})\left(\dfrac{0.9 \text{ m}}{1 \text{ yd}}\right) = 9 \text{ meters}$

33. $505 \text{ m} = (505 \text{ m})\left(\dfrac{1 \text{ yd}}{0.9 \text{ m}}\right) = 561.\overline{1} \approx 561.11 \text{ yd}$

34. $175 \text{ m} = (175 \text{ m})\left(\dfrac{1 \text{ yd}}{0.9 \text{ m}}\right) = 194.\overline{4} \approx 194.44 \text{ yd}$

35. $344 \text{ m} = (344 \text{ m})\left(\dfrac{100 \text{ cm}}{1 \text{ m}}\right)\left(\dfrac{1 \text{ ft}}{30 \text{ cm}}\right) = 1146.\overline{6} \approx 1146.67 \text{ ft}$

36. $303 \text{ m} = (303 \text{ m})\left(\dfrac{100 \text{ cm}}{1 \text{ m}}\right)\left(\dfrac{1 \text{ ft}}{30 \text{ cm}}\right) = 1010 \text{ ft}$

37. $60 \text{ km} = (60 \text{ km})\left(\dfrac{1 \text{ mi}}{1.6 \text{ km}}\right) = 37.5 \text{ mph}$

38. $105 \text{ mi} = (105 \text{ mi})\left(\dfrac{1.6 \text{ km}}{1 \text{ mi}}\right) = 168 \text{ km}$

39. $(6 \text{ yd})(9 \text{ yd}) = 54 \text{ yd}^2$

$54 \text{ yd}^2 = (54 \text{ yd}^2)\left(\dfrac{0.8 \text{ m}^2}{1 \text{ yd}^2}\right) = 43.2 \text{ m}^2$

40. $110 \text{ mi} = (110 \text{ mi})\left(\dfrac{1.6 \text{ km}}{1 \text{ mi}}\right) = 176 \text{ km}$

41. $80 \text{ km} = (80 \text{ km})\left(\dfrac{1 \text{ mi}}{1.6 \text{ km}}\right) = 50 \text{ mph}$

42. $8 \text{ fl oz} = (8 \text{ fl oz})\left(\dfrac{30 \text{ m}\ell}{1 \text{ fl oz}}\right) = 240 \text{ m}\ell$

43. $6 \text{ g} = (6 \text{ g})\left(\dfrac{1 \text{ oz}}{28 \text{ g}}\right) \approx 0.21 \text{ oz}$

44. $12{,}500 \text{ gal} = (12{,}500 \text{ gal})\left(\dfrac{3.8 \ \ell}{1 \text{ gal}}\right)\left(\dfrac{1 \text{ k}\ell}{1000 \ \ell}\right) = 47.5 \text{ k}\ell$

45. $(50 \text{ ft})(30 \text{ ft})(8 \text{ ft}) = 12{,}000 \text{ ft}^3$

    $12{,}000 \text{ ft}^3 = (12{,}000 \text{ ft}^3)\left(\dfrac{0.03 \text{ m}^3}{1 \text{ ft}^3}\right) = 360 \text{ m}^3$

46. $1189 \text{ mi}^2 = (1189 \text{ mi}^2)\left(\dfrac{2.6 \text{ km}^2}{1 \text{ mi}^2}\right) = 3091.4 \text{ km}^2$

47. $1 \text{ kg} = (1 \text{ kg})\left(\dfrac{1 \text{ lb}}{0.45 \text{ kg}}\right) = 2.\overline{2} \text{ lb}$

    $\dfrac{\$1.10}{2.\overline{2}} = \$0.495 \text{ per pound}$

48. a) $3.5 \text{ t} = (3.5 \text{ t})\left(\dfrac{1 \text{ T}}{0.9 \text{ t}}\right) = 3.\overline{8} \approx 3.89 \text{ T}$

    b) $3.\overline{8} \text{ T} = (3.\overline{8} \text{ T})\left(\dfrac{2000 \text{ lb}}{1 \text{ T}}\right) = 7777.\overline{7} \approx 7777.8 \text{ lb}$

49. $34.5 \text{ k}\ell = (34.5 \text{ k}\ell)\left(\dfrac{1000 \text{ }\ell}{1 \text{ k}\ell}\right)\left(\dfrac{1 \text{ gal}}{3.8 \text{ }\ell}\right) = 9078.947368 \approx 9078.95 \text{ gal}$

50. $0.25 \text{ oz} = (0.25 \text{ oz})\left(\dfrac{28 \text{ g}}{1 \text{ oz}}\right) = 7 \text{ g}$

    $\dfrac{\$80}{7} = 11.42857143 \approx \$11.43 \text{ per gram}$

51. $5.7 \text{ }\ell = (5.7 \text{ }\ell)\left(\dfrac{1 \text{ qt}}{0.95 \text{ }\ell}\right) = 6 \text{ qt}$

52. $\dfrac{1}{8} \text{ carat} = (0.125 \text{ carat})\left(\dfrac{1 \text{ g}}{5 \text{ carat}}\right) = 0.025 \text{ g}$

53. a) $-282 \text{ ft} = (-282 \text{ ft})\left(\dfrac{30 \text{ cm}}{1 \text{ ft}}\right) = -8460 \text{ cm}$

    b) $-8460 \text{ cm} = (-8460 \text{ cm})\left(\dfrac{1 \text{ m}}{100 \text{ cm}}\right) = -84.6 \text{ m}$

54. a) $105 \text{ m} = (105 \text{ m})\left(\dfrac{1 \text{ km}}{1000 \text{ m}}\right) = 0.105 \text{ km}$

    b) $105 \text{ m} = (105 \text{ m})\left(\dfrac{100 \text{ cm}}{1 \text{ m}}\right)\left(\dfrac{1 \text{ ft}}{30 \text{ cm}}\right) = 350 \text{ ft}$

55. a) $1 \text{ m}^2 = (1 \text{ m}^2)\left(\dfrac{(3.3)^2 \text{ ft}^2}{1 \text{ m}^2}\right) = 10.89 \text{ ft}^2$

    b) $1 \text{ m}^3 = (1 \text{ m}^3)\left(\dfrac{(3.3)^3 \text{ ft}^3}{1 \text{ m}^3}\right) = 35.937 \text{ ft}^3$

56. a) $15.3 \text{ acres} = (15.3 \text{ acres})\left(\dfrac{0.4 \text{ ha}}{1 \text{ acre}}\right) = 6.12 \text{ ha}$

    b) $6.12 \text{ ha} = (6.12 \text{ ha})\left(\dfrac{10{,}000 \text{ m}^2}{1 \text{ ha}}\right) = 61{,}200 \text{ m}^2$

57. $56 \text{ lb} = (56 \text{ lb})\left(\dfrac{0.45 \text{ kg}}{1 \text{ lb}}\right)\left(\dfrac{1 \text{ mg}}{1 \text{ kg}}\right) = 25.2 \text{ mg}$

58. $170 \text{ lb} = (170 \text{ lb})\left(\dfrac{0.45 \text{ kg}}{1 \text{ lb}}\right)\left(\dfrac{1.5 \text{ mg}}{1 \text{ kg}}\right) = 114.75 \text{ mg}$

59. $76 \text{ lb} = (76 \text{ lb})\left(\dfrac{0.45 \text{ kg}}{1 \text{ lb}}\right)\left(\dfrac{200 \text{ mg}}{1 \text{ kg}}\right) = 6840 \text{ mg};\ 6840 \text{ mg} = (6840 \text{ mg})\left(\dfrac{1 \text{ g}}{1000 \text{ mg}}\right) = 6.84 \text{ g}$

60. $82 \text{ lb} = (82 \text{ lb})\left(\dfrac{0.45 \text{ kg}}{1 \text{ lb}}\right)\left(\dfrac{5 \text{ mg}}{1 \text{ kg}}\right) = 184.5 \text{ mg}$

61. a) $2 \text{ teaspoons} = (2 \text{ teaspoons})\left(\dfrac{12.5 \text{ mg}}{1 \text{ teaspoon}}\right) = 25 \text{ mg}$

    b) $12 \text{ fl oz} = (12 \text{ fl oz})\left(\dfrac{30 \text{ m}\ell}{1 \text{ fl oz}}\right)\left(\dfrac{12.5 \text{ mg}}{5 \text{ m}\ell}\right) = 900 \text{ mg}$

62. a) $2 \text{ tablespoons} = (2 \text{ tablespoons})\left(\dfrac{236 \text{ mg}}{1 \text{ tablespoon}}\right) = 472 \text{ mg}$

    b) $8 \text{ fl oz} = (8 \text{ fl oz})\left(\dfrac{30 \text{ m}\ell}{1 \text{ fl oz}}\right)\left(\dfrac{1 \text{ tablespoon}}{15 \text{ m}\ell}\right)\left(\dfrac{236 \text{ mg}}{1 \text{ tablespoon}}\right) = 3776 \text{ mg}$

63. a) $964 \text{ ft} = (964 \text{ ft})\left(\dfrac{30 \text{ cm}}{1 \text{ ft}}\right)\left(\dfrac{1 \text{ m}}{100 \text{ cm}}\right) = 289.2 \text{ m}$

    b) $85,000 \text{ tons} = (85,000 \text{ tons})\left(\dfrac{0.9 \text{ tonne}}{1 \text{ ton}}\right) = 76\ 500 \text{ t}$

    c) $28 \text{ mi} = (28 \text{ mi})\left(\dfrac{1.6 \text{ km}}{1 \text{ mi}}\right) = 44.8 \text{ kph}$

64. $(0.5 \text{ c})\left(\dfrac{0.24 \ \ell}{1 \text{ c}}\right) = 0.12 \ \ell \ \text{ graham cracker crumbs}$

    $(12 \text{ oz})\left(\dfrac{28 \text{ g}}{1 \text{ oz}}\right) = 336 \text{ g} \ \text{ nuts}$

    $(8 \text{ oz})\left(\dfrac{28 \text{ g}}{1 \text{ oz}}\right) = 224 \text{ g} \ \text{ chocolate pieces}$

    $\left(\dfrac{4}{3} \text{ c}\right)\left(\dfrac{0.24 \ \ell}{1 \text{ c}}\right) = 0.32 \ \ell \ \text{ flaked coconut}$

    $\left(\dfrac{4}{3} \text{ c}\right)\left(\dfrac{0.24 \ \ell}{1 \text{ c}}\right) = 0.32 \ \ell \ \text{ condensed milk}$

    $(9 \text{ in.})\left(\dfrac{2.54 \text{ cm}}{1 \text{ in.}}\right) \times (13 \text{ in.})\left(\dfrac{2.54 \text{ cm}}{1 \text{ in.}}\right) = 22.86 \text{ cm} \times 33.02 \text{ cm} \ \text{ baking pan}$

    $350° \text{ F} = \dfrac{5}{9}(350 - 32) = 176.\overline{6} \approx 176.7° \text{ C}$

    $(1.5 \text{ in.})\left(\dfrac{2.54 \text{ cm}}{1 \text{ in.}}\right) \times (3 \text{ in.})\left(\dfrac{2.54 \text{ cm}}{1 \text{ in.}}\right) = 3.81 \text{ cm} \times 7.62 \text{ cm} \ \text{ bars}$

65. a) $\dfrac{2.00\ \text{€}}{1\ \text{kg}}=\left(\dfrac{2.00\ \text{€}}{1\ \text{kg}}\right)\left(\dfrac{1\ \text{kg}}{2.2\ \text{lb}}\right)\approx\dfrac{0.9\ \text{€}}{1\ \text{lb}}$ b) $\dfrac{0.9\ \text{€}}{1\ \text{lb}}=\left(\dfrac{0.9\ \text{€}}{1\ \text{lb}}\right)\left(\dfrac{\$1.30}{1\ \text{€}}\right)=\dfrac{\$1.17}{1\ \text{lb}}$

66. a) $\dfrac{7.00\ \text{€}}{100\ \text{g}}=\left(\dfrac{7.00\ \text{€}}{100\ \text{g}}\right)\left(\dfrac{1000\ \text{g}}{1\ \text{kg}}\right)\approx\dfrac{70\ \text{€}}{1\ \text{kg}}$ b) $\dfrac{70\ \text{€}}{1\ \text{kg}}=\left(\dfrac{70\ \text{€}}{1\ \text{kg}}\right)\left(\dfrac{0.45\ \text{kg}}{1\ \text{lb}}\right)\approx\dfrac{31.5\ \text{€}}{1\ \text{lb}}$

  c) $\dfrac{31.5\ \text{€}}{1\ \text{lb}}=\left(\dfrac{31.5\ \text{€}}{1\ \text{lb}}\right)\left(\dfrac{\$1.30}{1\ \text{€}}\right)=\dfrac{\$40.95}{1\ \text{lb}}$

67. $(0.2\ \text{mg})\left(\dfrac{1\ \text{grain}}{60\ \text{mg}}\right)\left(\dfrac{1\ \text{m}\ell}{\frac{1}{300}\ \text{grain}}\right)=1.0\ \text{cc, or b)}$

68. $15(130\ \text{lb})=1950\ \text{lb};(1950\ \text{lb})\left(\dfrac{0.18\ \text{kg}}{100\ \text{lb}}\right)\left(\dfrac{1\ \text{lb}}{0.45\ \text{kg}}\right)=7.8\ \text{lb}$

69. a) $(4.0\ \ell)\left(\dfrac{1000\ \text{m}\ell}{1\ \text{l}}\right)\left(\dfrac{1\ \text{cm}^3}{1\ \text{m}\ell}\right)=4000\ \text{cc}$

  b) $(4000\ \text{cm}^3)\left(\dfrac{1\ \text{in.}^3}{(2.54)^3\ \text{cm}^3}\right)=\dfrac{4000}{16.387064}=244.094...\approx244.09\ \text{in.}^3$

70. A meter
71. A kilogram
72. A hectare
73. A liter
74. A tonne
75. A decimeter
76. 1 microscope
77. wonton
78. 1 pound cake $\left(1\ \text{lb}=16\ \text{oz};16\ \text{oz}\left(\dfrac{28\ \text{g}}{1\ \text{oz}}\right)=448\ \text{g}\right)$
79. 1 kilohurtz
80. 2 megacycles
81. 1 megaphone
82. 1 decacards
83. 2 kilomockingbirds
84. 1 microfiche
85. 1 decoration

Review Exercises

1. $\dfrac{1}{100}$ of base unit
2. $1000\times$ base unit
3. $\dfrac{1}{1000}$ of base unit
4. $100\times$ base unit
5. 10 times base unit
6. $\dfrac{1}{10}$ of base unit
7. 40 cg = 0.040 g
8. 3.2 ℓ = 320 cℓ
9. 0.0016 cm = 0.016 mm
10. 1 000 000 mg = 1 kg
11. 4.62 kℓ = 4620 ℓ
12. 192.6 dag = 19 260 dg
13. 2.67 kℓ = 2 670 000 mℓ
   14 630 cℓ = 146 300 mℓ
   3000 mℓ, 14 630 cℓ, 2.67 kℓ
14. 0.047 km = 47 m
   47 000 cm = 470 m
   0.047 km, 47 000 cm, 4700 m
15. Centimeters
16. Grams
17. Degrees Celsius
18. Millimeters or centimeters
19. Square meters
20. Milliliters or cubic centimeters
21. Millimeters
22. Kilograms or tonnes
23. Kilometers
24. Meters or centimeters
25. a) and b) Answers will vary.
26. a) and b) Answers will vary.
27. c

28. b   29. c   30. a

31. a   32. b

33. $3600 \text{ kg} = (3600 \text{ kg})\left(\dfrac{1 \text{ t}}{1000 \text{ kg}}\right) = 3.6 \text{ t}$

34. $4.3 \text{ t} = (4.3 \text{ t})\left(\dfrac{1000 \text{ kg}}{1 \text{ t}}\right)\left(\dfrac{1000 \text{ g}}{1 \text{ kg}}\right) = 4\ 300\ 000 \text{ g}$

35. $24° \text{C} = \dfrac{9}{5}(24) + 32 = 75.2° \text{ F}$

36. $68° \text{F} = \dfrac{5}{9}(68 - 32) = 20° \text{ C}$

37. $-6° \text{F} = \dfrac{5}{9}(-6 - 32) = -21.\overline{1} \approx -21.1° \text{ C}$

38. $39° \text{C} = \dfrac{9}{5}(39) + 32 = 102.2° \text{ F}$

39. $l = 4 \text{ cm}, \ w = 1.6 \text{ cm}; \ A = lw = 4(1.6) = 6.4 \text{ cm}^2$

40. $r = 1.5 \text{ cm}; \ A = \pi r^2 \approx 3.14(1.5)^2 = 7.065 \approx 7.07 \text{ cm}^2$

41. a) $V = lwh = (10)(4)(2) = 80 \text{ m}^3$

    b) $(80 \text{ m}^3)\left(\dfrac{1 \text{ kl}}{1 \text{ m}^3}\ell\right)\left(\dfrac{1000 \ \ell}{1 \text{ k}\ell}\right)\left(\dfrac{1 \text{ kg}}{1 \ \ell}\right) = 80\ 000 \text{ kg}$

42. a) $A = lw = (33.7)(26.7) = 899.79 \text{ cm}^2$

    b) $899.79 \text{ cm}^2 = (899.79 \text{ cm}^2)\left(\dfrac{1 \text{ m}^2}{10,000 \text{ cm}^2}\right) = 0.089979 \text{ m}^2$

43. a) $V = lwh = (80)(40)(30) = 96\ 000 \text{ cm}^3$

    b) $96\ 000 \text{ cm}^3 = (96\ 000 \text{ cm}^3)\left(\dfrac{1 \text{ m}^3}{(100)^3 \text{ cm}^3}\right) = 0.096 \text{ m}^3$

    c) $96\ 000 \text{ cm}^3 = (96\ 000 \text{ cm}^3)\left(\dfrac{1 \text{ m}\ell}{1 \text{ cm}^3}\right) = 96\ 000 \text{ m}\ell$

    d) $0.096 \text{ m}^3 = (0.096 \text{ m}^3)\left(\dfrac{1 \text{ k}\ell}{1 \text{ m}^3}\right) = 0.096 \text{ k}\ell$

44. Since $1 \text{ km} = 100 \times 1 \text{ dam}, \ 1 \text{ km}^2 = 100^2 \times 1 \text{ dam}^2 = 10\ 000 \text{ dam}^2$.

    Thus, 1 square kilometer is 10,000 times larger than a square dekameter.

45. $(25 \text{ cm})\left(\dfrac{1 \text{ in.}}{2.54 \text{ cm}}\right) = 9.842... \approx 9.84 \text{ in.}$

46. $(105 \text{ kg})\left(\dfrac{1 \text{ lb}}{0.45 \text{ kg}}\right) = 233.\overline{3} \approx 233.33 \text{ lb}$

47. $(83 \text{ yd})\left(\dfrac{0.9 \text{ m}}{1 \text{ yd}}\right) = 74.7 \text{ m}$

48. $(100 \text{ m})\left(\dfrac{1 \text{ yd}}{0.9 \text{ m}}\right) = 111.\overline{1} \approx 111.11 \text{ yd}$

49. $(45 \text{ mi})\left(\dfrac{1.6 \text{ km}}{1 \text{ mi}}\right) = 72 \text{ kph}$

50. $(60 \ \ell)\left(\dfrac{1 \text{ qt}}{0.95 \ \ell}\right) = 63.157... \approx 63.16 \text{ qt}$

51. $(20 \text{ gal})\left(\dfrac{3.8 \ \ell}{1 \text{ gal}}\right) = 76 \ \ell$

52. $(60 \text{ m}^3)\left(\dfrac{1 \text{ yd}^3}{0.76 \text{ m}^3}\right) = 78.947... \approx 78.95 \text{ yd}^3$

53. $(83 \text{ cm}^2)\left(\dfrac{1 \text{ in.}^2}{6.45 \text{ cm}^2}\right) = 12.86821705 \approx 12.87 \text{ in.}^2$

54. $(4 \text{ qt})\left(\dfrac{0.95 \ \ell}{1 \text{ qt}}\right) = 3.8 \ \ell$

55. $(15 \text{ yd}^3)\left(\dfrac{0.729 \text{ m}^3}{1 \text{ yd}^3}\right) = 10.9 \text{ m}^3$

56. $(62 \text{ mi})\left(\dfrac{1.6 \text{ km}}{1 \text{ mi}}\right) = 99.2 \text{ km}$

57. $(27 \text{ cm})\left(\dfrac{1 \text{ ft}}{30 \text{ cm}}\right) = 0.9 \text{ ft}$

58. $(3.25 \text{ in.})\left(\dfrac{2.54 \text{ cm}}{1 \text{ in.}}\right)\left(\dfrac{10 \text{ mm}}{1 \text{ cm}}\right) = 82.55 \text{ mm}$

59. a) $700(1.5 \text{ kg}) = 1050 \text{ kg}$

    b) $1050 \text{ kg} = (1050 \text{ kg})\left(\dfrac{1 \text{ lb}}{0.45 \text{ kg}}\right) = 2333.\overline{3} \approx 2333.33 \text{ lb}$

60. $A = lw = (24)(15) = 360 \text{ ft}^2; \ 360 \text{ ft}^2 = \left(360 \text{ ft}^2\right)\left(\dfrac{0.09 \text{ m}^2}{1 \text{ ft}^2}\right) = 32.4 \text{ m}^2$

61. a) $\left(50{,}000 \text{ gal}\right)\left(\dfrac{3.8 \ \ell}{1 \text{ gal}}\right)\left(\dfrac{1 \text{ k}\ell}{1000 \ \ell}\right) = 190 \text{ k}\ell$ b) $\left(190 \text{ k}\ell\right)\left(\dfrac{1000 \ \ell}{1 \text{ k}\ell}\right)\left(\dfrac{1 \text{ kg}}{1 \ \ell}\right) = 190 \ 000 \text{ kg}$

62. a) $65 \text{ mi/hr} = \left(65 \text{ mi/hr}\right)\left(\dfrac{1.6 \text{ km}}{1 \text{ mi}}\right) = 104 \text{ km/hr}$ b) $104 \text{ km/hr} = \left(104 \text{ km/hr}\right)\left(\dfrac{1000 \text{ m}}{1 \text{ km}}\right) = 104{,}000 \text{ m/hr}$

63. a) $V = lwh = (90)(70)(40) = 252 \ 000 \text{ cm}^3; \ 252 \ 000 \text{ cm}^3 = \left(252 \ 000 \text{ cm}^3\right)\left(\dfrac{1 \text{ m}\ell}{1 \text{ cm}^3}\right)\left(\dfrac{1 \ \ell}{1000 \text{ m}\ell}\right) = 252 \ \ell$

  b) $252 \ \ell = \left(252 \ \ell\right)\left(\dfrac{1 \text{ kg}}{1 \ \ell}\right) = 252 \text{ kg}$

64. $1 \text{ kg} = \left(1 \text{ kg}\right)\left(\dfrac{1 \text{ lb}}{0.45 \text{ kg}}\right) = 2.\overline{2} \text{ lb}; \ \dfrac{\$3.50}{2.\overline{2}} = \$1.575 \approx \$1.58 \text{ per pound}$

Chapter Test

1. $4497 \text{ c}\ell = 0.497 \text{ da}\ell$

2. $273 \text{ hm} = 2{,}730{,}000 \text{ m}$

3. $1 \text{ km} = \left(1 \text{ km}\right)\left(\dfrac{100 \text{ dam}}{1 \text{ km}}\right) = 100 \text{ dam} \ \text{ or } 100 \text{ times greater}$

4. $400(6) = 2400 \text{ m}; \ \left(2400 \text{ m}\right)\left(\dfrac{1 \text{ km}}{1000 \text{ m}}\right) = 2.4 \text{ km}$ 5. b

6. a   7. c

8. c   9. b

10. $1 \text{ m}^2 = \left(1 \text{ m}^2\right)\left(\dfrac{100^2 \text{ cm}^2}{1 \text{ m}^2}\right) = 10 \ 000 \text{ cm}^2 \ \text{ or } 10{,}000 \text{ times greater}$

11. $1 \text{ m}^3 = \left(1 \text{ m}^3\right)\left(\dfrac{1000^3 \text{ mm}^3}{1 \text{ m}^3}\right) = 1 \ 000 \ 000 \ 000 \text{ mm}^3 \ \text{ or } 1{,}000{,}000{,}000 \text{ times greater}$

12. $225 \text{ oz} = \left(225 \text{ oz}\right)\left(\dfrac{28 \text{ g}}{1 \text{ oz}}\right) = 6300 \text{ g}$

13. $45 \text{ km} = \left(45 \text{ km}\right)\left(\dfrac{1 \text{ mi}}{1.6 \text{ km}}\right) = 28.125 \text{ mi}$

14. $-15° \text{ F} = \dfrac{5}{9}\left(-15 - 32\right) = -26.\overline{1} \approx -26.11° \text{ C}$ 15. $20° \text{ C} = \dfrac{9}{5}\left(20\right) + 32 = 68° \text{ F}$

16. a) $300 \text{ kg} = \left(300 \text{ kg}\right)\left(\dfrac{1000 \text{ g}}{1 \text{ kg}}\right) = 300{,}000 \text{ g}$ b) $300 \text{ kg} = \left(300 \text{ kg}\right)\left(\dfrac{1 \text{ lb}}{0.45 \text{ kg}}\right) = 666.\overline{6} \text{ lb} \approx 670 \text{ lb}$

17. a) $V = lwh = 20(20)(8) = 3200 \text{ m}^3$ b) $3200 \text{ m}^3 = \left(3200 \text{ m}^3\right)\left(\dfrac{1000 \text{ k}\ell}{1 \text{ m}^3}\right) = 3200 \ k\ell$

  c) $3200 \text{ k}\ell = \left(3200 \text{ k}\ell\right)\left(\dfrac{1000 \ \ell}{1 \text{ k}\ell}\right)\left(\dfrac{1 \text{ kg}}{1 \ \ell}\right) = 3 \ 200 \ 000 \text{ kg}$

18. Total surface area: $2lh + 2wh = 2(20)(6) + 2(15)(6) = 420 \text{ m}^2$

Liters needed for first coat: $\left(420 \text{ m}^2\right)\left(\dfrac{1 \, \ell}{10 \text{ m}^2}\right) = 42 \, \ell$

Liters needed for second coat: $\left(420 \text{ m}^2\right)\left(\dfrac{1 \, \ell}{15 \text{ m}^2}\right) = 28 \, \ell$

Total liters needed: $42 + 28 = 70 \, \ell$

Total cost: $\left(70 \, \ell\right)\left(\dfrac{\$3.50}{1 \, \ell}\right) = \$245$

Group Projects

1. a) $(196 \text{ lb})\left(\dfrac{0.45 \text{ kg}}{1 \text{ lb}}\right)\left(\dfrac{20 \text{ mg}}{1 \text{ kg}}\right) = 1764 \text{ mg}$ b) $\left(\dfrac{250 \text{ cc}}{1 \text{ hr}}\right)\left(\dfrac{1 \text{ hr}}{60 \text{ min}}\right) = 4.1\overline{6} \approx 4.17 \text{ cc/min}$

2. a) $(60 \text{ lb})\left(\dfrac{0.45 \text{ kg}}{1 \text{ lb}}\right) = 27 \text{ kg};$ child's dose: $\dfrac{27 \text{ kg}}{67.5 \text{ kg}}(70 \text{ mg}) = 28 \text{ mg}$

  b) $\dfrac{\text{child's weight in kg}}{67.5 \text{ kg}} \times 70 \text{ mg} = 70 \text{ mg};$ $\dfrac{\text{child's weight in kg}}{67.5 \text{ kg}} = 1$

  Child's weight: $67.5 \text{ kg} = \left(67.5 \text{ kg}\right)\left(\dfrac{1 \text{ lb}}{0.45 \text{ kg}}\right) = 150 \text{ lb}$

3. a) $5 \text{ ft } 2 \text{ in.} = 62 \text{ in.}; 62 \text{ in.} = \left(62 \text{ in.}\right)\left(\dfrac{2.54 \text{ cm}}{1 \text{ in.}}\right) = 157.48 \text{ cm}$

  $157.48 \text{ cm} \; - \; 5 \text{ cm} \; = \; 152.48 \text{ cm}$ (length of the kimono)

  b) $8695.5 \text{ yen} = \left(8695.5 \text{ yen}\right)\left(\dfrac{\$1 \text{ U.S.}}{117.25 \text{ yen}}\right) = \$74.162 \text{ U.S.} \approx \$74.16 \text{ U.S.}$

  c) $6 \text{ lb} = \left(6 \text{ lb}\right)\left(\dfrac{16 \text{ oz}}{1 \text{ lb}}\right)\left(\dfrac{28 \text{ g}}{1 \text{ oz}}\right) = 2688 \text{ g}$

  $2688 \text{ g} = \left(2688 \text{ g}\right)\left(\dfrac{10 \text{ pesos}}{100 \text{ g}}\right)\left(\dfrac{\$0.092 \text{ U.S.}}{1 \text{ peso}}\right) = 24.729... \approx \$24.73$

  Note: If you use different conversion factors, your answer will be slightly different because the conversion factors are rounded values.

  d) To fill the tank in Euros:

  $53 \, \ell\left(\dfrac{1.238 \text{ €}}{1 \, \ell}\right) = 65.614 \approx 65.61 \text{ €}$

  To fill the tank in U.S. dollars:

  $65.614 \text{ €} = \left(65.614 \text{ €}\right)\left(\dfrac{\$1.17}{1 \text{ €}}\right) = \$76.768... \approx \$76.77; \$76.77 \text{ for } 53 \, \ell$

  $\dfrac{1.238 \text{ €}}{1 \, \ell} = \left(\dfrac{1.238 \text{ €}}{1 \, \ell}\right)\left(\dfrac{\$1.17}{1 \text{ €}}\right)\left(\dfrac{3.8 \, \ell}{1 \text{ gal}}\right) = \$5.504... \text{ per gal; The cost is approximately } \$5.50 \text{ per gallon}$

CHAPTER NINE

GEOMETRY

Exercise Set 9.1

1. a) Undefined terms, definitions, postulates (axioms), and theorems

   b) First, Euclid introduced **undefined terms**. Second, he introduced certain **definitions**. Third, he stated primitive propositions called **postulates (axioms)** about the undefined terms and definitions. Fourth, he proved, using deductive reasoning, other propositions called **theorems**.

2. An **axiom (postulate)** is a statement that is accepted as being true on the basis of its "obviousness" and its relation to the physical world. A **theorem** is a statement that has been proven using undefined terms, definitions, and axioms.

3. Two lines that do not lie in the same plane and do not intersect are called **skew lines**.

4. Two lines in the same plane that do not intersect are **parallel lines**.

5. Two angles in the same plane are **adjacent angles** when they have a common vertex and a common side but no common interior points.

6. Two angles the sum of whose measure is 90° are called **complementary angles**.

7. Two angles the sum of whose measure is 180° are called **supplementary angles**.

8. An angle whose measure is 180° is a **straight angle**.

9. An angle whose measure is greater than 90° but less than 180° is an **obtuse angle**.

10. An angle whose measure is 90° is a **right angle**.

11. An angle whose measure is less than 90° is an **acute angle**.

12. In the pair of intersecting lines below, $\angle$ 1 and $\angle$ 3 are vertical angles as are $\angle$ 2 and $\angle$ 4.

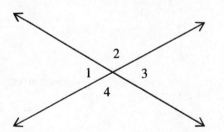

13. Ray, $\overrightarrow{BA}$	14. Open line segment, $\overset{\circ\!\!\!-\!\!\!\circ}{AB}$	15. Half line, $\overset{\circ}{\overrightarrow{BA}}$	16. Line, $\overleftrightarrow{AB}$
17. Ray, $\overrightarrow{AB}$	18. Line segment, $\overline{AB}$	19. Half open line segment, $\overset{\circ\!\!\!-}{AB}$	20. Half line, $\overset{\circ}{\overrightarrow{AB}}$
21. $\overline{BG}$	22. $\overline{EG}$	23. $\overset{\circ}{\overline{BD}}$	24. $\overline{AD}$
25. $\{B, F\}$	26. $\{F\}$	27. $\{C\}$	28. $\overset{\circ\!\!-\!\!\circ}{BC}$

305

29. $\angle CFG$ 30. $\triangle BCF$ 31. $\overline{BC}$ 32. $\varnothing$

33. $\{B\}$ 34. $\overleftrightarrow{ED}$ 35. $\overline{BC}$ 36. $\overrightarrow{DE}$

37. $\angle ABE$ 38. $\angle FBE$ 39. $\overline{BF}$ 40. $\overline{DE}$

41. $\overset{\circ\;\circ}{AC}$ 42. $\varnothing$ 43. $\overset{\circ\;\circ}{BE}$ 44. $\overline{FG}$

45. Obtuse   46. Straight   47. Straight   48. Acute

49. Right   50. None of these   51. None of these   52. Right

53. $90° - 26° = 64°$ 54. $90° - 89° = 1°$ 55. $90° - 32\frac{3}{4}° = 57\frac{1}{4}°$

56. $90° - 31\frac{2}{5}° = 58\frac{3}{5}°$ 57. $90° - 64.7° = 25.3°$ 58. $90° - 0.01° = 89.99°$

59. $180° - 89° = 91°$ 60. $180° - 8° = 172°$ 61. $180° - 20.5° = 159.5°$

62. $180° - 148.7° = 31.3°$ 63. $180° - 43\frac{5}{7}° = 136\frac{2}{7}°$ 64. $180° - 64\frac{7}{16}° = 115\frac{9}{16}°$

65. b   66. d   67. f

68. c   69. a   70. e

71. Let x = measure of $\angle 2$

$x + 8$ = measure of $\angle 1$

$$x + x + 8 = 90$$
$$2x + 8 = 90$$
$$2x = 82$$
$$x = \frac{81}{2} = 41°, m\angle 2$$
$$x + 8 = 41 + 8 = 49°, m\angle 1$$

72. Let x = measure of $\angle 1$

$90 - x$ = measure of $\angle 2$

$$x - (90 - x) = 62$$
$$x - 90 + x = 16$$
$$2x - 90 = 16$$
$$2x = 106$$
$$x = \frac{106}{2} = 53°, m\angle 1$$
$$90 - x = 90 - 53 = 37°, m\angle 2$$

73. Let x = measure of $\angle 1$

$180 - x$ = measure of $\angle 2$

$$x - (180 - x) = 88$$
$$x - 180 + x = 88$$
$$2x - 180 = 88$$
$$2x = 268$$
$$x = \frac{268}{2} = 134°, m\angle 1$$
$$180 - x = 180 - 134 = 46°, m\angle 2$$

74. Let x = measure of $\angle 1$

$17x$ = measure of $\angle 2$

$$x + 17x = 180$$
$$18x = 180$$
$$x = \frac{180}{18} = 10°, m\angle 1$$
$$17x = 17(10) = 170°, m\angle 2$$

75. $m\angle 1 + 125° = 180°$

$m\angle 1 = 55°$

$m\angle 2 = m\angle 1$ (vertical angles)

$m\angle 3 = 125°$ (vertical angles)

$m\angle 5 = m\angle 2$ (alternate interior angles)

$m\angle 4 = m\angle 3$ (alternate interior angles)

$m\angle 7 = m\angle 4$ (vertical angles)

$m\angle 6 = m\angle 5$ (vertical angles)

Measures of angles 3, 4, and 7 are each 125°.

Measures of angles 1, 2, 5, and 6 are each 55°.

76. $m\angle 3 + 30° = 180°$

$m\angle 3 = 150°$

$m\angle 1 = 30°$ (vertical angles)

$m\angle 2 = m\angle 3$ (vertical angles)

$m\angle 4 = m\angle 1$ (corresponding angles)

$m\angle 7 = m\angle 4$ (vertical angles)

$m\angle 6 = m\angle 3$ (alternate interior angles)

$m\angle 5 = m\angle 6$ (vertical angles)

Measures of angles 1, 4, and 7 are each 30°.

Measures of angles 2, 3, 5, and 6 are each 150°.

77. $m\angle 3 + 120° = 180°$

   $m\angle 3 = 60°$

   $m\angle 4 = 120°$ (vertical angles)

   $m\angle 7 = m\angle 3$ (vertical angles)

   $m\angle 6 = m\angle 3$ (alternate interior angles)

   $m\angle 1 = m\angle 6$ (vertical angles)

   $m\angle 5 = m\angle 4$ (alternate exterior angles)

   $m\angle 2 = m\angle 5$ (vertical angles)

   Measures of angles 2, 4, and 5 are each 120°.

   Measures of angles 1, 3, 6, and 7 are each 60°.

78. $m\angle 1 + 25° = 180°$

   $m\angle 1 = 155°$

   $m\angle 3 = m\angle 1$ (vertical angles)

   $m\angle 2 = 25°$ (vertical angles)

   $m\angle 4 = m\angle 3$ (alternate interior angles)

   $m\angle 7 = m\angle 4$ (vertical angles)

   $m\angle 5 = m\angle 2$ (corresponding angles)

   $m\angle 6 = m\angle 5$ (vertical angles)

   Measures of angles 2, 5, and 6 are each 25°.

   Measures of angles 1, 3, 4, and 7 are each 155°.

79.
$$x + 2x + 12 = 90$$
$$3x + 12 = 90$$
$$3x = 78$$
$$x = \frac{78}{3} = 26°, \; m\angle 2$$
$$90 - x = 90 - 26 = 64°, \; m\angle 1$$

80.
$$x + 5x - 6 = 90$$
$$6x - 6 = 90$$
$$6x = 96$$
$$x = \frac{96}{6} = 16°, \; m\angle 1$$
$$90 - x = 90 - 16 = 74°, \; m\angle 2$$

81.
$$x + 2x - 9 = 90$$
$$3x - 9 = 90$$
$$3x = 99$$
$$x = \frac{99}{3} = 33°, \; m\angle 1$$
$$90 - x = 90 - 33 = 57°, \; m\angle 2$$

82.
$$x + 8x - 9 = 90$$
$$9x - 9 = 90$$
$$9x = 99$$
$$x = \frac{99}{9} = 11°, \; m\angle 2$$
$$90 - x = 90 - 11 = 79°, \; m\angle 1$$

83.
$$x + 3x - 4 = 180$$
$$4x - 4 = 180$$
$$4x = 184$$
$$x = \frac{184}{4} = 46°, \; m\angle 2$$
$$180 - x = 180 - 46 = 134°, \; m\angle 1$$

84.
$$x + 7x - 12 = 180$$
$$8x - 12 = 192$$
$$8x = 192$$
$$x = \frac{192}{8} = 24°, \; m\angle 2$$
$$180 - x = 180 - 24 = 156°, \; m\angle 1$$

85.
$$x + 5x + 6 = 180$$
$$6x + 6 = 180$$
$$6x = 174$$
$$x = \frac{174}{6} = 29°, \; m\angle 1$$
$$180 - x = 180 - 29 = 151°, \; m\angle 2$$

86.
$$x + 6x + 5 = 180$$
$$7x + 5 = 180$$
$$7x = 175$$
$$x = \frac{175}{7} = 25°, \; m\angle 1$$
$$180 - x = 180 - 25 = 155°, \; m\angle 2$$

87. a) An infinite number of lines can be drawn through a given point.

   b) An infinite number of planes can be drawn through a given point.

88. If the two planes are not parallel, the intersection is a straight line.

89. An infinite number of planes can be drawn through a given line.

90. a) Yes, any three noncollinear points always determine a plane.

   b) No, the plane determined is unique.

   c) An infinite number of planes can be drawn through three collinear points.

For Exercises 91 - 98, the answers given are one of many possible answers.

91. Plane *ABG* and plane *JCD*

92. $\overleftrightarrow{EF}$ and $\overleftrightarrow{DG}$

93. $\overleftrightarrow{BG}$ and $\overleftrightarrow{DG}$

94. Plane *ABG* and plane *BCD*

95. Plane $AGB \cap$ plane $ABC \cap$ plane $BCD = \{B\}$

96. Plane $HGD \cap$ plane $FGD \cap$ plane $BGD = \overleftrightarrow{GD}$

97. $\overleftrightarrow{BC} \cap$ plane $ABG = \{B\}$

98. $\overline{AB} \cap$ plane $ABG = \overline{AB}$

99. Always true. If any two lines are parallel to a third line, then they must be parallel to each other.

100. Sometimes true. A triangle must always contain at least two acute angles. Some triangles contain three acute angles.

101. Sometimes true. Vertical angles are only complementary when each is equal to 45°.

102. Sometimes true. Alternate exterior angles are only supplementary when each is equal to 90°.

103. Sometimes true. Alternate interior angles are only complementary when each is equal to 45°.

104. Never true. The sum of two obtuse angles is greater than 180°.

105. Answers will vary.

106. No. Line *m* and line *n* may intersect.

107. No. Line *l* and line *n* may be parallel or skew.

108.

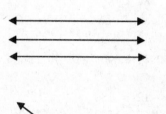

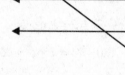

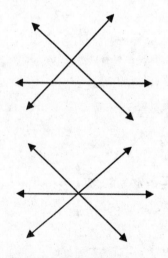

109.

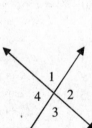

$m\angle 1 + m\angle 2 = 180°$
$m\angle 3 + m\angle 4 = 180°$
$180° + 180° = 360°$

110. a)

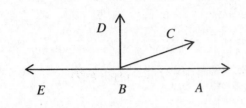

Other answers are possible.

b) Let $m\angle ABC = x$ and $m\angle CBD = y$.

$x + y = 90°$ and $y = 2x$

Substitute $y = 2x$ into $x + y = 90°$.

$x + 2x = 90°$

$3x = 90°$

$\dfrac{3x}{3} = \dfrac{90°}{3}$

$x = 30° = m\angle ABC$

c) $m\angle CBD = y$

$y = 2x = 2(30°) = 60°$

d) $m\angle ABD + m\angle DBE = 180°$

$m\angle ABD = x + y = 30° + 60° = 90°$.

$90° + m\angle DBE = 180°$

$m\angle DBE = 180° - 90° = 90°$.

Exercise Set 9.2

1. A **polygon** is a closed figure in a plane determined by three or more straight line segments.

2. A **regular polygon** is one whose sides are all the same length and whose interior angles all have the same measure; other polygons may have sides of different length and interior angles with different measures.

3. The different types of triangles are acute, obtuse, right, isosceles, equilateral, and scalene. Descriptions will vary.

4. The different types of quadrilaterals are trapezoid, parallelogram, rhombus, rectangle, and square. Descriptions will vary.

5. If the corresponding sides of two similar figures are the same length, the figures are **congruent figures**.

6. Figures that have the same shape but may be of different sizes are **similar figures**.

7. a) Triangle
   b) Regular

8. a) Rectangle
   b) Not regular

9. a) Octagon
   b) Regular

10. a) Trapezoid
    b) Not regular

11. a) Rhombus
    b) Not regular

12. a) Pentagon
    b) Regular

13. a) Octagon
    b) Not regular

14. a) Dodecagon
    b) Not regular

15. a) Isosceles
    b) Acute

16. a) Scalene
    b) Right

17. a) Isosceles
    b) Right

18. a) Isosceles
    b) Obtuse

19. a) Scalene
    b) Acute

20. a) Equilateral
    b) Acute

21. a) Scalene
    b) Right

22. a) Scalene
    b) Obtuse

23. Rectangle

24. Trapezoid

25. Square

26. Parallelogram

27. Rhombus

28. Trapezoid

29. The measures of the other two angles of the triangle are 138° and 180° − 155° (supplementary angles). Therefore, the measure of angle x is $180° - 138° - (180° - 155°) = 17°$.

30. The measures of two angles of the triangle are 180° − 105° and 180° − 133° (supplementary angles). The measure of the third angle of the triangle is $180° - (180° - 105°) - (180° - 133°) = 58°$. Since angle x is a vertical angle with the 58° angle, the measure of angle x is 58°.

31. The measure of one angle of the triangle is 27° (by vertical angles). The measure of another angle of the triangle is 180° - 57° = 123°. The measure of the third angle of the triangle is 180° - 27° - 123° = 30°. The measure of angle x is 180° - 30° = 150° (The 30° angle and angle x form a straight angle.).

32. The given measure of one angle of the triangle is 35°. The measure of another angle of the triangle is 30° (by vertical angles). The measure of the third angle of the triangle is 180° - 35° - 30° = 115°. The measure of angle x is 180° - 115° = 65° (The 115° angle and angle x form a straight angle.).

33.

Angle	Measure	Reason
1	90°	$\angle 1$ and $\angle 7$ are vertical angles
2	50°	$\angle 2$ and $\angle 4$ are corresponding angles
3	130°	$\angle 3$ and $\angle 4$ form a straight angle
4	50°	Vertical angle with the given 50° angle
5	50°	$\angle 2$ and $\angle 5$ are vertical angles
6	40°	Vertical angle with the given 40° angle
7	90°	$\angle 2$, $\angle 6$, and $\angle 7$ form a straight angle
8	130°	$\angle 3$ and $\angle 8$ are vertical angles
9	140°	$\angle 9$ and $\angle 10$ form a straight angle
10	40°	$\angle 10$ and $\angle 12$ are vertical angles
11	140°	$\angle 9$ and $\angle 11$ are vertical angles
12	40°	$\angle 6$ and $\angle 12$ are corresponding angles

34.

Angle	Measure	Reason
1	50°	$\angle 1$ and $\angle 5$ are vertical angles
2	63°	Vertical angle with the given 63° angle
3	67°	$\angle 1$, $\angle 2$, and $\angle 3$ form a straight angle
4	67°	$\angle 3$ and $\angle 4$ are vertical angles
5	50°	$\angle 5$ and $\angle 12$ are corresponding angles
6	113°	$\angle 6$ and the given 67° angle form a straight angle
7	50°	The sum of the measures of the interior angles of a triangle is 180°
8	130°	$\angle 8$ and $\angle 12$ form a straight angle
9	67°	$\angle 4$ and $\angle 9$ are corresponding angles
10	113°	$\angle 6$ and $\angle 10$ are vertical angles
11	130°	$\angle 8$ and $\angle 11$ are vertical angles
12	50°	$\angle 7$ and $\angle 12$ are vertical angles

35. $n = 6$
$(6 - 2) \times 180° = 4 \times 180° = 720°$

36. $n = 7$
$(7 - 2) \times 180° = 5 \times 180° = 900°$

37. $n = 8$
$(8 - 2) \times 180° = 6 \times 180° = 1080°$

38. $n = 10$
$(10 - 2) \times 180° = 8 \times 180° = 1440°$

39. $n = 20$
$(20 - 2) \times 180° = 18 \times 180° = 3240°$

40. $n = 12$
$(12 - 2) \times 180° = 10 \times 180° = 1800°$

41. a) The sum of the measures of the interior angles of a triangle is 180°. Dividing by 3, the number of angles, each interior angle measures 60°.

    b) Each exterior angle measures $180° - 60° = 120°$.

42. a) The sum of the measures of the interior angles of a quadrilateral is $(4 - 2) \times 180° = 2 \times 180° = 360°$. Dividing by 4, the number of angles, each interior angle measures 90°.

    b) Each exterior angle measures $180° - 90° = 90°$.

43. a) The sum of the measures of the interior angles of a pentagon is $(5 - 2) \times 180° = 3 \times 180° = 540°$. Dividing by 5, the number of angles, each interior angle measures 108°.

    b) Each exterior angle measures $180° - 108° = 72°$.

44. a) The sum of the measures of the interior angles of a nonagon is $(9 - 2) \times 180° = 7 \times 180° = 1260°$. Dividing by 9, the number of angles, each interior angle measures 140°.

    b) Each exterior angle measures $180° - 140° = 40°$.

45. a) The sum of the measures of the interior angles of a decagon is $(10 - 2) \times 180° = 8 \times 180° = 1440°$. Dividing by 10, the number of angles, each interior angle measures 144°.

    b) Each exterior angle measures $180° - 144° = 36°$.

46. a) The sum of the measures of the interior angles of an icosagon is $(20 - 2) \times 180° = 18 \times 180° = 3240°$. Dividing by 20, the number of angles, each interior angle measures 162°.

    b) Each exterior angle measures $180° - 162° = 18°$.

47. Let $x = A'C'$
$$\frac{A'C'}{AC} = \frac{A'B'}{AB}$$
$$\frac{x}{5} = \frac{1}{2.5}$$
$$2.5x = 5$$
$$x = 2$$

Let $y = B'C'$
$$\frac{B'C'}{BC} = \frac{A'B'}{AB}$$
$$\frac{y}{4} = \frac{1}{2.5}$$
$$2.5y = 4$$
$$y = \frac{4}{2.5} = 1.6$$

48. Let $x = BC$
$$\frac{BC}{B'C'} = \frac{AB}{A'B'}$$
$$\frac{x}{12} = \frac{50}{20} = \frac{5}{2}$$
$$2x = 60$$
$$x = 30$$

Let $y = A'C'$
$$\frac{A'C'}{AC} = \frac{A'B'}{AB}$$
$$\frac{y}{40} = \frac{2}{5}$$
$$5y = 80$$
$$y = 16$$

49. Let $x = DC$
$$\frac{DC}{D'C'} = \frac{AB}{A'B'}$$
$$\frac{x}{6} = \frac{4}{10}$$
$$10x = 24$$
$$x = \frac{24}{10} = \frac{12}{5}$$

Let $y = B'C'$
$$\frac{B'C'}{BC} = \frac{A'B'}{AB}$$
$$\frac{y}{3} = \frac{10}{4}$$
$$4y = 30$$
$$y = \frac{30}{4} = \frac{15}{2}$$

50. Let $x = AB$

$$\frac{AB}{A'B'} = \frac{AD}{A'D'}$$

$$\frac{x}{5} = \frac{5}{12}$$

$$12x = 25$$

$$x = \frac{25}{12}$$

Let $y = C'D'$

$$\frac{C'D'}{CD} = \frac{A'D'}{AD}$$

$$\frac{y}{1} = \frac{12}{5}$$

$$5y = 12$$

$$y = \frac{12}{5}$$

51. Let $x = D'C'$

$$\frac{D'C'}{DC} = \frac{A'D'}{AD}$$

$$\frac{x}{16} = \frac{22.5}{18}$$

$$18x = 360$$

$$x = 20$$

Let $y = A'B'$

$$\frac{A'B'}{AB} = \frac{A'D'}{AD}$$

$$\frac{y}{17} = \frac{22.5}{18}$$

$$18y = 382.5$$

$$y = 21.25$$

52. Let $x = B'C'$

$$\frac{BC}{B'C'} = \frac{AB}{A'B'}$$

$$\frac{12}{x} = \frac{27}{36}$$

$$27x = 432$$

$$x = 16$$

Let $y = D'C'$

$$\frac{DC}{D'C'} = \frac{AB}{A'B'}$$

$$\frac{15}{y} = \frac{27}{36}$$

$$27y = 540$$

$$y = 20$$

53. Let $x = BC$

$$\frac{BC}{EC} = \frac{AB}{DE}$$

$$\frac{x}{1} = \frac{3}{1}$$

$$x = 3$$

54. Let $x = DC$

$$\frac{DC}{AC} = \frac{DE}{AB}$$

$$\frac{x}{5} = \frac{1}{3}$$

$$3x = 5$$

$$x = \frac{5}{3}$$

55. $AD = AC - DC = 5 - \dfrac{5}{3} = \dfrac{15}{3} - \dfrac{5}{3} = \dfrac{10}{3}$

56. $BE = BC - EC = 3 - 1 = 2$

57. $AC = A'C' = 28$

58. $A'B' = AB = 14$

59. $B'C' = BC = 30$

60. $m\angle B'A'C' = m\angle BAC = 84°$

61. $m\angle ACB = m\angle A'C'B' = 28°$

62. $m\angle ABC = m\angle A'B'C' = 180° - 84° - 28° = 68°$

63. $AD = A'D' = 6$

64. $B'C' = BC = 16$

65. $A'B' = AB = 8$

66. $m\angle BCD = m\angle B'C'D' = 50°$

67. $m\angle A'D'C' = m\angle ADC = 70°$

68. $m\angle DAB = m\angle D'A'B'$
$= 360° - 130° - 70° - 50° = 110°$

69. $180° - 125° = 55°$

70. $55°$

71. $180° - 90° - 55° = 35°$

72. $90° + 35° = 125°$

73.   Let x = height of silo

$$\frac{x}{6} = \frac{105}{9}$$

$$9x = 630$$

$$x = 70 \text{ ft}$$

74. $m\angle BAC + m\angle BCA + 80° = 180°$

$m\angle BAC + m\angle BCA = 100°$

$m\angle BAC = m\angle BCA$

$m\angle BAC = 50°, m\angle BCA = 50°$

$m\angle x = 50°$ since $\angle x$ and $\angle BAC$ are alternate interior angles.

The measure of the angle adjacent to $\angle y$ is $180° - 50° - 80° = 50°$.

$m\angle y = 180° - 50° = 130°$

75.   a) $\dfrac{44 \text{ mi}}{0.875 \text{ in.}} = \dfrac{\text{SP-A}}{2.25 \text{ in.}}$

$\text{SP-A} = \dfrac{(44)(2.25)}{0.875} \text{ mi} = 113.14 \text{ mi}$

b) $\dfrac{44 \text{ mi}}{0.875 \text{ in.}} = \dfrac{\text{SP-R}}{1.5 \text{ in.}}$

$\text{SP-R} = \dfrac{(44)(1.5)}{0.875} \text{ mi} = 75.43 \text{ mi}$

76.   a) $\dfrac{90 \text{ mi}}{2 \text{ in.}} = \dfrac{\text{C-B}}{3 \text{ in.}}$

$\text{C-B} = \dfrac{(90)(3)}{2} \text{ mi} = 135 \text{ mi}$

b) $\dfrac{90 \text{ mi}}{2 \text{ in.}} = \dfrac{\text{B-R}}{3 \text{ in.}}$

$\text{C-B} = \dfrac{(90)(3.1)}{2} \text{ mi} = 139.5 \text{ mi}$

77.

$\dfrac{DE}{D'E'} = 3$ $\dfrac{EF}{E'F'} = 3$ $\dfrac{DF}{D'F'} = 3$

$\dfrac{12}{D'E'} = 3$ $\dfrac{15}{E'F'} = 3$ $\dfrac{9}{D'F'} = 3$

$3D'E' = 12$ $3E'F' = 15$ $3D'F' = 9$

$\overline{D'E'} = 4$ $\overline{E'F'} = 5$ $\overline{D'F'} = 3$

78.

$\dfrac{E'F'}{EF} = \dfrac{1}{3}$ $\dfrac{F'G'}{FG} = \dfrac{1}{3}$ $\dfrac{G'H'}{GH} = \dfrac{1}{3}$ $\dfrac{E'H'}{EH} = \dfrac{1}{3}$

$\dfrac{E'F'}{21} = \dfrac{1}{3}$ $\dfrac{F'G'}{9} = \dfrac{1}{3}$ $\dfrac{G'H'}{9} = \dfrac{1}{3}$ $\dfrac{E'H'}{12} = \dfrac{1}{3}$

$3E'F' = 21$ $3F'G' = 9$ $3G'H' = 9$ $3E'H' = 12$

$\overline{E'F'} = 7$ $\overline{F'G'} = 3$ $\overline{G'H'} = 3$ $\overline{E'H'} = 4$

79.   a) $m\angle HMF = m\angle TMB, \; m\angle HFM = m\angle TBM, \; m\angle MHF = m\angle MTB$

b)   Let x = height of the wall

$$\frac{x}{20} = \frac{5.5}{2.5}$$

$$2.5x = 110$$

$$x = \frac{110}{2.5} = 44 \text{ ft}$$

80. a) $m\angle CED = m\angle ABC; m\angle ACB = m\angle DCE$ (vertical angles); $m\angle BAC = m\angle CDE$ (alternate interior angles)

  b) Let $x = DE$

$$\frac{x}{AB} = \frac{CE}{BC}$$

$$\frac{x}{543} = \frac{1404}{356}$$

$$356x = 762,372; \quad x = 2141.494... \approx 2141.49 \text{ ft}$$

Exercise Set 9.3

Throughout this section, on exercises involving π, we used the π key on a scientific calculator to determine the answer. If you use 3.14 for π, your answers may vary slightly.

1. a) The **perimeter** of a two-dimensional figure is the sum of the lengths of the sides of the figure.

  b) The **area** of a two-dimensional figure is the region within the boundaries of the figure.

  c)

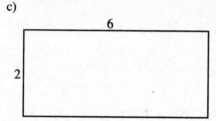

$A = lw = 6(2) = 12$ square units

$P = 2l + 2w = 2(6) + 2(2) = 12 + 4 = 16$ units

2. The **radius** of a circle is half the **diameter** or the **diameter** of a circle is twice the **radius**.

3. a) To determine the number of square feet, multiply the number of square yards by $3 \times 3 = 9$.

  b) To determine the number of square yards, divide the number of square feet by $3 \times 3 = 9$.

4. a) To determine the number of square inches, multiply the number of square feet by $12 \times 12 = 144$.

  b) To determine the number of square feet, divide the number of square inches by $12 \times 12 = 144$.

5. $A = \frac{1}{2}bh = \frac{1}{2}(5)(7) = 17.5 \text{ in.}^2$

6. $6 \text{ yd} = 3(8) = 18 \text{ ft}$

$$A = \frac{1}{2}bh = \frac{1}{2}(2)(18) = 18 \text{ ft}^2 = \frac{18}{9} = 2 \text{ yd}^2$$

7. $A = \frac{1}{2}bh = \frac{1}{2}(7)(5) = 17.5 \text{ cm}^2$

8. $A = \frac{1}{2}bh = \frac{1}{2}(2)(\sqrt{3}) = \sqrt{3} \text{ m}^2$

9. $A = lw = 21(10) = 210 \text{ ft}^2$

$P = 2l + 2w = 2(21) + 2(10) = 62 \text{ ft}$

10. $A = bh = (7)(14) = 98 \text{ in.}^2$

$P = 2l + 2w = 2(9) + 2(14) = 46 \text{ in.}$

11. $3 \text{ m} = 3(100) = 300 \text{ cm}$

$A = bh = 300(20) = 6000 \text{ cm}^2$

$P = 2l + 2w = 2(300) + 2(27) = 654 \text{ cm}$

12. $2 \text{ yd} = 2(3) = 6 \text{ ft}$

$A = s^2 = (6)^2 = 36 \text{ ft}^2$

$P = 4s = 4(6) = 24 \text{ ft}$

13. $2 \text{ ft} = 2(12) = 24 \text{ in.}$

$A = \frac{1}{2}h(b_1 + b_2) = \frac{1}{2}(24)(5 + 19) = 288 \text{ in.}^2$

$P = s_1 + s_2 + b_1 + b_2 = 25 + 25 + 5 + 19 = 74 \text{ in.}$

14. $A = \frac{1}{2}h(b_1 + b_2) = \frac{1}{2}(12)(6 + 16)$

$= \frac{1}{2}(12)(22) = 132 \text{ in.}^2$

$P = s_1 + s_2 + b_1 + b_2 = 13 + 13 + 6 + 16 = 48 \text{ in.}$

15. $A = \pi r^2 = \pi(4)^2 = 16\pi \approx 50.27$ in.^{2}

$C = 2\pi r = 2\pi(4) = 8\pi \approx 25.13$ in.

16. $r = \dfrac{28}{2} = 14$ yd

$A = \pi r^2 = \pi(14)^2 = 196\pi \approx 615.75$ yd^2

$C = \pi d = \pi(28) \approx 87.96$ yd

17. $r = \dfrac{13}{2} = 6.5$ ft

$A = \pi r^2 = \pi(6.5)^2 = 42.25\pi \approx 132.73$ ft^2

$C = \pi d = \pi(13) \approx 40.84$ ft

18. $A = \pi r^2 = \pi(13)^2 = 169\pi \approx 530.93$ mm^2

$C = 2\pi r = 2\pi(13) = 26\pi \approx 81.68$ mm

19. a) $c^2 = 15^2 + 8^2$

$c^2 = 225 + 64$

$c^2 = 289$

$c = \sqrt{289} = 17$ yd

b) $P = s_1 + s_2 + s_3 = 8 + 15 + 17 = 40$ yd

c) $A = \dfrac{1}{2}bh = \dfrac{1}{2}(8)(15) = 60$ yd^2

20. a) $a^2 + 12^2 = 15^2$

$a^2 + 144 = 225$

$a^2 = 81$

$a = \sqrt{81} = 9$ in.

b) $P = s_1 + s_2 + s_3 = 9 + 12 + 15 = 36$ in.

c) $A = \dfrac{1}{2}bh = \dfrac{1}{2}(9)(12) = 54$ in.^{2}

21. a) $b^2 + 5^2 = 13^2$

$b^2 + 25 = 169$

$b^2 = 144$

$c = \sqrt{144} = 12$ km

b) $P = s_1 + s_2 + s_3 = 5 + 12 + 13 = 30$ km

c)

$A = \dfrac{1}{2}bh = \dfrac{1}{2}(5)(12) = 30$ km^2

22. a) $c^2 = 10^2 + 24^2$

$c^2 = 100 + 576$

$c^2 = 676$

$c = \sqrt{676} = 26$ cm

b) $P = s_1 + s_2 + s_3 = 10 + 24 + 26 = 60$ cm

c)

$A = \dfrac{1}{2}bh = \dfrac{1}{2}(10)(24) = 120$ cm^2

23. Area of square: $(10)^2 = 100$ m^2

Area of circle: $\pi(5)^2 = 25\pi = 78.53981634$ m^2

Shaded area:

$100 - 78.53981634 = 21.46018366 \approx 21.46$ m^2

24. Area of larger circle:

$\pi(4)^2 = 16\pi = 50.26548246$ cm^2

Area of smaller circle:

$\pi(3)^2 = 9\pi = 28.27433388$ cm^2

Shaded area:

$50.26548246 - 28.27433388 = 21.99114858$

≈ 21.99 cm^2

25. Use the Pythagorean Theorem to find the length of a side of the shaded square.

$x^2 = 2^2 + 2^2$

$x^2 = 4 + 4$

$x^2 = 8$

$x = \sqrt{8}$

Shaded area: $\sqrt{8}\left(\sqrt{8}\right) = 8$ in.^{2}

26. Area of rectangle: $7(4) = 28$ ft^2

Area of trapezoid: $\dfrac{1}{2}(4)(3+7) = \dfrac{1}{2}(4)(10) = 20$ ft^2

Shaded area: $28 - 20 = 8$ ft^2

27. Find area of trapezoid minus area of unshaded triangle.

Trapezoid: $18\left(\dfrac{9+11}{2}\right)=180$

Triangle: $\dfrac{1}{2}(18)(10)=90$

Shaded area: $180-90=90$ yd^2

28. Find area of large semicircle minus area of small semicircle.

Large: $\dfrac{1}{2}\pi\left(2.5^2\right)$ Small: $\dfrac{1}{2}\pi\left(5^2\right)$

Shaded area: $\dfrac{1}{2}\pi(25-6.25)=\dfrac{1}{2}\pi(18.75)$

≈ 29.45 in^2

29. Area of trapezoid:

$\dfrac{1}{2}(8)(9+20)=\dfrac{1}{2}(8)(29)=116$ in.^{2}

Area of circle: $\pi(4)^2=16\pi=50.26548246$ in.^{2}

Shaded area:

$116-50.26548246=65.73451754\approx 65.73$ in.^{2}

30. Area of circle: $\pi(5)^2=25\pi=78.53981634$ m^2

Area of rectangle: $8(6)=48$ m^2

Shaded area:

$78.53981634-48=30.53981634\approx 30.54$ m^2

31. Radius of larger circle: $\dfrac{28}{2}=14$ cm

Area of large circle:

$\pi(14)^2=196\pi=615.7521601$ cm^2

Radius of each smaller circle: $\dfrac{14}{2}=7$ cm

Area of each smaller circle:

$\pi(7)^2=49\pi=153.93804$ cm^2

Shaded area:

$615.7521601-153.93804-153.93804$

$=307.8760801\approx 307.88$ cm^2

32. Area of small rectangle on the right side:

$12(6)=72$ ft^2

Area of semi-circle on the right side:

$\dfrac{1}{2}\pi(6)^2=18\pi=56.54866776$ ft^2

Area of shaded region on the right side:

$72-56.54866776=15.45133224$ ft^2

Area of shaded region on the left side:

15.45133224 ft^2

Area of triangle: $\dfrac{1}{2}(14)(12)=84$ ft^2

Shaded area:

$15.45133224+15.45133224+84$

$=114.9026645\approx 114.90$ ft^2

33. $\dfrac{1}{x}=\dfrac{9}{207}$

$9x=207$

$x=\dfrac{207}{9}=23$ yd^2

34. $\dfrac{1}{x}=\dfrac{9}{15.2}$

$9x=15.2$

$x=\dfrac{15.2}{9}=1.6\overline{8}\approx 1.69$ yd^2

35. $\dfrac{1}{14.7}=\dfrac{9}{x}$

$x=14.7(9)=132.3$ ft^2

36. $\dfrac{1}{15.2}=\dfrac{9}{x}$

$x=15.2(9)=136.8$ ft^2

37. $\dfrac{1}{23.4} = \dfrac{10,000}{x}$

$x = 23.4(10,000) = 234,000 \text{ cm}^2$

38. $\dfrac{1}{0.375} = \dfrac{10,000}{x}$

$x = 0.375(10,000) = 3750 \text{ cm}^2$

39. $\dfrac{1}{x} = \dfrac{10,000}{8625}$

$10,000x = 8625$

$x = \dfrac{8625}{10,000} = 0.8625 \text{ m}^2$

40. $\dfrac{1}{x} = \dfrac{10,000}{608}$

$10,000x = 608$

$x = \dfrac{608}{10,000} = 0.0608 \text{ m}^2$

41. Area of living/dining room: $25(22) = 550 \text{ ft}^2$

    a) $550(10.86) = \$5973$ b) $550(13.86) = \$7623$

42. Area of living/dining room: $25(22) = 550 \text{ ft}^2$

    a) $550(5.89) = \$3239.50$ b) $550(8.89) = \$4889.50$

43. Area of kitchen: $12(14) = 168 \text{ ft}^2$

    Area of first floor bathroom: $6(10) = 60 \text{ ft}^2$

    Area of second floor bathroom: $8(14) = 112 \text{ ft}^2$

    Area of kitchen and both bathrooms: 340 ft^2

    Cost: $340(\$8.50) = \$2890$

44. Total area: $168 + 60 + 112 = 340 \text{ ft}^2$
    (See Exercise 43.)

    Cost: $340(\$5) = \$1700$

45. Area of bedroom 1: $10(14) = 140 \text{ ft}^2$

    Area of bedroom 2: $10(20) = 200 \text{ ft}^2$

    Area of bedroom 3: $10(14) = 140 \text{ ft}^2$

    Total area: $140 + 200 + 140 = 480 \text{ ft}^2$

    Cost: $480(\$6.06) = \$2908.80$

46. Area of all three bedrooms: 480 ft^2
    (See Exercise 45.)

    Cost: $480(\$5.56) = \$2668.80$

47. Area of entire lawn if all grass:
    $400(300) = 120,000 \text{ ft}^2$

    Area of house: $\dfrac{1}{2}(50)(100 + 150) = 6250 \text{ ft}^2$

    Area of goldfish pond:
    $\pi(20)^2 = 400\pi = 1256.637061 \text{ ft}^2$

    Area of privacy hedge: $200(20) = 4000 \text{ ft}^2$

    Area of garage: $70(30) = 2100 \text{ ft}^2$

    Area of driveway: $40(25) = 1000 \text{ ft}^2$

    Area of lawn:
    $120,000 - 6250 - 1256.637061 - 4000 - 2100 - 1000$

    $= 105,393.3629 \text{ ft}^2 = \dfrac{105,393.3629}{9}$

    $= 11,710.37366 \text{ yd}^2$

    Cost:

    $11,710.37366(\$0.02) = \$234.2074732 \approx \$234.21$

48. Area of entire lawn if all grass:
    $200(100) = 20,000 \text{ ft}^2$

    Area of patio: $40(10) = 400 \text{ ft}^2$

    Area of shed: $10(8) = 80 \text{ ft}^2$

    Area of house: $50(25) = 1250 \text{ ft}^2$

    Area of drive: $30(10) = 300 \text{ ft}^2$

    Area of pool: $\pi(12)^2 = 144\pi = 452.3893421 \text{ ft}^2$

    Area of lawn:
    $20,000 - 400 - 80 - 1250 - 300 - 452.3893421$

    $= 17,517.61066 \text{ ft}^2 = \dfrac{17,517.61066}{9}$

    $= 1946.401184 \text{ yd}^2$

    Cost:
    $1946.401184(\$0.02) = \$38.92802368 \approx \$38.93$

49. a) Perimeter $= 2(94) + 2(50) = 288$ ft
     b) Area $= (94)(50) = 4700$; 4700 tiles

50. a) Total area:
$$(3.5)(6) + (2.5)(8) + (3)(11.5) = 75.5 \text{ ft}^2$$
     b) Total cost: $(75.5)(87) = \$6568.50$

51. Let a = height on the wall that the ladder reaches
$$a^2 + 20^2 = 29^2$$
$$a^2 + 400 = 841$$
$$a^2 = 441$$
$$a = \sqrt{441} = 21 \text{ ft}$$

52. Let a = horizontal distance from dock to boat
$$a^2 + 9^2 = 41^2$$
$$a^2 + 81 = 1681$$
$$a^2 = 1600$$
$$a = \sqrt{1600} = 40 \text{ ft}$$

53. Let d be the distance.
$$d^2 = 37^2 + 310^2$$
$$d^2 = 97494$$
$$d = \sqrt{97494} \approx 312 \text{ ft}$$

54.

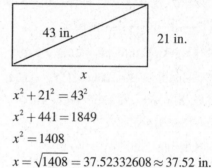

$$x^2 + 21^2 = 43^2$$
$$x^2 + 441 = 1849$$
$$x^2 = 1408$$
$$x = \sqrt{1408} = 37.52332608 \approx 37.52 \text{ in.}$$

55. a) $A = s^2$
     b) $A = (2s)^2 = 4s^2$
     c) The area of the square in part b) is four times larger than the area of the square in part a).

56. a) $A = bh$
     b) $A = 2b(2h) = 4bh$
     c) The area of the parallelogram in part b) is four times larger than the area of the parallelogram in part a).

57. $s = \dfrac{1}{2}(a+b+c) = \dfrac{1}{2}(8+6+10) = 12$
$$A = \sqrt{12(12-8)(12-6)(12-10)}$$
$$= \sqrt{12(4)(6)(2)} = \sqrt{576} = 24 \text{ cm}^2$$

58. a) $A = a^2$
     b) $A = ab$
     c) $A = ab$
     d) $A = b^2$
     e) $(a+b)^2 = a^2 + ab + ab + b^2 = a^2 + 2ab + b^2$

Exercise Set 9.4

In this section, we use the π key on the calculator to determine answers in calculations involving π. If you use 3.14 for π, your answers may vary slightly.

1. a) **Volume** is a measure of the capacity of a figure.
    b) **Surface area** is the sum of the areas of the surfaces of a three-dimensional solid.
2. **Solid geometry** is the study of three-dimensional solid figures.
3. A **polyhedron** is a closed surface formed by the union of polygonal regions.
    A **regular polyhedron** is one whose faces are all regular polygons of the same size and shape.
4. A **prism** is a polyhedron whose bases are congruent polygons and whose sides are parallelograms.
    A **right prism** is one in which all of the lateral faces are rectangles.

5. A **prism** and a **pyramid** are both polyhedrons, but a prism has a top and a bottom base while a pyramid only has one base.

6. For any polyhedron, the number of vertices minus the number of edges plus the number of faces equals two.

7. a) $V = lwh = (1)(4)(2) = 8 \text{ m}^3$

   b) $SA = 2lw + 2wh + 2lh$

   $SA = 2(1)(4) + 2(4)(2) + 2(1)(2) = 28 \text{ m}^2$

8. a) $V = lwh = (6)(3)(2) = 36 \text{ yd}^3$

   b) $SA = 2lw + 2wh + 2lh$

   $SA = 2(3)(2) + 2(2)(6) + 2(3)(6) = 72 \text{ yd}^2$

9. a) $V = s^3; \; V = 5^3 = 125 \text{ ft}^3$

   b) $SA = 6s^2; \; SA = 6(5^2) = 150 \text{ ft}^2$

10. a) $V = s^3; \; V = 7^3 = 343 \text{ cm}^3$

    b) $SA = 6s^2; \; SA = 6(7^2) = 294 \text{ cm}^2$

11. a) $V = \pi r^2 h = \pi(2^2)(12) = 48\pi$

    $V \approx 150.80 \text{ in.}^3$

    b) $SA = 2\pi r^2 + 2\pi rh$

    $SA = 2\pi(2^2) + 2\pi(2)(12) = 56\pi$

    $SA \approx 175.93 \text{ in}^2$

12. a) $V = \pi r^2 h = \pi(6^2)(24) = 864\pi$

    $V \approx 2714.34 \text{ in.}^3$

    b) $SA = 2\pi r^2 + 2\pi rh$

    $SA = 2\pi(6^2) + 2\pi(6)(24) = 360\pi$

    $SA \approx 1130.97 \text{ in}^2$

13. a) $V = \dfrac{1}{3}\pi r^2 h = \dfrac{1}{3}\pi(3^2)(14) = 42\pi$

    $V \approx 131.95 \text{ cm}^3$

    b) $SA = \pi r^2 + \pi r\sqrt{r^2 + h^2}$

    $SA = \pi\left(3^2 + 3\sqrt{3^2 + 14^2}\right) = \pi\left(9 + 3\sqrt{205}\right)$

    $SA \approx 163.22 \text{ cm}^2$

14. a) $r = \dfrac{10}{2} = 5 \text{ ft}$

    $V = \dfrac{1}{3}\pi r^2 h = \dfrac{1}{3}\pi(5^2)(24) = 200\pi$

    $V \approx 628.32 \text{ ft}^3$

    b) $SA = \pi r^2 + \pi r\sqrt{r^2 + h^2}$

    $SA = \pi\left(5^2 + 5\sqrt{5^2 + 24^2}\right) = \pi\left(25 + 5\sqrt{601}\right)$

    $SA \approx 463.63 \text{ ft}^2$

15. a) $r = \dfrac{9}{2} = 4.5 \text{ cm}$

    $V = \dfrac{4}{3}\pi r^3$

    $V = \dfrac{4}{3}\pi(4.5^3) = \dfrac{4}{3}\pi(91.125) \approx 381.70 \text{ cm}^3$

    b) $SA = 4\pi r^2$

    $SA = 4\pi(4.5^2) = 4\pi(20.25) \approx 254.47 \text{ cm}^2$

16. a) $V = \dfrac{4}{3}\pi r^3$

    $V = \dfrac{4}{3}\pi(7^3) = \dfrac{4}{3}\pi(343) \approx 1436.76 \text{ mi}^3$

    b) $SA = 4\pi r^2$

    $SA = 4\pi(6^2) = 4\pi(49) \approx 615.75 \text{ mi}^2$

17. Area of the base: $B = \dfrac{1}{2}bh = \dfrac{1}{2}(8)(8) = 32 \text{ in.}^2$

    $V = Bh = 32(12) = 384 \text{ in.}^3$

18. Area of the base:

    $B = \dfrac{1}{2}h(b_1 + b_2) = \dfrac{1}{2}(10)(8 + 12) = 100 \text{ in.}^2$

    $V = Bh = 100(24) = 2400 \text{ in.}^3$

19. Area of the base: $B = s^2 = 11^2 = 121 \text{ cm}^2$

    $V = \dfrac{1}{3}Bh = \dfrac{1}{3}(121)(13) = 524.\overline{3} \approx 524.33 \text{ cm}^3$

20. Area of the base: $B = \dfrac{1}{2}bh = \dfrac{1}{2}(9)(15) = 67.5 \text{ ft}^2$

    $V = \dfrac{1}{3}Bh = \dfrac{1}{3}(67.5)(13) = 292.5 \text{ ft}^3$

21. $V = $ vol. of large prism $-$ vol. of small prism

    $V = (6)(6)(12) - (3)(3)(12) = (36 - 9)(12)$

    $V = (27)(12) = 324 \text{ mm}^3$

22. $V = $ vol. cone $-$ vol. of cylinder

    $V = \dfrac{1}{3}\pi\left(2.5^2\right)(11) - \pi\left(2^2\right)(4)$

    $V = \pi\left[\dfrac{(6.25)(11)}{3} - (4)(4)\right] \approx 21.73 \text{ in}^3$

23. $V = 2(\text{volume of one small trough})$

    depth of trough $= 7$

    area of triangular ends $= \dfrac{1}{2}(4)(7) = 14$

    $V = 2(14)(14) = 392 \text{ ft}^3$

24. $V = $ volume of rect. solid $-$ volume of sphere

    $= 4(4)(4) - \dfrac{4}{3}\pi\left(2^3\right) \approx 30.49 \text{ ft}^3$

25. $V = $ volume of cylinder $-$ volume of 3 spheres

    $= \pi\left(3.5\right)^2(20.8) - 3\left[\dfrac{4}{3}\pi\left(3.45\right)^3\right]$

    $= 254.8\pi - 164.2545\pi = 90.5455\pi$

    $V \approx 284.46 \text{ cm}^3$

26. $V = $ vol. of large cylinder $-$ vol. of small cylinder

    $= \pi\left(1.5\right)^2(5) - \pi\left(0.5\right)^2(5) = 11.25\pi - 1.25\pi = 10\pi$

    $V \approx 31.42 \text{ m}^3$

27. $V = $ volume of rect. solid $-$ volume of pyramid

    $= 3(3)(4) - \dfrac{1}{3}\left(3^2\right)(4) = 36 - 12 = 24 \text{ ft}^3$

28. $V = $ volume of prism $-$ volume of rectangular solid

    $= \dfrac{1}{2}(6)(8)(11) - 3(4)(11)$

    $= 264 - 132 = 132 \text{ in.}^3$

29. $79 \text{yd}^3 = 9(27) = 243 \text{ ft}^3$

30. $7.25 \text{ yd}^3 = 7.25(27) = 195.75 \text{ ft}^3$

31. $153 \text{ ft}^3 = \dfrac{153}{27} = 5.\overline{6} \approx 5.67 \text{ yd}^3$

32. $2457 \text{ ft}^3 = \dfrac{2457}{27} = 91 \text{ yd}^3$

33. $3.7 \text{ m}^3 = 3.7(1,000,000) = 3,700,000 \text{ cm}^3$

34. $17.6 \text{ m}^3 = 17.6(1,000,000) = 17,600,000 \text{ cm}^3$

35. $7,500,000 \text{ cm}^3 = \dfrac{7,500,000}{1,000,000} = 7.5 \text{ m}^3$

36. $7,300,000 \text{ cm}^3 = \dfrac{7,300,000}{1,000,000} = 7.3 \text{ m}^3$

37. Tubs: $V = \pi r^2 h = \pi\left(3\right)^2(5) = 45\pi$

    $= 141.3716694 \approx 141.37 \text{ in.}^3$

    Boxes: $V = s^3 = \left(5\right)^3 = 125 \text{ in.}^3$

38. a) $V = 46(25)(25) = 28,750 \text{ in.}^3$

    b) $\left(1 \text{ ft}\right)^3 = (12 \text{ in.})(12 \text{ in.})(12 \text{ in.}) = 1728 \text{ in.}^3$

    $28,750 \text{ in.}^3 = \dfrac{28,750}{1728} = 16.63773148 \approx 16.64 \text{ ft}^3$

39. $SA = 2lw + 2wh + 2lh$

    $SA = 2(142)(125) + 2(125)(10) + 2(10)(142)$

    $SA = 40,840 \text{ mm}^2$

40. $r = \dfrac{20}{2} = 10$

    $r = SA = 4\pi r^2$

    $SA = 4\pi\left(10^2\right) = 400\pi$

    $SA \approx 1256.64 \text{ in}^2$

41. $V = 12(4)(3) = 144$ in.^{3}

 144 in.$^3 = 144(0.01736) = 2.49984 \approx 2.50$ qt

42. a) Cylinder 1:

 $V = \pi\left(\dfrac{10}{2}\right)^2(12) = 300\pi = 942.4777961 \approx 942.48$ in.^{3}

 Cylinder 2:

 $V = \pi\left(\dfrac{12}{2}\right)^2(10) = 360\pi$

 $= 1130.973355 \approx 1130.97$ in.^{3}

 The container with the larger diameter holds more.

 b) $1130.97 - 942.48 = 188.49 \approx 188.50$ in.^{3}

43. a) $V = 80(50)(30) = 120,000$ cm^3

 b) $120,000$ mℓ

 c) $120,000$ m$\ell = \dfrac{120,000}{1000} = 120\ \ell$

44. $V = \dfrac{1}{3}Bh = \dfrac{1}{3}(720)^2(480) = 82,944,000$ ft^3

45. $r = \dfrac{3.875}{2} = 1.9375$ in.

 Volume of each cylinder:

 $\pi r^2 h = \pi(1.9375)^2(3)$

 $= 11.26171875\pi = 35.37973289$

 Total volume:

 $8(35.37973289) = 283.0378631 \approx 283.04$ in.^{3}

46. a) 4 in. $= \dfrac{4}{12} = \dfrac{1}{3}$ ft

 $V = lwh = 9(18)\left(\dfrac{1}{3}\right) = 54$ ft^3

 $\dfrac{54}{27} = 2$ yd^3

 b) $2(\$32.95) = \$65.90$

47. a) 5.5 ft $= 5.5(12) = 66$ in.

 $r = \dfrac{2.5}{2} = 1.25$ in.

 $V = \pi r^2 h = \pi(1.25)^2(66) = 103.125\pi$

 $= 323.9767424 \approx 323.98$ in.^{3}

 b) $\dfrac{323.98}{1728} = 0.187488426 \approx 0.19$ ft^3

48. a) Round pan:

 $A = \pi r^2 = \pi\left(\dfrac{9}{2}\right)^2 = 20.25\pi$

 $= 63.61725124 \approx 63.62$ in.^{2}

 Rectangular pan: $A = lw = 7(9) = 63$ in.^{2}

 b) Round pan:

 $V = \pi r^2 h \approx 63.62(2) = 127.24$ in.^{3}

 Rectangular pan: $V = lwh = 7(9)(2) = 126$ in.^{3}

 c) Round pan

49. $V = \dfrac{1}{3}\pi r^2 h = \dfrac{1}{3}\pi\left(\dfrac{3}{2}\right)^2(6) = 4.5\pi$

 $= 14.13716694 \approx 14.14$ in.^{3}

50. a) $B =$ area of trapezoid $= \dfrac{1}{2}(9)(8+12) = 90$ in.^{2}

 4 ft $= 4(12) = 48$ in.

 $V = Bh = 90(48) = 4320$ in.^{3}

 b) 1 ft$^3 = (12)(12)(12) = 1728$ in.^{3}

 4320 in.$^3 = \dfrac{4320}{1728} = 2.5$ ft^3

51. $8 - x + 4 = 2$

 $12 - x = 2$

 $-x = -10$

 $x = 10$ edges

52. $12 - 16 + x = 2$

 $-4 + x = 2$

 $x = 6$ faces

53. $x - 8 + 4 = 2$
    $x - 4 = 2$
    $x = 6$ vertices

54. $7 - 12 + x = 2$
    $-5 + x = 2$
    $x = 7$ faces

55. $11 - x + 5 = 2$
    $16 - x = 2$
    $-x = -14$
    $x = 14$ edges

56. $x - 10 + 4 = 2$
    $x - 6 = 2$
    $x = 8$ vertices

57. $r_E = \dfrac{12,756.3}{2} = 6378.15 \text{ km}$

    $r_M = \dfrac{3474.8}{2} = 1737.4 \text{ km}$

    a) $SA_E = 4\pi\left(6378.15^2\right) \approx 5.11 \times 10^8 \text{ km}^2$

    b) $SA_M = 4\pi\left(1737.4^2\right) \approx 3.79 \times 10^7 \text{ km}^2$

    c) $\dfrac{SA_E}{SA_M} = \dfrac{5.11 \times 10^8}{3.79 \times 10^7} \approx 13$

    d) $V_E = \dfrac{4}{3}\pi\left(6378.15^3\right) \approx 1.09 \times 10^{12} \text{ km}^3$

    e) $V_M = \dfrac{4}{3}\pi\left(1737.4^3\right) \approx 2.20 \times 10^{10} \text{ km}^3$

    f) $\dfrac{V_E}{V_M} = \dfrac{1.09 \times 10^{12}}{2.20 \times 10^{10}} \approx 50$

58. Let $r =$ the radius of one of the cans of orange juice
    The length of the box $= 6r$ and the width of the box $= 4r$
    Volume of box − volume of cans:

    $$lwh - 6\left(\pi r^2 h\right) = (6r)(4r)h - 6\pi r^2 h = 24r^2 h - 6\pi r^2 h = 6r^2 h(4 - \pi)$$

    Percent of the volume of the interior of the box that is not occupied by the cans:

    $$\frac{6r^2 h(4 - \pi)}{lwh} = \frac{6r^2(4 - \pi)}{(6r)(4r)} = \frac{4 - \pi}{4} = 0.2146018366 \approx 21.46\%$$

59. a) – e) Answers will vary.
    f) If we double the length of each edge of a cube, the new volume will be eight times the original volume.

60. a) – e) Answers will vary.
    f) If we double the radius of a sphere, the new volume will be eight times the original volume.

61. a) Find the volume of each numbered region. Since the length of each side is $a + b$, the sum of the volumes of each region will equal $(a + b)^3$.

    b) $V_1 = a(a)(a) = a^3 \qquad V_2 = a(a)(b) = a^2 b \qquad V_3 = a(a)(b) = a^2 b \qquad V_4 = a(b)(b) = ab^2$

    $V_5 = a(a)(b) = a^2 b \qquad V_6 = a(b)(b) = ab^2 \qquad V_7 = b(b)(b) = b^3$

    c) The volume of the piece not shown is ab^2.

62. a) $5.5 \text{ ft} = 5.5(12) = 66 \text{ in.}$

    $V = Bh = 5(66) = 330 \text{ in.}^3$

    b) Radius of cylinder: $\dfrac{0.75}{2} = 0.375 \text{ in.}$

    Volume of cylinder: $\pi r^2 h = \pi(0.375)^2(66) = 9.28125\pi = 29.15790682 \text{ in.}^3$

    Volume of hollow noodle: $330 - 29.15790682 = 300.8420932 \approx 300.84 \text{ in.}^3$

Exercise Set 9.5

1. The act of moving a geometric figure from some starting position to some ending position without altering its shape or size is called **rigid motion**. The four main rigid motions studied in this section are reflections, translations, rotations, and glide reflections.

2. **Transformational geometry** is a type of geometry in which we study how to use a geometric figure to obtain other geometric figures by conducting one of several changes, called rigid motions, to the figure.

3. A **reflection** is a rigid motion that moves a figure to a new position that is a mirror image of the figure in the starting position.

4. Answers will vary.

5. A **rotation** is a rigid motion performed by rotating a figure in the plane about a specific point.

6. Answers will vary.

7. A **translation** is a rigid motion that moves a figure by sliding it along a straight line segment in the plane.

8. Answers will vary.

9. A **glide reflection** is a rigid motion formed by performing a translation (or glide) followed by a reflection.

10. Answers will vary.

11. A geometric figure is said to have **reflective symmetry** if the positions of a figure before and after a reflection are identical (except for vertex labels).

12. A geometric figure is said to have **rotational symmetry** if the positions of a figure before and after a rotation are identical (except for vertex labels).

13. A **tessellation** is a pattern consisting of the repeated use of the same geometric figures to entirely cover a plane, leaving no gaps.

14. Answers will vary.

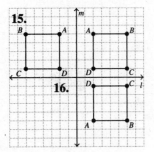

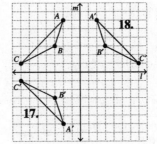

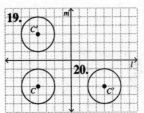

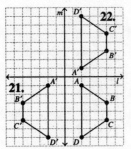

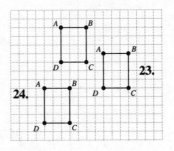

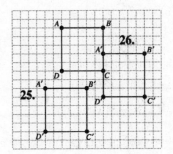

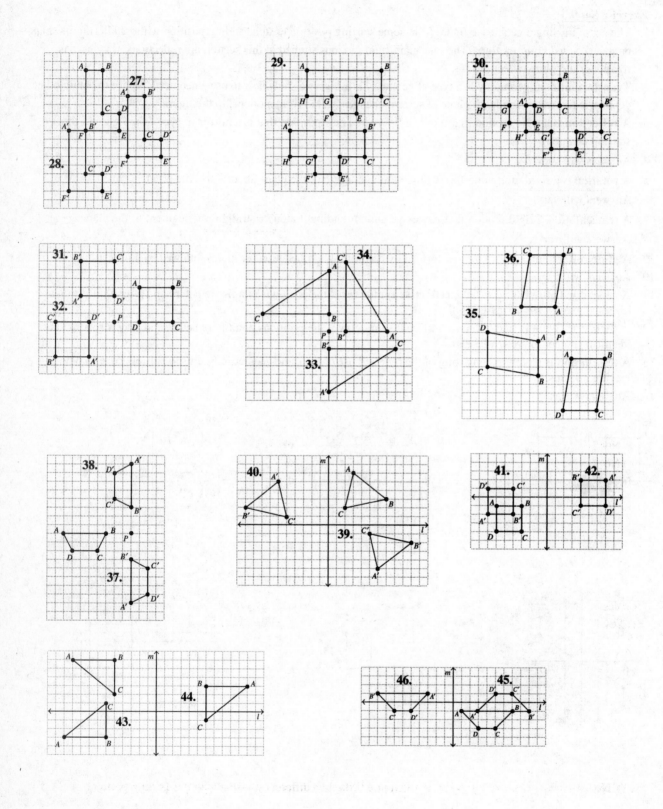

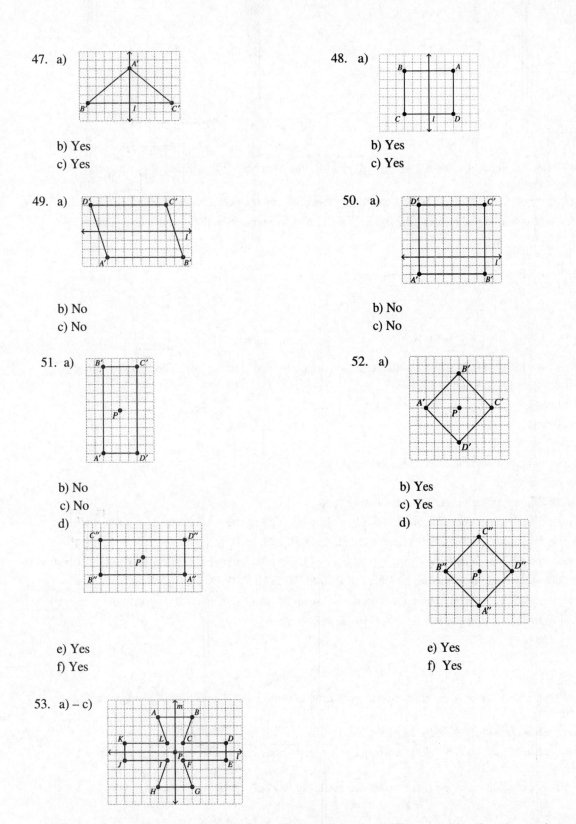

47. a)

  b) Yes
  c) Yes

48. a)

  b) Yes
  c) Yes

49. a)

  b) No
  c) No

50. a)

  b) No
  c) No

51. a)

  b) No
  c) No
  d)

  e) Yes
  f) Yes

52. a)

  b) Yes
  c) Yes
  d)

  e) Yes
  f) Yes

53. a) – c)

  d) No. Any 90° rotation will result in the figure being in a different position than the starting position.

54. a)

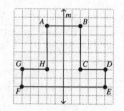

b) No. Any reflection about any horizontal line will result in the figure being in a different position than the starting position.

c) No. Any 90° rotation will result in the figure being in a different position than the starting position.

d) No. Any 180° rotation will result in the figure being in a different position than the starting position.

55. a) – b)

c)   No

d)   The order in which the translation and the reflection are performed is important. The figure obtained in part b) is the glide reflection.

56. Answers will vary.

57. Answers will vary.

58. a) Answers will vary.

   b) A regular octagon cannot be used as a tessellating shape.

59. a) Answers will vary.

   b) A regular pentagon cannot be used as a tessellating shape.

60. Although answers will vary depending on the font, the following capital letters have reflective symmetry about a horizontal line drawn through the center of the letter: B, C, D, E, H, I, K, O, X.

61. Although answers will vary depending on the font, the following capital letters have reflective symmetry about a vertical line drawn through the center of the letter: A, H, I, M, O, T, U, V, W, X, Y.

62. Although answers will vary depending on the font, the following capital letters have 180° rotational symmetry about a point in the center of the letter: H, I, N, O, S, X, Z.

Exercise Set 9.6

1. Topology is sometimes referred to as "rubber sheet geometry" because it deals with bending and stretching of geometric figures.

2. A **Möbius strip** is a one-sided, one-edged surface.

3. You can construct a Möbius strip by taking a strip of paper, giving one end a half twist, and taping the ends together.

4. A **Klein bottle** is a topological object that resembles a bottle but has only one side.

5. Four

6. a) Six

   b) Seven

7. A **Jordan curve** is a topological object that can be thought of as a circle twisted out of shape.

8. Since you must cross the curve to get from outside to inside, two crosses puts you back where you started. Thus, if you cross the curve twice (or any even number of times) to get outside, you must have started outside. Also, if you cross the curve once (or any odd number of times) to get outside, you must have started inside.

9. The number of holes in the object determines the **genus** of an object.

10. Two figures are **topologically equivalent** if one figure can be elastically twisted, stretched, bent, or shrunk into the other figure without ripping or puncturing the original figure.

11. 1, 5 – Red; 2, 4 – Green; 3 – Blue

12. 1, 7 – Red; 4, 6, 8 – Green; 2, 3, 5 – Blue

13. 1 – Red; 2, 5 – Yellow; 3, 6 – Blue; 4 – Green

14. 1, 4, 6 – Red; 2,3 – Yellow; 7 – Green; 5 – Blue

15. 1, 3, 7 – Red; 2, 6, 8 – Blue; 4,5 – Green

16. 1, 4, 6 – Red; 2, 5, 8 – Blue; 3, 7, 9 – Yellow

17. CA, WA, MT, UT – Red
OR, WY, AZ – Green
ID, NM – Blue
NV, CO – Yellow

18. TX, KS, MS, KY, SC, FL – Red
OK, LA, TN – Green
MO, GA, VA – Blue
AR, AL, NC – Yellow

19. YT, NU, AB, ON – Red
NT, QC – Blue
BC, SK – Green
MB – Yellow

20. BCS, SON, DGO, NLE – Red
BCA, CHH, ZAC, TMP – Blue
SIN, COA – Green
NAY, SLP – Yellow

21. Outside; a straight line from point *A* to a point clearly outside the curve crosses the curve an even number of times.

22. Inside; a straight line from point *B* to a point clearly outside the curve crosses the curve an odd number of times.

23. Inside; a straight line from point *F* to a point clearly outside the curve crosses the curve an odd number of times.

24. Inside; a straight line from point *E* to a point clearly outside the curve crosses the curve an odd number of times.

25. Outside; a straight line from point *D* to a point clearly outside the curve crosses the curve an even number of times.

26. Outside; a straight line from point *C* to a point clearly outside the curve crosses the curve an even number of times.

27. Outside; a straight line from point *B* to a point clearly outside the curve crosses the curve an even number of times.

28. Outside; a straight line from point *A* to a point clearly outside the curve crosses the curve an even number of times.

29. 1

30. 1

31. 5

32. 5

33. Larger than 5

34. 0

35. 5

36. 1

37. 0

38. 0

39. larger than 5

40. 0

41. a) - d) Answers will vary.

42. One

43. One

44. One

45. Two

46. The smaller one is a Möbius strip; the larger one is not.

47. a) No, it has an inside and an outside.
b) Two   c) Two
d) Two strips, one inside the other

48. No, it does not.

49. Answers will vary.

50. Ecuador, Brazil, Chile – Red
Colombia, Guyana, French Guiana, Bolivia – Green
Peru, Venezuela, Suriname, Paraguay,
Uruguay – Yellow
Argentina - Blue

51. Answers will vary.

52. a) 1
b) 1
c) Answers will vary.

Exercise Set 9.7

1. Benoit Mandelbrot – first to use the word fractal to describe shapes that had several common characteristics, including some form of "self-similarity"

2. G.F. Bernhard Riemann - discovered elliptical geometry

3. Nikolay Ivanovich Lobachevsky - discovered hyperbolic geometry

4. Carl Friedrich Gauss - discovered hyperbolic geometry

5. Janos Bolyai - discovered hyperbolic geometry

6. Girolamo Saccheri - proved many theorems of hyperbolic geometry

7. a) Euclidean - Given a line and a point not on the line, one and only one line can be drawn parallel to the given line through the given point.

   b) Hyperbolic - Given a line and a point not on the line, two or more lines can be drawn through the given point parallel to the given line.

   c) Elliptical - Given a line and a point not on the line, no line can be drawn through the given point parallel to the given line.

8. a) Euclidean - The sum of the measures of the angles of a triangle is 180°.

   b) Hyperbolic - The sum of the measures of the angles of a triangle is less than 180°.

   c) Elliptical - The sum of the measures of the angles of a triangle is greater than 180°.

9. A plane

10. A sphere

11. A pseudosphere

12. Each type of geometry can be used in its own frame of reference.

13. Spherical - elliptical geometry; flat - Euclidean geometry; saddle-shaped - hyperbolic geometry

14. Coastlines, trees, mountains, galaxies, polymers, rivers, weather patterns, brains, lungs, blood supply

15.

16.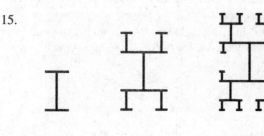

17.

18.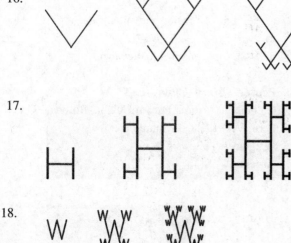

19.a)

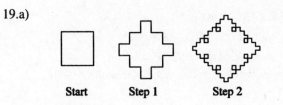

Start   Step 1   Step 2

b) Infinite.

c) Finite since it covers a finite or closed area.

20. a)

Step	Perimeter
1	$3\left(\dfrac{4}{3}\right)^0 = 3(1) = 3$
2	$3\left(\dfrac{4}{3}\right)^1 = 3\left(\dfrac{4}{3}\right) = 4$
3	$3\left(\dfrac{4}{3}\right)^2 = 3\left(\dfrac{16}{9}\right) = \dfrac{16}{3}$
4	$3\left(\dfrac{4}{3}\right)^3 = 3\left(\dfrac{64}{27}\right) = \dfrac{64}{9}$
5	$3\left(\dfrac{4}{3}\right)^4 = 3\left(\dfrac{256}{81}\right) = \dfrac{256}{27}$
6	$3\left(\dfrac{4}{3}\right)^5 = 3\left(\dfrac{1024}{243}\right) = \dfrac{1024}{81}$

b) At each stage, the perimeter is $\dfrac{4}{3}$ multiplied by the previous perimeter.

c) The area is finite because it encloses a finite region.
   The perimeter is infinite.

Review Exercises

In the Review Exercises and Chapter Test questions, the π key on the calculator is used to determine answers in calculations involving π. If you use 3.14 for π, your answers may vary slightly.

1. $\{B\}$

2. $\overline{AD}$

3. $\triangle BFC$

4. $\overline{BH}$

5. $\{F\}$

6. $\{\ \}$

7. $90° - 23.7° = 66.3°$

8. $180° - 124.7° = 55.3°$

9. Let $x = BC$

$$\frac{BC}{B'C} = \frac{AC}{A'C}$$

$$\frac{x}{3.4} = \frac{12}{4}$$

$$4x = 40.8$$

$$x = \frac{40.8}{4} = 10.2 \text{ in.}$$

10. Let $x = A'B'$

$$\frac{A'B'}{AB} = \frac{A'C}{AC}$$

$$\frac{x}{6} = \frac{4}{12}$$

$$12x = 24$$

$$x = \frac{24}{12} = 2 \text{ in.}$$

11. $m\angle ABC = m\angle A'B'C$

   $m\angle A'B'C = 180° - 88° = 92°$

   Thus, $m\angle ABC = 92°$

   $m\angle BAC = 180° - 30° - 92° = 58°$

12. $m\angle ABC = m\angle A'B'C$

   $m\angle A'B'C = 180° - 88° = 92°$

   Thus, $m\angle ABC = 92°$

13. $m\angle 1 = 50°$

   $m\angle 6 = 180° - 110° = 70°$

   $m\angle 2 = m\angle 1 + m\angle 6 = 120°$

   $m\angle 3 = m\angle 2 = 120°$

   $m\angle 4 = m\angle 6 = 70°$

   $m\angle 5 = 180° - m\angle 4 = 180° - 70° = 110°$

14. $n = 5$

   $(n-2)180° = (5-2)180° = 3(180°) = 540°$

15. a) $A = lw = 10(8) = 80 \text{ cm}^2$

   b) $P = 2l + 2w = 2(10) + 2(8) = 36 \text{ cm}$

16. a) $A = \dfrac{1}{2}h(b_1 + b_2) = \dfrac{1}{2}(2)(4+9) = 13 \text{ in.}^2$

   b) $P = 3.2 + 4 + 3.2 + 9 = 19.4 \text{ in.}$

17. a) $A = bh = 12(7) = 84 \text{ in.}^2$

   b) $P = 2(9) + 2(12) = 42 \text{ in.}$

18. a) $A = \dfrac{1}{2}bh = \dfrac{1}{2}(3)(4) = 6 \text{ km}^2$

   b) $P = 3 + 4 + \sqrt{3^2 + 4^2} = 7 + \sqrt{25} = 12 \text{ km}$

19. a) $A = \pi r^2 = \pi(13)^2 \approx 530.93 \text{ cm}^2$

   b) $C = 2\pi r = 2\pi(13) = 26\pi \approx 81.68 \text{ cm}$

20. $A = $ area of rectangle $- 3($area of one circle$)$

   Length of rectangle $= 3($diameter of circle$)$

   $\qquad\qquad\qquad = 3(8) = 24$

   Area of rectangle: $(8)(24) = 192$

   Area of circle: $\pi(4^2) = 16\pi$

   Shaded area: $192 - 3(16\pi) \approx 41.20 \text{ in}^2$

21. Shaded area is the area of an 8 by 8 square minus the four corner squares (each 2 by 2) and minus the area of a circle of diameter 4.

   Shaded area $= (8)(8) - 4(2)(2) - \pi(2^2)$

   $\qquad\qquad\quad = 48 - 4\pi \approx 35.43 \text{ cm}^2$

22. $A = lw = 14(16) = 224 \text{ ft}^2$

   Cost: $224(\$5.25) = \$1176$

23. a) $V = lwh = 10(3)(4) = 120 \text{ cm}^3$

   b) $SA = 2lw + 2wh + 2lh$

   $SA = 2(10)(3) + 2(3)(4) + 2(10)(4) = 164 \text{ cm}^2$

24. a) $V = \pi r^2 h = \pi(6^2)(18) = 648\pi \approx 2035.75 \text{ in}^3$

   b) $SA = 2\pi r^2 + 2\pi rh$

   $SA = 2\pi(6^2) + 2\pi(6)(18) = 288\pi$

   $SA \approx 904.78 \text{ in}^2$

25. a) $r = \dfrac{12}{2} = 6$ mm

$$V = \dfrac{1}{3}\pi r^2 h = \dfrac{1}{3}\pi\left(6^2\right)(16) = 192\pi$$

$$V \approx 603.19 \text{ mm}^3$$

b) $SA = \pi r^2 + \pi r\sqrt{r^2 + h^2}$

$$SA = \pi\left(6^2 + 6\sqrt{6^2 + 16^2}\right) = \pi\left(36 + 6\sqrt{292}\right)$$

$$SA \approx 435.20 \text{ mm}^2$$

27. $B = \dfrac{1}{2}bh = \dfrac{1}{2}(9)(12) = 54 \text{ m}^2$

$$V = Bh = 54(8) = 432 \text{ m}^3$$

26. a) $V = \dfrac{4}{3}\pi r^3$

$$V = \dfrac{4}{3}\pi\left(4^3\right) = \dfrac{4}{3}\pi(64) \approx 268.08 \text{ ft}^3$$

b) $SA = 4\pi r^2$

$$SA = 4\pi\left(4^2\right) = 4\pi(16) \approx 201.06 \text{ ft}^2$$

28. If h represents the height of the triangle which is the base of the pyramid, then

$$
\begin{aligned}
h^2 + 3^2 &= 5^2 \\
h^2 + 9 &= 25 \\
h^2 &= 16 \\
h &= \sqrt{16} = 4 \text{ ft}
\end{aligned}
$$

$$B = \dfrac{1}{2}bh = \dfrac{1}{2}(6)(4) = 12 \text{ ft}^2$$

$$V = \dfrac{1}{3}Bh = \dfrac{1}{3}(12)(7) = 28 \text{ ft}^3$$

29. $V = $ volume of cylinder $-$ volume of cone

$$= \pi(2)^2(9) - \dfrac{1}{3}\pi(2)^2(9) = 36\pi - 12\pi = 24\pi$$

$$= 75.39822369 \approx 75.40 \text{ cm}^3$$

31.
$$
\begin{aligned}
h^2 + 1^2 &= 3^2 \\
h^2 + 1 &= 9 \\
h^2 &= 8 \\
h &= \sqrt{8}
\end{aligned}
$$

$$A = \dfrac{1}{2}h(b_1 + b_2) = \dfrac{1}{2}\left(\sqrt{8}\right)(2 + 4) = 8.485281374 \text{ ft}^2$$

a) $V = Bh = 8.485281374(8)$

$$= 67.88225099 \approx 67.88 \text{ ft}^3$$

30. $V = $ vol. of large sphere $-$ vol. of small sphere

$$= \dfrac{4}{3}\pi(6)^3 - \dfrac{4}{3}\pi(3)^3 = 288\pi - 36\pi = 252\pi$$

$$= 791.6813487 \approx 791.68 \text{ cm}^3$$

31. b) Weight:

$$67.88(62.4) + 375 = 4610.7 \text{ lb}$$

Yes, it will support the trough filled with water.

c) $(4610.7 - 375) = 4235.7$ lb of water

$$\dfrac{4235.7}{8.3} = 510.3253 \approx 510.3 \text{ gal}$$

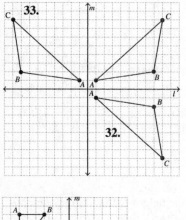

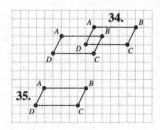

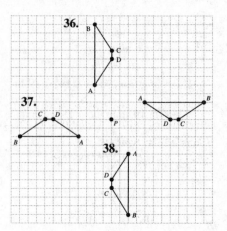

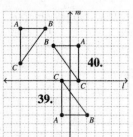

41. Yes   42. No   43. No   44. Yes

45. a) – d) Answers will vary.

46. Saarland, North Rhine-Westphalia, Bremen, Mecklenburg-Western Pomerania, Berlin, Thuringia, Baden-Württemberg, Hamburg – Red

    Rhineland-Palatinate, Lower Saxony, Saxony – Green

    Schleswig-Holstein, Hesse, Brandenburg – Yellow

    Bavaria, Saxony-Anhalt – Blue

47. Outside; a straight line from point A to a point clearly outside the curve crosses the curve an even number of times.

48. Euclidean: Given a line and a point not on the line, one and only one line can be drawn parallel to the given line through the given point.

    Elliptical: Given a line and a point not on the line, no line can be drawn through the given point parallel to the given line.

    Hyperbolic: Given a line and a point not on the line, two or more lines can be drawn through the given point parallel to the given line.

49.

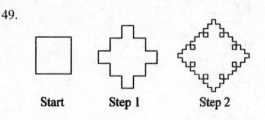

50.

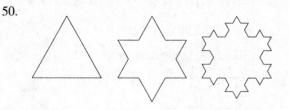

Chapter Test

1. $\overset{\circ}{\overrightarrow{EF}}$

2. $\triangle BCD$

3. $\{D\}$

4. $\overleftrightarrow{AC}$

5. $90° - 12.4° = 77.6°$

6. $180° - 51.7° = 128.3°$

7. The other two angles of the triangle are $48°$ (by vertical angles) and $180° - 112° = 68°$. Thus, the measure of angle $x = 180° - 48° - 68° = 64°$.

8. $n = 10$

   $(n-2)180° = (10-2)180° = 8(180°) = 1440°$

9. Let $x = B'C'$

   $$\frac{B'C'}{BC} = \frac{A'C'}{AC}$$

   $$\frac{x}{7} = \frac{5}{13}$$

   $$13x = 35$$

   $$x = \frac{35}{13} = 2.692307692 \approx 2.69 \text{ cm}$$

10. a)
    $$x^2 + 5^2 = 13^2$$
    $$x^2 + 25 = 169$$
    $$x^2 = 144$$
    $$x = \sqrt{144} = 12 \text{ in.}$$

    b) $P = 5 + 13 + 12 = 30 \text{ in.}$

    c) $A = \frac{1}{2}bh = \frac{1}{2}(5)(12) = 30 \text{ in.}^2$

11. $r = \frac{14}{2} = 7 \text{ cm}$

    a) $V = \frac{4}{3}\pi r^3 = \frac{4}{3}\pi(7^3) \approx 1436.76 \text{ cm}^3$

    b) $SA = 4\pi r^2$

    $SA = 4\pi(7^2) = 4\pi(49) \approx 615.75 \text{ cm}^2$

12. Shaded volume =
    volume of prism $-$ volume of cylinder

    Volume of prism: $V = lwh = (6)(4)(3) = 72 \text{ m}^3$

    Volume of cylinder: $V = \pi r^2 h = \pi(1^2)4 = 4\pi \text{ m}^3$

    Shaded volume $= 72 - 4\pi \approx 59.43 \text{ m}^3$

13. $B = lw = 4(7) = 28 \text{ ft}^2$

    $V = \frac{1}{3}Bh = \frac{1}{3}(28)(12) = 112 \text{ ft}^3$

14.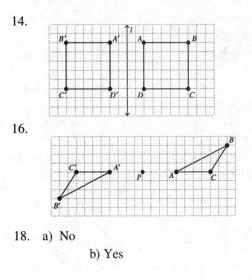

15.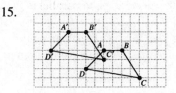

16.

17.

18. a) No

    b) Yes

19. A **Möbius strip** is a surface with one side and one edge.

20. a) and b) Answers will vary.

21. **Euclidean:** Given a line and a point not on the line, one and only one line can be drawn parallel to the given line through the given point. **Elliptical:** Given a line and a point not on the line, no line can be drawn through the given point parallel to the given line. **Hyperbolic:** Given a line and a point not on the line, two or more lines can be drawn through the given point parallel to the given line.

Group Projects

1. a) $B = \pi r^2 = \pi \left(\dfrac{12}{2}\right)^2 = 36\pi = 113.0973355$

$V = Bh = 113.0973355(4) = 452.3893421 \approx 452 \text{ ft}^3$

b) $452.3893421(7.5) = 3392.920066 \approx 3393 \text{ gal}$

c) $452.3893421(52.4) = 23,705.20153 \approx 23,705 \text{ lb}$

d) Weight of Jacuzzi and water: $475 + 23,705.20153 = 24,180.20153 \text{ lb}$; yes

e) Weight of Jacuzzi, water, and four people: $24,180.20153 + 4(115) = 24,640.20153 \text{ lb}$; yes

2. a) 12 ft

b) $12.5 \text{ ft} \times 3.5 \text{ ft} \times \dfrac{1}{3} \text{ ft}$

c) $V = \dfrac{4}{12} \text{ ft} \times 3.5 \text{ ft} \times 12.5 \text{ ft} = 14.58\overline{3} \text{ ft}^3$

$14.58\overline{3} \text{ ft}^3 = \dfrac{14.58\overline{3}}{27} = 0.5401234568 \text{ yd}^3$

d) $0.5401234568(45) = 24.30\overline{5} \approx \$24.31$

e) Area of two triangular sides $= 2 \cdot \dfrac{1}{2}(2 \text{ ft})(12 \text{ ft}) = 24 \text{ ft}^2$

area of rectangular end $= (2 \text{ ft})(3 \text{ ft}) = 6 \text{ ft}^2$

total area of form $= 24 + 6 = 30 \text{ ft}^2$

area of 1 sheet $= (4 \text{ ft})(8 \text{ ft}) = 48 \text{ ft}^2$

Only 1 sheet is needed.

f) $18.95

h) $5(\$2.14) = \$10.70$

g) Five 8 ft 2×4's

i) $B = \dfrac{1}{2}bh = \dfrac{1}{2}(2)(12) = 12 \text{ ft}^2$

$V = Bh = 12(3) = 36 \text{ ft}^3$

$36 \text{ ft}^3 = \dfrac{36}{27} = 1.\overline{3} \text{ yd}^3 \approx 1.33 \text{ yd}^3$

j) $1.\overline{3}(\$45) = \$60$

l) $2^2 + 12^2 = x^2$

$4 + 144 = x^2$

$x^2 = 148$

$x = \sqrt{148} = 12.16552506 \approx 12.17 \text{ ft}$

k) $\$24.31 + \$18.95 + \$10.70 + \$60 = \$113.96$

m) Since each board is 6 in. wide and the top of the ramp is 3 ft wide, it will take $\dfrac{3}{0.5} = 6$ boards.

Each 10-ft board leaves $12.17 \text{ ft} - 10 \text{ ft} = 2.17 \text{ ft}$ of space to fill to the end of the ramp. So, the boards leave $(2.17)(6) = 13.02 \text{ ft}$. Since each board is 10 ft long, 2 boards are needed. The total number of boards needed is $6 + 2 = 8$ boards.

n) $8(\$6.47) = \$51.76$

p) $\$24.31 + \$51.76 + \$24.40 = \$100.47$

o) $10(\$2.44) = \$24.40$

q) The materials are less expensive for the wooden ramp.

CHAPTER TEN

MATHEMATICAL SYSTEMS

Exercise Set 10.1

1. A binary operation is an operation that is performed on two elements, and the result is a single element.

2. A set of elements and at least one binary operation.

3. Each of these operations can be performed on only two elements at a time and the result is always a single element.   a) $2 + 3 = 5$ b) $5 - 3 = 2$ c) $2 \times 3 = 6$ d) $6 \div 3 = 2$

4. Closure, identity, each element must have a unique inverse, associative property.

5. Closure, identity, each element must have a unique inverse, associative property, commutative property.

6. Abelian group

7. An identity element is an element in a set such that when a binary operation is performed on it and any given element in the set, the result is the given element. The additive identity element is 0, and the multiplicative identity element is 1.   Examples: $5 + 0 = 5$, $5 \times 1 = 5$

8. If a binary operation is performed on any two elements of a set and the result is an element of the set, then that set is closed under the given binary operation. For all integers a and b, $a + b$ is an integer. Therefore, the set of integers is closed under the operation of addition.

9. When a binary operation is performed on two elements in a set and the result is the identity element for the binary operation, then each element is said to be the inverse of the other. The additive inverse of 2 is (-2) since $2 + (-2) = 0$, and the multiplicative inverse of 2 is $(1/2)$ since $2 \times 1/2 = 1$.

10. A specific example illustrating that a specific property is not true is called a counterexample.

11. Yes. For a group, the Commutative property need not apply.

12. No. Every commutative group is also a group.

13. d   The Commutative property need not apply.

14. Squaring, finding square roots, finding the reciprocal, finding the absolute value

15. The commutative property of addition stated that $a + b = b + a$, for any elements a, b, and c.
    Example: $3 + 4 = 4 + 3$

16. The commutative property of multiplication stated that $a \times b = b \times a$, for any real numbers a, b, and c.
    Example: $3 \times 4 = 4 \times 3$

17. The associative property of multiplication states that $(a \times b) \times c = a \times (b \times c)$, for any real numbers a, b, and c.   Example: $(3 \times 4) \times 5 = 3 \times (4 \times 5)$

18. The associative property of addition states that $(a + b) + c = a + (b + c)$, for any elements a, b, and c.
    Example: $(3 + 4) + 5 = 3 + (4 + 5)$

19. $8 \div 4 = 2$, but $4 \div 8 = \frac{1}{2}$

20. $7 - 3 = 4$, BUT $3 - 7 = -4$

21. $(6 - 3) - 2 = 3 - 2 = 1$, but $6 - (3 - 2) = 6 - 1 = 5$

22. $(16 \div 4) \div 2 = 4 \div 2$, $= 2$ but $16 \div (4 \div 2) = 16 \div 2 = 8$

23. Yes. Satisfies 5 properties needed

24. Yes. Satisfies 4 properties needed

25. No. No identity element

26. No. No identity element

27. No. Not closed
28. No. Not closed
29. No. No identity element
30. No. Not all elements have inverses
31. No. Not all elements have inverses
32. No. Not closed
33. Yes. Satisfies 4 properties needed
34. No. Not all elements have inverses
35. No. Not closed   ie.: 1/0 is undefined
36. No. Does not satisfy Associative property
37. No. Does not satisfy Associative property
38. No. Not closed
39. Yes. Closure: The sum of any two real numbers is a real number. The identity element is zero.   Example: $5 + 0 = 0 + 5 = 5$

    Each element has a unique inverse.

    Example: $6 + (-6) = 0$

    The associative property holds:

    Example: $(2 + 3) + 4 = 2 + (3 + 4)$
40. No. Closure: The product of any two real numbers is a real number. The identity element is one.   Example: $5 \bullet 1 = 1 \bullet 5 = 5$

    Not every element has an inverse.

    Example: $0 \bullet ? = 1$

    The associative property holds:

    Example: $(2 \bullet 3) \bullet 4 = 2 \bullet (3 \bullet 4)$
41. No; the system is not closed, $\pi + (-\pi) = 0$ which is not an irrational number.
42. No. The system is not closed, $\sqrt{2} \cdot \sqrt{2} = 2$ which
    is rational.
43. Answers will vary.

Exercise Set 10.2

1. The clock addition table is formed by adding all pairs of integers between 1 and 12 using the 12 hour clock to determine the result. Example: If the clock is at 7 and we add 8, then the clock will read 3.
   Thus, $7 + 8 = 3$ in clock arithmetic.
2. $12 + 12 = 12.$ Start at 12 move clockwise 12 hours, the result is 12.
3. a) First add $(2 + 11)$ on the clock, then add that result to 5 on the clock to obtain the final answer.
   b) $(2 + 11) + 5 = 2$ $(1) + 5 = 6$

4. a) Start at the first number on the face of the clock, then count counterclockwise the number being subtracted. The number you end at is the difference.
   b) $3 - 5 = 10$
5. a) Add 12 to 2 to get 14, which is larger than 6. Then subtract 6 from 14.
   b) $2 - 6$ $2 + 12 = 14$ $14 - 6 = 8$
   c) Since 12 is the identity element, you can add 12 to any number without changing the answer.
6. The system is commutative if the elements in the table are symmetric about the main diagonal.
7. Yes. 12
8. Yes, the sum of any two numbers in clock 12 arithmetic is a number in clock 12 arithmetic.
9. Yes. 1 and 11 are inverses, 2 and 10 are inverses, 3 and 9 are inverses, 4 and 8 are inverses, 5 and 7 are inverses, 6 is its own inverse, and 12 is its own inverse.
10. $(2 + 3) + 8 = 2 + (3 + 8)$

    $5 + 8 = 2 + 11$

    $1 = 1$
11. Yes. $6 + 9 = 3$ and $9 + 6 = 3$

12. Yes, the five properties are met.
    1) The system is closed. All results are from the set $\{1, 2, 3, 4, 5, 6, 7, 8, 9, 10, 11, 12\}$
    2) The identity element is 12.
    3) Each element has an inverse.
    4) The associative property holds true.
    5) The system is commutative.

13. a) Identity element = 7
    b) Additive inverse of 2 is 5. $2 + 5 = 7$

14. a) Identity element = 6
    b) Additive inverse of 3 is 3. $3 + 3 = 6$

15. No. Not commutative, Non-symmetrical around main diagonal

16. Yes. Commutative, symmetrical around main diagonal

17. Identity element = C, Row 3 is identical to top row and column 3 is identical to left column

18. There is no identity. While the top row = 3rd row, the left column ≠ any other column.

19. a) The inverse of A is B because A ⊕ B = C.
    b) The inverse of B is A because B ⊕ A = C.
    c) The identity C is its own inverse.

20. a) The inverse of A is A because A ╫ A = C.
    b) The inverse of B is B because B ╫ B = C.
    c) The identity C is its own inverse.

21. $2 + 5 = 7$

22. $6 + 10 = 4$

23. $8 + 8 = 4$

24. $11 + 7 = 6$

25. $4 + 12 = 4$

26. $12 + 12 = 12$

27. $3 + (8 + 9) = 3 + 5 = 8$

28. $(8 + 7) + 6 = 3 + 6 = 9$

29. $(6 + 4) + 8 = 10 + 8 = 6$

30. $(6 + 10) + 12 = 4 + 12 = 4$

31. $(7 + 8) + (9 + 6) = 3 + 3 = 6$

32. $(7 + 11) + (9 + 5) = 6 + 2 = 8$

33. $11 - 6 = 5$

34. $12 - 5 = 7$

35. $6 - 7 = 11$

36. $8 - 11 = 9$

37. $11 - 8 = 3$

38. $4 - 10 = 6$

39. $1 - 12 = 1$

40. $6 - 10 = 8$

41. $5 - 5 = 12$

42. $8 - 8 = 12$

43. $12 - 12 = 12$

44. $5 - 8 = 9$

45.

+	1	2	3	4	5	6
1	2	3	4	5	6	1
2	3	4	5	6	1	2
3	4	5	6	1	2	3
4	5	6	1	2	3	4
5	6	1	2	3	4	5
6	1	2	3	4	5	6

55.

+	1	2	3	4	5	6	7
1	2	3	4	5	6	7	1
2	3	4	5	6	7	1	2
3	4	5	6	7	1	2	3
4	5	6	7	1	2	3	4
5	6	7	1	2	3	4	5
6	7	1	2	3	4	5	6
7	1	2	3	4	5	6	7

46. $3 + 4 = 1$

47. $4 + 5 = 3$

48. $5 + 6 = 5$

49. $5 - 2 = 3$

50. $4 - 5 = 5$

51. $2 - 6 = 2$

52. $3 - 4 = 5$

53. $4 - 6 = 4$

54. $2 + (1 - 3) = 2 + 4 = 6$

55. See above.

56. $6 + 6 = 5$

57. $4 + 7 = 4$

58. $3 + 6 = 2$

59. $7 + 6 = 6$

60. $2 - 3 = 6$

61. $3 - 6 = 4$

62. $2 - 4 = 5$

63. $(4 - 5) - 6 = 6 - 6 = 7$

64. $3 - (2 - 6) = 3 - 3 = 7$

65. Yes. Satisfies 5 required properties

66. No, not necessarily. It may not have an inverse, identity element, or satisfy the Commutative or Associative properties.

67. a) {0, 2, 4, 6}
    b) £
    c) Yes. All elements in the table are in the original set.
    d) Identity element is 0.
    e) Yes; $0 £ 0 = 0$, $2 £ 6 = 0$, $4 £ 4 = 0$, $6 £ 2 = 0$
    f) $(2 £ 4) £ 4 = 6 £ 4 = 2$
       and $2 £ (4 £ 4) = 2 £ 0 = 2$
    g) Yes; $2 £ 6 = 0 = 6 £ 2$
    h) Yes, system satisfies five properties needed.

69. a) {*, 5, L}
    b) 🐎
    c) Yes. All elements in the table are in the original set.
    d) Identity element is L.
    e) Yes; $* 🐎 5 = L$, $5 🐎 * = L$, $L 🐎 L = L$
    f) $(* 🐎 5) 🐎 5 = L 🐎 5 = 5$
       and $* 🐎 (5 🐎 5) = * 🐎 * = 5$
    g) Yes; $L 🐎 * = *$ and $* 🐎 L = *$
    h) Yes, system satisfies five properties needed.

71. a) {f, r, o, m}   b) 🐕
    c) The system is closed. All elements in the table are elements of the set.
    d) $(r 🐕 o) 🐕 f = m 🐕 f = m$
    e) $(f 🐕 r) 🐕 m) = r 🐕 m = f$
    f) Identity element is f.
    g) Inverse of r is m since $m 🐕 r = f = r 🐕 m$.
    h) Inverse of m is r since $r 🐕 m = f = m 🐕 r$.

74. a) Is closed; all elements in the table are in the original set.   b) Identity = ⊡
    c) Inverse: of ⊡ is ⊡ ; of M is M; of △ is △
    d) $(M ⊗ △) ⊗ M = △ ⊗ M = M$
       $M ⊗ (△ ⊗ M) = M ⊗ M = ⊡$
       Not associative since M   ⊡
    e) $△ ⊗ M = M$ $M ⊗ △ = △$
       Not commutative since M ≠ △

68. a) {♣, ♦, ♥, ♠}   b) ®
    c) Yes. All elements in the table are in the original set.
    d) Yes, the identity element is ♥.
    e) Yes; $♣ ® ♣ = ♥$, $♦ ® ♠ = ♥$,
       $♥ ® ♥ = ♥$, $♠ ® ♦ = ♥$
    f) $(♣ ® ♦) ® ♠ = ♠ ® ♠ = ♣$
       and $♣ ® (♦ ® ♠) = ♣ ® ♥ = ♣$
    g) Yes; $♦ ® ♣ = ♠$ and $♣ ® ♦ = ♠$
    h) Yes, system satisfies five properties needed.

70. a) {3, 5, 8, 4}   b) ☊
    c) Yes. elements in the table are in the original set.
    d) Identity element is 4.
    e) Yes. $3 ☊ 8 = 4$, $5 ☊ 5 = 4$, $8 ☊ 3 = 4$,
       $4 ☊ 4 = 4$
    f) $(5 ☊ 8) ☊ 4 = 3 ☊ 4 = 3$
       and $5 ☊ (8 ☊ 4) = 5 ☊ 8 = 3$
    g) Yes. $8 ☊ 5 = 3 = 5 ☊ 8$
    h) Yes, system satisfies five properties needed.

72. a) No, there is no identity element.
    b) $(1 w 3) w 4 ≠ 1 w (3 w 4)$
       $4 w 4 ≠ 1 w 3$

73. Not closed, since $Γ ‡ Γ = Π$, which is not in the original set of elements.

75. No inverses for ⊙ and *
    $(* ⊡ *) ⊡ T = ⊙ ⊡ T = *$
    $* ⊡ (* ⊡ T) = * ⊡ T = P$
    Not associative since * ≠ P

76. (a ☺ a) ☺ △ = △ ☺ △ = a

    a ☺ (a ☺ △) = a ☺ 0 = π

    Not associative since a ≠ π

    △ ☺ π = π   π ☺ △ = a

    Not commutative since π ≠ a

78. No inverses for 0, 2, 3, and 4

79. a)

+	E	O
E	E	O
O	O	E

    b) The system is closed, the identity element is E, each element is its own inverse, and the system is commutative since the table is symmetric about the main diagonal. Since the system has fewer than 6 elements and satisfies the above properties, it is a commutative group.

83. a) All elements in the table are in the set {1, 2, 3, 4, 5, 6} so the system is closed. The identity is 6. 5 and 1 are inverses of each other, and 2, 3, 4, and 6 are their own inverses. Thus, if the associative property is assumed, the system is a group.

    b) $4 \infty 5 = 2$, but $5 \infty 4 = 3$

84. a) Is closed   Identity = F

    (C ☺ D) ☺ A = E ☺ A = F

    An example of associativity:

    C ☺ (D ☺ A) = C ☺ C = F

    Inverses of: A ☺ E = F,   B ☺ B = F,

    C ☺ C = F,   D ☺ D = F,

    E ☺ A = F,   F ☺ F = F

    B ☺ C = E   C ☺ B = A

    Not Commutative since E ≠ A

86. $4^3 = 64$ ways

87.

+	0	1	2	3	4
0	0	1	2	3	4
1	1	2	3	4	0
2	2	3	4	0	1
3	3	4	0	1	2
4	4	0	1	2	3

77. No identity element and therefore no inverses.

    (d ⇔ e) ⇔ d = d ⇔ d = e

    d ⇔ (e ⇔ d) = d ⇔ e = d

    Not associative since e ≠ d

    e ⇔ d = e   d ⇔ e = d

    Not commutative since e ≠ d

80. a)

×	E	O
E	E	E
O	E	O

    b) The identity is O, but since E has no inverse, the system is not a group.

81. Student activity - Answers will vary.

82. Student activity - Answers will vary.

83. Examples of associativity

    $(2 \infty 3) \infty 4 = 5 \infty 4 = 3$ and

    $2 \infty (3 \infty 4) = 2 \infty 5 = 3$

    $(1 \infty 3) \infty 5 = 4 \infty 5 = 2$ and

    $1 \infty (3 \infty 5) = 1 \infty 4 = 2$

85. a)

*	R	S	T	U	V	I
R	V	T	U	S	I	R
S	U	I	V	R	T	S
T	S	R	I	V	U	T
U	T	V	R	I	S	U
V	I	U	S	T	R	V
I	R	S	T	U	V	I

    b) Is a group: Is closed; identity = I; each element has a unique inverse; an example of associativity:

    R * (T * V) = R * U = S

    (R * T) * V = U * V = S

    c) R * S = T   S * R = U

    Not Commutative since T ≠ U

88.

+	0	1	2	3	4	5
0	0	1	2	3	4	5
1	1	2	3	4	5	0
2	2	3	4	5	0	1
3	3	4	5	0	1	2
4	4	5	0	1	2	3
5	5	0	1	2	3	4

89. 1) Add number in left column to number in top row
    2) Divide this sum by 4
    3) Replace remainder in table

90. a) Yes   d) Yes
    b) Yes, 1   e) Yes
    c) Yes, 1   f) Yes

91. a) Matrix addition is commutative because addition of real numbers is commutative.

    b) For example:

$$\begin{bmatrix} 1 & 4 \\ 3 & 7 \end{bmatrix}\begin{bmatrix} 5 & 0 \\ 1 & 2 \end{bmatrix} = \begin{bmatrix} 9 & 8 \\ 22 & 14 \end{bmatrix} \text{ but } \begin{bmatrix} 5 & 0 \\ 1 & 2 \end{bmatrix}\begin{bmatrix} 1 & 4 \\ 3 & 7 \end{bmatrix} = \begin{bmatrix} 5 & 20 \\ 7 & 18 \end{bmatrix}$$

Exercise Set 10.3

1. A modulo m system consists of m elements, 0 through m – 1, and a binary operation.

2. a) a is congruent to b modulo m, written $a \equiv b$ (mod m), means a and b have the same remainder when divided by m.

   b) 27 and 2 have the same remainder, 2, when divided by 5.

3. In a modulo 3 system there will be 3 modulo classes. When a number is divided by 3 the remainder will be 0, 1, or 2.

0	1	2
0	1	2
3	4	5
6	7	8
.	.	.

4. In any modulo system, modulo classes are developed by placing all numbers with the same remainder in the same modulo class.

5. In a modulo 16 system there will be 16 modulo classes. When a number is divided by 16 the remainder will be a number 0 – 15.

6. In a modulo n system there will be n modulo classes. When a number is divided by n the remainder will be a number from 0 – (n–1).

7. $29 \equiv 4$ (mod 5): 4, 9, and 204 have the same remainder, 4, when divided by 5.

8. $50 \equiv 1$ (mod 7): 78 and 71 have the same remainder, 1, when divided by 7.

9. Today is Thursday = Day 4, so $17 \equiv 0$ (mod 7) is Sunday

10. $161 \div 7 = 23$ remainder 0, so 161 days later is the same as today, or Thursday.

11. $365 \div 7 = 52$ remainder 1. So 365 days is 1 day later than today (Thursday), or Friday.

12. 3 years $= (3 \cdot 365)$ days $= 1095$ days; $1095 \div 7 = 156$ remainder 3. So 3 years is 3 days later than today (Thursday), or Sunday.

13. 3 years, 34 days = (3)(365 + 34) days = 1129 days $1129 \div 7 = 161$ remainder 2. So 3 years, 34 days is 2 days later than today (Thursday), or Saturday.

14. $463 \div 7 = 66$ remainder 1. So 463 days is 1 day later than today (Thursday), or Friday.

15. 400 days / 7 = 57 remainder 1. So 400 days is one day after today, or Friday.

16. 3 yrs. 27 days = 1122 days $1122 / 7 = 160$ remainder 2. So 1122 days is 2 days later than today (Thursday), or Saturday.

17. $9+16 \equiv 1 \pmod{12}$, so 16 months after October is February.

18. $48 \equiv 0 \pmod{12}$, so 48 months after October is October.

19. Since 2 years = 24 months and $24 \equiv 0 \pmod{12}$, 2 years 7 months is the same as 7 months; $9+7 \equiv 4$
    $\pmod{12}$ so 7 months after October is May.

20. Since 4 years = 48 months and $48 \equiv 0 \pmod{12}$, 4 years 8 months is the same as 8 months; 8 months after October is June.

21. $83 \div 12 = 6$ remainder 11. So 83 months is 11 months after October, which is September.

22. Since 7 years = 84 months and $84 \equiv 0 \pmod{12}$, 7 years after October is October.

23. $105 \div 12 = 8$ remainder 9. So 105 months is 9 months after October, which is July.

24. Since 5 years = 60 months and $60 \equiv 0 \pmod{12}$, 5 years 9 months is the same as 9 months; 9 months after October is July.

25. $4 + 7 = 11 \qquad 11 \equiv 1 \pmod 5$

26. $5 + 10 = 15 \qquad 15 \equiv 0 \pmod 5$

27. $2 + 5 + 5 = 12 \qquad 12 \equiv 2 \pmod 5$

28. $9 - 3 = 6 \qquad 6 \equiv 1 \pmod 5$

29. $5 - 12 \equiv (10 + 5) - 12 \pmod 5$
    $\equiv 15 - 12 \pmod 5$
    $\equiv 3 \pmod 5$

30. $8 \bullet 7 = 56 \qquad 56 \equiv 1 \pmod 5$

31. $8 \bullet 9 = 72 \qquad 72 \equiv 2 \pmod 5$

32. $1 - 4 \equiv (1 + 5) - 4 \pmod 5$
    $\equiv 2 \pmod 5$

33. $4 - 8 \equiv (5 + 4) - 8 \pmod 5$
    $\equiv 9 - 8 \pmod 5$
    $\equiv 1 \pmod 5$

34. $3 - 7 \equiv (5 + 3) - 7 \pmod 5$
    $\equiv 8 - 7 \pmod 5$
    $\equiv 1 \pmod 5$

35. $(15 \bullet 4) - 8 = 60 - 8 = 52 \qquad 52 \equiv 2 \pmod 5$

36. $(4 - 9) \cdot 7 \equiv (5 + 4 - 9) \cdot 7 \pmod 5$
    $\equiv (9 - 9) \cdot 7 \pmod 5$
    $\equiv 0 \pmod 5$

37. $10 \pmod 5 \equiv 0$

38. $23 \pmod 7 \equiv 2$

39. $48 \pmod{12} \equiv 0$

40. $43 \pmod 6 \equiv 1$

41. $41 \pmod 9 \equiv 5$

42. $75 \pmod 8 \equiv 3$

43. $30 \pmod 7 \equiv 2$

44. $53 \pmod 4 \equiv 1$

45. $-1 \pmod 7 \equiv 6$

46. $-7 \pmod 4 \equiv 1$

47. $-13 \pmod{11} \equiv 9$

48. $-11 \pmod{13} \equiv 2$

49. $205 \pmod{10} \equiv 5$

50. $-12 \pmod 4 \equiv 0$

51. $2 + 3 = 5 \equiv 5 \pmod 6$

52. $6 + 5 \equiv 3 \pmod 8$

53. $1 + 3 \equiv 4 \pmod 5$

54. $4 + 5 \equiv 3 \pmod 6$

55. $4 - 5 \equiv 5 \pmod 6$

56. $2 \bullet 5 \equiv 3 \pmod 7$

57. $5 \bullet 5 \equiv 7 \pmod 9$

58. $3 \bullet \{ \} \equiv 5 \pmod 6$
    No solution

59. $2 \bullet \{ \} \equiv 1 \pmod 6$
    No solution

60. $3 \bullet \{ \} \equiv 3 \pmod{12}$
    $\{1, 5, 9\}$

61. $4 \bullet \{ \} \equiv 4 \pmod{10}$
    $\{1, 6\}$

62. $7 - 3 \equiv 4 \pmod 8$

63. $5 - 8 \equiv 9 \pmod{12}$

64. $6 - 7 \equiv 8 \pmod 9$

65. $3 \bullet 0 \equiv 0 \pmod{10}$

66. $4 \bullet \{ \} \equiv 5 \pmod 8$
    No solution

67. a) 2020, 2024, 2028, 2032, 2036

    b) 3004

    c) 2552, 2556, 2560, 2564, 2568, 2572

68. f f f f f r r   cycle is 8 days

      ↑

      today

a) $60 \equiv 4 \pmod 8$; 4 days after 2nd rest day she will be flying.

b) $90 \equiv 2 \pmod 8$; 2 days after 2nd rest day she will be flying.

c) $240 \equiv 0 \pmod 8$; 240 days from today is the same as 2nd rest day, so she will be resting.

d) 6 days before today is the first fly day, so she was flying.

e) $20 \equiv 4 \pmod 8$; 4 days before today is the third fly day, so she was flying.

70. a) $20/10 = 2 \text{ R } 0$ twice a day

b) $49/10 = 4 \text{ R } 9$ twice a day

c) $103/10 = 10 \text{ R } 3$ twice a day

d) $78/10 = 7 \text{ R } 8$ yes, rest

72. a) $6 \cong 1 \pmod 5$

If this is week 3, then $3 + 1 \cong 4 \pmod 5$ indicates the 3 P.M. - 11 P.M. shift.

b) $7 \cong 2 \pmod 5$

If this is week 4, then $4 + 2 \cong 1 \pmod 5$ indicates the 7 A.M. - 3 P.M. shift.

c) $11 \cong 1 \pmod 5$

If this is week 1, then $1 + 1 \cong 2 \pmod 5$ indicates the 7 A.M. - 3 P.M. shift.

73. The waiter's schedule in a mod 14 system is given in the following table:

Day: 0 1 2 3 4 5 6 7 8 9 10 11 12 13

shift: d d d d d e e e d d d d e e

      ↑

      today

a) $20 \equiv 6 \pmod{14}$; 6 days from today is an evening shift.

b) $52 \equiv 10 \pmod{14}$; 10 days from today is the day shift.

c) $365 \equiv 1 \pmod{14}$; 1 day from today is the day shift.

69. am/pm am/pm am/pm r am am r r

              ↑

            today

a) $28 \equiv 4 \pmod 8$; 4 days after today she rests.

b) $60 \equiv 4 \pmod 8$; 4 days after today she rests.

c) $127 \equiv 7 \pmod 8$; 7 days after today she has morning and afternoon practice.

d) $82 \equiv 2 \pmod 8$; 2 days after today she has a morning practice, so she does not have an off day.

71. The manager's schedule is repeated every seven weeks. If this is week two of her schedule, then this is her second weekend that she works, or week 1 in a mod 7 system. Her schedule in mod 7 on any given weekend is shown in the following table:

Weekend (mod 7):

Work/off 0 1 2 3 4 5 6

         w w w w w w o

a) If this is weekend 1, then in 5 more weeks $(1 + 5 = 6)$ she will have the weekend off.

b) $25 \equiv 7 = 3$, remainder 4. Thus $25 \cong \pmod 7$ and 4 weeks from weekend 1 will be weekend 5. She will not have off.

c) $50 \equiv 7 = 7$, remainder 1. One week from weekend 1 will be weekend 2. It will be 4 more weeks before she has off. Thus, in 54 weeks she will have the weekend off.

74. The truck driver's schedule is repeated every 17 days as indicated by the following table:

Days	Activity
0 - 2	N.Y. - Chicago
3	Rest in Chicago
4 - 6	Chicago - L.A.
7 - 8	Rest in L.A.
9 - 13	L.A. - N.Y.
14 – 16	Rest in N.Y.

a) $30 \equiv 13 \pmod{17}$ indicates that he will be driving from L.A. to N.Y.

b) $70 \equiv 2 \pmod{17}$ indicates that he will be driving from N.Y. to Chicago.

c) 2 years = 730 days $\equiv 16 \pmod{17}$ indicates that he will be resting in N.Y.

75. a)

+	0	1	2
0	0	1	2
1	1	2	0
2	2	0	1

b) Yes. All the numbers in the table are from the set {0, 1, 2, 3}.
c) The identity element is 0.
d) Yes. element + inverse = identity
$0 + 0 = 0$ $1 + 2 = 0$ $2 + 1 = 0$
e) $(1 + 2) + 2 = 2$ $1 + (2 + 2) = 1 + 1 = 2$
Associative since $2 = 2$.
f) Yes, the table is symmetric about the main diagonal. $1 + 2 = 0 = 2 + 1$
g) Yes. All five properties are satisfied.
h) Yes. The modulo system behaves the same no matter how many elements are in the system.

76. a)

+	0	1	2	3	4	5	6	7
0	0	1	2	3	4	5	6	7
1	1	2	3	4	5	6	7	0
2	2	3	4	5	6	7	0	1
3	3	4	5	6	7	0	1	2
4	4	5	6	7	0	1	2	3
5	5	6	7	0	1	2	3	4
6	6	7	0	1	2	3	4	5
7	7	0	1	2	3	4	5	6

b) Yes. All the numbers in the table are from the set {0, 1, 2, 3, 4, 5, 6, 7}.
c) The identity element is 0.
d) elem. + inverse = identity
$0 + 0 = 0$ $1 + 7 = 0$ $2 + 6 = 0$ $3 + 5 = 0$
$4 + 4 = 0$ $5 + 3 = 0$ $6 + 2 = 0$ $7 + 1 = 0$
e) $(1 + 2) + 5 = 3 + 5 = 0$
$1 + (2 + 5) = 1 + 7 = 0$ Yes, Associative
f) Yes. $2 + 4 = 6 = 4 + 2$
g) Yes. All five properties are satisfied.
h) Same answer as problem 75 part h.

77. a)

×	0	1	2	3
0	0	0	0	0
1	0	1	2	3
2	0	2	0	2
3	0	3	2	1

b) Yes. All the elements in the table are from the set {0, 1, 2, 3}.
c) Yes. The identity element is 1.
d) elem. × inverse = identity
$0 \times$ none $= 1$ $1 \times 1 = 1$ $2 \times$ none $= 1$
$3 \times 3 = 1$ Elements 0 and 2 do not have inverses.
e) $(1 \times 3) \times 0 = 3 \times 0 = 0$
$1 \times (3 \times 0) = 1 \times 0 = 0$ Yes, Associative
f) Yes. $2 \times 3 = 2 = 3 \times 2$
g) No. Not all elements have inverses.

78. a)

×	0	1	2	3	4	5	6
0	0	0	0	0	0	0	0
1	0	1	2	3	4	5	6
2	0	2	4	6	1	3	5
3	0	3	6	2	5	1	4
4	0	4	1	5	2	6	3
5	0	5	3	1	6	4	2
6	0	6	5	4	3	2	1

b) Yes. All the elements in the table are from the set {0, 1, 2, 3, 4, 5, 6}.
c) Yes. The identity element is 1.
d) No. elem. → inverse $0 \to$ none $1 \to 1$
$2 \to 4$ $3 \to 5$ $4 \to 2$ $5 \to 3$ $6 \to 6$
The element 0 does not have an inverse.
e) $(1 \times 2) \times 4 = 2 \times 4 = 1$
$1 \times (2 \times 4) = 1 \times 1 = 1$ Yes, Associative
f) Yes. $2 \times 3 = 6 = 3 \times 2$
g) No. 0 does not have an inverse.

For the operation of division in modular systems, we define $n \div d = n \bullet i$, where i is the multiplicative inverse of d.
79. $? \div 5 \equiv 5 \pmod 9$
Since $5 \cdot 2 \equiv 1 \pmod 9$, 2 is the inverse of 5.
$? \div 5 \pmod 9 \equiv ? \cdot 2 \pmod 9 \equiv 5 \pmod 9$
Since $7 \cdot 2 \equiv 5 \pmod 9$, $? = 7$

80. $5 \div 7 \equiv ? \pmod 9$
Since $7 \bullet 4 = 28 \equiv 1 \pmod 9$, 4 is the inverse of 7.
$5 \div 7 \pmod 9 \equiv 5 \cdot 4 \pmod 9 \equiv 2 \pmod 9$; $? = 2$

81. $? \div ? \equiv 1 \pmod 4$ $0 \div 0$ is undefined.
    $1 \div 1 \equiv 1 \pmod 4$ $2 \div 2 \equiv 1 \pmod 4$
    $3 \div 3 \equiv 1 \pmod 4$ $? = \{1, 2, 3\}$

82. Since $2 \cdot 3 = 6 \equiv 1 \pmod 5$, 3 is the inverse of 2.
    $1 \div 2 \pmod 5 \equiv 1 \cdot 3 \pmod 5 \equiv 3 \pmod 5$.
    So $1 \div 2 \equiv 3 \pmod 5$.

83. $5k \equiv x \pmod 5$ $5(1) \equiv 0 \pmod 5$
    $5(2) = 10 \equiv 0 \pmod 5$ $x = 0$

84. $5k + 4 \equiv x \pmod 5$ $5(1) + 4 = 9 \equiv 4 \pmod 5$
    $5(2) + 4 = 14 \equiv 4 \pmod 5$ $x = 4$

85. $4k - 2 \equiv x \pmod 4$ $4(0) - 2 = -2 \equiv 2 \pmod 4$
    $4(1) - 2 = 2 \equiv 2 \pmod 4$ $4(2) - 2 = 6 \equiv 2 \pmod 4$
    $x = 2$

86. Check the numbers divisible by 5 until you find
    one that is also congruent to 2 in modulo 6.
    $20 \cong 2 \pmod 6$ and 20 is also divisible by 5.

87. a) $365 \equiv 1 \pmod 7$ so his birthday will be one day
       later in the week next year and will fall on
       Tuesday.
    b) $366 \equiv 2 \pmod 7$ so if next year is a leap year
       his birthday will again fall Wednesday.

88. a) The three years following a leap year each have
       365 days, so her birthday will advance one day
       in the week each year and will fall on a Friday
       in three years.
    b) The following year will be a leap year and thus
       her birthday will advance *two* days, skipping
       Saturday and landing on Sunday. Five more
       years will add $1 + 1 + 1 + 2 + 1$ or six days,
       so after nine years her birthday will finally be
       on a Saturday.

89. (365 days)(24 hrs./day)(60 min./hr.) = 525,600 hrs.
    (525,600)/(4) = 131,400 rolls $131400 \cong 0 \pmod 4$

90. If 10 is subtracted from each number on the wheel,
    23 11   3 18 10 19   2 10 16   4 24   becomes
    13   1 20   8   0   9 19   0   6 21 14   which is equivalent to
    M   A T H   I S   F U N

Review Exercises

1. A set of elements and at least one binary operation.
2. A binary operation is an operation that can be performed on two and only two elements of a set. The result is a single element.
3. No. Example: $2 - 3 = -1$, but -1 is not a whole number.
4. Yes. The difference of any two real numbers is always a real number.
5. $8 + 7 = 15 \equiv 3 \pmod{12}$
6. $5 + 12 = 17 \equiv 5 \pmod{12}$
7. $4 - 9 = -3 \equiv 9 \pmod{12}$
8. $4 + 7 + 9 = 20 \equiv 8 \pmod{12}$
9. $7 - 4 + 6 = 9 \equiv 9 \pmod{12}$
10. $2 - 8 - 7 = -13 \equiv 11 \pmod{12}$
11. a) The system is closed. If the binary operation is $\boxdot$ then for any elements a and b in the set, a $\boxdot$ b is a member of the set.
    b) There exists an identity element in the set. For any element a in the set, if a $\boxdot$ i = i $\boxdot$ a = a, then i is called the identity element.
    c) Every element in the set has a unique inverse. For any element a in the set, there exists an element b such that a $\boxdot$ b = b $\boxdot$ a = i. Then b is the inverse of a, and a is the inverse of b.
    d) The set is associative under the operation For elements a, b, and c in the set, (a $\boxdot$ b) $\boxdot$ c = a $\boxdot$ (b $\boxdot$ c).

12. An Abelian group is a group in which the operation has the commutative property.

13. Yes

14. The set of integers with the operation of multiplication does not form a group since not all elements have an inverse. Example: $4 \cdot \dfrac{1}{4} = 1$, but $\dfrac{1}{4}$ is not an integer. Only 1 and –1 have inverses.

15. No, there is no identity element.

16. The set of rational numbers with the operation of multiplication does not form a group since zero does not have an inverse. $0 \bullet \underline{?} = 1$

17. There is no identity element. Therefore the system does not form a group.

18. Not every element has an inverse.
    Not Associative   Example: (P ? P) ? 4 = L ? 4 = #   P ? (P ? 4) = P ? L = 4;   # ≠ 4

19. Not Associative   Example: (! □ p) □ ? = p □ ? = ! and   ! □ (p □ ?) = ! □ ! = ?;   ! ≠ ?

20. a) { ☺ , ●, ♀, ♂ }

    b) ⌂

    c) Yes. All the elements in the table are from the set { ☺ , ●, ♀, ♂ }.

    d) The identity element is ☺ .

    e) Yes.

    ☺ ⌂ ☺ = ☺   ● ⌂ ♂ = ☺

    ♀ ⌂ ♀ = ☺   ♂ ⌂ ● = ☺

    Every element has an inverse.

    f) Yes, Associative

    (☺ ⌂ ♀) ⌂ ♂ = ♀ ⌂ ♂ = ●

    ☺ ⌂ (♀ ⌂ ♂) = ☺ ⌂ ● = ●

    g) Yes. The elements in the table are symmetric around the diagonal.

    ♂ ⌂ ♀ = ● = ♀ ⌂ ♂

    h)   Yes, all five properties are satisfied.

21. 15 ÷ 5 = 3, remainder 0   15 ≡ 0 (mod 5)

22. 26 ÷ 7 = 3, remainder 5   26 ≡ 5 (mod 7)

23. 31 ÷ 6 = 5, remainder 1   31 ≡ 1 (mod 6)

24. 59 ÷ 8 = 7, remainder 3   59 ≡ 3 (mod 8)

25. 71 ÷ 12 = 5, remainder 11   71 ≡ 11 (mod 12)

26. 54 ÷ 4 = 13, remainder 2   54 ≡ 2 (mod 4)

27. 52 ÷ 12 = 4, remainder 4   52 ≡ 4 (mod 12)

28. 54 ÷ 14 = 3, remainder 12   54 ≡ 12 (mod 14)

29. 97 ÷ 11 = 8, remainder 9   97 ≡ 9 (mod 11)

30. 31 ÷ 20 = 1, remainder 1   31 ≡ 11 (mod 20)

31. 3 + 7 = 10 ≡ 1 (mod 9); ? = 1

32. ? – 4 ≡ 2 (mod 5)

    0 – 4 ≡ 1 (mod 5)   1 – 4 ≡ 2 (mod 5)

    2 – 4 ≡ 3 (mod 5)   3 – 4 ≡ 4 (mod 5)

    ? = 1

33. 4 • ? ≡ 3 (mod 7)

    4 • 0 ≡ 0 (mod 7)   4 • 1 ≡ 4 (mod 7)

    4 • 2 = 8 ≡ 1 (mod 7)   4 • 3 = 12 ≡ 5 (mod 7)

    4 • 4 = 16 ≡ 2 (mod 4)   4 • 5 = 20 ≡ 6 (mod 7)

    4 • 6 = 24 ≡ 3 (mod 7)

    ? = 6

34. $6 - ? \equiv 5 \pmod 7$

$6 - 0 \equiv 6 \pmod 7$ $6 - 1 \equiv 5 \pmod 7$

$6 - 2 \equiv 4 \pmod 7$ $6 - 3 \equiv 3 \pmod 7$

$6 - 4 \equiv 2 \pmod 7$ $6 - 5 \equiv 1 \pmod 7$

Replace ? with 1.

35. $? \bullet 4 \equiv 0 \pmod 8$

$0 \bullet 4 \equiv 0 \pmod 8$ $1 \bullet 4 \equiv 4 \pmod 8$

$2 \bullet 4 = 8 \equiv 0 \pmod 8$ $3 \bullet 4 = 12 \equiv 4 \pmod 8$

$4 \bullet 4 = 16 \equiv 0 \pmod 8$ $5 \bullet 4 = 20 \equiv 4 \pmod 8$

$6 \bullet 4 = 24 \equiv 0 \pmod 8$ $7 \bullet 4 = 28 \equiv 4 \pmod 8$

Replace ? with $\{0, 2, 4, 6\}$.

36. $10 \bullet 7 \equiv ? \pmod{11}$

$10 \bullet 7 = 70$; $70 \div 11 \equiv 6$, remainder 4

Thus, $10 \bullet 7 \equiv 4 \pmod{11}$.

Replace ? with 4.

37. $3 - 5 \equiv ? \pmod 7$

$3 - 5 = (3+7) - 5 = 5 \equiv 5 \pmod 7$

Replace ? with 5.

38. $? \bullet 7 \equiv 3 \pmod{10}$

$0 \bullet 7 \equiv 0 \pmod{10}$ $1 \bullet 7 \equiv 7 \pmod{10}$

$2 \bullet 7 = 14 \equiv 4 \pmod{10}$ $3 \bullet 7 = 21 \equiv 1 \pmod{10}$

$4 \bullet 7 = 28 \equiv 8 \pmod{10}$ $5 \bullet 7 = 35 \equiv 5 \pmod{10}$

$6 \bullet 7 = 42 \equiv 2 \pmod{10}$ $7 \bullet 7 = 49 \equiv 9 \pmod{10}$

$8 \bullet 7 = 56 \equiv 6 \pmod{10}$ $9 \bullet 7 = 63 \equiv 3 \pmod{10}$

$10 \bullet 7 = 70 \equiv 0 \pmod{10}$

Replace ? with 9.

39. $5 \bullet ? \equiv 3 \pmod 8$

$5 \bullet 0 \equiv 0 \pmod 8$ $5 \bullet 1 \equiv 5 \pmod 8$

$5 \bullet 2 = 10 \equiv 2 \pmod 8$ $5 \bullet 3 = 15 \equiv 7 \pmod 8$

$5 \bullet 4 = 20 \equiv 4 \pmod 8$ $5 \bullet 5 = 25 \equiv 1 \pmod 8$

$5 \bullet 6 = 30 \equiv 6 \pmod 8$ $5 \bullet 7 = 35 \equiv 3 \pmod 8$

Replace ? with 7.

40. $7 \bullet ? \equiv 2 \pmod 9$

$7 \bullet 0 \equiv 0 \pmod 9$ $7 \bullet 1 \equiv 7 \pmod 9$

$7 \bullet 2 = 14 \equiv 5 \pmod 9$ $7 \bullet 3 = 21 \equiv 3 \pmod 9$

$7 \bullet 4 = 28 \equiv 1 \pmod 9$ $7 \bullet 5 = 35 \equiv 7 \pmod 9$

$7 \bullet 6 = 42 \equiv 6 \pmod 9$ $7 \bullet 7 = 49 \equiv 4 \pmod 9$

$7 \bullet 8 = 56 \equiv 2 \pmod 9$

Replace ? with 8.

41. a)

+	0	1	2	3	4	5
0	0	1	2	3	4	5
1	1	2	3	4	5	0
2	2	3	4	5	0	1
3	3	4	5	0	1	2
4	4	5	0	1	2	3
5	5	0	1	2	3	4

41. b) Since all the numbers in the table are elements of $\{0, 1, 2, 3, 4, 5\}$, the system has the closure property.

c) The identity element is 0 and the inverses of each element are $0 - 0$, $1 - 5$, $2 - 4$, $3 - 3$, $4 - 2$, $5 - 1$

d) The associative property holds as illustrated by the example:

$(2 + 3) + 5 = 4 = 2 + (3 + 5)$

e) The commutative property holds since the elements are symmetric about the main diagonal

f) The modulo 6 system forms a commutative group under addition.

42. a)

×	0	1	2	3
0	0	0	0	0
1	0	1	2	3
2	0	2	0	2
3	0	3	2	1

b) The identity element is 1, but because 0 and 2 have no inverses, the modulo 4 system does not form a group under multiplication.

43. Day (mod 10):   0   1   2   3   4   5   6   7   8   9   10   11   12   13

       Work/off :   w   w   w   o   o   o   o   w   w   w   w   o   o   o

                      ↑

               today

     a) Since $30 \equiv 2$ (mod 14), Linda will be working 30 days after today.

     b) Since $45 \equiv 3$ (mod 14), Linda will have the day off in 45 days.

Chapter Test

1. A mathematical system consists of a set of elements and at least one binary operation.

2. Closure, identity element, inverses, associative property, and commutative property.

3. Yes.

4.

+	1	2	3	4	5
1	2	3	4	5	1
2	3	4	5	1	2
3	4	5	1	2	3
4	5	1	2	3	4
5	1	2	3	4	5

5. Yes. It is closed since the only elements in the table are from the set $\{1, 2, 3, 4, 5\}$. The identity element is 5. The inverses are $1 \leftrightarrow 4, 2 \leftrightarrow 3, 3 \leftrightarrow 2$, $4 \leftrightarrow 1$, and $5 \leftrightarrow 5$. The system is associative. The system is commutative since the table is symmetric about the main diagonal. Thus, all five properties are satisfied.

6. $1 + 3 + 4 = 8 = 3$

7. On a clock with numbers 1 to 5, starting at 2 and moving counterclockwise 5 places ends back at 2. So $2 - 5 = 2$.

8. a) The binary operation is □ .

     b) Yes. All elements in the table are from the set $\{W, S, T, R\}$.

     c) The identity element is T, since $T \square x = x = x \square T$, where x is any member of the set $\{W, S, T, R\}$.

     d) The inverse of R is S, since $R \square S = T$ and $S \square R = T$.

     e) $(T \square R) \square W = R \square W = S$

9. The system is not a group. It does not have the closure property since $c * c = d$, and d is not a member of $\{a, b, c\}$.

10. Since all the numbers in the table are elements of $\{1, 2, 3\}$, the system is closed. The commutative property holds since the elements are symmetric about the main diagonal. The identity element is 2 and the inverses are $1 - 3, 2 - 2, 3 - 1$. If it is assumed the associative property holds as illustrated by the example: $(1 ? 2) ? 3 = 2 = 1 ? (2 ? 3)$, then the system is a commutative group.

11. Since all the numbers in the table are elements of $\{@, \$, \&, \%\}$, the system is closed. The commutative property holds since the elements are symmetric about the main diagonal. The identity element is $\$$ and the inverses are $@ - \&, \$ - \$, \& - @, \% - \%$. It is assumed the associative property holds as illustrated by the example: $(@ \, O \, \$) \, O \, \% = \& = @ \, O \, (\$ \, O \, \%)$, then the system is a commutative group.

12. $27 \div 5 = 5$, remainder 2 $27 \equiv 2$ (mod 5)   13. $91 \div 13 = 7$, remainder 0 $91 \equiv 0$ (mod 13)

14. $7 + 7 \equiv 6 \pmod 8$

16. $3 - 5 \equiv 7 \pmod 9$

   $3 - 5 = (3 + 9) - 5 = 12 - 5 \equiv 7 \pmod 9$

   $12 - 5 \equiv 7 \pmod 9$

   Replace ? with 5.

18. $3 \bullet ? \bullet \equiv 2 \pmod 6$

   $3 \bullet 0 \equiv 0 \pmod 6$ $\quad 3 \bullet 1 \equiv 3 \pmod 6$

   $3 \bullet 2 \equiv 0 \pmod 6$ $\quad 3 \bullet 3 \equiv 3 \pmod 6$

   $3 \bullet 4 \equiv 0 \pmod 6$ $\quad 3 \bullet 5 \equiv 3 \pmod 6$

   There is no solution for ? The answer is { }.

20. a)

×	0	1	2	3	4
0	0	0	0	0	0
1	0	1	2	3	4
2	0	2	4	1	3
3	0	3	1	4	2
4	0	4	3	2	1

   b) The system is closed. The identity is 1. However, 0 does not have an inverse, so the system is not a group.

15. $2 - 3 = (5 + 2) - 3 = 4 \equiv 4 \pmod 5$; replace ? with 2.

17. $4 \bullet 2 = 8$ and $8 \equiv 2 \pmod 6$

   $4 \bullet 2 \equiv 2 \pmod 6$

   Replace ? with 2.

19. $239 \div 7 = 29$, remainder 7

   $293 \equiv 7 \pmod 8$

Group Projects

1. a)

♣	A	B	C	D
A	B	C	D	A
B	C	D	A	B
C	D	A	B	C
D	A	B	C	D

   b) The system is closed. The identity is D.

   c) $(A \clubsuit B) \clubsuit C = C \clubsuit C = B$

   $A \clubsuit (B \clubsuit C) = A \clubsuit A = B$

   Yes, Associative

   d) $A \clubsuit C = D$ $\quad B \clubsuit B = D$ $\quad C \clubsuit A = D$

   $D \clubsuit D = D$ $\quad$ All elements have inverses.

   e) $A \clubsuit B = C = B \clubsuit A$

   Yes, Commutative, symmetrical around the main diagonal

   Therefore, the system is a commutative group.

2. a) Yes, see Group Project exercise 3. a).

   b) Product = 0 when factors $\neq$ 0

   mod 4, mod 6, mod 8, mod 9

   c) Product = 0 only when at least 1 factor = 0

   mod 3, mod 5, mod 7

   d) The systems in which the modulus is a composite number have products of 0 when neither factor is 0.

3. a)

mod 3

•	0	1	2
0	0	0	0
1	0	1	2
2	0	2	1

mod 4

•	0	1	2	3
0	0	0	0	0
1	0	1	2	3
2	0	2	0	2
3	0	3	2	1

mod 5

•	0	1	2	3	4
0	0	0	0	0	0
1	0	1	2	3	4
2	0	2	4	1	3
3	0	3	1	4	2
4	0	4	3	2	1

mod 6

•	0	1	2	3	4	5
0	0	0	0	0	0	0
1	0	1	2	3	4	5
2	0	2	4	0	2	4
3	0	3	0	3	0	3
4	0	4	2	0	4	2
5	0	5	4	3	2	1

mod 7

•	0	1	2	3	4	5	6
0	0	0	0	0	0	0	0
1	0	1	2	3	4	5	6
2	0	2	4	6	1	3	5
3	0	3	6	2	5	1	4
4	0	4	1	5	2	6	3
5	0	5	3	1	6	4	2
6	0	6	5	4	3	2	1

mod 8

•	0	1	2	3	4	5	6	7
0	0	0	0	0	0	0	0	0
1	0	1	2	3	4	5	6	7
2	0	2	4	6	0	2	4	6
3	0	3	6	1	4	7	2	5
4	0	4	0	4	0	4	0	4
5	0	5	2	7	4	1	6	3
6	0	6	4	2	0	6	4	2
7	0	7	6	5	4	3	2	1

mod 9

•	0	1	2	3	4	5	6	7	8
0	0	0	0	0	0	0	0	0	0
1	0	1	2	3	4	5	6	7	8
2	0	2	4	6	8	1	3	5	7
3	0	3	6	0	3	6	0	3	6
4	0	4	8	3	7	2	6	1	5
5	0	5	1	6	2	7	3	8	4
6	0	6	3	0	6	3	0	6	3
7	0	7	5	3	1	8	6	4	2
8	0	8	7	6	5	4	3	2	1

3. b) mod 3, mod 5, mod 7

c) mod 4, mod 6, mod 8, mod 9

d) Modulo systems with prime modulus have multiplicative inverses for all nonzero numbers.

CHAPTER ELEVEN

CONSUMER MATHEMATICS

Exercise Set 11.1

1. A percent is a ratio of some number to 100.
2. (i) Divide the number by 100.　　(ii) Remove the percent sign.
3. (i) Divide the number by the denominator.
   (ii) Multiply the quotient by 100 (which has the effect of moving the decimal point two places to the right).
   (iii) Add a percent sign.
4. Multiply the decimal number by 100 and add a percent sign.

5. Percent change $= \dfrac{(\text{Amount in latest period}) - (\text{Amount in previous period})}{\text{Amount in previous period}} \times 100$

6. Percent markup on cost $= \dfrac{\text{Selling Price } - \text{ Dealer's Cost}}{\text{Dealer's Cost}} \times 100$

7. $\dfrac{3}{4} = 0.75 = (0.75)(100)\% = 75.0\%$

8. $\dfrac{3}{5} = 0.60 = (0.60)(100)\% = 60.0\%$

9. $\dfrac{11}{20} = 0.55 = (0.55)(100)\% = 55.0\%$

10. $\dfrac{7}{8} = 0.875 = (0.875)(100)\% = 87.5\%$

11. $0.007654 = (0.007654)(100)\% = 0.8\%$

12. $0.5688 = (0.5688)(100)\% = 56.9\%$

13. $3.78 = (3.78)(100)\% = 378\%$

14. $13.678 = (13.678)(100)\% = 1367.8\%$

15. $5\% = \dfrac{5}{100} = 0.05$

16. $3.2\% = \dfrac{3.2}{100} = 0.032$

17. $5.15\% = \dfrac{5.15}{100} = 0.0515$

18. $0.75\% = \dfrac{0.75}{100} = 0.0075$

19. $\dfrac{1}{4}\% = 0.25\% = \dfrac{0.25}{100} = 0.0025$

20. $\dfrac{3}{8}\% = 0.375\% = \dfrac{0.375}{100} = 0.00375$

21. $\dfrac{1}{5}\% = 0.2\% = \dfrac{0.2}{100} = 0.002$

22. $135.9\% = \dfrac{135.9}{100} = 1.359$

23. $1\% = \dfrac{1}{100} = 0.01$

24. $0.50\% = \dfrac{0.50}{100} = 0.005$

25. $\dfrac{5}{20} = \dfrac{25}{100} = 25\%$

26. $\dfrac{95}{3500} \approx .0271428... = (0.0271428... \times 100)\% =$

    $2.714\ \%$

27. $8(.4125) = 3.3$ $\quad 8.0 - 3.3 = 4.7$ g

28. $(693,905)(.36) = 249,805.8$ miles

29. $(2,604,262)(.08) = \$208,341$

30. $(2,604,262)(.11) = \$286,469$

31. $(2,604,262)(.25) = \$651,066$

32. $(2,604,262)(.56) = \$1,548,388$

33. $(5000)(0.31) = \$1550$

34. $(5000)(0.01) = \$50$

35. $(5000)(0.42) = \$2100$

36. $(5000)(0.13) = \$650$

37. $\dfrac{231\text{million}}{559\text{ million}} = 0.413$ $\quad 0.413 = 41.3\%$

38. $\dfrac{180\text{ million}}{559\text{ million}} = 0.322$ $\quad 0.322 = 32.2\%$

39. $\dfrac{56\text{ million}}{559\text{ million}} = 0.100$ $\quad 0.100 = 10.0\%$

40. $\dfrac{53\text{ million}}{559\text{ million}} = 0.095$ $\quad 0.095 = 9.5\%$

41. $\dfrac{636,677 - 642,200}{642,200} = -0.009 = 0.9\%$ decrease

42. $\dfrac{298.3 - 248.7}{248.7} = 0.199 \approx 19.9\%$ increase

43. a) $\dfrac{0.654 - 0.329}{0.329} = 0.988 = 98.8\%$ increase

    b) $\dfrac{2.125 - 0.654}{0.645} = 2.249 = 224.9\%$ increase

    c) $\dfrac{5.225 - 2.125}{2.125} = 1.459 = 145.9\%$ increase

    d) $\dfrac{8.283 - 5.225}{5.225} = 0.585 = 58.5\%$ increase

44. a) $\dfrac{70.3 - 74.8}{74.8} = -0.06 = 6\%$ decrease

    b) $\dfrac{73.0 - 70.3}{70.3} = 0.038 = 3.8\%$ increase

    c) $\dfrac{74.9 - 73.0}{73.0} = 0.026 = 2.6\%$ increase

    d) $\dfrac{71.6 - 74.9}{74.9} = -0.044 = 4.4\%$ decrease

45. a) $\dfrac{11,500 - 6450}{6450} = 0.783 = 78.3\%$ increase

    b) $\dfrac{8340 - 11,500}{11,500} = 0.275 = 27.5\%$ decrease

    c) $\dfrac{10,720 - 8340}{8340} = 0.285 = 28.5\%$ increase

    d) $\dfrac{10,720 - 6450}{6450} = 0.662 = 66.2\%$ increase

46. a) $\dfrac{50,000 - 25,000}{25,000} = 1.00 = 100.0\%$ increase

    b) $\dfrac{100,000 - 75,000}{75,000} = 0.333 \pm 33.3\%$ increase

    c) $\dfrac{400,000 - 200,000}{200,000} = 1.00 = 100\%$ increase

    d) $\dfrac{400,000 - 25,000}{25,000} = 15 = 1500\%$ increase

47. $(.15)(45) = \$ 6.75$

48. $(.065)(150) = \$ 9.75$

49. $24/96 = .25;\ (.25)(100) = 25\%$

50. $15/75 = .20;\ (.20)(100) = 20\%$

51. $.05x = 75;\quad x = 75/.05 = 300$

52. $10x = 75;\quad x = 75/.10 = 750$

53. a) tax $= 6\%$ of $\$43.50 = (0.06)(43.50) = \$2.61$
    b) total bill before tip $= \$43.50 + \$2.61 = \$46.11$
    c) tip $= 15\%$ of $46.11 = 0.15(46.11) = \$6.92$
    d) total cost $= 46.11 + 6.92 = \$53.03$

54. 25% of what number is 10?

    $0.25x = 10 \qquad x = \dfrac{10}{0.25} = 40$

    original number of crew is 40.

55. $1.50(x) = 18 \qquad x = \dfrac{18}{1.50} = 12$

12 students got an A on the 2nd test.

56. $0.30(x) = 57 \qquad x = \dfrac{57}{0.30} = 190$

The original number of employees was 190.

57. Mr. Browns' increase was $0.07(36,500) = \$2,555$
His new salary $= \$36,500 + \$2,555 = \$39,055$

58. $(0.17)(300) = x = 51 \qquad$ 51 prefer Ranch.

59. Percent change $= \left(\dfrac{407-430}{430}\right)(100) =$

$\left(\dfrac{-23}{430}\right)(100) = -5.3\%$

There was a 5.3% decrease in the # of units sold.

60.

Percent markup $= \left(\dfrac{699-320}{320}\right)(100) = \dfrac{379}{320} = 1.184$

$(1.184)(100) = 118.4\,\%$

61. $\dfrac{37.0-32.9}{32.9} = 0.125 = 12.5\%$ increase

62. $\dfrac{210-235}{235} = -0.106 = 10.6\%$ decrease

63. Percent decrease from regular price $=$

$\left(\dfrac{\$439-539.62}{539.62}\right)(100) = \left(\dfrac{-100.62}{539.62}\right)(100) =$

$-18.6\,\%$

The sale price is 18.6% lower than the regular price.

64. Percent markup $= \left(\dfrac{11.95-7.95}{7.95}\right)(100) =$

$(0.5031)(100) = 50.3\,\%$

65. $(0.18)(\text{sale price}) = \$675$

sale price $= \dfrac{675}{0.18} = \$3,750$

66. No, 15% of $115 is $(0.15)(\$115) = \$17.25$
The sale price should be $115 - 17.25 = \$97.75$
not $100.

67. $1000 increased by 10% is $\$1000 + 0.10(\$1000) = \$1000 + \$100 = \$1,100$.
$1,100 decreased by 10% is $\$1,100 - 0.10(\$1,100) = \$1,100 - \$110 = \$990$.
Therefore if he sells the car at the reduced price he will lose $10.

68. a) No, the 25% discount is greater. (see part b)
  b) $189.99 - 0.10(189.99) = 189.99 - 19.00 = 170.99 \qquad 170.99 - 0.15(170.99) = 170.99 - 25.65 = \$145.34$
  c) $189.99 - 0.25(189.99) = 189.99 - 47.50 = \$142.49$
  d) Yes

69. The profit must be $0.40(\$5901.79) = \$2,360.72$. With a 40% profit, the total revenue must be
$5901.79 + 2360.72 = \$8,262.51$; the revenue from the first sale would be $100 \times \$9.00 = \$900$, and the
revenue from the second sale would be $150 \times \$12.50 = \$1,875.00$. The revenue needed for the 250 ties
would be $8,262.51 - \$900.00 - \$1,875.00 = \$5,487.51$. Thus, the selling price should be

$\dfrac{\$5,487.51}{250} = \$21.95$.

70. a) $200 decreased by 25% b) $100 increased by 50% c) $100 increased by 100%

Exercise Set 11.2
1. Interest is the money the borrower pays for the use of the lender's money.
2. The amount of money that a bank is willing to lend to a person is called credit.
3. Security is anything of value pledged by the borrower that the lender may sell or keep if the borrower does not repay the loan.
4. A cosigner is a person, other than the person who received the loan, who guarantees that a loan will be repaid.
5. i = interest, p = principal, r = interest rate, t = time
   The rate and time must be expressed for the same period of time, i.e. days, months or years.

6. A personal note is an agreement that states the conditions of the loan.

7. The United States Rule states that if a partial payment is made on a loan, interest is computed on the principal from the first day of the loan (or previous partial payment) up to the date of the partial payment. For each partial payment, the partial payment is used to pay the interest first, then the remainder of the payment is applied to the principle. On the due date of the loan the interest is calculated from the date of the last partial payment.

8. The difference between ordinary interest and interest calculated using the Banker's rule is the way in which time is used in the simple interest formula. Ordinary interest: a month is 30 days and year is 360 days. Banker's rule: any fractional part of a year is the exact number of days, and a year is 360 days.

9. $i = prt = (250)(.03)25) = \$15.00$

10. $i = (375)(.045)(5) = \$84.38$

11. $i = (1100)(.0875)(90/360) = \$24.06$

12. $i = (2500)(0.03785)\left(\dfrac{9}{12}\right) = \$72.66$

13. $i = prt = (587)(0.00045)(60) = \$15.85$

14. $i = (6,742.75)(0.0605)\left(\dfrac{90}{360}\right) = \$101.98$

15. $i = (2,756.78)(0.1015)\left(\dfrac{103}{360}\right) = \$80.06$

16. $i = (550.31)(0.089)\left(\dfrac{67}{360}\right) = \$9.12$

17. $i = (1372.11)(.01375)(6) = \$113.20$

18. $i = (4,1864)(.000375)(60) = \$941.94$

19. $(2000)(r)(4) = 400 \qquad r = \dfrac{400}{(2000)(4)}(100) = 5\%$

20. $p(.06)\left(\dfrac{30}{360}\right) = 26.90 \qquad p = \dfrac{(360)(26.90)}{(30)(0.06)} = \$5380$

21. $12.00 = p(0.08)\left(\dfrac{3}{12}\right) = p(0.02) \quad p = \dfrac{12.00}{0.02} = \$600$

22. $64.00 = (800)(0.06)(t) = 48t$
$t = \dfrac{64.00}{48} = 1.\overline{3}$ years, or 1 yr. 4 months

23. $124.49 = (957.62)(0.065)(t) = 62.2453t$
$\dfrac{124.49}{62.2453} = t \qquad t = 2$ years

24. $343.20 = (1650.00)(r)(6.5) = 10725r$
$\dfrac{343.20}{10725} = r \qquad r = 0.032$ or 3.2% per year

25. $i = (6000)(0.035)(3) = 630$
Repayment $= p + i = 6000 + 630 = \$6630$

26. a) $(4500)(.0475)(3) = \$641.25$
b) $4500 + 641.25 = \$5,141.25$

27. a) $i = prt \qquad i = (3500)(0.075)(6/12) = \$131.25$
b) $A = p + i \qquad A = 3500 + 131.25 = \$3,631.25$

28. a) $i = prt \qquad I = (2500)(0.08)(5/12) = \$83.33$
b) $2500.00 - 83.33 = \$2416.67$
c) $i = prt \qquad 83.33 = (2416.67)(5/12) = 1006.95r$
$\dfrac{83.33}{1006.95} = r = 0.08275$ or 8.3%

29. a) $i = prt \qquad I = (3650)(0.075)(8/12) = \$182.50$
b) $3650.00 - 182.50 = \$3467.50$, which is the amount Julie received.
c) $i = prt \qquad 182.50 = (3467.50)(r)(8/12) = 2311.67r$
$\dfrac{182.50}{2311.67} = r = 0.0789$ or 7.9%

30. a) $0.80x = 350 \qquad x = 350/0.80 = \$437.50$
$\$437.50$ is needed in savings
b) $3\dfrac{1}{4}\% + 2\% = 5\dfrac{1}{4}\%$
c) $i = prt \qquad i = (350)(0.0525)(0.5) = \$9.19$
$A = p + i = 350 + 9.19 = \$359.19$

31. Amt. collected = (470)(4500/2) = $1,057,500
    i = prt = (1,057,500)(0.054)(5/12) = $23,793.75

32. i = 80.25 − 75.00 = 5.25
    5.25 = (75.00)(r)(14/360) = 2.92r
    $r = \dfrac{5.25}{2.92} = 1.80$ or 180%

33. [Feb 14–Nov 25]: 329 − 45 = 284 days

34. [01/17–10/10]: 283 − 17 = 266 days

35. [02/02–03/17]: 304 − 33 = 271 days
    Because of Leap Year, 271 + 1 = 272 days

36. [06/14–01/24]: (365 − 165) + 24 = 200 + 24 = 224 days

37. [08/24–05/15]: (365 − 236) + 135 = 129 + 135 = 264 days

38. [01/24–06/14]: (365 − 355) + 118 = 10 + 118 = 128 days

39. [03/15] for 90 days: 74 + 90 = 164, which is June 13

40. [05/11] for 120 days: 131 + 120 = 251, which is September 8

41. [11/25] for 120 days: 329 + 120 = 449;
    449 − 365 = 84   84 − 1 leap year day = day 83, which is March 24

42. July 5 for 210 days: 186 + 210 = 396;
    396 − 365 = day 31, which is January 31

43. [05/01 to 06/01]: 152 − 121 = 31 days
    (3000)(.04)(31/360) = 10.33
    1000.00 − 10.33 = 989.67
    3000.00 − 989.67 = $2010.33

    [06/01 to 07/01]: 182 − 152 = 30 days
    (2010.33)(.04)(30/360) = 6.70
    2010.33 + 6.70 = $2017.03

44. [01/15 to 03/01]: 60 − 15 = 45 days
    (6000)(.07)(45/360) = 52.50
    2500.00 − 52.50 = $2447.50
    6000.00 − 2447.50 = $3552.50

    [03/1 to 04/15]: 105 − 60 = 45 days
    (3552.50)(.07)(45/360) = $31.08
    3552.50 + 31.09 = $3583.58

45. [02/01 to 05/01]: = 121 − 32 = 89 days
    (2400)(.055)(89/360) = $32.63
    1000.00 − 32.63 = $967.37
    2400 − 967.37 = $1432.63

    [05/01 to 08/31]: = 243 − 121 = 122 days
    (1432.63)(.055)(122/360) = $26.70
    1432.63 + 26.70 = $1459.33

46. [09/01 to 10/31]: 304 − 244 = 60 days
    (8500)(.115)(60/360) = $162.92
    4250.00 − 162.92 = $730.00
    8500.00 − 730.00 = $4412.92

    [10/31 to 10/01]: 365 − 304 = 61 days
    (4412.92)(.115)(61/360) = $85.99
    4412.92 + 85.99 = $4498.91

47. [07/15 to 12/27]: 361 − 196 = 165 days
    (9000)(.06)(165/360) = $247.50
    4000.00 − 247.50 = $3752.50
    9000.00 − 3752.50 = $5247.50

    [12/27 to 02/01]: (365 − 361) + 32 = 36 days
    (5247.50)(.06)(36/360) = $31.49
    5247.50 + 31.49 = $5278.99

48. [01/01 to 01/15]: 15 − 1 = 14 days
    (1000)(.125)(14/360) = $4.86
    300.00 − 4.86 = $295.14
    1000.00 − 295.14 = $704.86

    [01/15 to 02/15]: 46 − 15 = 31 days
    (704.86)(.125)(31/360) = $7.59
    704.86 + 7.59 = $712.45

49. [08/01 to 09/01]:   244 – 213 = 31 days
    (1800)(.15)(31/360) =$ 23.25
    500.00 – 23.25 = $476.75
    1800.00 – 476.75 = $1323.25

    [09/01 to 10/01]:   274 – 244 = 30 days
    (1323.25)(.15)(30/360) = $16.54
    500.00 – 16.54 = $483.46
    1323.25 – 483.46 = $839.79

    [10/01 to 11/01]:   305 – 274 = 31 days
    (839.79)(.15)(31/360) = $10.85
    839.79 + 10.85 = $850.64

51. [03/01 to 08/01]:   213 – 60 = 153 days
    (11600)(.06)(153/360) = $95.80
    2000.00 – 295.80 = $1704.20
    11600.00 – 1704.20 = $9895.80

    [08/01 to 11/15]:   319 – 213 = 106 days
    (9895.80)(.06)(106/360) = $174.83
    4000.00 – 174.83 = $3825.17
    9895.8 – 3825.17 = $6070.63

    [11/15 to 12/01]:   335 – 319 = 16 days
    (6070.63)(.06)(16/360) = $16.19
    6070.63 + 16.19 = $6086.82

53. [03/01 to 05/01]:   121 – 60 = 61 days
    (6500)(.105)(61/360) = $115.65
    1750.00 – 115.65 = $1634.35
    6500.00 – 1634.35 = $4865.65

    [05/01 to 07/01]:   182 – 121 = 61 days
    (4865.65)(.105)(61/360) = $86.57
    2350.00 – 86.57 = $2263.43
    4865.65 – 2263.43 = $2602.22

    Since the loan was for 180 days, the maturity
    date occurs in 180 – 61 – 61 = 58 days
    (2602.22)(.105)(58/360) = $44.02
    2602.22 + 44.02 = $2646.24

50. [10/15 to 11/15]:   319 – 288 = 31 days
    (5000)(.14)(31/360) = $60.28
    800.00 – 60.28 = $739.72
    5000.00 – 739.72 = $4260.28

    [11/15 to 12/15]:   349 – 319 = 30 days
    (4260.28)(.14)(30/360) = $49.70
    800.00 – 49.70 = $750.30
    4260.28 – 750.30 = $3509.98

    [12/15 to 01/01]:   (365 – 349) + 1 = 16 days
    (3509.98)(.14)(16/360) = $21.84
    3509.98 + 21.84 = $3531.82

52. [07/12 to 10/10]:   283 – 193 = 90 days
    (21000)(.04375)(90/360) = $229.69
    8000.00 – 229.69 = $7770.31
    21000.00 – 7770.31 = $13229.69

    [10/10 to 12/08]:   342 – 283 = 59 days
    (13229.69)(.04375)(59/360) = $94.86
    6000.00 – 94.86 = $5905.14
    13229.69 – 5905.14 = $7324.55

    [12/08 to 01/30]:   (365 – 342) + 30 = 53 days
    (7324.55)(.04375)(53/360) = $47.18
    7324.55 + 47.18 = $7371.73

54. [05/15 to 06/15]:   166 – 135 = 31 days
    (3000)(.11)(31/360) = $28.42
    875.00 – 28.42 = $846.58
    3000.00 – 846.58 = $2153.42

    [06/15 to 08/01]:   213 – 166 = 47 days
    (2153.42)(.11)(47/360) = $30.93
    940.00 – 30.93 = $909.07
    2153.42 – 909.07 = $1244.35

    [08/01 to 09/01]:   244 – 2135 = 31 days
    (1244.35)(.11)(31/360) = $11.79
    1244.35 + 11.79 = $1256.14

55. a) May 5 is day 125 $125 + 182 = 307$
   day 307 is Nov. 3
   b) i = $(1000)(0.0434)(182/360) = \$21.94$
   Amt. paid = $1000 - 21.94 = \$978.06$
   c) interest = $\$21.94$
   d) $r = \dfrac{i}{pt} = \dfrac{21.94}{978.06\left(\frac{182}{360}\right)} = 0.0444$ or 4.44%

56. a) Aug. 31 is day 243 $243 + 364 = 607$
   $(607 - 1) - 365 = 241$ day 241 is Aug. 29
   b) i = $(6000)(0.044)(364/360) = \$266.93$
   Amt. paid = $6000 - 266.93 = \$5,733.07$
   c) interest = $\$266.93$
   d) $r = \dfrac{266.93}{5733.07\left(\frac{364}{360}\right)} = 0.0460$ or 4.6%

57. a) Amt. received = $743.21 - 39.95 = \$703.26$
   $i = prt$
   $39.95 = (703.26)(r)(5/360)$
   $39.95 = (9.7675)(r)$
   $r = 39.95/9.7675 = 4.09$ or 409%
   b) $39.95 = (703.26)(r)10/360$
   $39.95 = (19.535)(r)$
   $r = 39.95/19.535 = 2.045$ or 204.5%
   c) $39.95 = (703.26)(r)(20/360)$
   $39.95 = (39.07)r$
   $r = 39.95/39.07 = 1.023$ or 102.3%

58. a) $(600)(.0675)(30/360) = 3.38$
   $200.00 + 3.38 = \$203.38$

   $(400)(.07)(30/360) = 2.33$
   $200.00 + 2.33 = \$202.33$

   $(200)(.0725)(30/360) = 1.21$
   $200.00 + 1.21 = \$201.21$

   b) $3.38 + 2.33 + 1.21 = \$6.92 =$ total interest

59. a) $\dfrac{93337}{100000} = 0.93337$
   $1.00000 - 0.93337 = .06663$ or 6.663 %
   b) $\dfrac{100000}{93337} = 1.071386$
   $1.071386 - 1.000000 = .071386$ or 7.139 %
   c) $100000 - 93337 = \$6663.00$
   d) $(6663)(.05)(1) = 33.15$
   $6663.00 + 33.15 = \$6696.15$

60. a) [08/03/1492 to 12/01/1620]
   1492 to 1620 = 127 years = 45720 days
   08/03 to 12/31 = $365 - 215 = 150$ days
   01/01 to 12/01 = 335 days
   $45720 + 150 + 335 = 46205$ days
   $(1)(.05)(46205/360) = 6.417361 = \$6.42$
   b) [07/04/1776 to 08/03/1492]
   284 yrs. minus 30 days = 102,210
   $(1)(.05)(102,210/360) = 14.1958 = \$14.20$
   c) [08/03/1492 to 12/07/1941]
   449 yrs plus 126 days = 161,766 days
   $(1)(.05)(161,766/360) = \$22.47$
   d) Answers will vary.

Exercise Set 11.3

1. An investment is the use of money or capital for income or profit.
2. With a fixed investment the amount invested as principal is guaranteed and interest is computed at a fixed rate.
3. For a variable investment neither the principal nor the interest is guaranteed.
4. Interest that is computed on the principal and any accumulated interest is called compound interest.
5. The effective annual yield on an investment is the simple interest rate that gives the same amount of interest as a compound rate over the same period of time.
6. The principal that would have to be invested today to have a fixed amount of money in the future.
7. $n = 1$, $r = 0.04$, $t = 5$, $p = 1000$
   a) $A = 1000\left(1 + \dfrac{0.04}{1}\right)^{(1)(5)} = \$1216.65$
   b) $i = 1216.56 - 1000 = \$216.65$

8. $n = 2$, $r = 0.05$, $t = 2$, $p = 3000$
   a) $A = 3000\left(1 + \dfrac{0.05}{1}\right)^{(2)(2)} = \$3311.44$
   b) $i = 3311.44 - 3000 = \$311.44$

9. $n = 4$, $r = 0.03$, $t = 4$, $p = 2000$

   a) $A = 2000\left(1 + \dfrac{0.03}{4}\right)^{(4)(4)} = \$2253.98$

   b) $i = 2253.98 - 2000 = \$253.98$

10. $n = 4$, $r = 0.07$, $t = 3$, $p = 5000$

   a) $A = 5000\left(1 + \dfrac{0.07}{4}\right)^{(4)(3)} = \$6157.20$

   b) $i = 6157.20 - 5000 = \$1157.20$

11. $n = 12$, $r = 0.055$, $t = 3$, $p = 7000$

   a) $A = 7000\left(1 + \dfrac{0.055}{1}\right)^{(12)(3)} = \$8252.64$

   b) $i = 8252.64 - 7000 = \$1252.64$

12. $n = 2$, $r = 0.06$, $t = 2$, $p = 4000$

   a) $A = 4000\left(1 + \dfrac{0.06}{2}\right)^{(2)(2)} = \$4502.04$

   b) $i = 4502.04 - 4000 = \$502.04$

13. $n = 360$, $r = 0.04$, $t = 2$, $p = 8000$

   a) $A = 8000\left(1 + \dfrac{0.04}{360}\right)^{(360)(2)} = \$8666.26$

   b) $i = 8666.26 - 8000 = \$666.26$

14. $n = 12$, $r = 0.045$, $t = 5$, $p = 8500$

   a) $A = 8500\left(1 + \dfrac{0.045}{12}\right)^{(12)(5)} = \$10,640.26$

   b) $i = 10,640.26 - 8500 = \$2140.26$

15. $n = 1$, $r = 0.05$, $t = 10$, $A = 50,000$

   $p = \dfrac{50,000}{\left(1 + \dfrac{0.05}{1}\right)^{(1)(10)}} = \$30,695.66$

16. $n = 2$, $r = 0.04$, $t = 5$, $A = 75,000$

   $p = \dfrac{50,000}{\left(1 + \dfrac{0.04}{2}\right)^{(2)(5)}} = \$61,526.12$

17. $n = 4$, $r = 0.04$, $t = 4$, $A = 100,000$

   $p = \dfrac{100,000}{\left(1 + \dfrac{0.04}{4}\right)^{(4)(4)}} = \$85,282.13$

18. $n = 4$, $r = 0.12$, $t = 20$, $A = 25,000$

   $p = \dfrac{25,000}{\left(1 + \dfrac{0.12}{4}\right)^{(4)(20)}} = \$2349.43$

19. $A = 50,000\left(1 + \dfrac{0.04}{4}\right)^{(4)(2)} = \$54,142.84$

20. $A = 2500\left(1 + \dfrac{0.03}{12}\right)^{(12)(4)} = \$2818.32$

21. $A = 1500\left(1 + \dfrac{0.039}{12}\right)^{12 \bullet 2.5} = \$1653.36$

22. $p = 250,000 - 10,000 = 240,000$

   $A = 240,000\left(1 + \dfrac{0.015}{12}\right)^{12 \bullet 10} = \$278,814.10$

23. $p = 800 + 150 + 300 + 1000 = \$2250$

   $A = 2250\left(1 + \dfrac{0.02}{360}\right)^{360 \bullet 2} = \$2,341.82$

24. $A = 5000\left(1 + \dfrac{0.0335}{4}\right)^{4 \bullet 5} = \$5907.60$

25. a) $A = 2000\left(1 + \dfrac{0.05}{2}\right)^{2 \bullet 15} = \$4,195.14$

   b) $A = 2000\left(1 + \dfrac{0.05}{4}\right)^{2 \bullet 15} = \$4,214.36$

26. $A = 2000\left(1 + \dfrac{0.06}{2}\right)^{2 \cdot 10} = \$3612.22$ - 1st 10 yrs.

   $A = 3612.22\left(1 + \dfrac{0.06}{4}\right)^{4 \cdot 8} = \$5,816.85$ - 18 yrs.

27. $A = 3000\left(1 + \dfrac{0.0175}{4}\right)^{4 \bullet 2} = \$3106.62$

28. $A = 6000\left(1 + \dfrac{0.0525}{12}\right)^{24} = \$6,662.74$

   $i = \$6662.74 - \$6000 = \$662.74$

29. $A = 6000\left(1 + \dfrac{0.08}{4}\right)^{12} = \$7,609.45$

30. Let $p = \$1.00$. Then

   $A = 1\left(1 + \dfrac{0.056}{360}\right)^{360} = \$1.0576$

   $i = 1.0576 - 1.00 = 0.0576$

   The effective annual yield is 5.76%

31. $A = 1\left(1+\dfrac{0.035}{12}\right)^{12\bullet1} \approx 1.0356$

    $i = A-1 = 1.0356 - 1 = 0.0356$

    APY = 3.56%

32. $A = 1\left(1+\dfrac{0.0475}{12}\right)^{12\bullet1} \approx 1.0485$

    $i = A-1 = 1.0485 - 1 = 0.0485$

    APY = 4.85%

33. $A = 1\left(1+\dfrac{0.024}{12}\right)^{12\bullet1} \approx 1.0243$

    $i = A-1 = 1.0243 - 1 = 0.0243$

    Yes, APY = 2.43 %, not 2.6 %

34. $A = 1\left(1+\dfrac{0.045}{12}\right)^{4\bullet1} \approx 1.0458$

    $i = A-1 = 1.0458 - 1 = 0.0458$

    Yes, APY = 4.58 %

35. The effective rate of the 4.75% account is:

    $A = 1\left(1+\dfrac{0.0475}{12}\right)^{12} \approx 1.0485$

    APY = 1.0485 − 1.00 = 0.0485 or 4.85%

    Therefore the 5% simple interest account pays
    more interest.

36. The amount Tom owes the bank after two years is:

    $A = 1500\left(1+\dfrac{0.10}{4}\right)^{4\bullet2} = \$1{,}827.60$

    Bank's interest charge:

    $i = 1827.60 - 1500 = \$327.60$

    Grandfather's interest charge:

    $i = prt = (1500)(0.07)(2) = \$210.00$

    Tom will save 327.60 − 210.00 = $117.60

37. a) $925{,}000 - 370{,}000 = \$555{,}000$

    b) $\dfrac{555{,}000}{\left(1+\dfrac{0.075}{12}\right)^{(12)(30)}} = \$58{,}907.60$

    c) surcharge $= \dfrac{58{,}907.60}{598} = \$98.518$

38. a) $\dfrac{1{,}750{,}000}{\left(1+\dfrac{0.09}{360}\right)^{(360)(20)}} = \$289{,}338.14$

    b) $\dfrac{289{,}338.14 - 100{,}000}{2753} = \$68.78$

39. Present value $= \dfrac{275{,}000}{\left(1+\dfrac{0.0515}{12}\right)^{(12)(5)}} = \$212{,}687.10$

40. Present value $= \dfrac{200{,}000}{\left(1+\dfrac{0.075}{4}\right)^{80}} = \$45{,}250.17$

41. Present value $= \dfrac{50{,}000}{\left(1+\dfrac{0.08}{4}\right)^{72}} = \$12{,}015.94$

42. Present value $= \dfrac{20{,}000}{\left(1+\dfrac{0.07}{4}\right)^{60}} = \$7{,}062.61$

43. a) $A = 1000\left(1+\dfrac{0.02}{2}\right)^{4} = \$1{,}040.60$

    $i = \$1040.60 - \$1000 = \$40.60$

    b) $A = 1000\left(1+\dfrac{0.04}{2}\right)^{4} = \$1{,}082.43$

    $i = \$1082.43 - \$1000 = \$82.43$

    c) $A = 1000\left(1+\dfrac{0.08}{2}\right)^{4} = \$1{,}169.86$

    $i = \$1169.86 - \$1000 = \$169.86$

    d) No predictable outcome.

44. a) $A = 100\left(1+\dfrac{0.12}{12}\right)^{24} = \$126.97$

    $i = \$126.97 - \$100 = \$26.97$

    b) $A = 200\left(1+\dfrac{0.12}{12}\right)^{24} = \$253.95$

    $i = \$253.95 - \$200 = \$53.95$

    c) $A = 400\left(1+\dfrac{0.12}{12}\right)^{24} = \$507.89$

    $i = \$507.89 - \$400 = \$107.89$

    d) The interest doubles also.

45. $p = 1.35$, $r = 0.025$, $t = 5$, $n = 1$

  $A = 1.35(1 + 0.025)^5 = \$1.53$

46. $p = 2000$, $A = 3586.58$, $n = 12$, $t = 5$

  $$3586.58 = 2000\left(1+\frac{r}{12}\right)^{60}$$

  $$\frac{3586.58}{2000} = \left(1+\frac{r}{12}\right)^{60}$$

  $$(1.79329)^{1/60} = 1 + \frac{r}{12} = 1.00978$$

  $$0.00978 = \frac{r}{12} \quad r = 0.00978(12) = .117 \text{ or } 11.7\%$$

47. a) $72/3 = 24$ years   b) $72/6 = 12$ years

  c) $72/8 = 9$ years   d) $72/12 = 6$ years

  e) $72/r = 22$ $72 = 22r$ $r = 72/22 = 0.0327$

    $r = 3.27\%$

48. $A = 2000\,[1 + (.08/2)]^6 = 2000\,(1.04)^6 = \$2530.64$

  $i = \$2530.64 - 2000 = \$530.64$

  Simple interest: $i = prt = 530.64 = 2000(r)(3)$

  $530.64 = 6000r \quad r = \dfrac{530.64}{6000} = 0.0884 \text{ or } 8.84\ \%$

49. $i = prt = (100{,}000)(0.05)(4) = \$20{,}000$

  $$A = 100{,}000\left(1+\frac{0.05}{360}\right)^{360\cdot 4} = \$122{,}138.58$$

  interest earned: $\$122{,}138.58 - 100{,}000 = \$22{,}138.58$

  Select investing at the compounded daily interest because the compound interest is greater by $2,138.58.

Exercise Set 11.4

1. An open-end installment loan is a loan on which you can make different payment amounts each month. A fixed installment loan is one in which you pay a fixed amount each month for a set number of months.

2. With an installment plan, the borrower repays the principal plus the interest with weekly or monthly payments that usually begin shortly after the loan is made. With a personal note, the borrower repays the principal plus the interest as a single payment at the end of the specified time period.

3. The APR is the true rate of interest charged on a loan.

4. The finance charge is the total amount of money the borrower must pay for the use of the money borrowed.

5. The total installment price is the sum of all the monthly payments and the down payment, if any.

6. a) Unearned interest is the interest saved by paying off a loan early.

  b) The actuarial method.

7. The unpaid balance method and the average daily balance method.

8. A cash advance is a loan obtained through a credit card.

9. a) Amount financed = $10{,}000 - 0.15(10{,}000) = \$8500.00$

    From Table 11.2 the finance charge per $100 at 7.5 % for 60 payments is 20.23.

    Total finance charge = $(20.23)\left(\dfrac{8500}{100}\right) = \$1719.55$

  b) Total amount due after down payment = $8500.00 + 1719.55 = \$10{,}219.55$

    Monthly payment = $\dfrac{10{,}219.55}{60} = \$170.33$

10. a) Amount financed = $7000 - 0.20(7000) = \$5600.00$

    From Table 11.2, the finance charge per $100 financed at 5% for 36 months is 7.90.

    Total finance charge = $(7.90)\left(\dfrac{5600}{100}\right) = \$442.40$

  b) Total amount due after down payment = $5600.00 + 442.40 = \$6042.40$

    Monthly payment = $\dfrac{6042.40}{36} = \$167.84$

11. a) Amount financed = 9900 – 0.10(9900) = $8910

From Table 11.2, the finance charge per $100 financed at 9.5% for 48 months is $20.59.

Total finance charge is $(20.59)\left(\dfrac{8910}{100}\right) = \$1834.57$

b) Total amount due = 8910 + 1834.57 = $10,744.57

Monthly payment = $\dfrac{10,744.57}{48} = \$223.85$

12. a) From Table 11.2, the finance charge per $100 financed at 8% for 60 months is $21.66.

Total finance charge = $(21.66)\left(\dfrac{25,000}{100}\right) = \$5415.00$

b) Total amount due = 25,000 + 5415.00 = $30,415.00

Monthly payment = $\dfrac{30,415.00}{60} = \$506.92$

13. a) Down payment = 0.20(3200) = $640; Cheryl borrowed 3200 – 640 = $2560

Total installment price = (60 • 53.14) = $3188.40

Finance charge = 3188.40 – 2560 = $628.40

b) $\left(\dfrac{\text{finance charge}}{\text{amt. financed}}\right)(100) = \left(\dfrac{628.40}{2560}\right)(100) = 24.55$

From Table 11.2 for 60 payments, the value of 24.55 corresponds with an APR of 9.0 %.

14. a) Down payment = (0.05)(1495) = $74.75; Ilga financed $1495 – 74.75 = $1420.25

Total installment price = (64)(24) = $1536.00

Finance charge = 1536.00 – 1420.25 = $115.75

b) $\left(\dfrac{\text{finance charge}}{\text{amt. financed}}\right)(100) = \left(\dfrac{115.75}{1420.25}\right)(100) = 8.15$

From Table 11.2, for 24 payments, the value of $8.15 is closest to $8.00 which corresponds with an APR of 7.5 %.

15. a) Total installment price = (224)(48) = $10752.00

Finance charge = 10752.00 – 9000.00 = $1752.00

b) $\left(\dfrac{\text{finance charge}}{\text{amt. financed}}\right)(100) = \left(\dfrac{1752.00}{9000}\right)(100) = 19.47$

From Table 11.2, for 48 payments, the value of $19.47 is closest to $19.45 which corresponds with an APR of 9.0 %.

16. Down payment = (0.25)(3450) = $862.50   Amount financed = 3450 – 862.50 = $2587.50

a) Installment price = (6)(437) = 2622

Finance charge = $2622.00 – $2587.50 = $34.50

b) $\left(\dfrac{\text{finance charge}}{\text{amt. financed}}\right)(100) = \left(\dfrac{34.50}{2587.50}\right)(100) = 1.33$

From Table 11.2, for 6 payments, the value of $1.33 is closest to $1.32 which corresponds with an APR of 4.5 %.

17. Down payment = $0.00   Amount financed = $12,000.00   Monthly payments = $232.00
   a) Installment price = (60)(232) = 13,920
       Finance charge = $13,920.00 – $12,000.00 = $1920.00

   $$\left(\frac{\text{finance charge}}{\text{amt. financed}}\right)(100) = \left(\frac{1920.00}{12000}\right)(100) = 16.00$$

   From Table 11.2, for 6 payments, the value of $16.00 corresponds to an APR of 6.0 %.
   b) From Table 11.2, the monthly payment per $100 for the remaining 36 months at 6.0% APR is $9.52.

   $$u = \frac{nPV}{100+V} = \frac{(36)(232)(9.52)}{(100+9.52)} = \frac{79511.04}{109.52} = 725.9956 = \$726.00$$

   c) (232)(23) = 5336;   5336 + 726 = 6062;   13920 – 6062 = $7858.00

18. (83.81)(48) = 4022.88   4022.88 – 3500.00 = 522.88
   a) $\left(\dfrac{522.88}{3500}\right)(100) = \$14.94$ per $100   From Table 11.2, $14.94 corresponds to an APR of 7 %.

   b) From Table 11.2, the monthly payment per $100 for the remaining 30 months at 7% APR is $9.30.

   $$u = \frac{nPV}{100+V} = \frac{(30)(83.81)(9.30)}{(100+9.30)} = \$213.93$$

   c) (83.81)(17) = 1424.77;   1424.77 + 213.93 = 1638.70;   4022.88 – 1638.70 = $2384.18

19. a) Amount financed = 32000 – 10000 = $22000
       From Table 11.2, the finance charge per 100 financed at 8 % for 36 payments is 12.81.

   $$\text{Total finance charge} = (12.81)\left(\frac{22000}{100}\right) = 2818.20$$

   b) Total amt. due = 22000 + 2818.20 = $24,818.20

   $$\text{Monthly payment} = \frac{24818.20}{36} = \$689.39$$

   c) From Table 11.2, the monthly payment per $100 for the remaining 12 months at 8.0% APR is $4.39.

   $$u = \frac{nPV}{100+V} = \frac{(12)(689.89)(4.39)}{100+4.39} = \frac{36317.07}{104.39} = \$347.90$$

   d) (23)(689.39) = 15855.97;   15855.97 – 347.90 = 16203.87;   24818.20 – 16203.87 = $8614.17

20. a) Amount financed = $1150;   finance charges = (24)(50.71) – 1150 = $67.04

   $$\left(\frac{67.04}{1150}\right)(100) = 5.83$$

   From Table 11.2, the interest rate that would generate a finance charge of $5.83 is 5.5 % for 24 payments.
   b) From Table 11.2, the monthly payment per $100 for the remaining 12 months at 5.5% APR is $3.00.

   $$u = \frac{(50.71)(12)(3.00)}{100+3.00} = \$17.72$$

   c) Total for all payments: (24)(50.71) = $1217.04

       (11)(50.71) = 557.81;   557.81 + 17.72 = 575.53;   1217.04 – 575.53 = $641.51

21. a) $(0.01)(2600) = \$26$

    b) Principal on which interest is paid during April:

    $2600 - 500 = \$2100$

    Interest for April:

    $(2100)(0.00039698)(30) = \$25.01$

    1% of outstanding principal:

    $(0.01)(2100) = \$21.00$

    Minimum monthly payment:

    $25.01 + 21.00 = 46.01$ which rounds up to \$47.

22. a) $(0.02)(3200) = \$64$

    b) Principal on which interest is paid during October:

    $3200 - 1200 = \$2000$

    Interest for October:

    $(2000)(0.0004238)(31) = \$26.28$

    2% of outstanding principal:

    $(0.02)(2000) = \$40.00$

    Minimum monthly payment:

    $26.28 + 40.00 = 66.28$ which rounds up to \$67.

23. a) Total charges: $677 + 452 + 139 + 141 = \$1409$

    $(0.015)(1409) = \$21.14$ which rounds up to \$22

    b) Principal on which interest is paid during December:

    $1409 - 300 = \$1109$

    Interest for December:

    $(1109)(0.0005163)(31) = \$17.75$

    1.5% of outstanding principal:

    $(0.015)(1109) = \$16.64$

    Minimum monthly payment:

    $17.75 + 16.64 = 34.39$ which rounds up to \$35.

24. a) Total charges: $359 + 273 + 653 + 315 + 225 = \$1825$

    $(0.025)(1825) = \$45.63$ which rounds up to \$46

    b) Principal on which interest is paid during September:

    $1825 - 750 = \$1075$

    Interest for September:

    $(1075)(0.0003164)(30) = \$10.20$

    2.5% of outstanding principal:

    $(0.025)(1075) = \$26.88$

    Minimum monthly payment:

    $10.20 + 26.88 = 37.08$ which rounds up to \$38.

25. a) Finance charge = (1097.86)(0.018)(1) = $19.76

    b) Bal. due May 5 = (1097.86 + 19.76 + 425.79) – 800 = $743.41

26. a) Finance charge = (567.20)(0.011)(1) = $6.24

    b) old balance + finance charge – payment + airline ticket + hotel bill + clothing = new balance

    567.20 + 6.24 – 275.00 + 330.00 + 190.80 + 84.75 = $903.99

27. a) Finance charge = (124.78)(0.0125)(1) = $1.56

    b) old balance + finance charge – payment + art supplies + flowers + music CD = new balance

    124.78 + 1.56 – 100.00 + 25.64 + 67.23 + 13.90 = $133.11

28. a) Finance charge = (57.88)(0.0135)(1) = $0.78

    b) old balance + finance charge – payment + paint + curtains + chair = new balance

    57.88 + 0.78 – 45.00 + 64.75 + 72.85 + 135.50 = $286.76

29. a)

Date	Balance Due	Number of Days	(Balance)(Days)
May 12	$378.50	1	(378.50)(1) = $ 378.50
May 13	$508.29	2	(508.29)(2) = 1,016.58
May 15	$458.29	17	(458.29)(17) = 7,790.93
June 01	$594.14	7	(594.14)(7) = 4,158.98
June 08	$631.77	4	(631.77)(4) = 2,527.08
		31	sum = $15,872.07

Average daily balance = $\dfrac{15872.07}{31}$ =

$512

b) Finance charge = prt =

   (512.00)(0.013)(1) = $6.66

c) Balance due = 631.77 + 6.66 = $638.43

30. a)

Date	Balance Due	Number of Days	(Balance)(Days)
Mar. 23	$1,578.25	3	(1578.25)(3) = $4,734.75
Mar. 26	$1,658.23	4	(1658.23)(4) = 6,632.92
Mar. 30	$1,710.99	4	(1710.99)(4) = 6,843.96
Apr. 03	$1,460.99	12	(1460.99)(12) = 17,531.88
Apr. 15	$1,651.51	7	(1651.51)(7) = 11,560.57
Apr. 22	$1,842.36	1	(1842.36)(1) = 1,842.36
		31	sum = $49,146.44

Average daily balance = $\dfrac{49146.44}{31}$ =

$1585.37

b) Finance charge = prt =

   (1585.37)(0.013)(1) = $20.61

c) Balance due = 1842.36 + 20.61 = $1,862.97

31. a)

Date	Balance Due	Number of Days	(Balance)(Days)
Feb. 03	$124.78	5	(124.78)(5) = $623.90
Feb. 08	$150.42	4	(150.42)(4) = 601.68
Feb. 12	$ 50.42	2	(50.42)(2) = 100.84
Feb. 14	$117.65	11	(117.65)(11) = 1294.15
Feb. 25	$131.55	6	(131.55)(6) = 789.30
Mar 3		28	sum = $3,409.87

Average daily balance = $\dfrac{3409.87}{28}$ =

$121.78

b) Finance charge = prt =

   (121.78)(0.0125)(1) = $1.52

c) Balance due = 131.55 + 1.52 = $133.07

d) The finance charge using the avg. daily balance method is $0.04 less than the finance charge using the unpaid balance method.

32. a)

Date	Balance Due	Number of Days	(Balance)(Days)
Sept. 05	$567.20	3	(567.20)(3) = $1701.60
Sept. 08	$292.20	13	(292.20)(13) = $3798.60
Sept. 21	$622.20	6	(622.20)(6) = $3733.20
Sept. 27	$813.00	5	(813.00)(5) = $4065.00
Oct. 02	$897.75	3	(897.75)(3) = $2693.25
Oct. 05		30	sum = $15,991.65

Average daily balance $= \dfrac{15,991.65}{30} =$ $533.06

b) Finance charge = prt =
   (533.06)(0.011)(1) = $5.86

c) Balance due = 897.75 + 5.86 = $903.61

d) The finance charge using the avg. daily balance method is $0.38 less than the finance charge using the unpaid balance method.

33. a) i = (875)(0.0004273)(32) = $11.96   b) A = 875 + 11.96 = $886.96

34. 0.05477 % per day = 0.0005477   a) (600)(0.0005477)(27) = $8.87   b) 600.00 + 8.87 = $608.87

35. $1000.00   5 %   6 payments
   a) State National Bank (SNB): (1000)(.05)(.5) = $25.00
   b) Consumers Credit Union (CCU): (1000)(x)(1) = 35.60   (86.30)(12) = 1035.60
      1035.60 – 1000.00 = $35.60
   c) $\left(\dfrac{25}{1000}\right)(100) = 2.50$ In Table 11.2, $2.49 is the closest value to $2.50, which corresponds to an

      APR of 8.5 %.
   d) $\left(\dfrac{35.60}{1000}\right)(100) = 3.56$ In Table 11.2, $3.56 corresponds to an APR of 6.5 %.

36. The interest on $890 at 5.25% annually for 1 month is: i = (890)(0.0525)(1/12) = $3.89
   She will be saving $3.89 by using her credit card.

37. Let p = amount Ken borrowed
       p + 2500 = purchase price
   Installment price: 2500 + (379.50)(36) = $16,162
   Interest = Installment price – purchase price
   i = 16,162 – (p + 2500) = 16,162 – p – 2500 = 13,662 – p

   Since i = prt we have:
   13,662 – p = (p)(.06)(3) = 13,662 – p = .18p
   13,662 = .18p + p   p = 11,577.97
   purchase price = 11,577.97 + 2500 = $14,077.97

38. a) Amount financed = 3450 – 862.50 = $2587.50

Month	Finance charge	Payment	Balance
1	None	$432.00	$2155.50
2	(2155.50)(0.013) = $28.02	460.02	1723.50
3	(1723.50)(0.013) = $22.41	454.41	1291.50
4	(1291.50)(0.013) = $16.79	448.79	859.50
5	(859.50)(0.013) = $11.17	443.17	427.50
6	(427.50)(0.013) = $ 5.56	433.06	0.00

a) It will take 6 months to repay the loan.

b) The total amount of interest paid is $83.95

c) The installment loan saves them
   83.95 – 34.50 = $49.45

39. $35,000   15 % down payment   60 month fixed loan   APR = 8.5 %

   $(35000)(.15) = 5250$ $35000 - 5250 = 29750$

   a) From Table 11.2, 60 payments at an APR of 8.5 % yields a finance charge of $23.10 per $100.

   $$\left(\frac{29750}{100}\right)(23.10) = \$6872.25$$

   b) $29750.00 + 6872.25 = 36622.25$ $\dfrac{36622.25}{60} = \$610.37$

   c) In Table 11.2, 36 payments at an APR of 8.5 % yields a finance charge of $13.64 per $100.

   $$u = \frac{(36)(610.37)(13.64)}{100+13.64} = \frac{299716.08}{113.64} = \$2637.42$$

   d) $u = \dfrac{f \cdot k(k+1)}{n(n+1)} = \dfrac{(6872.25)(36)(37)}{60(61)} = \dfrac{9153837}{3660} = \$2501.05$

40. $23,000   10 % down payment   48 month fixed loan   APR = 6.0 %

   $(23000)(.10) = 2300$ $23000 - 2300 = 20700$

   a) From Table 11.2, 48 payments at an APR of 6.0 % yields a finance charge of $12.73 per $100.

   $$\left(\frac{20700}{100}\right)(12.73) = \$2635.11$$

   b) $20700.00 + 2635.11 = 23335.11$ $\dfrac{23335.11}{48} = \$486.15$

   c) In Table 11.2, 36 payments at an APR of 6.0 % yields a finance charge of $9.52 per $100.

   $$u = \frac{(36)(486.15)(9.52)}{100+9.52} = \frac{166613.33}{109.52} = \$1521.31$$

   d) $u = \dfrac{f \cdot k(k+1)}{n(n+1)} = \dfrac{(2635.11)(36)(37)}{48(49)} = \dfrac{3509966.52}{2352} = \$1492.33$

41. $m = \dfrac{4500\left(\dfrac{0.07}{12}\right)}{1-\left(1+\dfrac{0.07}{12}\right)^{-(12)(2)}} = \$201.48$

Exercise Set 11.5

1. A mortgage is a long-term loan in which the property is pledged as security for payment of the difference between the down payment and the sale price.
2. The down payment is the amount of cash the buyer must pay the seller before the lending institution will grant the buyer a mortgage.
3. The major difference between these two types of loans is that the interest rate for a conventional loan is fixed for the duration of the loan, whereas the interest rate for a variable-rate loan may change every period, as specified in the loan agreement.
4. a) A point is 1% of the mortgage.   b) For x points multiply the mortgage by 0.01x.
5. A buyer's adjusted monthly income is found by subtracting any fixed monthly payment with more than 10 months remaining from the gross monthly income.
6. An add on rate, or margin, is the percent added to the interest rate on which the adjustable rate mortgage is based.

7. An amortization schedule is a list of the payment number, interest, principal, and balance remaining on the loan.

8. The FHA insures the loan and a bank provides the money for the loan.

9. Equity is the difference between the appraised value of your home and the loan balance.

10. A home equity loan is a loan in which the equity in your home is used as collateral.

11. a) Down payment = 20% of $350,000
$(0.20)(350000) = \$70,000$

   b) amt. of mortgage = 350000 – 70,000 = 28,000
Table 11.4 yields $8.71 per $1000 of mortgage

    Monthly payment = $\left(\dfrac{28,000}{1000}\right)(8.71)$
                 $= \$2438.80$

12. a) Down payment = 10% of $289,000
$(0.10)(289000) = \$28,900$

   b) amt. of mortgage = 289,000 – 28,900 = 260,100
Table 11.4 yields $7.34 per $1000 of mortgage

    Monthly payment = $\left(\dfrac{260,100}{1000}\right)(7.34)$
                 $= \$1909.13$

13. a) Down payment = 15% of $1,750,000
$(0.15)(1750000) = \$262,500$

   b) amt. of mortgage =
1750000 – 262500 = 1487500
Table 11.4 yields $6.44 per $1000 of mortgage

    Monthly payment = $\left(\dfrac{1,487,500}{1000}\right)(6.44)$
                 $= \$9579.50$

14. a) Down payment = 3% of $275,000
$(0.03)(275000) = \$8250$

   b) amt. of mortgage = 275000 – 8250 = 266750
Table 11.4 yields $6.99 per $1000 of mortgage

    Monthly payment = $\left(\dfrac{266750}{1000}\right)(6.99)$
                 $= \$1864.58$

15. a) Down payment = 20% of $195,000
$(0.20)(195000) = \$39,000$

   b) amt. of mortgage = 195,000 – 39000 = $156,000

   c) $(156000)(.02) = \$3120.00$

16. a) 245000 – 45000 = $200,000.00

   b) $(200000)(.015) = \$3000.00$

17. $3200 = monthly income
3200 – 335 = 2865 = adjusted income

   a) $(0.28)(2865) = \$802.20$

   b) Table 11.4 yields $7.91 per $1000 of mortgage

    $\left(\dfrac{150000}{1000}\right)(7.91) = \$1186.50$

    1186.50 + 225.00 = $1411.50

   c) No; $1411.50 > $802.20

18. $4,100 = monthly income
4100 – 505 = $3595.00 = adjusted income

   a) $(3595)(.28) = \$1006.60$

   b) Table 11.4 yields $9.00 per $1000 of mortgage

    $\left(\dfrac{275000}{1000}\right)(9.00) = \$2475.00$

    2475 + 425 = $2900.00

   c) No; $2900.00 > $1006.60

19. a) $(490.24)(30)(12) = \$176,486.40$
176486.40 + 11250.00 = $187,736.40

   b) 187736.40 – 75000 = $112,736.40

   c) i = prt = $(63750)(.085)(1/12) = 451.56$
490.24 – 451.56 = $38.68

20. a) Down payment = 160,000 – 110,000 = $50,000
Total cost of house
= 50000 + (1038.40)(12)(25) + (0.02)(110000)
= $363,720

   b) interest and points
= $363,720 – $160,000 = $203,720

   c) interest on first payment   i = prt
$(110,000)(0.105)(1/12) = \$962.50$
amount applied to principal =
1038.40 – 962.50 = $75.90

21. a) down payment = $(0.15)(113500) = \$17,025$

    b) amount of loan = $113500 - 17025$

    b) amount of mortgage = $113500 - 17,025$
    $$= \$96,475$$

    cost of three points = $(0.03)(96475) = \$2894.25$

    c) $4750 - 420 = \$4330.00$ adjusted monthly income
    $(0.28)(4330.00) = \$1212.40 = 28\%$ of adjusted income

    d) At a rate of 10% for 20 years, Table 11.4 yields 9.66.
    $$\text{mortgage payment} = \left(\frac{96475}{1000}\right)(9.66) = \$931.95$$

    e) Insurance + taxes = $\dfrac{1200 + 320}{12} = \$126.67$ /mo.
    $931.95 + 126.67 = \$1058.62$ total mo. payment

    f) Since \$1,212.40 is greater than \$1058.62, the Rosens qualify.

    g) interest on first payment = i = prt =
    $(96475)(0.10)(1/12) = \$803.96$
    amount applied to principal = $931.95 - 803.96 = \$127.99$

22. Cost of house = \$95,000.00

    a) $(95000)(.20) = \$19,000.00$

    b) $4000 - 135 = \$3865 \qquad (3865)(.28) = \$1082.20$

    c) Table 11.4 yields \$8.74 per \$1000 of mortgage
    $$\left(\frac{76000}{1000}\right)(8.74) = \$664.24$$

    d) Insurance + taxes = $\dfrac{1500 + 336}{12} = \$153$ /mo.
    $664.24 + 153 = \$817.24$

    e) Yes; $\$817.24 < \$1082.20$

    f) $i = prt = (76000)(.095)(1/12) = \$601.67$;
    $664.24 - 601.67 = \$62.57$

    g) $(664.24)(25)(12) = 199272$
    $199272 + 19000 = \$218,272.00$

    h) $218272 - 95000 = \$123,272.00$

23. Bank A   Down payment = $(0.10)(105000) = \$10,500$
    amount of mortgage $105000 - 10500 = \$94,500$
    At a rate of 10% for 30 years, Table 11.4 yields \$8.70 .
    monthly mortgage payment =
    $$\left(\frac{94500}{1000}\right)(8.70) = \$822.15$$
    cost of three points = $(0.03)(94500) = \$2835$
    Total cost of the house =
    $10500 + 2835 + (822.15)(12)(30) = \$309,309$

    Bank B   Down payment = $(0.20)(105000) = \$21,000$
    amount of mortgage $105000 - 21000 = \$84,000$
    At a rate of 11.5% for 25 years, Table 11.4 yields \$10.16.
    monthly mortgage payment =
    $$\left(\frac{84000}{1000}\right)(10.16) = \$853.44$$
    cost of the house = $21000 + (853.44)(12)(25) = \$277,032$

    The Riveras should select Bank B.

24. Condominium   \$525,000.00
    GCTCU   20% down payment, 7.5%, 15 years,
    $\qquad\qquad$ 1 point at closing
    SCCU   15% down payment, 8.5%, 20 years,
    $\qquad\qquad$ No points
    GCTU:
    Down payment: $(0.20)(525000) = 105000$
    Mortgage: $(0.80)(525000) = 420000$
    1 pt.: $(420000)(.01) = 4200$
    At 7.5% for 15 yrs., Table 11.4 yields \$9.27.
    $$(9.27)\left(\frac{420000}{1000}\right) = \$3893.40$$
    Total monthly payments:
    $\qquad (15)(12)(3893.40) = \$700,812$
    Total payments:
    $\qquad 105000.00 + 4200.00 + 700,812.00 = \$810,012$
    SCCU:
    Down payment: $(0.15)(525000) = 78750$
    Mortgage: $(0.85)(525000) = 446250$
    At 8.5% for 20 yrs., Table 11.4 yields \$8.68.
    $$(8.68)\left(\frac{446250}{1000}\right) = \$3873.45$$
    Total monthly payments:
    $\qquad (20)(12)(3873.45) = \$929,628.00$
    Total payments:
    $\qquad 929628 + 78750 = \$1,008,378.00$
    GCTU would provide a lower cost.

25. Down payment: $(0.20)(450000) = \$90,000$
   Amount of mortgage: $450000 - 90000 = \$360,000$
   1 point: $(0.01)(360000) = \$3600$

   a) Monthly payment: $(13.22)\left(\dfrac{360000}{1000}\right) = \$4759.20$

   Total payments: $90000 + 3600 + (10)(12)(4759.20) = \$664,704$

   b) Monthly payment: $(9.65)\left(\dfrac{360000}{1000}\right) = \$3474.00$

   Total payments: $90000 + 3600 + (20)(12)(3474.00) = \$927,360$

   c) Monthly payment: $(8.78)\left(\dfrac{360000}{1000}\right) = \$3160.80$

   Total payments: $90000 + 3600 + (30)(12)(3160.80) = \$1,231,488$

26. a) $m = \dfrac{200000\left(\dfrac{0.0675}{12}\right)}{1 - \left(1 + \dfrac{0.0675}{12}\right)^{-(12)(30)}} = \$1297.20$
       b) $m = \dfrac{200000\left(\dfrac{0.13}{52}\right)}{1 - \left(1 + \dfrac{0.13}{52}\right)^{-(52)(15)}} = \$583.17$

   c) $m = \dfrac{200000\left(\dfrac{0.09}{12}\right)}{1 - \left(1 + \dfrac{0.09}{12}\right)^{-(12)(40)}} = \$1542.72$
       d) $m = \dfrac{200000\left(\dfrac{0.039}{24}\right)}{1 - \left(1 + \dfrac{0.039}{24}\right)^{-(25)(50)}} = \$379.01$

27. a) Amount of mortgage $= 105000 - 5000 = \$100000$ Initial monthly payment $= \left(\dfrac{100000}{1000}\right)(8.05) = \$805.00$

   b)

Payment #	Interest	Principal	Balance
1	$750.00	$55.00	$99,945.00
2	749.59	55.41	99,889.59
3	749.17	55.83	99,833.76

   c) effective interest rate $= 6.13\% + 3.25\% = 9.38\%$.   The new rate is 9.38%.

   d)

Payment #	Interest	Principal	Balance
4	$780.37	$24.63	$99,809.13
5	780.17	24.83	99,784.30
6	779.98	25.02	99,759.28

   e) New rate $= 6.21\% + 3.25\% = 9.46\%$

28. a) amount of mortgage: $\$95000 - \$13000 = \$82,000$
   At a rate of 8.5% for 30 years, Table 11.4 yields $7.69.
   initial monthly payment =

   $\left(\dfrac{82000}{1000}\right)(7.69) = \$630.58$

   b) effective interest rate: $5.65 + 3.25 = 8.9\%$
   8.9% is less than 1% above the old rate of 8.5%.
   Thus, the new rate is 8.9%.

   c) effective new interest rate: $4.85 + 3.25 = 8.1$

29. a) The variable rate mortgage would be the cheapest.

   b) To find the payments for the variable rate mortgage, add the 6 monthly rates and multiply by 12, giving $52,336.80. The payments over 6 years for the fixed rate mortgage are 6 times 12 times 90 times the table value 8.41 for a 30-year mortgage at 9.5%. This yields $54,496.80. The variable rate saves $2160.

Exercise Set 11.6

1. An annuity is an account into which, or out of which, a sequence of scheduled payments is made.

2. A is the accumulated amount, p is the periodic payment, r is the interest rate, n is the number of payments per year, and t is the number of years over which payments are made.

3. a) An annuity into which payments are made at regular intervals, with interest compounded at the end of each interval and with a fixed interest rate for each compounding period, is called an ordinary annuity.

   b) A sinking fund is a type of annuity in which the goal is to save a specific amount of money in a specified amount of time.

4. A variable annuity is an annuity that is invested in stocks, bonds, mutual funds, or other investments that do not provide a guaranteed interest rate.

5. An immediate annuity is an annuity that is established with a lump sum of money for the purpose of providing the investor with regular, usually monthly, payments for the rest of the investor's life.

6. With a traditional IRA, the money invested is not subject to taxes; however, when money is withdrawn, it is subject to income taxes. With a Roth IRA, the investor has already paid taxes on the money invested and money withdrawn is not subject to income taxes.

7. With a 410k plan, the money invested is not subject to taxes; however, when money is withdrawn, it is subject to income taxes. With a Roth 401k plan, the investor has already paid taxes on the money invested, and money withdrawn is not subject to income taxes.

8. A 403b plan is a retirement plan similar to a 401k plan, but available only to employees of schools, civil governments, hospitals, charities, and other not-for-profit organizations.

9. $A = \dfrac{3000\left[\left(1+\dfrac{0.05}{1}\right)^{(1)(30)}-1\right]}{\dfrac{0.05}{1}} = \$199{,}316.54$

10. $A = \dfrac{800\left[\left(1+\dfrac{0.07}{2}\right)^{(2)(25)}-1\right]}{\dfrac{0.07}{2}} = \$104{,}798.33$

11. $A = \dfrac{400\left[\left(1+\dfrac{0.08}{4}\right)^{(4)(35)}-1\right]}{\dfrac{0.08}{4}} = \$299{,}929.32$

12. $A = \dfrac{200\left[\left(1+\dfrac{0.06}{12}\right)^{(12)(40)}-1\right]}{\dfrac{0.06}{12}} = \$398{,}298.15$

13. $p = \dfrac{20{,}000\left(\dfrac{0.04}{2}\right)}{\left(1+\dfrac{0.04}{2}\right)^{(2)(15)}-1} = \$493.00$

14. $p = \dfrac{35{,}000\left(\dfrac{0.05}{1}\right)}{\left(1+\dfrac{0.05}{1}\right)^{(1)(20)}-1} = \$1058.50$

15. $p = \dfrac{250{,}000\left(\dfrac{0.06}{12}\right)}{\left(1+\dfrac{0.06}{12}\right)^{(12)(35)}-1} = \$175.48$

16. $p = \dfrac{1{,}000{,}000\left(\dfrac{0.10}{4}\right)}{\left(1+\dfrac{0.10}{4}\right)^{(4)(40)}-1} = \$490.41$

17. $A = \dfrac{50\left[\left(1+\dfrac{0.03}{12}\right)^{(12)(35)}-1\right]}{\dfrac{0.03}{12}} = \$37{,}078.18$

18. $A = \dfrac{200\left[\left(1+\dfrac{0.05}{4}\right)^{(4)(20)}-1\right]}{\dfrac{0.05}{4}} = \$27{,}223.76$

19. $A = \dfrac{2000\left[\left(1+\dfrac{0.07}{2}\right)^{(2)(10)}-1\right]}{\dfrac{0.07}{2}} = \$56{,}559.36$

20. $A = \dfrac{500\left[\left(1+\dfrac{0.06}{12}\right)^{(12)(18)}-1\right]}{\dfrac{0.06}{12}} = \$193{,}676.60$

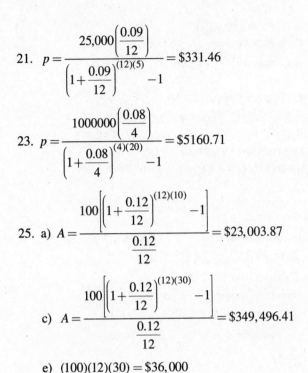

21. $p = \dfrac{25,000\left(\dfrac{0.09}{12}\right)}{\left(1+\dfrac{0.09}{12}\right)^{(12)(5)}-1} = \$331.46$

22. $p = \dfrac{500,000\left(\dfrac{0.06}{12}\right)}{\left(1+\dfrac{0.06}{12}\right)^{(12)(10)}-1} = \$3051.03$

23. $p = \dfrac{1000000\left(\dfrac{0.08}{4}\right)}{\left(1+\dfrac{0.08}{4}\right)^{(4)(20)}-1} = \$5160.71$

24. $p = \dfrac{25,000,000\left(\dfrac{0.075}{2}\right)}{\left(1+\dfrac{0.075}{2}\right)^{(2)(50)}-1} = \$24,223.66$

25. a) $A = \dfrac{100\left[\left(1+\dfrac{0.12}{12}\right)^{(12)(10)}-1\right]}{\dfrac{0.12}{12}} = \$23,003.87$

b) $A = 23,003.87\left(1+\dfrac{0.12}{12}\right)^{(12)(30)} = \$826,980.88$

c) $A = \dfrac{100\left[\left(1+\dfrac{0.12}{12}\right)^{(12)(30)}-1\right]}{\dfrac{0.12}{12}} = \$349,496.41$

d) $(100)(12)(10) = \$12,000$

e) $(100)(12)(30) = \$36,000$

f) Alberto

Review Exercises

1. $3/4 = 0.75 = 75.0\%$

2. $5/6 \approx 0.833 = 83.3\%$

3. $5/8 = 0.625 = 62.5\%$

4. $0.041 = 4.1\%$

5. $0.0098 = 0.98\% \approx 1.0\%$

6. $3.141 = 314.1\%$

7. 9% $\dfrac{9}{100} = .09$

8. 14.1% $\dfrac{14.1}{100} = 0.141$

9. 123% $\dfrac{123}{100} = 1.23$

10. $\dfrac{1}{4}\% = 0.25\%$ $\dfrac{.25}{100} = .0025$

11. $\dfrac{5}{6} = 0.8\overline{3}\%$ $\dfrac{0.8\overline{3}}{100} = 0.008\overline{3}$

12. 0.00045% $\dfrac{0.00045}{100} = 0.0000045$

13. $\dfrac{71,500-60,790}{60,790} \approx 0.176 = 17.6\%$

14. $\dfrac{51,300-46,200}{46,200} \approx 0.1104 = 11.0\%$

15. $(x\%)(80) = 15$ $x\% = 15/80 = .1875$
    $0.1875 = 18.75\%$
    15 is 18.75% of 80.

16. $0.55x = 44$ $x = 44/0.55 = 80$
    44 is 5% of 80.

17. $(0.17)(540) = x$ $91.8 = x$
    17% of 540 is 91.8.

18. Tip = 15% of $42.79 = (0.15)(42.79) = \$6.42$

19. $0.20(x) = 8$ $x = 8/0.20 = 40$
    The original number was 40 people.

20. $\dfrac{(95-75)}{75} = \dfrac{20}{75} = .2\overline{6}$ $(.267)(100) = 26.7$
    The increase was 26.7%.

21. $i = (6000)(.02)(30/360) = \$10.00$

22. $37.50 = (2700)(r)(100/360)$

$$37.50 = \left(\frac{270000}{360}\right)(r) \qquad r = 0.05 \text{ or } 5\%$$

23. $114.75 = (p)(0.085)(3)$
    $114.75 = (p)(0.255) \qquad \$450 = p$

24. $316.25 = (5500)(0.115)(t)$
    $316.25 \qquad = (632.50)(t) \quad t = 0.5 \text{ yrs. or } 6 \text{ mos.}$

25. $i = (5300)(.0575)(3) = 914.25$
    Total amount due at maturity $= 5300 + 914.25 =$
    $\$6214.25$

26. a) $i = (3000)(0.081)(240/360) = \$162$
    She paid $3000 + 162 = \$3,162$

27. a) $i = (6000)(0.115)(24/120 = \$1380.00$
    b) amount received: $6000.00 - 1380.00 = 4,620.00$
    c) $i = prt \qquad 1380 = (4620)(r)(24/12) = 9240r$
    $r = (1380)(9240) = .1494 \quad (.1494)(100) = 14.9\%$

28. a) $5\frac{1}{2}\% + 2\% = 7\frac{1}{2}\%$
    b) $i = (800)(0.75)(6/12) = \$30$
    $A = \$800 + \$30 = \$830.00$
    c) $x = $ amount of money in the account
    85% of $x = 800 \quad 0.85x = 800 \quad x = \$941.18$

29. a) $A = 5000\left(1 + \dfrac{0.06}{1}\right)^{(1)(5)} = \$6691.13 \quad \$6691.13 - \$5000 = \$1691.13$

    b) $A = 5000\left(1 + \dfrac{0.06}{2}\right)^{(2)(5)} = \$6719.58 \quad \$6719.58 - \$5000 = \$1719.58$

    c) $A = 5000\left(1 + \dfrac{0.06}{4}\right)^{(4)(5)} = \$6734.28 \quad \$6734.28 - \$5000 = \$1734.28$

    d) $A = 5000\left(1 + \dfrac{0.06}{12}\right)^{(12)(5)} = \$6744.25 \quad \$6744.25 - \$5000 = \$1744.25$

    e) $A = 5000\left(1 + \dfrac{0.06}{360}\right)^{(360)(5)} = \$6749.13 \quad \$6749.13 - \$5000 = \$1749.13$

30. $A = p\left(1 + \dfrac{r}{n}\right)^{nt}$

    $A = 2500\left(1 + \dfrac{0.0475}{4}\right)^{4 \bullet 15} = \$5,076.35$

31. Let $p = 1.00$. Then $A = 1\left(1 + \dfrac{0.56}{360}\right)^{360} = 1.05759$

    $i = 1.05759 - 1.00 = 0.05759$
    The effective annual yield is 5.76%.

32. $p\left(1 + \dfrac{0.055}{4}\right)^{80} = 40000 \qquad p = \dfrac{40000}{(1.01375)^{80}} = 13415.00 \qquad$ You need to invest $\$13,415.00$

33. 48 mo. $\$176.14$/mo. $\$7500$ 24 payments

    a) $(176.14)(48) = 8454.72 \qquad 8454.72 - 7500 = \$954.72 \qquad \left(\dfrac{954.72}{7500}\right)(100) = \$12.73/\$100$

    From Table 11.2, $\$12.73$ indicates an APR of 6.0%

    b) $n = 24, p = 176.14, v = 6.37 \qquad u = \dfrac{(24)(176.14)(6.37)}{100 + 6.37} = \dfrac{26928.28}{106.37} = \$253.16$

    c) $(176.14)(48) = 8454.72 \qquad (176.14)(23) = 4051.22 \qquad 8454.72 - 4051.22 = \$4403.50$
    $4403.50 - 253.16 = \$4150.34$

34. Amount borrowed: $4000 − $500 = $3500

   a) Total of payments: $(24)(155.91) = \$3741.84$

   Finance charge: $3741.84 - 3500 = \$241.84$

   $$\left(\frac{241.84}{3500}\right)(100) = \$6.91\,/\$100$$

   From Table 11.2, $6.91 for a 24-month loan indicates an APR of 6.5%

   b) n = 12, p = 155.91, v = 6.37 $u = \dfrac{(12)(155.91)(3.56)}{100 + 3.56} = \$64.32$

   c) $(155.91)(11) = 1715.01$ $3741.84 - 1715.01 = \$2026.83$
      $2026.83 - 64.32 = \$1962.51$

35. 24 mo. $111.73/mo. Down payment = $860 24 payments

   a) $3420 - 860 = \$2560.00$ $(111.73)(24) = 2681.52$ $2681.52 - 2560.00 = \$121.52$

   $$\left(\frac{121.52}{2560}\right)(100) = \$4.75\,/\$100$$

   From Table 11.2, $4.75 indicates an APR of 4.5%

   b) n = 12, p = 111.73, v = 2.45 $u = \dfrac{(12)(111.73)(2.45)}{100 + 2.45} = \dfrac{3284.86}{102.45} = \$32.06$

   c) $(111.73)(11) = 1229.03$ $2681.52 - 1229.03 = 1452.49$ $1452.49 - 32.06 = \$1420.43$

36. Balance = $485.75 as of June 01   i = 1.3%

   June 04: $485.75 - 375.00) = \$110.75$ June 08: $110.75 + 370.00 = \$480.75$
   June 21: $480.75 + 175.80 = \$656.55$ June 28: $656.55 + 184.75 = \$841.30$

   a) $(485.75)(.013)(1) = \$6.31$ b) $841.30 + 6.31 = \$847.61$

   c) $(485.75)(3) + (110.75)(4) + (480.75)(13) + (656.55)(7) + (841.30)(3) = \$15269.75$
      $15269.75/30 = \$508.99$

   d) $(508.99)(.013)(1) = \$6.62$ e) $841.30 + 6.62 = \$847.92$

37. a) $i = (185.72)(0.14)(1) = \$2.60$

   b) Aug. 01: $185.72
      Aug. 05: $185.72 + 2.60 = \$188.32$
      Aug. 08: $188.32 + 85.75 = \$274.07$
      Aug. 10: $274.07 - 75.00 = \$199.07$
      Aug. 15: $199.07 + 72.85 = \$271.92$
      Aug. 21: $271.92 + 275.00 = \$546.92$
      As of Sep 5, the new account balance
      is $546.92.

   d) $i = (\$382.68)(0.014)(1) = \$5.36$

   c)

Date	Balance	# of Days	(Balance)(Days)
Aug. 05	185.72	3	(185.72)(3) = 557.16
Aug. 08	271.47	2	(271.47)(2) = 542.94
Aug. 10	196.47	5	(196.47)(5) = 982.35
Aug. 15	269.32	6	(269.32)(6) = 1615.92
Aug. 21	544.32	15	(544.32)(15) = 8164.80
Sep 05		31	sum = $11,863.17

   avg. daily balance = $\dfrac{11,863.17}{31} = \$382.68$

   e) $544.32 + 5.36 = \$549.68$ is the amount due on Sep 5.

38. a) $(\$72{,}000)(0.20) = \$14{,}400$

    b) $72{,}000 - 14{,}400 = \$57{,}600$

    c) $(1100.26)(60) = \$66{,}015.60;$
    $66{,}015.60 - 57{,}600 = \$8415.60$

    d) $\left(\dfrac{\text{finance charge}}{\text{amount financed}}\right)(100)$

    $= \left(\dfrac{8415.60}{57{,}600}\right)(100) = 14.61;$

    Using Table 11.2, where no. of payments is 60, APR = 5.5%

39. a) $275 - 50 = \$225;$ $(19.62)(12) = \$235.44;$
    $235.44 - 225 = \$10.44$ interest paid

    b) $\left(\dfrac{\text{finance charge}}{\text{amount financed}}\right)(100)$

    $= \left(\dfrac{10.44}{225}\right)(100) = 4.64;$

    Using Table 11.2, where no. of payments is 12, \$4.64 is closest to \$4.66, which yields an APR of 8.5%

40. a) down payment $= (0.25)(135700) = \$33{,}925$

    b) gross monthly income $= 64000/12 = \$5{,}333.33$
    adjusted monthly income:
    $5333.33 - 528.00 = \$4{,}805.33$
    28% of adjusted monthly income:
    $(0.28)(4805.33) = \$1{,}345.49$

    c) $\left(\dfrac{101{,}775}{1000}\right)(8.41) = \$855.93$

    d) total monthly payment:
    $855.93 + 316.67 = \$1172.60$

    e) Yes, \$1345.49 is greater than \$1172.60.

41. a) down payment $= (0.15)(89900) = \$13{,}485$

    b) amount of mortgage $= 89{,}900 - 13{,}485 = \$76{,}415$
    At 11.5% for 30 years, Table 11.4 yields 9.90.
    monthly mortgage payment:

    $\left(\dfrac{76415}{1000}\right)(9.90) = \$756.51$

    c) $i = prt = (76415)(0.115)(1/12) = \$732.31$
    amount applied to principal:
    $756.51 - 732.51 = \$24.20$

    d) total cost of house: $13485 + (756.51)(12)(30) = \$285{,}828.60$

    e) total interest paid: $285{,}828.60 - 89900 = \$195{,}928.60$

42. a) amount of mortgage: $105{,}000 - 26{,}250 = \$78{,}750$

    b) $5.00\% + 3.00\% = 8.00\%$ c) $4.75\% + 3.00\% = 7.75\%$

    First payment $= \left(\dfrac{78{,}750}{1000}\right)(6.99) = \$550.46$

43. $A = \dfrac{250\left[\left(1+\dfrac{0.09}{12}\right)^{(12)(10)} - 1\right]}{\dfrac{0.09}{12}} = \$48{,}378.57$

44. $p = \dfrac{100{,}000\left(\dfrac{0.07}{4}\right)}{\left(1+\dfrac{0.07}{4}\right)^{(4)(15)} - 1} = \$955.34$

Chapter Test

1. a) $i = (2000)(0.04)(1/2) = \$40.00$

   b) $288 = (1200)(0.08)(t); \ 288 = 96t; \ t = 3$ years

2. $i = prt = (5700)(0.0575)(30/12) = \$819.38$

3. Total amount paid to the bank
   $5700 + 819.38 = \$6519.38$

4. Partial payment on Sept. 15 (45 days)
   $i = (5400)(0.125)(45/360) = \$84.375$
   $\$3000.00 - 84.375 = \$2,915.625$
   $5400.00 - 2915.625 = \$2484.375$

   $i = (2484.375)(0.125)(45/360) = \$38.82$
   $2484.38 + 38.82 = \$2523.20$

5. $84.38 + 38.82 = \$123.20$

6. a) $A = 7500\left(1 + \dfrac{0.03}{4}\right)^{8} = \$7961.99$

   interest $= 7961.99 - 7500.00 = \$461.99$

   b) $A = 2500\left(1 + \dfrac{0.065}{12}\right)^{36} = \$3036.68$

   interest $= 3036.68 - 2500.00 = \$536.68$

7. $(2350)(.15) = 352.50$
   $2350 - 352.50 = \$1997.50$

8. $(90.79)(24) = 2178.96$
   $2178.96 - 1997.50 = \$181.46$

9. $\left(\dfrac{181.46}{1997.50}\right)(100) = \$9.08 \ /\$100$ In Table 11.2, \$9.08 is closest to \$9.09 which yields an APR of 8.5%.

10. \$7500   36 mo.   \$223.10 per mo. $(223.10)(36) = 8031.60$ $8031.60 - 7500.00 = 531.60$

   a) $\left(\dfrac{181.46}{1997.50}\right)(100) = \$9.08$ In Table 11.2, \$9.08 yields an APR of 4.5%.

   b) $u = \dfrac{n \cdot P \cdot V}{100 + V} = \dfrac{(12)(223.10)(2.45)}{100 + 2.45} = \dfrac{6559.14}{102.45} = \$64.02$

   c) $(223.10)(23) = 5131.30$ $8031.60 - 5131.30 = \$2900.30$ $2900.30 - 64.02 = \$2836.28$

11. Mar. 23: \$878.25
    Mar. 26: $878.25 + 95.89 = \$974.14$
    Mar. 30: $974.14 + 68.76 = \$1042.90$
    Apr. 03: $1042.90 - 450.00 = \$592.90$
    Apr. 15: $592.90 + 90.52 = \$683.42$
    Apr. 22: $683.42 + 450.85 = \$1134.27$

    a) $i = (878.25)(.014)(1) = \$12.30$
    b) $1134.27 + 12.30 = \$1146.57$

   c)

Date	Balance	# of Days	Balance-Days
Mar. 23	878.25	3	$(878.25)(3) = 2634.75$
Mar. 26	974.14	4	$(974.14)(4) = 3896.56$
Mar. 30	1042.90	4	$(1042.90)(4) = 4171.60$
Apr. 03	592.90	12	$(592.90)(12) = 7114.80$
Apr. 15	683.42	7	$(683.42)(7) = 4783.94$
Apr. 22	1134.27	1	$(1134.27)(1) = 1134.27$
Apr 23		31	sum $= \$23,735.92$

   avg. daily balance $= \dfrac{23,735.92}{31} = \$765.67$

   d) $(765.67)(.014)(1) = \$10.72$
   e) $1134.27 + 10.72 = \$1144.99$

12. down payment = $(0.15)(144500) = \$21{,}675.00$

13. amount of loan = $144500 - 21675 = \$122{,}825$

    points = $(0.02)(122825) = \$2456.50$

14. gross monthly income = $86500 \div 12 = \$7208.33$

    $7{,}208.33 - 605.00 = \$6{,}603.33$ adj. mo. income

    maximum monthly payment = $(0.28)(6603.33) = \$1{,}848.93$

15. At 10.5% interest for 30 years, Table 11.4 yields $9.15.

    monthly payments = $\left(\dfrac{122825}{1000}\right)(9.15) = \$1{,}123.85$

16. $1123.85 + 304.17 = \$1428.02$ total mo. payment

17. Yes.

18. a) Total cost of the house:

    $21675 + 2456.50 + (1123.85)(12)(30)$

    $= \$428{,}717.50$

    b) interest = $428{,}717.50 - 144{,}500 = \$284{,}217.50$

19. $A = \dfrac{500\left[\left(1 + \dfrac{0.06}{12}\right)^{(12)(20)} - 1\right]}{\dfrac{0.06}{12}} = \$231{,}020.45$

20. $p = \dfrac{15{,}000\left(\dfrac{0.06}{12}\right)}{\left(1 + \dfrac{0.06}{12}\right)^{(12)(4)} - 1} = \$277.28$

Group Projects

1. a) $\left(\dfrac{130{,}000}{1000}\right)(8.74) = \$1136.20$ (monthly payment) ; $(1136.20)(300) = \$340{,}860$

   b) $130{,}000 - 20{,}000 = 110{,}000;$ $\left(\dfrac{110{,}000}{1000}\right)(8.74) = \$961.40$ (monthly payment)

      $(961.40)(300) = \$288{,}420$

   c) $A = 20{,}000\left(1 + \dfrac{0.10}{4}\right)^{4 \cdot 25} = \$236{,}274.33$

   d) $1136.20 - 961.40 = \$174.80$

   e) $S = \dfrac{R\left[\left(1 + \frac{r}{n}\right)^{nt} - 1\right]}{\frac{r}{n}} = \dfrac{174.80\left[\left(1 + \frac{0.06}{12}\right)^{12 \cdot 25} - 1\right]}{\frac{0.06}{12}} = \$121{,}135.34$

   f) The Youngs should not make a down payment and keep the $20,000 invested.

CHAPTER TWELVE

PROBABILITY

Exercise Set 12.1

1. An experiment is a controlled operation that yields a set of results.

2. a) The possible results of an experiment are called its outcomes.

   b) An event is a subcollection of the outcomes of an experiment.

3. Empirical probability is the relative frequency of occurrence of an event. It is determined by actual observation of an experiment.

$$P(E) = \frac{\text{number of times the event occurred}}{\text{number of times the experiment was performed}}$$

4. The possible outcomes of an experiment.

5. Relative frequency over the long run can accurately be predicted, not individual events or totals.

6. The best way to determine the likelihood of death for a person is to observe others with similar characteristics.

7. Not necessarily, but it does mean that if a coin was flipped many times, about one-half of the tosses would land heads up.

8. Not necessarily, but it does mean that the average person with traits similar to Mr. Duncan's will live another 43.21 years.

9. a) Roll a die 100 times and determine the number of times that a 5 occurs out of 100.

   b) Answers will vary (AWV).   c) AWV

10. Not necessarily, but it does mean that if a die were rolled many times, about one-sixth of the outcomes would be 4's.

11. AWV   12. AWV   13. AWV   14. AWV

15. Of 30 birds: 14 finches   10 cardinals   6 blue jays

   a) P(f) = 14/30 = 7/15   b) P(c) = 10/30 = 1/3   c) P(bj) = 6/30 = 1/5

16. Of 60 music lovers: 12 like rock   16 like country   8 like classical   24 like other types

   a) P(r) = 12/60 = 1/5   b) P(c) = 16/60 = 4/15   c) P(other) = 24/60 = 2/5

17. Of 105 animals: 45 are dogs.   40 are cats   15 are birds   5 are rabbits

   a) P(dog) = 45/105 = 3/7   b) P(cat) = 8/21   c) P(rabbit) = 5/105 = 1/21

18. 5/50000 = 1/10000 = 0.0001

19. a) $\dfrac{4737}{129,098} \approx 0.0367$ b) $\dfrac{21,922}{129,098} \approx 0.1698$ c) $\dfrac{11,418}{129,098} \approx 0.0884$

20. a) $\dfrac{14,200,000}{74,600,000} \approx 0.1903$ b) $\dfrac{11,200,000}{74,600,000} \approx 0.1501$ c) $\dfrac{7,100,000}{74,600,000} \approx 0.0952$

21. a) $\dfrac{29}{186}$

    b) $\dfrac{98}{186} = \dfrac{1}{2}$

    c) $\dfrac{12}{186} = \dfrac{2}{31}$

22. a) $P(A) = \dfrac{43}{645} \approx 0.067$

    b) $P(C) = \dfrac{260}{645} \approx 0.403$

    c) $P(D \text{ or higher}) = \dfrac{90 + 260 + 182 + 43}{645} = 0.891$

23. Of 80 votes: 22 for Allison   18 for Emily   20 for Kimberly   14 for Johanna   6 for others
    a) $P(A) = 22/80 = 11/40$ b) $P(E) = 18/80 = 9/40$ c) $P(K) = 20/80 = 1/4$ d) $P(J) = 14/80 = 7/40$
    e) $P(\text{others}) = 6/80 = 3/40$

24. a) 0.23   b) 0.13   c) 0.26

25. a) $P(\text{bulls-eye}) = \dfrac{6}{20} = \dfrac{3}{10}$

    b) $P(\text{not bulls-eye}) = \dfrac{14}{20} = \dfrac{7}{10}$

    c) $P(\text{at least 20 pts.}) = \dfrac{14}{20} = \dfrac{7}{10}$

    d) $P(\text{does not score}) = \dfrac{2}{20} = \dfrac{1}{10}$

26. $P(\text{side 4}) = \dfrac{13}{100} = 0.13$

27. a) $P(\text{affecting circular}) = \dfrac{0}{150} = 0$

    b) $P(\text{affecting elliptical}) = \dfrac{50}{250} = 0.2$

    c) $P(\text{affecting irregular}) = \dfrac{100}{100} = 1$

28. Of 4,112,052 babies born, 2,104,661 were male and 2,007,391 were female.
    a) $P(m) = \dfrac{2,104,661}{4,112,052} = 0.51$ b) $P(f) = \dfrac{2,007,391}{4,112,052} = 0.49$

29. a) $P(\text{white flowers}) = \dfrac{224}{929} = 0.24$ b) $P(\text{purple flowers}) = \dfrac{705}{929} = 0.76$

30. a) $P(\text{tall plants}) = \dfrac{787}{1064} = 0.74$ b) $P(\text{short plants}) = \dfrac{277}{1064} = 0.26$

31. Answers will vary.

32. Answers will vary.

Exercise Set 12.2

1. If each outcome of an experiment has the same chance of occurring as any other outcome, they are said to be equally likely outcomes.

2. $P(event) = \dfrac{\text{no. of outcomes favorable to the event}}{\text{total number of possible outcomes}}$

3. $P(A) + P(not\ A) = 1$

4. $P(\text{event will not occur}) = 1 - \dfrac{3}{7} = \dfrac{7}{7} - \dfrac{3}{7} = \dfrac{4}{7}$

5. $P(\text{event will not occur}) = 1 - 0.7 = 0.3$

6. $P(\text{event will occur}) = 1 - 0.65 = 0.35$

7. $P(\text{event will occur}) = 1 - \dfrac{5}{12} = \dfrac{12}{12} - \dfrac{5}{12} = \dfrac{7}{12}$

8. a) 52   b) 13   c) 26   d) 4   e) 26
   f) 12   g) 4   h) 4

9. None of the possible outcomes is the event in question.

10. The event must include all possible outcomes.

11. All probabilities are between 0 and 1.

12. The sum of the probabilities of all outcomes = 1.

13. a) $P(correct) = 1/5$ b) $P(correct) = 1/4$

14. a) $P(\text{channel 3}) = 1/10$
    b) $P(\text{even channel}) = 5/10 = 1/2$
    c) $P(\text{less than 7}) = 7/10$

15. $P(\text{you win}) = \dfrac{\text{one choice}}{40\text{ possible choices}} = \dfrac{1}{40}$

16. $P(\text{you win}) = \dfrac{\text{one choice}}{52\text{ possible choices}} = \dfrac{1}{52}$

17. $P(5) = \dfrac{4}{52} = \dfrac{1}{13}$

18. $P(\text{5 or 7}) = \dfrac{4+4}{52} = \dfrac{8}{52} = \dfrac{2}{13}$

19. $P(\text{not 5}) = \dfrac{48}{52} = \dfrac{12}{13}$

20. $P(\text{5 of diamonds}) = \dfrac{1}{52}$

21. $P(black) = \dfrac{13+13}{52} = \dfrac{26}{52} = \dfrac{1}{2}$

22. $P(diamond) = \dfrac{13}{52} = \dfrac{1}{4}$

23. $P(\text{red or black}) = \dfrac{26+26}{52} = \dfrac{52}{52} = \dfrac{1}{1} = 1$

24. $P(\text{red and black}) = 0$

25. $P(>4 \text{ and} <9) = P(5,6,7,8) = \dfrac{16}{52} = \dfrac{4}{13}$

26. $P(\text{king and club}) = P(\text{king of clubs}) = \dfrac{1}{52}$

27. a) $P(red) = \dfrac{2}{4} = \dfrac{1}{2}$ b) $P(green) = \dfrac{1}{4}$
    c) $P(yellow) = \dfrac{1}{4}$ d) $P(blue) = 0$

28. a) $P(red) = \dfrac{1}{4}$ b) $P(green) = \dfrac{1}{2}$
    c) $P(yellow) = \dfrac{1}{4}$ d) $P(blue) = 0$

29. a) $P(red) = \dfrac{2}{6} = \dfrac{1}{3}$ b) $P(green) = \dfrac{1}{6}$
    c) $P(yellow) = \dfrac{2}{6} = \dfrac{1}{3}$ d) $P(blue) = \dfrac{1}{6}$

30. a) $P(\text{red}) = \dfrac{4}{8} = \dfrac{1}{2}$ b) $P(\text{green}) = \dfrac{1}{8}$ c) $P(\text{yellow}) = \dfrac{1}{8}$ d) $P(\text{blue}) = \dfrac{2}{8} = \dfrac{1}{4}$

Of 100 cans: 30 are cola (c)   40 are orange (o)   10 are ginger ale (ga)   20 are root beer (rb)

31. $P(\text{rb}) = \dfrac{20}{100} = \dfrac{1}{5}$ 32. $P(\text{c or o}) = \dfrac{70}{100} = \dfrac{7}{10}$ 33. $P(\text{c, rb, o}) = \dfrac{90}{100} = \dfrac{9}{10}$ 34. $P(\text{ga}) = \dfrac{10}{100} = \dfrac{1}{10}$

35. $P(600) = \dfrac{1}{12}$ 36. $P(> 700) = \dfrac{2}{12} = \dfrac{1}{6}$ 37. $P(\text{lose/bankrupt}) = \dfrac{2}{12} = \dfrac{1}{6}$ 38. $P(2500/\text{surprise}) = \dfrac{2}{12} = \dfrac{1}{6}$

Of 30 basketballs: 10 are Wilson (w)   15 are Spalding (s)   5 are other (o)

39. $P(\text{s}) = \dfrac{15}{30} = \dfrac{1}{2}$ 40. $P(\text{w}) = \dfrac{10}{30} = \dfrac{1}{3}$ 41. $P(\text{not w}) = \dfrac{20}{30} = \dfrac{2}{3}$ 42. $P(\text{w or s}) = \dfrac{25}{30} = \dfrac{5}{6}$

For a traffic light: 25 seconds on red (r)   5 seconds on yellow (y)   55 seconds on green (g)

43. $P(\text{g}) = \dfrac{55}{85} = \dfrac{11}{17}$ 44. $P(\text{y}) = \dfrac{5}{85} = \dfrac{1}{17}$ 45. $P(\text{not r}) = \dfrac{60}{85} = \dfrac{12}{17}$ 46. $P(\text{not g}) = \dfrac{30}{85} = \dfrac{6}{17}$

Of 9 letters: 1 = T   4 = E   2 = N   2 = S

47. $P(S) = \dfrac{2}{9}$ 48. $P(\text{not S}) = 1 - \dfrac{2}{9} = \dfrac{7}{9}$ 49. $P(\text{consonant}) = \dfrac{5}{9}$

50. $P(\text{T or N}) = \dfrac{1+2}{9} = \dfrac{1}{3}$ 51. $P(W) = 0$ 52. $P(\text{V not selected}) = 1$

53. $\dfrac{3}{51}$ 54. $\dfrac{5}{51}$ 55. $\dfrac{27}{51}$ 56. $\dfrac{15}{51}$

57. $P(15) = \dfrac{1}{26}$ 58. $P(\text{orange}) = \dfrac{13}{26} = \dfrac{1}{2}$ 59. $P(\geq 22) = \dfrac{5}{26}$ 60. $P(\leq 6 \text{ and/or } \leq 9) =$ $P(7,8,9) = \dfrac{3}{26}$

61. $P(\text{car}) = \dfrac{85}{130} = \dfrac{17}{26}$ 62. $P(\text{SUV}) = \dfrac{45}{130} = \dfrac{9}{26}$ 63. $P(\text{GM}) = \dfrac{83}{130}$ 64. $P(\text{Toyota}) = \dfrac{47}{130}$

65. $P(\text{GM car}) = \dfrac{55}{130} = \dfrac{11}{26}$ 66. $P(\text{GM SUV}) = \dfrac{28}{130} = \dfrac{14}{65}$ 67. $P(\text{Jif}) = \dfrac{12}{38} = \dfrac{6}{19}$ 68. $P(\text{Skippy}) = \dfrac{7}{38}$

69. $P(\text{chunky}) = \dfrac{15}{38}$ 70. $P(\text{smooth}) = \dfrac{23}{38}$ 71. $P(\text{Peter Pan smooth}) = \dfrac{10}{38} = \dfrac{5}{19}$ 72. $P(\text{Jif chunky}) = \dfrac{5}{38}$

73. $P(\text{red}) = \dfrac{2}{18} + \dfrac{1}{12} + \dfrac{1}{6} = \dfrac{4}{36} + \dfrac{3}{36} + \dfrac{6}{36} = \dfrac{13}{36}$ 74. $P(\text{green}) = \dfrac{1}{18} + \dfrac{2}{12} + \dfrac{1}{12} = \dfrac{1}{18} + \dfrac{3}{12} = \dfrac{2}{36} + \dfrac{9}{36} = \dfrac{11}{36}$

75. $P(\text{yellow}) = \dfrac{1}{6} + \dfrac{1}{12} + \dfrac{1}{12} = \dfrac{2}{12} + \dfrac{2}{12} = \dfrac{4}{12} = \dfrac{1}{3}$

76. $P(\text{red or green}) = \dfrac{13}{36} + \dfrac{11}{36} = \dfrac{24}{36} = \dfrac{2}{3}$

77. $P(\text{yellow or green}) = \dfrac{1}{3} + \dfrac{11}{36} = \dfrac{23}{36}$

78. $P(\text{red or yellow}) = \dfrac{13}{36} + \dfrac{1}{3} = \dfrac{25}{36}$

79. a) $P(CC) = 0$ b) $P(CC) = 1$

80. a) $P(SCA) = P(S_1 S_2) = \dfrac{1}{4}$

   b) $P(SCT) = P(S_1 S_2 \text{ or } S_2 S_1) = \dfrac{1}{2}$

   c) $P(NSCA \text{ or } NSCT) = 1 - \left(\dfrac{1}{2} + \dfrac{1}{4}\right) = 1 - \dfrac{3}{4} = \dfrac{1}{4}$

81. a) $P(R/R) = \dfrac{2}{4} \cdot \dfrac{2}{4} = \dfrac{4}{16} = \dfrac{1}{4}$

   b) $P(G/G) = \dfrac{2}{4} \cdot \dfrac{2}{4} = \dfrac{4}{16} = \dfrac{1}{4}$

   c) $P(R/G) = \dfrac{2}{4} \cdot \dfrac{2}{4} = \dfrac{4}{16} = \dfrac{1}{4}$

82. a) $P(\text{sparrow w/low attract. to PK}) = \dfrac{2}{7}$

   b) $P(\text{high attract. to CC / low attract to PK}) = 0$

   c) $P(\text{high attract. to BSSS / low attract to PK}) = \dfrac{4}{7}$

83. $4 \cdot 7 + 1 = 29$

Exercise Set 12.3

1. a) The odds against an event are found by dividing the probability that the event will not occur by the probability that the event will occur.

   b) The odds in favor of an event are found by dividing the probability that the event will occur by the probability that the event will not occur.

2. Answers will vary.

3. Odds against are more commonly used.

4. If the odds against an event are a to b, then $P(\text{event occurs}) = \dfrac{b}{a+b}$ and $P(\text{event does not occur}) = \dfrac{a}{a+b}$.

5. $7 : 2$ or 7 to 2

6. $3 : 8$ or 3 to 8

7. a) $P(\text{event occurs}) = \dfrac{1}{1+1} = \dfrac{1}{2}$

   b) $P(\text{event fails to occur}) = \dfrac{1}{1+1} = \dfrac{1}{2}$

8. a) $P(\text{event fails}) = 1 - P(\text{event occurs}) = 1 - \dfrac{1}{2} = \dfrac{1}{2}$

   b) odds against the event $= \dfrac{P(\text{event fails to occur})}{P(\text{event occurs})} =$

   $\dfrac{1/2}{1/2} = \left(\dfrac{1}{2}\right)\left(\dfrac{2}{1}\right) = \dfrac{1}{1}$ or $1:1$

   c) odds in favor of the event are $1:1$.

9. a) P(tie goes well) = $\dfrac{8}{15}$

   b) P(tie does not go well) = $\dfrac{7}{15}$

   c) odds against tie going well =

   $\dfrac{\text{P(tie does not go well)}}{\text{P(tie goes well)}} = \dfrac{7/15}{8/15} = \dfrac{7}{8}$ or 7 : 8

   d) odds in favor of it going well are 8 : 7

10. 12 bills: 6 - \$1; 2 - \$5; 3 - \$10; 1 - \$20

    a) P(\$5) = $\dfrac{2}{12} = \dfrac{1}{6}$

    b) P(not \$5) = $\dfrac{10}{12} = \dfrac{5}{6}$

    c) 1 : 5

    d) 5 : 1

11. Against: 6 : 1; in favor: 1 : 6

12. Against: 3 : 1; in favor: 1 : 3

13. Since there is only one 4, the odds against a 4 are 5 : 1.

14. Since half the numbers are odd, the odds against an odd number are 1 : 1.

15. odds against rolling less than 3 = $\dfrac{\text{P(3 or greater)}}{\text{P(less than 3)}} =$

    $\dfrac{4/6}{2/6} = \dfrac{4}{6} \cdot \dfrac{6}{2} = \dfrac{4}{2} = \dfrac{2}{1}$ or 2:1

16. odds against rolling greater than 4 =

    $\dfrac{\text{P(failure to roll greater than 4)}}{\text{P(roll greater than 4)}} =$

    $\dfrac{4/6}{2/6} = \dfrac{2}{1}$ or 2 : 1

17. odds against a queen =

    $\dfrac{\text{P(failure to pick a queen)}}{\text{P(pick a queen)}} =$

    $\dfrac{48/52}{4/52} = \dfrac{48}{52} \cdot \dfrac{52}{4} = \dfrac{48}{4} = \dfrac{12}{1}$ or 12:1

    Therefore, odds in favor of picking a queen are 1:12.

18. odds against a heart = $\dfrac{\text{P(failure to pick a heart)}}{\text{P(pick a heart)}} =$

    $\dfrac{39/52}{13/52} = \dfrac{39}{52} \cdot \dfrac{52}{13} = \dfrac{39}{13} = \dfrac{3}{1}$ or 3:1

    Therefore, odds in favor of picking a heart are 1:3.

19. odds against a picture card =

    $\dfrac{\text{P(failure to pick a picture)}}{\text{P(pick a picture)}} = \dfrac{40/52}{12/52} = \dfrac{40}{12} = \dfrac{10}{3}$

    or 10:3

    Therefore, odds in favor of picking a picture card are 3:10.

20. odds against card greater than 5 =

    $\dfrac{\text{P(failure to pick a card greater than 5)}}{\text{P(pick a card greater than 5)}} =$

    $\dfrac{20/52}{32/52} = \dfrac{20}{52} \cdot \dfrac{52}{32} = \dfrac{20}{32} = \dfrac{5}{8}$ or 5:8

    Therefore, odds in favor of picking a card greater than 5 are 8:5.

21. odds against red =

    $\dfrac{\text{P(not red)}}{\text{P(red)}} = \dfrac{1/2}{1/2} = \dfrac{1}{2} \cdot \dfrac{2}{1} = \dfrac{2}{2} = \dfrac{1}{1}$ or 1:1

22. odds against red =

    $\dfrac{\text{P(not red)}}{\text{P(red)}} = \dfrac{2/3}{1/3} = \dfrac{2}{3} \cdot \dfrac{3}{1} = \dfrac{6}{3} = \dfrac{2}{1}$ or 2:1

23. odds against red = $\dfrac{\text{P(not red)}}{\text{P(red)}} = \dfrac{5/8}{3/8} = \dfrac{5}{8} \cdot \dfrac{8}{3} = \dfrac{5}{3}$

    or 5:3

24. odds against red = $\dfrac{\text{P(not red)}}{\text{P(red)}} = \dfrac{5/8}{3/8} = \dfrac{5}{8} \cdot \dfrac{8}{3} = \dfrac{5}{3}$

    or 5:3

25. a) odds against selecting female =

$$\frac{P(\text{failure to select female})}{P(\text{select female})} = \frac{16/30}{14/30} = \frac{16}{14} = \frac{8}{7}$$

    or 8 : 7 .

  b) odds against selecting male =

$$\frac{P(\text{failure to select male})}{P(\text{select male})} = \frac{14/30}{16/30} = \frac{14}{16} = \frac{7}{8}$$

    or 7 : 8 .

26. a) odds against winning = $\dfrac{P(\text{failure to win})}{P(\text{win})} =$

$$\frac{999999/1000000}{1/1000000} = \frac{999999}{1} \text{ or } 999{,}999 : 1$$

  b) odds against winning = $\dfrac{P(\text{failure to win})}{P(\text{win})} =$

$$\frac{999990/1000000}{10/1000000} = \frac{99999}{1} \text{ or } 99{,}999 : 1$$

27. odds against a stripe = $\dfrac{P(\text{not a stripe})}{P(\text{stripe})} =$

$$\frac{8/15}{7/15} = \frac{8}{15} \cdot \frac{15}{7} = \frac{8}{7} \text{ or } 8:7$$

28. odds in favor of not the 8 ball are

$$\frac{P(\text{not the 8 ball})}{P(\text{the 8 ball})} = \frac{14/15}{1/15} = \frac{14}{15} \cdot \frac{15}{1} = \frac{14}{1} \text{ or } 14:1$$

29. odds in favor of even are $\dfrac{P(\text{even})}{P(\text{not even})} =$

$$\frac{7/15}{8/15} = \frac{7}{15} \cdot \frac{15}{8} = \frac{7}{8} \text{ or } 7:8$$

30. odds against a ball with red are

$$\frac{P(\text{no red})}{P(\text{red})} = \frac{13/15}{2/15} = \frac{13}{15} \cdot \frac{15}{2} = \frac{13}{2} \text{ or } 13:2$$

31. odds against a ball with 9 or greater are

$$\frac{P(\text{less than 9})}{P(\text{9 or greater})} = \frac{8/15}{7/15} = \frac{8}{15} \cdot \frac{15}{7} = \frac{8}{7} \text{ or } 8:7$$

32. The odds in favor of two digits =

$$\frac{P(\text{two digits})}{P(\text{not two digits})} = \frac{6/15}{9/15} = \frac{6}{9} = \frac{2}{3} \text{ or } 2:3$$

33. a) $\dfrac{3}{10}$

  b) 7 : 3

34. a) P(2 dots) = $\dfrac{1}{3}$

  b) Odds against rolling 2 dots   4 : 2 or 2 : 1

35. The odds against testing negative =

$$\frac{P(\text{test positive})}{P(\text{test negative})} = \frac{4/76}{72/76} = \frac{4}{72} = \frac{1}{18} \text{ or } 1:18$$

36. The odds against red = $\dfrac{P(\text{red})}{P(\text{not red})} = \dfrac{2/11}{9/11} = \dfrac{2}{9}$

  or 2:9

37. a) P(Wendy wins) = $\dfrac{7}{7+4} = \dfrac{7}{11}$

  b) P(Wendy loses) = $\dfrac{4}{7+4} = \dfrac{4}{11}$

38. a) P(Boris wins) = $\dfrac{3}{3+8} = \dfrac{3}{11}$

  b) P(Boris loses) = $\dfrac{8}{3+8} = \dfrac{8}{11}$

39. Odds against   4 : 11   P(promoted) = $\dfrac{11}{4+11} = \dfrac{11}{15}$

40. Odds against   7 : 2   a) P(wins) = $\dfrac{2}{7+2} = \dfrac{2}{9}$

  b) P(loses) = $\dfrac{7}{7+2} = \dfrac{7}{9}$

41. P(G) = $\dfrac{15}{75} = \dfrac{1}{5}$

42. P(not G) = $1 - \dfrac{1}{5} = \dfrac{4}{5}$

43. Odds in favor of G = $\dfrac{P(G)}{P(\text{not G})} = \dfrac{1/5}{4/5} = \dfrac{1}{4} \text{ or } 1:4$

44. Odds against B9 =

$$\frac{P(\text{not B9})}{P(\text{B9})} = \frac{74/75}{1/75} = \left(\frac{74}{75}\right)\left(\frac{75}{1}\right) = \frac{74}{1} \text{ or } 74:1$$

45. Odds against G are 4:1

46. Odds in favor of B9 are 1:74

47. $P(A+) = \dfrac{34}{100} = 0.34$

48. $P(B-) = \dfrac{2}{100} = 0.02$

49. $\dfrac{66}{34} = \dfrac{33}{17}$ or $33 : 17$

50. $\dfrac{2}{98} = \dfrac{1}{49}$ or $1 : 49$

51. $P(\text{O or O-}) = \dfrac{43}{100} = \dfrac{43}{43+57}$ or $43 : 57$

52. $P(\text{A+ or O+}) = \dfrac{71}{100} = \dfrac{71}{71+29}$ or $29 : 71$

53. If $P(\text{selling out}) = 0.9 = \dfrac{9}{10}$, then

  $P(\text{do not sell your car this week}) = 1 - \dfrac{9}{10} = \dfrac{1}{10}$.

  The odds against selling out $= \dfrac{1/10}{9/10} = \dfrac{1}{9}$ or 1:9.

54. Odds in favor of high blood pressure: $1 : 3$

55. If $P(\text{all parts are present}) = \dfrac{7}{8}$, then the odds in

  favor of all parts being present are $7 : 1$.

56. a) $P(\text{on time}) = \dfrac{138}{175}$

  b) Number that did not arrive on time:
     $175 - 138 = 37$
     Odds against on-time arrival: $37 : 138$

57. a) $P(\text{birth defect}) = \dfrac{1}{33}$

  b) Number without birth defect: $33 - 1 = 32$
     Odds against birth defect: $32 : 1$

58. $P(\text{even or} > 3) = P(2, 4, 5 \text{ or } 6) = \dfrac{4}{6} = \dfrac{2}{3}$

  Odds against even or > 3 are $\dfrac{1/3}{2/3} = \dfrac{1}{2}$ or $1 : 2$.

59. $P(\#\ 1 \text{ wins}) = \dfrac{2}{9}$ $P(\#\ 2 \text{ wins}) = \dfrac{1}{3}$

  $P(\#\ 3 \text{ wins}) = \dfrac{1}{16}$ $P(\#\ 4 \text{ wins}) = \dfrac{5}{12}$

  $P(\#\ 5 \text{ wins}) = \dfrac{1}{2}$

60. a) $P(R) = \dfrac{9}{19}$

  b) Odds against red are $10 : 9$

  c) $P(0 \text{ or } 00) = \dfrac{1}{19}$

  d) Odds in favor of 0 or 00 are 1:18.

61. If multiple births are 3% of births, then single births are 97% of births, and the odds against a multiple birth are $97 : 3$.

Exercise Set 12.4

1. Expected value is used to determine the average gain or loss of an experiment over the long run.

2. a) An expected value of 0 indicates that the individual would break even over the long run.

   b) A negative expected value predicts a long-run loss or failure

   c) A positive expected value predicts a long run gain or positive outcome.

3. The fair price is the amount charged for the game to be fair and result in an expected value of 0.

4. a) $E = P_1A_1 + P_2A_2$ b) $E = P_1A_1 + P_2A_2 + P_3A_3$

5. To obtain fair price, add the cost to play to the expected value.

6. No, fair price is the price to pay to make the expected value 0. The expected value is the expected outcome of an experiment when the experiment is performed many times

7. $0.50. Since you would lose $1.00 on average for each game you played, the fair price of the game should be $1.00 less. Then the expected value would be 0, and the game would be fair.

8. $1.00. Since you would lose $2.00 on average for each game you played, the fair price of the game should be $2.00 less. Then the expected value would be 0, and the game would be fair.

9. $3(-\$0.40) = -\$1.20$

10. Paul's expected value on a $5 bet is $5(0.20) = \$1.00$.

11. $E = P_1A_1 + P_2A_2 = 0.30(14,000) + 0.70(8400) = $ 10,080 people

12. $E = P_1A_1 + P_2A_2 = 0.60(80000) + 0.40(-20000) = 48000 - 8000 = \$40000$

13. $E = P_1A_1 + P_2A_2 = 0.50(78) + 0.50(62) = 39 + 31 = 70$ points

14. $E = P_1A_1 + P_2A_2 = 0.40(50) + 0.60(65) = 59$ people

15. $E = P_1A_1 + P_2A_2 = 0.40(1.2 \text{ M}) + 0.60(1.6 \text{ M}) = .48 \text{ M} + .96 \text{ M} = 1.44 \text{ M}$ viewers

16. a) $E = P(\text{sunny})(1/2) + P(\text{cloudy})(1/4)$ $E = 0.75(1/2) + 0.25(1/4) = 0.375 + 0.0625 = 0.4375$ inches/day

    b) (0.4375 inches per day)(31 days) = 13.5625 inches of growth during July is expected

17. a) $E = P_1A_1 + P_2A_2 = (.60)(10000) + (.10)(0) + (.30)(-7200) = 6000 + 0 + -2160 = \$3840$

18. a) $(.7)(5) + (.3)(10) = .35 + 3 = \$6.50$ b) $200.00 - 6.50 = \$193.50$

19. $E = P_1A_1 + P_2A_2 + P_3A_3 = P(\$1 \text{ off})(\$1) + P(\$2 \text{ off})(\$2) + P(\$5 \text{ off})(\$5)$

    $E = (1/10)(1) + (2/10)(2) + (1/10)(5) = 7/10 + 4/10 + 5/10 = 16/10 = \$1.60$

20. a) $(1/4)(5) + (3/4)(-2) = 1.25 - 1.50 = -\$0.25$ for Mike

    b) Dave's expectation is the negative of Mike's, or $0.25

21. a) $(3/6)(5) + (2/6)(2) + (1/6)(-15) \approx -\$0.17$

    b) Gabriel's expectation is the negative of Alyssa's, or $0.17.

22. a) $(2/5)(-8) + (3/5)(5) = -16/5 + 3/1 = -3.20 + 3.00 = -\$0.20$

    b) Dolly's expectation is the negative of Chi's, or = $0.20

23. a) $(1/5)(5) + (0)(0) + (4/5)(-1) = 1 - 4/5 = 1/5$

    Yes, positive expectations = 1/5

    b) $(1/4)(5) + (0)(0) + (3/4)(-1) = 5/4 - 3/4 = 1/2$

    Yes, positive expectations = 1/2

24. a) $(1/4)(5) + (0)(0) + (3/4)(-2) = 5/4 - 6/4 = -1/4$

    No, negative expectations = -1/4

    b) $(1/3)(5) + (0)(0) + (2/3)(-2) = 5/3 - 4/3 = 1/3$

    Yes, positive expectations = 1/3

25. a) $\left(\dfrac{1}{500}\right)(398)+\left(\dfrac{499}{500}\right)(-2)=\dfrac{398-998}{500}=$

$\dfrac{-600}{500}=\dfrac{-300}{250}=-\$1.20$

    b) Fair price = -1.20 + 2.00 = \$.80

26. a) $\left(\dfrac{1}{1000}\right)(799)+\left(\dfrac{999}{1000}\right)(-1)=\dfrac{799-999}{1000}=$

$\dfrac{799}{1000}-\dfrac{999}{1000}=\dfrac{-200}{1000}=-\$0.20$

    b) Fair price = -0.20 + 1.00 = \$.80

27. a) $\left(\dfrac{1}{2000}\right)(997)+\left(\dfrac{2}{2000}\right)(497)+\left(\dfrac{1997}{2000}\right)(-3)=\dfrac{997+994-5991}{2000}=\dfrac{-4000}{2000}=-\$2.00$

    b) Fair price = -2.00 + 3.00 = \$1.00

28. a) $E = P_1A_1 + P_2A_2 + P_3A_3 + P_4A_4$

$E = \left(\dfrac{1}{10000}\right)(\$4{,}995) + \left(\dfrac{1}{10000}\right)(\$2{,}495) + \left(\dfrac{2}{10000}\right)(\$995) + \left(\dfrac{9996}{10000}\right)(-\$5)$

$= \dfrac{4995}{10000} + \dfrac{2495}{10000} + \dfrac{1990}{10000} - \dfrac{49980}{10000} = \dfrac{33000}{10000} = -\$4.05$

    b) The fair price is \$5.00 – \$4.05 = \$0.95

29. $\dfrac{1}{2}(1)+\dfrac{1}{2}(5)=\dfrac{1}{2}+\dfrac{5}{2}=3=\$3.00$

30. $\dfrac{1}{2}(5)+\dfrac{1}{4}(1)+\dfrac{1}{4}(10)=2.50+.25+2.50=\$5.25$

31. $\dfrac{1}{2}(10)+\dfrac{1}{4}(-5)+\dfrac{1}{4}(-20)=5-1.25-5=-\$1.25$

32. $\dfrac{1}{2}(-10)+\dfrac{1}{4}(2)+\dfrac{1}{4}(20)=-5+.50+5=\$0.50$

33. $(500)\left(\dfrac{2}{5}\right)+(1000)\left(\dfrac{3}{5}\right)=\$800$

34. $(1000)\left(\dfrac{4}{5}\right)+(5000)\left(\dfrac{1}{5}\right)=\$1800$

35. $\left(100+200+300+400+1000\right)\left(\dfrac{1}{5}\right)=\$400$

36. $(600)\left(\dfrac{2}{5}\right)+(2000)\left(\dfrac{2}{5}\right)+(5000)\left(\dfrac{1}{5}\right)=\$2040$

37. a) $(8)\left(\dfrac{1}{2}\right)+(1)\left(\dfrac{1}{2}\right)=\$5.50$

    b) Fair price = \$5.50 + 2.00 = \$7.50

38. a) $(8)\left(\dfrac{1}{2}\right)+(3)\left(\dfrac{1}{4}\right)+(-1)\left(\dfrac{1}{4}\right)=\$4.50$

    b) Fair price = 4.50 + 2.00 = \$6.50

39. a) $(8)\left(\dfrac{1}{4}\right)+(3)\left(\dfrac{1}{4}\right)+(-1)\left(\dfrac{1}{2}\right)=\$2.25$

    b) Fair price = 2.25 + 2.00 = \$4.25

40. a) $(8)\left(\dfrac{3}{8}\right)+(3)\left(\dfrac{1}{4}\right)+(-1)\left(\dfrac{3}{8}\right)=\$3.38$

    b) Fair price = 3.38 + 2.00 = \$5.38

41. a) $(5-10)\left(\dfrac{2}{4}\right)+(20-10)\left(\dfrac{2}{4}\right)=\$2.50$

    b) Fair price = 2.50 + 10.00 = \$12.50

42. a) $(15-10)\left(\dfrac{3}{4}\right)+(0-10)\left(\dfrac{1}{4}\right)=\$1.25$

    b) Fair price = 1.25 + 10.00 = \$11.25

43. a)

$(0-10)\left(\dfrac{1}{4}\right)+(1-10)\left(\dfrac{1}{4}\right)+(5-10)\left(\dfrac{1}{4}\right)+(10-10)\left(\dfrac{1}{4}\right)=-\$6.00$

    b) Fair price = –6.00 + 10.00 = \$4.50

44. a)

$(2-10)\left(\dfrac{2}{4}\right)+(10-10)\left(\dfrac{1}{4}\right)+(400-10)\left(\dfrac{1}{4}\right)=\$93.50$

    b) Fair price = 93.50 + 10.00 = \$103.50

45. $E = P_1A_1 + P_2A_2 + P_3A_3 + P_4A_4 + P_5A_5 =$
$0.17(1) + 0.10(2) + 0.02(3) + 0.08(4) + 0.63(0) =$
0.75 base

46. $E_{company} = P(\text{insured lives})(\text{amount gained}) +$
$\qquad P(\text{insured dies})(\text{amount lost})$
$E_{co} = (0.994)(100) + (0.006)(9,900) = 99.4 - 59.4$
$\qquad = \$40$, which is the amount the company gains
$\qquad$ on this type of policy.

47. $E = P_1A_1 + P_2A_2 + P_3A_3$
$\qquad = \dfrac{3}{10}(4) + \dfrac{5}{10}(3) + \dfrac{2}{10}(1) = 1.2 + 1.5 + 0.2$
$\qquad = 2.9$ points

48. $E = P_1A_1 + P_2A_2 + P_3A_3$
$\qquad = \dfrac{3}{10}(5) + \dfrac{5}{10}(2) + \dfrac{2}{10}(-3) = 1.5 + 1.0 - 0.6$
$\qquad = 1.9$ points

49. $E = (0.65)(75) + (0.35)(20) = 55.75$
Expected number of new employees is 56.

50. $E = (0.6)(450,000) + (0.3)(120,000)$
$\qquad + (0.1)(-275,000)$
$\qquad = \$278,500$

51. $E = (0.75)(10,000) + (0.1)(0) + (0.15)(-2,000)$
$\qquad = \$7200$

52. $E = (0.40)(2,000) + (0.5)(750) + (0.10)(0)$
$\qquad = \$1175$

53. $E = P(1)(1) + P(2)(2) + P(3)(3) + P(4)(4) + P(5)(5)$
$\qquad + P(6)(6)$
$\qquad = \dfrac{1}{6}(1) + \dfrac{1}{6}(2) + \dfrac{1}{6}(3) + \dfrac{1}{6}(4) + \dfrac{1}{6}(5) + \dfrac{1}{6}(6)$
$\qquad = \dfrac{21}{6} = 3.5$ points

44. $E = P_1A_1 + P_2A_2 + P_3A_3$
$\qquad = 0.70(40,000) + 0.10(0) + 0.20(-30,000)$
$\qquad = 28,000 + 0 - 6,000 = \$22,000$

45. $E = P_1A_1 + P_2A_2 + P_3A_3$
$\qquad = \dfrac{200}{365}(110) + \dfrac{100}{365}(160) + \dfrac{65}{365}(210)$
$\qquad = 60.27 + 43.84 + 37.40 = 141.51$ calls/day

56. Profit if Jorge sells the house $= 0.06(100,000)$
$\qquad = \$6,000$
Profit if another Realtor sells the house $=$
$0.03(100,000) = \$3,00$
$E = P_1A_1 + P_2A_2 + P_3A_3$
$\qquad = 0.2(5000) + 0.5(2000) + 0.3(1000)$
$\qquad = \$1,000 + \$1,000 - \$300 = \$1,700$ gain
Yes, in the long run if Jorge lists many of these
$\$100,000$ homes, he can expect to make, on
average, $\$1,700$ per listing.

57. a) $P(1) = \dfrac{1}{2} + \dfrac{1}{16} = \dfrac{8}{16} + \dfrac{1}{16} = \dfrac{9}{16}$,
$\qquad P(10) = \dfrac{1}{4} = \dfrac{4}{16}$,
$\qquad P(\$20) = \dfrac{1}{8} = \dfrac{2}{16}$, $P(\$100) = \dfrac{1}{16}$

b) $E = P_1A_1 + P_2A_2 + P_3A_3 + P_4A_4$
$\qquad = \dfrac{9}{16}(\$1) + \dfrac{4}{16}(\$10) + \dfrac{2}{16}(\$20) + \dfrac{1}{16}(\$100)$
$\qquad = \dfrac{9}{16} + \dfrac{40}{16} + \dfrac{40}{16} + \dfrac{100}{16} = \dfrac{189}{16} = \$11.81$

c) fair price $=$ expected value $-$ cost to play $=$
$\$11.81 - 0 = \$11.81$

58. a) $P(\$1) = \dfrac{1}{6} + \dfrac{1}{4} = \dfrac{2}{12} + \dfrac{3}{12} = \dfrac{5}{12} = \dfrac{10}{24}$,
$\qquad P(\$10) = \dfrac{1}{6} = \dfrac{4}{24}$,
$\qquad P(\$20) = \dfrac{1}{6} + \dfrac{1}{8} = \dfrac{4}{24} + \dfrac{3}{24} = \dfrac{7}{24}$,
$\qquad P(\$100) = \dfrac{1}{8} = \dfrac{3}{24}$

58. b) $E = P_1A_1 + P_2A_2 + P_3A_3 + P_4A_4$
$\qquad = \dfrac{10}{24}(1) + \dfrac{4}{24}(10) + \dfrac{7}{24}(20) + \dfrac{3}{24}(100)$
$\qquad = \dfrac{10}{24} + \dfrac{40}{24} + \dfrac{140}{24} + \dfrac{300}{24} = \dfrac{490}{24} = \$20.42$

c) fair price $=$ expected value $-$ cost to play $=$
$\$20.42 - 0 = \$20.42$

59. E = P(insured lives)(cost) + P(insured dies)(cost −
    $40,000)
    = 0.97(cost) + 0.03(cost − 40,000)
    = 0.97(cost) + 0.03(cost) − 1200
    = 1.00(cost) − 1200
    Thus, in order for the company to make a profit,
    the cost must exceed $1,200

60. No, you don't know how many others are
    selecting the same numbers that you are selecting.

61. E = P(win)(amount won) + P(lose)(amount lost)

$$= \left(\frac{1}{38}\right)(35) + \left(\frac{37}{38}\right)(-1) = \frac{35}{38} - \frac{37}{38} = -\frac{2}{38}$$

$$= -\$0.053$$

62. E = P(win)(amount won) + P(lose)(amount lost) = $\left(\frac{18}{38}\right)(1) + \left(\frac{20}{38}\right)(-1) = \frac{18}{38} - \frac{20}{38} = -\frac{2}{38} = -\$0.053$

63. a) E = $\frac{1}{12}(100) + \frac{1}{12}(200) + \frac{1}{12}(300) + \frac{1}{12}(400) + \frac{1}{12}(500) + \frac{1}{12}(600) + \frac{1}{12}(700) + \frac{1}{12}(800) + \frac{1}{12}(900)$

$\frac{1}{12}(1000) = \left(\frac{5500}{12}\right) = \$458.3\overline{3}$

b) E = $\frac{1}{12}(5500) + \frac{1}{12}(-1800) = \frac{3700}{12} = \$308.33$

Exercise Set 12.5

1. If a first experiment can be performed in *M* distinct ways and a second experiment can be performed in
   N distinct ways, then the two experiments in that specific order can be performed in *M·N* distinct
   ways.

2. a) A list of all the possible outcomes of an experiment.
   b) Each individual outcome in a sample space is a sample point.

3. (2)(7) = 14 ways. Using the counting principle.

4. Answers will vary.

5. The first selection is made. Then the second selection is made before the first selection is returned to the
   group of items being selected from.

6. (5)(3) = 15 ways

7. a) (50)(50) = 2500   b) (50)(49) = 2450

8. a) (365)(365) = 133,225   b) (365)(364) = 132,860

9. a) (7)(7)(7) = 343   b) (7)(6)(5) = 210

10. a) (10)(10) = 100   b) (10)(9) = 90

11. a) (2)(2) = 4 points
    b)

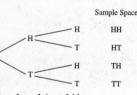

    c) P(no heads) = 1/4
    d) P(exactly one head) = 2/4 = 1/2
    e) P(two heads) = 1/4

12. a) (2)(2) = 4 points
    b)

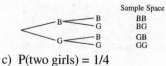

    c) P(two girls) = 1/4
    d) P(at least one girl) = 3/4
    e) P(girl 1ˢᵗ and boy 2ⁿᵈ) = 1/4

13. a) (3)(3) = 9 points

b)

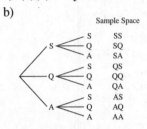

Sample Space

c) P(two apples) = 1/9

d) P(sun and then question mark) = 1/9

e) P(at least one apple) = 5/9

14. a) (3)(2) = 6 points

b)

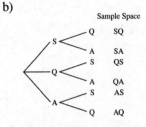

Sample Space

c) P(two apples) = 0/6 = 0

d) P(sun and then question mark) = 1/6

e) P(at least one apple) = 4/6 = 2/3

15. a) (4)(3) = 12 points

b)

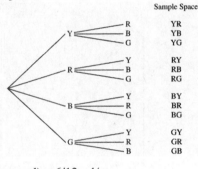

Sample Space

c) P(exactly one red) = 6/12 = ½

d) P(at least one is not red) = 12/12 = 1

e) P(no green) = 6/12 = 1/2

16. a) (2)(2)(2) = 8 points

b)

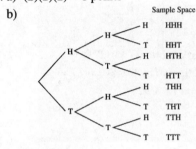

Sample Space

c) P(no heads) = 1/8

d) P(1 head) = 3/8

e) P(3 heads) = 1/8

17. a) (3)(3) = 9 points

b)

Sample Space

c) P(Java) = 1/3

d) P(Java and Oyster) = 1/9

e) P(paint other than Java) = 2/3

18. a) (4)(3) = 12 points

b)

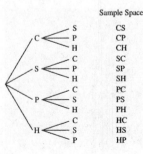

Sample Space

c) P(Persian cat) = 6/12 = 1/2

d) P(Persian cat and calico cat) = 2/12 = 1/6

e) P(not Persiann) = 6/12 = 1/2

19. a) (6)(6) = 36 points

b)

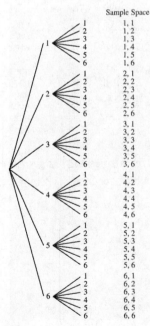

Sample Space

c) P(double) = 6/36 = 1/6

d) P(sum of 7) = 6/36 = 1/6

e) P(sum of 2) = 1/36

f) No; the P(sum of 2) < P(sum of 7)

20. a) (3)(3)(3) = 27 points
    b)

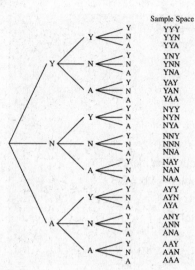

```
                                    Sample Space
                         Y          YYY
                   Y      N          YYN
                         A          YYA
                         Y          YNY
            Y      N      N          YNN
                         A          YNA
                         Y          YAY
                   A      N          YAN
                         A          YAA
                         Y          NYY
                   Y      N          NYN
                         A          NYA
                         Y          NNY
     N      N      N      N          NNN
                         A          NNA
                         Y          NAY
                   A      N          NAN
                         A          NAA
                         Y          AYY
                   Y      N          AYN
                         A          AYA
                         Y          ANY
     A      N      N                 ANN
                         A          ANA
                         Y          AAY
                   A      N          AAN
                         A          AAA
```

c) P(No vote on all three motions) = 1/27
d) P(Yes vote on exactly two motions) = 6/27 = 2/9
e) P(at least one yes vote) = 19/27

21. a) (3)(2)(1) = 6 points
    b)

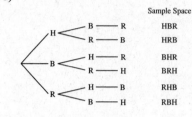

```
                              Sample Space
            B ——— R           HBR
     H <
            R ——— B           HRB
            H ——— R           BHR
     B <
            R ——— H           BRH
            H ——— B           RHB
     R <
            B ——— H           RBH
```

c) P(BB – 1st) = 2/6 = 1/3
d) P(Home Depot – 1st / RL - last) = 1/6
e) P(BB, RL, Home Depot) = 1/6

22. a) (3)(3)(2) = 18
    b)

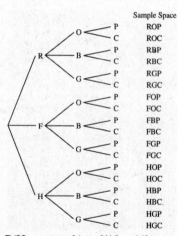

```
                              Sample Space
            P        ROP
     O <
            C        ROC
            P        RBP
R    B <
            C        RBC
            P        RGP
     G <
            C        RGC
            P        FOP
     O <
            C        FOC
            P        FBP
F    B <
            C        FBC
            P        FGP
     G <
            C        FGC
            P        HOP
     O <
            C        HOC
            P        HBP
H    B <
            C        HBC
            P        HGP
     G <
            C        HGC
```

c) P(Honeycomb) = 6/18 = 1/3
d) P(Rice Krispies and Ginger Ale) = 2/18 = 1/9
e) P(not black cherry) = 12/18 = 2/3

23. a) (3)(2)(3) = 18 points
    b)

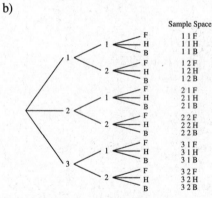

```
                              Sample Space
                   F          1 1 F
            1      H          1 1 H
                   B          1 1 B
     1             F          1 2 F
            2      H          1 2 H
                   B          1 2 B
                   F          2 1 F
            1      H          2 1 H
                   B          2 1 B
     2             F          2 2 F
            2      H          2 2 H
                   B          2 2 B
                   F          3 1 F
            1      H          3 1 H
                   B          3 1 B
     3             F          3 2 F
            2      H          3 2 H
                   B          3 2 B
```

c) P(two bedroom) = 6/18 = 1/3
d) P(two bedroom, fireplace) = 2/18 = 1/9
e) P(no balcony) = 12/18 = 2/3

24. a) (4)(2)(2) = 16 points
    b)

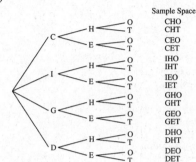

Sample Space

CHO
CHT
CEO
CET
IHO
IHT
IEO
IET
GHO
GHT
GEO
GET
DHO
DHT
DEO
DET

    c) P(Gateway) = 1/4
    d) P(H-P) = 1/2
    e) P(Gateway and H-P) = 2/16 = 1/8

25. a) (3)(3)(3) = 27
    b)

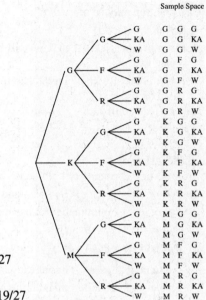

Sample Space

G G G
G G KA
G G W
G F G
G F KA
G F W
G R G
G R KA
G R W
K G G
K G KA
K G W
K F G
K F KA
K F W
K R G
K R KA
K R W
M G G
M G KA
M G W
M F G
M F KA
M F W
M R G
M R KA
M R W

    c) P(GE,GE,GE) = 1/27
    d) P(not GE) = 8/27
    e) P(at least 1 GE) = 19/27

26. a) (4)(2)(2) = 16 points
    b)

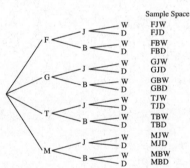

Sample Space

FJW
FJD
FBW
FBD
GJW
GJD
GBW
GBD
TJW
TJD
TBW
TBD
MJW
MJD
MBW
MBD

    c) P(*John Adams*) = 1/2
    d) P(*Farewell to Arms* or *Moby-Dick*) =
        2/4 = 1/2
    e) P(not *Moby-Dick*) = 3/4

27. a) (2)(4)(3) = 24 sample points
    b)

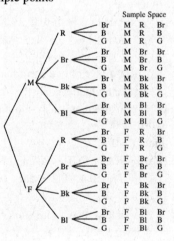

Sample Space

M R Br
M R B
M R G
M Br Br
M Br B
M Br G
M Bk Br
M Bk B
M Bk G
M Bl Br
M Bl B
M Bl G
F R Br
F R B
F R G
F Br Br
F Br B
F Br G
F Bk Br
F Bk B
F Bk G
F Bl Br
F Bl B
F Bl G

    c) P(M, black, blue) = 1/24
    d) P(F, blonde) = 3/24 = 1/8

28. a) (2)(2)(2)(2) = 16 sample points
    b)

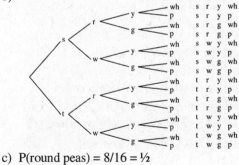

Sample Space

s r y wh
s r y p
s r g wh
s r g p
s w y wh
s w y p
s w g wh
s w g p
t r y wh
t r y p
t r g wh
t r g p
t w y wh
t w y p
t w g wh
t w g p

    c) P(round peas) = 8/16 = ½
    d) P(s, w, y, p) = 1/16

29. a) P(white) = 1/3
    b) P(red) = 2/3
    c) No; P(white) < P(red)
    d)

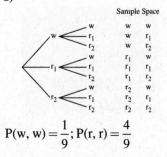

Sample Space

w w
w r_1
w r_2
r_1 w
r_1 r_1
r_1 r_2
r_2 w
r_2 r_1
r_2 r_2

$$P(w, w) = \frac{1}{9} ; P(r, r) = \frac{4}{9}$$

30. a) point up may be more likely
    b) {uu, ud, du, dd}
    c) If u is more likely than d, uu will be more likely than dd.
    d) Not unless we know the probabilities of the two outcomes.
    e) Answers will vary.

31. 1 red, 1 blue, and 1 brown

32. $60/(2 \cdot 6) = 5$; 5 faces

Exercise Set 12.6

1. a) A occurs, B occurs, or both occur   b) "and" means both events, A and B, must occur.
2. a) P(A or B) = P(A) + P(B) – P(A and B)
3. a) Two events are mutually exclusive if it is impossible for both events to occur simultaneously.
   b) P(A or B) = P(A) + P(B)
4. a) P(A and B) = P(A) $\cdot$ P(B)
5. We assume that event A has already occurred.
6. a) Two events are independent if the occurrence of either event in no way affects the probability of occurrence of the other event.
   b) Two events are dependent if the occurrence of either event affects the probability of occurrence of the other event.
7. a) No, it is possible for both to like classical music.
   b) No, if the mother likes classical music, the daughter might be more likely to like classical music.
8. a)   No; both events can occur at the same time
   b) Yes; the occurrence of one event has no effect on the occurrence of the other.
9. If the events are mutually exclusive, the events cannot happen simultaneously and thus P(A and B) = 0.

10. Answers will vary.

11. P(A and B) = 0.3
    P(A or B) = P(A) + P(B) – P(A and B)
    $= 0.6 + 0.4 - 0.3 = 1.0 - 0.3 = 0.7$

12. P(A or B) = 0.9
    P(A or B) = P(A) + P(B) – P(A and B)
    $0.9 = 0.7 + 0.5 - P(A \text{ and } B)$
    P(A and B) = 0.3

13. P(B) = P(A or B) + P(A and B) – P(A)
    $= 0.7 + 0.3 - 0.6 = 0.4$

14. P(A or B) = P(A) + P(B) – P(A and B)
    $0.6 = P(A) + 0.3 - 0.1$
    $0.6 = P(A) + 0.2$ $P(A) = 0.4$

15. P(M and E) = 0.55
    P(M or E) = P(M) + P(E) – P(M and E)
    $= 0.7 + 0.6 - 0.55 = 1.3 - 0.55 = 0.75$

16. P(O and B) = 0.2
    P(O or B) = P(O) + P(b) – P(O and B)
    $= 0.6 + 0.4 - 0.2 = 1.0 - 0.2 = 0.8$

17. P(2 or 5) = 1/6 + 1/6 = 2/6 = 1/3

18. P(odd number or greater than 4) =
    $P(1, 3, 5) + P(5, 6) - P(5) = \dfrac{1}{2} + \dfrac{3}{3} - \dfrac{1}{6} = \dfrac{2}{3}$

19. P(greater than 4 or less than 2) = P(5, 6. or 1) =
    2/6 + 1/6 = 3/6 = 1/2

20. All numbers on the die are either > 3 or < 5.
    P(> 3 or < 5) = 6/6 = 1

21. Since these events are mutually exclusive,
    P(ace or 2) = P(ace) + P(2) =
    $= \dfrac{4}{52} + \dfrac{4}{52} = \dfrac{8}{52} = \dfrac{2}{13}$

22. Since it is possible to obtain a card that is both a jack and a club when only one card is selected, these events are not mutually exclusive.
    P(jack or club) = P(jack) + P(club) –
    $P(\text{jack and club}) = \dfrac{4}{52} + \dfrac{13}{52} - \dfrac{1}{52} = \dfrac{16}{52} = \dfrac{4}{13}$

23. Since it is possible to obtain a card that is a picture card and a red card, these events are not mutually exclusive.

P(picture or red)

= P(pict.) + P(red) − P(pict. & red)

$$= \frac{12}{52} + \frac{26}{52} - \frac{6}{52} = \frac{32}{52} = \frac{8}{13}$$

24. Since it is impossible to obtain a card that is both a club and a red card, these events are mutually exclusive.

P(club or red) = P(club) + P(red) =

$$= \frac{13}{52} + \frac{26}{52} = \frac{39}{52} = \frac{3}{4}$$

25. Since it is possible to obtain a card less than 8 that is a club, these events are not mutually exclusive.

$$P(< 8 \text{ or club}) = \frac{28}{52} + \frac{13}{52} - \frac{7}{52} = \frac{34}{52} = \frac{17}{26}$$

26. Since it is possible to obtain a card greater than 9 that is black, these events are not mutually exclusive.

$$P(> 9 \text{ or black}) = \frac{16}{52} + \frac{26}{52} - \frac{8}{52} = \frac{34}{52} = \frac{17}{26}$$

27. a) P(monkey and monkey) =

$$\frac{5}{20} \cdot \frac{5}{20} = \frac{1}{4} \cdot \frac{1}{4} = \frac{1}{16}$$

   b) P(monkey and monkey) =

$$\frac{5}{20} \cdot \frac{4}{19} = \frac{1}{4} \cdot \frac{4}{19} = \frac{1}{19}$$

28. a) P(3 and 3) = $\dfrac{4}{20} \cdot \dfrac{4}{20} = \dfrac{1}{5} \cdot \dfrac{1}{5} = \dfrac{1}{25}$

   b) P(3 and 3) = $\dfrac{4}{20} \cdot \dfrac{3}{19} = \dfrac{1}{5} \cdot \dfrac{3}{19} = \dfrac{3}{95}$

29. a) P(lion and bird) = $\dfrac{5}{20} \cdot \dfrac{5}{20} = \dfrac{1}{4} \cdot \dfrac{1}{4} = \dfrac{1}{16}$

   b) P(lion and bird) = $\dfrac{5}{20} \cdot \dfrac{5}{19} = \dfrac{1}{4} \cdot \dfrac{5}{19} = \dfrac{5}{76}$

30. a) P(2 and 4) = $\dfrac{4}{20} \cdot \dfrac{4}{20} = \dfrac{1}{5} \cdot \dfrac{1}{5} = \dfrac{1}{25}$

   b) P(2 and 4) = $\dfrac{4}{20} \cdot \dfrac{4}{19} = \dfrac{1}{5} \cdot \dfrac{4}{19} = \dfrac{4}{95}$

31. a) P(red bird and monkey) =

$$\frac{3}{20} \cdot \frac{5}{20} = \frac{3}{20} \cdot \frac{1}{4} = \frac{3}{80}$$

   b) P(red bird and monkey) =

$$\frac{3}{20} \cdot \frac{5}{19} = \frac{15}{380} = \frac{3}{76}$$

32. a) P(even and even) = $\dfrac{8}{20} \cdot \dfrac{8}{20} = \dfrac{2}{5} \cdot \dfrac{2}{5} = \dfrac{4}{25}$

   b) P(even and even) = $\dfrac{8}{20} \cdot \dfrac{7}{19} = \dfrac{2}{5} \cdot \dfrac{7}{19} = \dfrac{14}{95}$

33. a) P(odd and odd) = $\dfrac{12}{20} \cdot \dfrac{12}{20} = \dfrac{3}{5} \cdot \dfrac{3}{5} = \dfrac{9}{25}$

   b) P(odd and odd) = $\dfrac{12}{20} \cdot \dfrac{11}{19} = \dfrac{3}{5} \cdot \dfrac{11}{19} = \dfrac{33}{95}$

34. a) P(lion and red bird) = $\dfrac{5}{20} \cdot \dfrac{3}{20} = \dfrac{1}{4} \cdot \dfrac{3}{20} = \dfrac{3}{80}$

   b) P(lion and red bird) = $\dfrac{5}{20} \cdot \dfrac{3}{19} = \dfrac{1}{4} \cdot \dfrac{3}{19} = \dfrac{3}{76}$

35. P(frog or even) = $\dfrac{5}{20} + \dfrac{8}{20} - \dfrac{2}{20} = \dfrac{11}{20}$

36. P(yellow bird or > 4) = $\dfrac{2}{20} + \dfrac{4}{20} = \dfrac{6}{20} = \dfrac{3}{10}$

37. P(lion or a 5) = $\dfrac{5}{20} + \dfrac{4}{20} - \dfrac{1}{20} = \dfrac{8}{20} = \dfrac{2}{5}$

38. P(red bird or even) = $\dfrac{3}{20} + \dfrac{8}{20} - \dfrac{1}{20} = \dfrac{10}{20} = \dfrac{1}{2}$

39. P(2 reds) = $\dfrac{1}{2} \cdot \dfrac{1}{2} = \dfrac{1}{4}$

40. P(red and then yellow) = $\dfrac{1}{2} \cdot \dfrac{1}{2} = \dfrac{1}{4}$

41. P(red and green) = $\frac{1}{4} \cdot \frac{1}{2} = \frac{1}{8}$

42. P(2 reds) = $\frac{1}{4} \cdot \frac{1}{4} = \frac{1}{16}$

43. P(2 yellows) = P(red and red) = $\frac{3}{8} \cdot \frac{3}{8} = \frac{9}{64}$

44. P(both not green = $\frac{6}{8} \cdot \frac{6}{8} = \frac{9}{16}$

45. P(2 reds) = $\frac{1}{2} \cdot \frac{1}{4} = \frac{1}{8}$

46. P(yellow then red) = $\frac{1}{2} \cdot \frac{1}{4} = \frac{1}{8}$

47. P(both not red) = $\frac{1}{2} \cdot \frac{3}{4} = \frac{3}{8}$

48. P(yellow and not yellow) = $\frac{1}{2} \cdot \frac{3}{4} = \frac{3}{8}$

49. P(green or red) = 4/7

50. P(not blue) = 5/7

51. P(both red) = (3/7)(3/7) = 9/49

52. P(blue then yellow) = (2/7)(1/7) = 2/49

53. P(all red) = (3/7)(2/6)(1/5) = 1/35

54. P(none red) = (4/7)(3/6)(2/5) = 4/35

55. P(R, B, B) = (3/7)(2/6)(1/5) = 1/35

56. P(R, G, R) = (3/7)(1/6)(2/5) = 1/35

57. P(3 girls) = P(1st girl) • P(2nd girl) • P(3rd girl)

$= \frac{1}{2} \cdot \frac{1}{2} \cdot \frac{1}{2} = \frac{1}{8}$

58. P(3 boys) = P(1st boy) • P(2nd boy) • P(3rd boy)

$= \frac{1}{2} \cdot \frac{1}{2} \cdot \frac{1}{2} = \frac{1}{8}$

59. P(G,G,B) = P(1st girl) • P(2nd girl) • P(3rd boy)

$= \frac{1}{2} \cdot \frac{1}{2} \cdot \frac{1}{2} = \frac{1}{8}$

60. P(G,B,G) = P(1st girl) • P(2nd boy) • P(3rd girl)

$= \frac{1}{2} \cdot \frac{1}{2} \cdot \frac{1}{2} = \frac{1}{8}$

61. a) P(5 boys) = P(b) • P(b) • P(b) • P(b) • P(b)

$= \frac{1}{2} \cdot \frac{1}{2} \cdot \frac{1}{2} \cdot \frac{1}{2} \cdot \frac{1}{2} = \frac{1}{32}$

b) P(next child is a boy) = $\frac{1}{2}$

62. a) P(8 girls) = $\frac{1}{2} \cdot \frac{1}{2} \cdot \frac{1}{2} \cdot \frac{1}{2} \cdot \frac{1}{2} \cdot \frac{1}{2} \cdot \frac{1}{2} \cdot \frac{1}{2} = \frac{1}{256}$

b) P(next child is a girl) = $\frac{1}{2}$

63. a) P(Titleist/Pinnacle) = $\frac{4}{7} \cdot \frac{1}{7} = \frac{4}{49}$

b) P(Titleist/Pinnacle) = $\frac{4}{7} \cdot \frac{1}{6} = \frac{4}{42} = \frac{2}{21}$

64. a) P(not Top Flite/not Top Flite) = $\frac{5}{7} \cdot \frac{5}{7} = \frac{25}{49}$

b) P(not Top Flite/not Top Flite)= $\frac{5}{7} \cdot \frac{4}{6} = \frac{20}{42} = \frac{10}{21}$

65. a) P(at least 1 Top Flite) = $\frac{2}{7} \cdot \frac{5}{7} + \frac{5}{7} \cdot \frac{2}{7} + \frac{2}{7} \cdot \frac{2}{7} = \frac{24}{49}$

b) P(at least 1 Top Flite)= $\frac{2}{7} \cdot \frac{5}{6} + \frac{5}{7} \cdot \frac{2}{6} + \frac{2}{7} \cdot \frac{1}{6} = \frac{11}{21}$

66. a) P(Pinnacle/Pinnacle) = $\frac{1}{7} \cdot \frac{1}{7} = \frac{1}{49}$

b) P(Pinnacle/Pinnacle) = $\frac{1}{7} \cdot \frac{0}{6} = 0$

67. P(neither had trad. ins.) = $\frac{31}{50} \cdot \frac{30}{49} = \frac{93}{245}$

68. P(both have managed care) = $\frac{24}{50} \cdot \frac{23}{49} = \frac{276}{1225}$

69. P(at least one trad.) = 1 – P(neither trad.) =
$1 - \dfrac{93}{245} = \dfrac{152}{245}$ (see Exercise 67)

70. P(trad. ins./managed care) = $\dfrac{19}{50} \cdot \dfrac{24}{49} = \dfrac{228}{1225}$

71. P(all recommended) = $\dfrac{23}{40} \cdot \dfrac{22}{39} \cdot \dfrac{21}{38} = \dfrac{1771}{9880}$

72. P(no/yes/yes) = $\dfrac{7}{40} \cdot \dfrac{23}{39} \cdot \dfrac{22}{38} = \dfrac{1771}{29,640}$

73. P(no/no/not sure) = $\dfrac{7}{40} \cdot \dfrac{6}{39} \cdot \dfrac{10}{38} = \dfrac{7}{988}$

74. P(yes/no/no) = $\dfrac{23}{40} \cdot \dfrac{7}{39} \cdot \dfrac{6}{38} = \dfrac{161}{9880}$

75. The probability that any individual reacts favorably is 70/100 or 0.7.
P(Mrs. Rivera reacts favorably) = 0.7

76. P(Mr. Rivera and Mrs. Rivera react favorably and Carlos is unaffected) = P(Mr. Rivera reacts favorably) • P(Mrs. Rivera reacts favorably) • P(Carlos is unaffected) = 0.7•0.7•0.2 = 0.098

77. P(all 3 react favorably) = 0.7•0.7•0.7 = 0.343

78. One does not react favorably if the reaction is unfavorable or if it is unaffected.
P(not favorable) = 0.1 + 0.2 = 0.3. Therefore,
P(none reacts favorably) = $(0.3)^3 = 0.027$

79. Since each question has four possible answers of which only one is correct, the probability of guessing correctly on any given question is 1/4.
P(correct answer on any one question) = ¼

80. If you have guessed correctly on only the first question, then you have missed the last four. The probability of missing any given question is 3/4.
P(only the 1st correct) = P(1st corr)•P(2nd incorr) •P(3rd incorr)•P(4th incorr)•P(5th incorr)
= (1/4)(3/4)(3/4)(3/4)(3/4) = 81/1024

81. P(only the 3rd and 4th questions correct) =
$\left(\dfrac{3}{4}\right)\left(\dfrac{3}{4}\right)\left(\dfrac{1}{4}\right)\left(\dfrac{1}{4}\right)\left(\dfrac{3}{4}\right) = \dfrac{27}{1024}$

82. P(all 5 questions correct) =
$\left(\dfrac{1}{4}\right)\left(\dfrac{1}{4}\right)\left(\dfrac{1}{4}\right)\left(\dfrac{1}{4}\right)\left(\dfrac{1}{4}\right) = \dfrac{1}{1024}$

83. P(none of the 5 questions correct) =
$\left(\dfrac{3}{4}\right)\left(\dfrac{3}{4}\right)\left(\dfrac{3}{4}\right)\left(\dfrac{3}{4}\right)\left(\dfrac{3}{4}\right) = \dfrac{243}{1024}$

84. P(at least one is correct) = 1 – P(none are correct) = $1 - \dfrac{243}{1024} = \dfrac{781}{1024}$

85. P(orange on 1st reel) = 5/22

86. P(bells on all 3 reels) =
P(Be on 1st)P(Be on 2nd)P(Be on 3rd) =
$\left(\dfrac{3}{22}\right)\left(\dfrac{4}{22}\right)\left(\dfrac{4}{22}\right) = \dfrac{48}{10648} = \dfrac{6}{1331}$

87. P(no bar/no bar/no bar) =
$\left(\dfrac{20}{22}\right)\left(\dfrac{20}{22}\right)\left(\dfrac{21}{22}\right) = \dfrac{1050}{1331}$

88. P(7/7/7) = $\left(\dfrac{1}{22}\right)\left(\dfrac{1}{22}\right)\left(\dfrac{1}{22}\right) = \dfrac{1}{10648}$

89. P(blue/blue) = $\left(\dfrac{2}{8}\right)\left(\dfrac{2}{12}\right) = \dfrac{4}{96} = \dfrac{1}{24}$

90. P(red on outer and blue on inner) =
$\dfrac{4}{12} \cdot \dfrac{2}{8} = \dfrac{1}{3} \cdot \dfrac{1}{4} = \dfrac{1}{12}$

91. P(not red on outer and not red on inner) =
$$\frac{8}{12}\cdot\frac{5}{8}=\frac{5}{12}$$

92. P(at least one is red) = 1 – P(neither is red) =
$$1-\frac{5}{12}=\frac{7}{12}$$

93. P(no hit/no hit) = (0.6)(0.6) = 0.36

94. P(hit/no hit) = (0.4)(0.1) = 0.04

95. P(both hit) = (0.4)(0.9) = 0.36

96. P(1st miss/2nd hit) = (0.6)(0.4) = 0.24

97. a) No; The probability of the 2nd depends on the outcome of the first.

   b) P(one afflicted) = .001

   c) P(both afflicted) = (.001)(.04) = .00004

   d) P(afflicted/not afflicted) = (0.001)(.96) = (.00096)

   e) P(not afflicted/afflicted) = (.999)(.001) = .000999

   f) P(not affl/not affl) = (.999)(.999) = .998001

98. a) P(Mrs. Jones # is selected) = (1/10)(1/10)(1/10) = .001

99. P(audit this year) = .036

100. P(audited next 2 years) = (.036)(.036) = .001296

101. P(audit/no audit) = (.036)(.964) = .034704

102. P(no audit/no audit) = (.964)(.964) = .929296

103. P(2 - same color) = P(2 r) + P(2 b) + P(2 y)
$$=\left(\frac{5}{10}\right)\left(\frac{4}{9}\right)+\left(\frac{3}{10}\right)\left(\frac{2}{9}\right)+\left(\frac{2}{10}\right)\left(\frac{1}{9}\right)$$
$$=\left(\frac{20}{90}\right)+\left(\frac{6}{90}\right)+\left(\frac{2}{90}\right)=\frac{28}{90}=\frac{14}{45}$$

104. P(at least 1 1-peso coin) =
   = 1 – P(neither coin is 1 peso)
$$=1-\left(\frac{7}{10}\right)\left(\frac{6}{9}\right)=\frac{8}{15}$$

105. P(no diamonds) = $\left(\frac{39}{52}\right)\left(\frac{38}{51}\right)=\frac{1482}{2652}=.56$

   The game favors the dealer since the probability of no diamonds is greater than 1/2.

106. The other card could be the ace or the queen and it is equally likely that it is either one.
   Thus, the probability the card is the queen is 1/2.

107. P(2/2) = (2/6)(2/6) = 4/36 = 1/9

108. P(3/3) = (3/6)(3/6) = 9/36 = 1/4

109. P(even or < 3) = 2/6 + 3/6 – 2/6 = 3/6 = 1/2

110. P(odd or > 1) = 4/6 + 5/6 -3/6 = 6/6 = 1

Exercise Set 12.7

1. The probability of E_2 given that E_1 has occurred.

2. $P(E_2\,|\,E_1)=\dfrac{n(E_1\text{ and }E_2)}{n(E_1)}$

3. $P(E_2\,|\,E_1)=\dfrac{n(E_1\text{ and }E_2)}{n(E_1)}=\dfrac{4}{12}=\dfrac{1}{3}$

4. $P(E_2\,|\,E_1)=\dfrac{5}{22}$

5. P(5 | orange) = 1/3

6. P(3 | yellow) = 0

7. P(even | not orange) = 2/3

8. P(> 2 | < 5) = 1/4

9. P(red | orange) = 2/3

10. P(> 3 | yellow) = 1/2

11. P(circle | odd) = 3/4

12. P(circle | ≥ 5) = 2/3

13. P(red | even) = 2/3

14. P(red or blue | even) = 1

15. P(circle or square | < 4) = 2/3

16. P(circle | even) = 0

17. P(4 | purple) = 1/5

18. P(even | red) = 1/3

19. P(purple | odd) = 2/6 = 1/3

20. P(> 6 | red) = 1/3

21. P(> 4 | purple) = 3/5

22. P(even | red or purple) = 4/8 = 1/2

23. P(gold | > 5) = 1/7

24. P(gold | > 10) = 0

25. P(1 and 1) = (1/4)(1/4) = 1/16

26. P(1 and 1) = 1/4

27. P(5 | at least a 5) = 1/7

28. P(> 5 | 2nd bill = 10) = 2/4 = ½

29. P(sum = 6) = 5/36

30. P(6 | 1) = 1/6

31. P(6 | 3) = 1/6

32. P(even | 2nd die = 2) = 3/6 = ½

33. P(> 7 | 2nd die = 5) = 4/6 = 2/3

34. P(7 or 11 | 1st die = 5) = 2/6 = 1/3

35. P(C4) = 3/9 = 1/3

36. P(at least $16B) = 2/9

37. P(at least $20B | C4) = 1/3

38. P(at least $10B | C3) = 2/4 = 1/2

39. P(C5 | at least $25B) = 1/2

40. P(C3 | at least $10B) = 2/5

41. $P(\text{car}) = \dfrac{1462}{2461} = 0.5941$

42. $P(\text{E-Z}) = \dfrac{843}{2461} = 0.3425$

43. $P(\text{E-Z} \,|\, \text{car}) = \dfrac{527}{1462} = 0.3605$

44. $P(\text{E-Z} \,|\, \text{truck}) = \dfrac{316}{999} = 0.3163$

45. $P(\text{car} \,|\, \text{E-Z}) = \dfrac{527}{843} = 0.6251$

46. $P(\text{truck} \,|\, \text{E-Z}) = \dfrac{316}{843} = 0.3749$

47. $P(\text{agg}) = \dfrac{350}{650} = \dfrac{7}{13}$

48. $P(\text{sale}) = \dfrac{320}{650} = \dfrac{32}{65}$

49. $P(\text{no sale} \,|\, \text{pass}) = \dfrac{80}{300} = \dfrac{4}{15}$

50. $P(\text{sale} \,|\, \text{agg}) = \dfrac{100}{350} = \dfrac{2}{7}$

51. $P(\text{sale} \,|\, \text{pass}) = \dfrac{220}{300} = \dfrac{11}{15}$

52. $P(\text{no sale} \,|\, \text{agg}) = \dfrac{250}{350} = \dfrac{5}{7}$

53. $P(\text{male}) = \dfrac{145}{295} = \dfrac{29}{59}$

54. $P(\text{15-64}) = \dfrac{198}{295}$

55. $P(\text{15-64} \,|\, \text{female}) = \dfrac{99}{150} = \dfrac{33}{50}$

56. $P(\text{65+} \,|\, \text{female}) = \dfrac{21}{150} = \dfrac{7}{50}$

57. $P(\text{female} \,|\, \text{0-14}) = \dfrac{30}{61}$

58. $P(\text{male} \,|\, \text{15-64}) = \dfrac{99}{198} = \dfrac{1}{2}$

59. $P(\text{good}) = \dfrac{300}{330} = \dfrac{10}{11}$

60. $P(\text{good} \,|\, \text{50 watts}) = \dfrac{100}{105} = \dfrac{20}{21}$

61. $P(\text{defective} \,|\, \text{20 watts}) = \dfrac{15}{95} = \dfrac{3}{19}$

62. $P(\text{good} \,|\, \text{100 watts}) = \dfrac{120}{130} = \dfrac{12}{13}$

63. P(good | 50 or 100 watts) = $\frac{220}{235} = \frac{44}{47}$

64. P(defective | not 50 watts) = $\frac{25}{225} = \frac{1}{9}$

65. P(ABC or NBC) = $\frac{110}{270} = \frac{11}{27}$

66. P(ABC | woman) = $\frac{50}{125} = \frac{2}{5}$

67. P(ABC or NBC | man) = $\frac{50}{145} = \frac{10}{29}$

68. P(not CBS | woman) = $\frac{105}{125} = \frac{21}{25}$

69. P(ABC,NBC,or CBS | man) = $\frac{55}{145} = \frac{11}{29}$

70. P(NBC or CBS | Woman) = $\frac{30}{125} = \frac{6}{25}$

71. P(large company stock) = 93/200

72. P(value stock) = 73/200

73. P(blend | medium co. stock) = 15/52

74. P(large co. stock | blend stock) = 23/50

75. a) n(A) = 140   b) n(B) = 120
    c) P(A) = 140/200 = 7/10
    d) P(B) = 120/200 = 6/10 = 3/5
    e) P(A | B) = $\frac{n(B\,and\,A)}{n(B)} = \frac{80}{120} = \frac{2}{3}$
    f) P(B | A) = $\frac{n(A\,and\,B)}{n(B)} = \frac{80}{140} = \frac{4}{7}$
    g) P(A)•P(B) = $\left(\frac{7}{10}\right)\left(\frac{3}{5}\right) = \frac{21}{50}$

    P(A | B)   P(A)•P(B) $\frac{2}{3} \neq \frac{21}{50}$

    A and B are not independent events.

76. P(E$_2$ | E$_1$) = $\dfrac{P(E_1 and\,E_2)}{P(E_1)} = \dfrac{\dfrac{n(E_1 and\,E_2)}{n}}{\dfrac{n(E_1)}{n}}$

    $= \dfrac{n(E_1 and\,E_2)}{n} \cdot \dfrac{n}{n(E_1)} = \dfrac{n(E_1 and\,E_2)}{n(E_1)}$

    $\therefore$ P(E$_2$ | E$_1$) = $\dfrac{n(E_1 and\,E_2)}{n(E_1)}$

77. a) $P(A|B) = \dfrac{P(A\,and\,B)}{P(B)} = \dfrac{0.15}{0.5} = 0.3$

    b) $P(B|A) = \dfrac{P(A\,and\,B)}{P(A)} = \dfrac{0.15}{0.3} = 0.5$

    c) Yes, $P(A) = P(A \mid B)$ and $P(B) = P(B \mid A)$.

78. P(green circle | +) = 1/3

79. P(+ | orange circle) = 1/2

80. P(yellow circle | -) = 1/3

81. P(green + | +) = 1/3

82. P(green or orange circle | green +) = 1

83. P(orange circle w/green + | +) = 0

Exercise Set 12.8

1. If a first experiment can be performed in M distinct ways and a second experiment can be performed in N distinct ways, then the two experiments in that specific order can be performed in $M \cdot N$ distinct ways.

2. A permutation is an ordered arrangement of a set of objects.

3. a) $n! = n(n-1)(n-2) \cdots 3 \cdot 2 \cdot 1$

    b) $\dfrac{n!}{n_1!n_2!\cdots n_r!}$

4. Multiply the counting numbers from n down to 1.

5. The number of permutations of n items taken r at a time.

6. Yes, because 0! = 1! = 1

7. $_nP_r = \dfrac{n!}{(n-r)!}$

8. a) All factors in the denominator have corresponding equal factors in the numerator, leaving only the factor 500 in the numerator.
   b) 500

9. $4! = 24$

10. $7! = 5040$

11. $_7P_2 = \dfrac{7!}{5!} = 7 \cdot 6 = 42$

12. $_5P_2 = \dfrac{5!}{3!} = 5 \cdot 4 = 20$

13. $0! = 1$

14. $_6P_4 = \dfrac{6!}{2!} = 6 \cdot 5 \cdot 4 \cdot 3 = 360$

15. $_8P_0 = \dfrac{8!}{8!} = 1$

16. $_6P_0 = \dfrac{6!}{6!} = 1$

17. $_9P_4 = \dfrac{9!}{5!} = 9 \cdot 8 \cdot 7 \cdot 6 = 3024$

18. $_3P_3 = \dfrac{3!}{0!} = 3! = 6$

19. $_8P_3 = \dfrac{8!}{5!} = 8 \cdot 7 \cdot 6 = 336$

20. $_{10}P_6 = \dfrac{10!}{4!} = 10 \cdot 9 \cdot 8 \cdot 7 \cdot 6 \cdot 5 = 151200$

21. $(10)(10)(10)(10) = 10000$

22. $(9)(8) = 72$

23. a) $(26)(25)(24)(10)(9) = 1,404,000$
    b) $(26)(26)(26)(10)(10) = 1,757,600$

24. a) $(36)(36)(36)(36) = 1,679,616$
    b) $(62)(62)(62)(62) = 14,776,336$

25. a) $5^5 = 3125$
    b) $\dfrac{1}{3125} = 0.00032$

26. $10^9 = 1,000,000,000$

27. $(34)(36)(36)(36)(36) = 57,106,944$

28. $7 \cdot 6 \cdot 5 = 210$

29. $(7)(4)(3)(4) = 336$

30. a) $5! = 120$ b) $5! = 120$
    c) $4! = 24$ d) $3! = 6$

31. a) $6! = 720$ b) $5! = 120$
    c) $4! = 24$ d) $5! \cdot 5 = 600$

32. $(15)(14)(13) = 2730$

33. $_{10}P_3 = \dfrac{10!}{(10-3)!} = \dfrac{10!}{7!} = \dfrac{10 \cdot 9 \cdot 8 \cdot 7!}{7!} = 720$

34. $10^{10} = 10,000,000,000$ possible ISBN numbers

35. a) There are 12 individuals and they can be arranged in $12! = 479,001,600$ ways
    b) $10! = 3,628,800$ different ways
    c) $5! \cdot 5! = 14,400$ different ways

36. a) $9! = 362,880$
    b) $5 \cdot 7! \cdot 4 = 100,800$
    c) $4 \cdot 3 \cdot 7! = 60,480$

37. $(26)(25)(24)(10)(9)(8)(7) = 78,624,000$

38. $(26)(26)(26)(10)(10)(10)(10) = 175,760,000$

39. $(26)(10)(9)(8)(7) = 131,040$

40. $(4)(25)(24)(10)(9)(8)(7) = 12,096,000$

41. $(10)(10)(10)(26)(26) = 676,000$

42. $(10)(9)(8)(26)(25) = 468,000$

43. $(5)(4)(8)(26)(25) = 104,000$

44. $(9)(9)(8)(26)(25) = 421,200$

45. a) $(8)(10)(10)(10)(10)(10)(10) = 8,000,000$
    b) $(8)(10)(10)(8,000,000) = 6,400,000,000$
    c) $(8)(10)(10)(8)(10^{10}) = (64)(10^{12})$
       $= 64,000,000,000,000$

46. $(12)(11)(10)(9) = 11,880$

47. $(15)(14)(13)(12)(11)(10) = 3,603,600$

48. $_{10}P_{10} = \dfrac{10!}{(10-10)!} = \dfrac{10!}{0!}$
    $= (10)(9)(8)(7)(6)(5)(4)(3)(2)(1) = 3,628,800$

49. $_7P_7 = \dfrac{7!}{0!} = \dfrac{7!}{1} = 7! = 5,040$

50. $(3)(3)(3)(3)(3)(3) = 3^6 = 729$ ways

51. $(5)(4)(7)(2) = 280$ systems

52. $(5)(2)(6) = 60$

53. $_9P_9 = \dfrac{9!}{0!} = 9! = 362,880$

54. $\dfrac{9!}{2!} = 181,440$

55. $\dfrac{10!}{3!2!} = 302,400$

56. $\dfrac{11!}{4!4!2!} = 34,650$

57. $\dfrac{7!}{2!2!2!} = 630$

    (There are 2 6's, 2 7's, and 2 8's.)

58. $\dfrac{7!}{3!2!} = 420$

    (There are 3 2's and 2 3's.)

59. The order of the flags is important. Thus, it is a permutation problem.

    $_9P_5 = \dfrac{9!}{(9-5)!} = \dfrac{9!}{4!} = (9)(8)(7)(6)(5) = 15,120$

60. $3^{12} = 531,441$

61. a) Since the pitcher must bat last, there is only one possibility for the last position. $\underline{1}$
       There are 8 possible batters left for the 1st position. Once the 1st batter has been selected, there are
       7 batters left for the 2nd position, 6 for the third, etc. $\underline{(8)}\,\underline{(7)}\,\underline{(6)}\,\underline{(5)}\,\underline{(4)}\,\underline{(3)}\,\underline{(2)}\,\underline{(1)}\,\underline{(1)} = 40,320$
    b) $9! = (9)(8)(7)(6)(5)(4)(3)(2)(1) = 362,880$

62. a) Since each arrangement is distinct, this is a permutation. Many problems of this type can be done with both the counting principle and the permutation formula.
       counting principle $= (5)(4)(3)(2)(1) = 120$
       permutation formula $= {}_5P_5$
       $= \dfrac{5!}{(5-5)!} = \dfrac{5!}{0!} = 120$

62. b) Consider the possible arrangements as indicated by the dashes. $\underline{}\,\underline{}\,\underline{}\,\underline{}\,\underline{}$ There is only one possibility for the middle position. $\underline{}\,\underline{}\,\underline{1}\,\underline{}\,\underline{}$ After the middle one is placed there are 4 possibilities for the 1st position, 3 for the 2nd, 2 for the 4th, and only 1 for the final position. $\underline{(4)}\,\underline{(3)}\,\underline{(1)}\,\underline{(2)}\,\underline{(1)} = 24$

63. a) $5^5 = 3125$ different keys
    b) $400,000 \div 3,125 = 128$ cars
    c) $\dfrac{1}{3125} = 0.00032$

64. $_8P_3 + 1 = \dfrac{8!}{5!} + 1 = 8 \cdot 7 \cdot 6 + 1 = 336 + 1 = 337$

65. $_7P_5 = \dfrac{7!}{2!} = \dfrac{7 \cdot 6 \cdot 5 \cdot 4 \cdot 3 \cdot 2!}{2!} = 2,520$ different

    letter permutations; $2500 \times \dfrac{1}{12} = 210$ minutes

    or $3\dfrac{1}{2}$ hours

66. $\dfrac{7!}{3!2!} = 420$,   Time $= 420 \times 5$ sec. $= 2{,}100$ sec.
or 35 min.

67. No, Ex. $_3P_2 \neq {_3}P_{(3\text{-}2)}$

$\dfrac{3!}{1!} \neq \dfrac{3!}{2!}$ because $6 \neq 3$

68. A $\bigcirc\ \bigcirc\ \bigcirc\ \bigcirc\ \bigcirc\ \bigcirc$ B
$(8)(7) = 56$ tickets

69. $(25)(24) = 600$ tickets

70. a) $\dfrac{6!}{2!} = 360$ b) CHOICE

71. a) $\dfrac{7!}{2!} = 2520$ b) SCROOGE

Exercise Set 12.9

1. The selection of a certain number of items without regard to their order.

2. The number of combinations possible when r items are selected from n items.

3. $_nC_r = \dfrac{n!}{(n-r)! \cdot r!}$

4. $_nC_r = \dfrac{_nP_r}{r!}$

5. If the order of the items is important then it is a permutation problem. If order is not important then it is a combination problem.

6. There will be more permutations.

7. $_4C_2 = \dfrac{4!}{(4-2)!2!} = \dfrac{(4)(3)(2)(1)}{(2)(1)(2)(1)} = 6$

8. $_8C_3 = \dfrac{8!}{5!3!} = \dfrac{(8)(7)(6)}{(3)(2)(1)} = 56$

9. a) $_6C_4 = \dfrac{6!}{2!4!} = \dfrac{(6)(5)}{(2)(1)} = 15$

   b) $_6P_4 = \dfrac{6!}{(6-4)!} = \dfrac{6!}{2!} = (6)(5)(4)(3) = 360$

10. a) $_8C_2 = \dfrac{8!}{6!2!} = \dfrac{(8)(7)}{(2)(1)} = 28$

    b) $_8P_2 = \dfrac{8!}{(8-2)!} = \dfrac{8!}{6!} = (8)(7) = 56$

11. a) $_8C_0 = \dfrac{8!}{8!0!} = 1$

    b) $_8P_0 = \dfrac{8!}{(8-0)!} = \dfrac{8!}{8!} = 1$

12. a) $_{12}C_8 = \dfrac{12!}{4!8!} = \dfrac{(12)(11)(10)(9)(8!)}{(4)(3)(2)(1)(8!)} = 495$

    b) $_{12}P_8 = \dfrac{12!}{(12-8)!} = \dfrac{12!}{4!}$

    $= (12)(11)(10)(9)(8)(7)(6)(5) = 19{,}958{,}400$

13. a) $_{10}C_3 = \dfrac{10!}{7!3!} = \dfrac{(10)(9)(8)(7!)}{(7!)(3)(2)(1)} = 120$

    b) $_{10}P_3 = \dfrac{10!}{(10-3)!} = \dfrac{(10)(9)(8)(7!)}{7!} = 720$

14. a) $_5C_5 = \dfrac{5!}{0!5!} = \dfrac{5!}{5!} = 1$

    b) $_5P_5 = \dfrac{5!}{(5-5)!} = \dfrac{5!}{1} = 120$

15. $\dfrac{_5C_3}{_5P_3} = \dfrac{\frac{5!}{2!3!}}{\frac{5!}{2!}} = \left(\dfrac{5!}{2!3!}\right)\left(\dfrac{2!}{5!}\right) = \dfrac{1}{3!} = \dfrac{1}{6}$

16. $\dfrac{_7C_2}{_7P_2} = \dfrac{\frac{7!}{5!2!}}{\frac{7!}{5!}} = \left(\dfrac{7!}{5!2!}\right)\left(\dfrac{5!}{7!}\right) = \dfrac{1}{2!} = \dfrac{1}{2}$

17. $_9C_4 \over _9C_2$ $= {9! \over 5!4! \over 9! \over 7!2!} = \left({9! \over 5!4!}\right)\left({7!2! \over 9!}\right) = {(7)(6) \over (4)(3)} = {7 \over 2}$

18. $_6C_6 \over _8C_0$ $= {6! \over 0!6! \over 8! \over 8!0!} = {1 \over 1} = 1$

19. $_9P_5 \over _{10}C_4$ $= {9! \over 4! \over 10! \over 6!4!} = {(9)(8)(7)(6)(5) \over (10)(9)(8)(7) \over (4)(3)(2)(1)} = {144 \over 2} = 72$

20. $_7P_0 \over _7C_0$ $= {7! \over 7! \over 7! \over 7!0!} = {1 \over 1} = 1$

21. $_8C_2 = {8! \over 6!2!} = {(8)(7)(6!) \over (2)(1)(6!)} = 28$ ways

22. $_{20}C_3 = {20! \over 17!3!} = {(20)(19)(18)(17!) \over (17!)(3)(2)(1)} = 1140$

23. $_5C_4 = {5! \over 1!4!} = 5$

24. $_9C_2 = {9! \over 7!2!} = {(9)(8) \over (2)(1)} = 36$

25. $_8C_3 = {8! \over 5!3!} = {(8)(7)(6) \over (3)(2)(1)} = 56$

26. $_{10}C_3 = {10! \over 7!3!} = {(10)(9)(8) \over (3)(2)(1)} = 120$

27. $_7C_4 = {7! \over 3!4!} = {(7)(6)(5) \over (3)(2)(1)} = 35$

28. $_{24}C_{20} = {24! \over 4!20!} = {(24)(23)(22)(21) \over (4)(3)(2)(1)} = 10{,}626$

29. $_{12}C_8 = {12! \over 4!8!} = {(12)(11)(10)(9) \over (4)(3)(2)(1)} = 495$

30. $_6C_4 = {6! \over 2!4!} = {(6)(5) \over (2)(1)} = 15$

31. $_8C_4 = {8! \over 4!4!} = {(8)(7)(6)(5) \over (4)(3)(2)(1)} = 70$

32. $_9C_3 \bullet _6C_2 =$

$\left({9! \over 6!3!}\right)\left({6! \over 4!2!}\right) = \left({(9)(8)(7) \over (3)(2)(1)}\right)\left({(6)(5) \over (2)(1)}\right) = 1260$

33. $_8C_2 = {8! \over 6!2!} = {(8)(7) \over (2)(1)} = 28$ tickets

34. Part I: $5C_3 = {5! \over 2!3!} = {(5)(4) \over (2)(1)} = 10$

Part II: $6C_4 = {6! \over 2!4!} = {(6)(5) \over (2)(1)} = 15$

$10 \cdot 15 = 150$ possible combinations

35. $_{12}C_3 \bullet _8C_2 =$

$\left({12! \over 9!3!}\right)\left({8! \over 6!2!}\right)$

$= \left({(12)(11)(10) \over (3)(2)(1)}\right)\left({(8)(7) \over (2)(1)}\right) = 6160$

36. $_{14}C_8 \bullet _{11}C_8 =$

$\left({14! \over 6!8!}\right)\left({11! \over 3!8!}\right)$

$= \left({(14)(13)(12)(11)(10)(9) \over (6)(5)(4)(3)(2)(1)}\right)\left({(11)(10)(9) \over (3)(2)(1)}\right)$

$= 495{,}495$

37. Red: $_{10}C_4 = {10! \over 6!4!} = {(10)(9)(8)(7) \over (4)(3)(2)(1)} = 210$

White. $_8C_2 = {8! \over 6!2!} = {(8)(7) \over (2)(1)} = 28$

$(210)(28) = 5880$ different choices

38. Town: $_7C_4 = {7! \over 3!4!} = {(7)(6)(5) \over (3)(2)(1)} = 35$

Citizens: $_5C_3 = {5! \over 2!3!} = {(5)(4) \over (2)(1)} = 10$

$(35)(10) = 350$ ways to form the committee

39. Regular: $_{10}C_5 =$

$$\frac{10!}{5!5!} = \frac{(10)(9)(8)(7)(6)}{(5)(4)(3)(2)(1)} = 252$$

Diet: $_7C_3 =$

$$\frac{7!}{3!4!} = \frac{(7)(6)(5)}{(3)(2)(1)} = 35$$

(252)(35) = 8820 ways to select the sodas

40. Difficult questions: $_6C_3 =$

$$\frac{6!}{3!3!} = \frac{(6)(5)(4)}{(3)(2)(1)} = 20$$

Average questions: $_{10}C_4 =$

$$\frac{10!}{6!4!} = \frac{(10)(9)(8)(7)}{(4)(3)(2)(1)} = 210$$

Easy questions: $_{12}C_3 =$

$$\frac{12!}{9!3!} = \frac{(12)(11)(10)}{(3)(2)(1)} = 220$$

Total number of 10-question tests =
(20)(210)(220) = 924,000

41. $_8C_4 \bullet {_5}C_2 =$

$$\left(\frac{8!}{4!4!}\right)\left(\frac{5!}{3!2!}\right) = \left(\frac{(8)(7)(6)(4)}{(4)(3)(2)(1)}\right)\left(\frac{(5)(4)}{(2)(1)}\right) = 700$$

42. $_6C_3 \bullet {_8}C_3 =$

$$\left(\frac{6!}{3!3!}\right)\left(\frac{8!}{5!3!}\right) = \left(\frac{(6)(5)(4)}{(3)(2)(1)}\right)\left(\frac{(8)(7)(6)}{(3)(2)(1)}\right) = 1120$$

43. $_6C_3 \bullet {_5}C_2 \bullet {_4}C_2 =$

$$\left(\frac{6!}{3!3!}\right)\left(\frac{5!}{3!2!}\right)\left(\frac{4!}{2!2!}\right) =$$

$$\left(\frac{(6)(5)(4)}{(3)(2)(1)}\right)\left(\frac{(5)(4)}{(2)(1)}\right)\left(\frac{(4)(3)}{(2)(1)}\right) = 1200$$

44. $_8C_3 \bullet {_9}C_5 \bullet {_4}C_2 =$

$$\left(\frac{8!}{5!3!}\right)\left(\frac{9!}{4!5!}\right)\left(\frac{4!}{2!2!}\right) =$$

$$\left(\frac{(8)(7)(6)}{(3)(2)(1)}\right)\left(\frac{(9)(8)(7)(6)}{(4)(3)(2)(1)}\right)\left(\frac{(4)(3)}{(2)(1)}\right) = 42,336$$

45. a) $_{10}C_8 = \frac{10!}{2!8!} = \frac{(10)(9)}{(2)(1)} = 45$

b) $_{10}C_9 = \frac{10!}{1!9!} = \frac{(10)(9!)}{(1)(9!)} = 10$

$_{10}C_{10} = \frac{10!}{10!} = 1$

$_{10}C_8 + {_{10}}C_9 + {_{10}}C_{10} = 45 + 10 + 1 = 56$

46. a) $_4C_2 = 6$

b) $_5C_2 = 10$

c) $_nC_2$

47. a)
```
              1
          1       1
        1     2     1
      1     3     3     1
    1     4     6     4     1
```

b)   1   5   10   10   5   1

48. a) $_{46}C_6 = \frac{46!}{40!6!} = 9,366,819$

b) $_{47}C_6 = \frac{47!}{41!6!} = 10,737,573$

c) $_{48}C_6 = \frac{48!}{42!6!} = 12,271,512$

d) $_{49}C_6 = \frac{49!}{43!6!} = 13,983,816$

e) No

49. a) 4! = 24   b) 4! = 24

50. $\displaystyle {}_nC_{(n-r)} = \frac{n!}{(n-(n-r))!(n-r)!} = \frac{n!}{(n-n+r)!(n-r)!}$

$\displaystyle = \frac{n!}{r!(n-r)!} = \frac{n!}{(n-r)!r!} = {}_nC_r$

51. $\displaystyle (15)(14)\cdot {}_{13}C_3 = (15)(14)\left(\frac{13!}{10!\,3!}\right)$

$\displaystyle = (15)(14)\left(\frac{(13)(12)(11)}{(3)(2)(1)}\right) = 60{,}060$

52. a) The order of the numbers is important. For example: if the combination is 12 - 4 - 23, the lock will not open if 4 - 12 - 23 is used. Since repetition is permitted, it is not a true permutation problem.

   b) $(40)(40)(40) = 64{,}000$

   c) $(40)(39)(38) = 59{,}280$

Exercise Set 12.10

1. $\displaystyle P(\text{4 red balls}) = \frac{\text{no. of 4 red ball comb.}}{\text{no. of 4 ball comb.}} = \frac{{}_8C_4}{{}_{12}C_4}$

2. $\displaystyle P(\text{all girls}) = \frac{\text{no. of all-girl comb.}}{\text{no. of student comb.}} = \frac{{}_{19}C_{12}}{{}_{34}C_{12}}$

3. $\displaystyle P(\text{3 vowels}) = \frac{\text{no. of 3 vowel comb.}}{\text{no. of 3 letter comb.}} = \frac{{}_5C_3}{{}_{26}C_3}$

4. $\displaystyle P(\text{3 aces}) = \frac{\text{3 aces of 3 cards}}{\text{no. of 3 letter comb.}} = \frac{{}_4C_3}{{}_{52}C_3}$

5. $P(\text{all 5 yellow Labs}) =$

   $\displaystyle \frac{\text{no. of 5 yellow Lab comb.}}{\text{no. of 5 puppy comb.}} = \frac{{}_8C_5}{{}_{15}C_5}$

6. $P(\text{4 dancers have college degrees}) =$

   $\displaystyle \frac{\text{no. of 4 college degree comb.}}{\text{no. 4-person comb.}} = \frac{{}_{28}C_4}{{}_{80}C_4}$

7. $P(\text{none of the 8 are Nike}) =$

   $\displaystyle \frac{\text{no. of 8 non-Nike comb.}}{\text{no. of 8 ball comb.}} = \frac{{}_{22}C_8}{{}_{50}C_8}$

8. $P(\text{none of the 9 have Oct. birthday}) =$

   $\displaystyle \frac{\substack{\text{no. of 3-person comb.}\\ \text{with no Oct. birthday}}}{\text{no. of 3 person groups}} = \frac{{}_{12}C_3}{{}_{16}C_3}$

9. $\displaystyle {}_5C_3 = \frac{5!}{2!3!} = \frac{(5)(4)}{(2)(1)} = 10$

   $\displaystyle {}_9C_3 = \frac{9!}{6!3!} = \frac{(9)(8)(7)}{(3)(2)(1)} = 84$

   $\displaystyle P(\text{3 reds}) = \frac{10}{84} = \frac{5}{42}$

10. $\displaystyle {}_4C_2 = \frac{4!}{2!2!} = 6$

    $\displaystyle {}_{10}C_2 = \frac{10!}{8!2!} = \frac{(10)(9)}{(2)(1)} = 45$

    $\displaystyle P(\text{2 defective}) = \frac{6}{45} = \frac{2}{15}$

11. $\displaystyle {}_8C_5 = \frac{8!}{3!5!} = \frac{(8)(7)(6)}{(3)(2)(1)} = 56$

    $\displaystyle {}_{14}C_5 = \frac{14!}{5!9!} = \frac{(14)(13)(12)(11)(10)}{(5)(4)(3)(2)(1)} = 2002$

    $\displaystyle P(\text{5 men's names}) = \frac{56}{2002} = \frac{4}{143}$

12. $\displaystyle {}_4C_2 = \frac{4!}{2!2!} = \frac{(4)(3)}{(2)(1)} = 6$

    $\displaystyle {}_8C_2 = \frac{8!}{6!2!} = \frac{(8)(7)}{(2)(1)} = 28$

    $\displaystyle P(\text{two \$5 bills}) = \frac{6}{28} = \frac{3}{14}$

13. $\displaystyle {}_5C_3 = \frac{5!}{2!3!} = \frac{(5)(4)}{(2)(1)} = 10$

    $\displaystyle {}_{10}C_3 = \frac{10!}{7!3!} = \frac{(10)(9)(8)}{(3)(2)(1)} = 120$

    $\displaystyle P(\text{3 greater than 4}) = \frac{10}{120} = \frac{1}{12}$

14. $\displaystyle {}_{12}C_4 = \frac{12!}{8!4!} = \frac{(12)(11)(10)(9)}{(4)(3)(2)(1)} = 495$

    $\displaystyle {}_{20}C_4 = \frac{20!}{16!4!} = \frac{(20)(19)(18)(17)}{(4)(3)(2)(1)} = 4845$

    $\displaystyle P(\text{all 4 mystery}) = \frac{495}{4845} = \frac{33}{323}$

15. $_6C_2 = \dfrac{6!}{4!2!} = \dfrac{(6)(5)}{(2)(1)} = 15$

$_2C_1 = 2$

$_{11}C_3 = \dfrac{11!}{8!3!} = \dfrac{(11)(10)(9)}{(3)(2)(1)} = 165$

P(2 from mfg, 1 from acct.) $= \dfrac{(15)(2)}{165} = \dfrac{2}{11}$

16. $_8C_2 = \dfrac{8!}{6!2!} = \dfrac{(8)(7)}{(2)(1)} = 28$

$_7C_2 = \dfrac{7!}{5!2!} = \dfrac{(7)(6)}{(2)(1)} = 21$

$_{15}C_4 = \dfrac{15!}{11!4!} = \dfrac{(15)(14)(13)(12)}{(4)(3)(2)(1)} = 1365$

P(2 teachers, 2 students) $= \dfrac{(28)(21)}{1365} = \dfrac{28}{65}$

17. $_{46}C_6 = \dfrac{46!}{40!6!} = 9{,}366{,}819 \qquad _6C_6 = 1$

P(win grand prize) $= \dfrac{1}{9{,}366{,}819}$

18. $_{52}C_5 = \dfrac{52!}{47!5!} = \dfrac{(52)(51)(50)(49)(48)}{(5)(4)(3)(2)(1)}$

$= 2{,}598{,}960$

$_{26}C_5 =$

$\dfrac{26!}{21!5!} = \dfrac{(26)(25)(24)(23)(22)}{(5)(4)(3)(2)(1)} = 65{,}700$

P(5 red) $= \dfrac{65700}{2598960} = \dfrac{253}{9996} = 0.0253$

19. $_3C_2 = \dfrac{3!}{1!2!} = 3 \qquad _5C_2 = \dfrac{5!}{3!2!} = \dfrac{(5)(4)}{(2)(1)} = 10$

P(no cars) $= \dfrac{3}{10}$

20. $_2C_2 = \dfrac{2!}{0!2!} = 1 \qquad _5C_2 = \dfrac{5!}{3!2!} = \dfrac{(5)(4)}{(2)(1)} = 10$

P(both cars) $= \dfrac{1}{10}$

21. P(at least 1 car) $= 1 - $ P(no cars) $=$

$1 - 1 - \dfrac{3}{10} = \dfrac{7}{10}$

22. $_2C_1 = \dfrac{2!}{1! \cdot 1!} = 2 \qquad _3C_1 = \dfrac{3!}{2! \cdot 1!} = 3$

$_5C_2 = \dfrac{5!}{3!2!} = 10$

P(exactly on car) $= \dfrac{2 \cdot 3}{10} = \dfrac{6}{10} = \dfrac{3}{5}$

23. $_6C_3 = \dfrac{6!}{3!3!} = \dfrac{(6)(5)(4)}{(3)(2)(1)} = 20$

$_{25}C_3 = \dfrac{25!}{3!22!} = \dfrac{(25)(24)(23)}{(3)(2)(1)} = 2300$

P(3 infielders) $= \dfrac{20}{2300} = \dfrac{1}{115}$

24. $_{15}C_3 = \dfrac{15!}{12! \cdot 3!} = \dfrac{(15)(14)(13)}{(3)(2)(1)} = 455$

P(no pitchers) $= \dfrac{455}{2300} = \dfrac{91}{460}$

25. $_{10}C_2 = \dfrac{10!}{8!2!} = 45 \qquad _6C_1 = \dfrac{6!}{5!1!} = 6$

P(2 pitchers and 1 infielder) $= \dfrac{(45)(6)}{2300} = \dfrac{27}{230}$

26. $_{10}C_1 = \dfrac{10!}{9!1!} = 10$

$_9C_2 = \dfrac{9!}{7!2!} = \dfrac{(9)(8)}{(2)(1)} = 36$

P(1 pitc. and 2 non-pitch/non-inf) $=$

$\dfrac{(10)(36)}{2300} = \dfrac{18}{115}$

For problems 27–30, use the fact that $_{25}C_6 = \dfrac{25!}{19!6!} = 177,100$

27. $_{10}C_6 = \dfrac{10!}{4!6!} = 210$

P(all mid) = $\dfrac{210}{177,100} = 0.0012$

28. $_{10}C_2 = \dfrac{10!}{8!2!} = 45$

$_{15}C_4 = \dfrac{15!}{11!4!} = 1365$

P(2 mid/4 compact) = $\dfrac{(45)(1365)}{117,100} = 0.3468$

29. $_{10}C_3 = \dfrac{10!}{7!3!} = 120$

$_{15}C_3 = \dfrac{15!}{12!3!} = 455$

P(2 mid/4 compact) = $\dfrac{(120)(455)}{117,100} = 0.3083$

30. P(at least one compact) = 1 – P(no compact)

$_{10}C_6 = \dfrac{10!}{4!6!} = 210$ (selections with all mid)

$= 1 - \dfrac{210}{177,100} = 0.9988$

For problems 31–34, use the fact that $_{12}C_4 = \dfrac{12!}{8!4!} = 495$

31. $_4C_2 = \dfrac{4!}{2!2!} = 6 \qquad _3C_2 = \dfrac{3!}{1!2!} = 3$

P(2 in FL, 2 in TX) = $\dfrac{(6)(3)}{495} = \dfrac{2}{55}$

33. $_4C_1 = 4$

$_5C_1 = 5$

$_3C_2 = 3$

P(1 in FL, 1 in CA, 2 in TX) =

$\dfrac{(4)(5)(3)}{495} = \dfrac{4}{33}$

32. $_5C_3 = \dfrac{5!}{3!2!} = 10 \qquad _4C_1 = \dfrac{4!}{3!1!} = 4$

P(3 in CA, 1 in FL) = $\dfrac{(10)(4)}{495} = \dfrac{8}{99}$

34. $_9C_4 = \dfrac{9!}{5!4!} = \dfrac{(9)(8)(7)(6)}{(4)(3)(2)(1)} = 126$

P(none in TX) = $\dfrac{126}{495}$

P($\geq$ 1 TX) = 1 – P(none in TX) =

$1 - \dfrac{126}{495} = \dfrac{41}{55}$

For problems 35 – 37, use the fact that $_{11}C_5 = \dfrac{11!}{6!5!} = \dfrac{(11)(10)(9)(8)(7)}{(5)(4)(3)(2)(1)} = 462$

35. $_6C_5 = \dfrac{6!}{1!5!} = 6$

P(5 women first) = $\dfrac{6}{462} = \dfrac{1}{77}$

36. $_5C_5 = \dfrac{5!}{0!5!} = 1 \qquad$ P(no women first) = $\dfrac{1}{462}$

P(at least 1 woman 1st) =

$1 - \dfrac{1}{462} = \dfrac{462}{462} - \dfrac{1}{462} = \dfrac{461}{462}$

37. Any one of the 6 women can sit in any one of the five seats - 30 possibilities.

P(exactly 1 woman) = $\dfrac{30}{462} = \dfrac{5}{77}$

38. P(3 women and then 2 men)

$\left(\dfrac{_6C_3}{_{11}C_3}\right)\left(\dfrac{_5C_2}{_8C_2}\right) = \left(\dfrac{20}{165}\right)\left(\dfrac{10}{28}\right) = \dfrac{10}{231}$

39. $_{24}C_3 = \dfrac{24!}{21!3!} = 2024$

$_{10}C_3 = \dfrac{10!}{7!3!} = 120$

P(all 3 are cashiers) = $\dfrac{120}{2024} = \dfrac{15}{253}$

40. $_4C_3 = \dfrac{4!}{1!3!} = 4 \qquad _4C_2 = \dfrac{4!}{2!2!} = \dfrac{(4)(3)}{(2)(1)} = 6$

and from problem 9, $_{52}C_5 = 2,598,960$

P(3 kings, 2 five's) = $\dfrac{4 \cdot 6}{2598960} = \dfrac{1}{108290}$

41.   a) P(royal spade flush) $= \dfrac{_{47}C_2}{_{52}C_7} = \dfrac{1}{123760}$

b) P(any royal flush) $= \dfrac{4}{123760} = \dfrac{1}{30,940}$

42. $\left[\dfrac{\left(_8C_3\right)\left(_{12}C_4\right)\left(_5C_2\right)}{_{25}C_9} \right] =$

$\dfrac{(8)(7)(6)(12)(11)(10)(9)(5)(4)}{(3)(2)(4)(3)(2)(2)} = \dfrac{277200}{2042975}$

P(3 waiters/4 waitresses/2 cooks) = 0.1357

43. a) $\left[\dfrac{\left(_4C_2\right)\left(_4C_2\right)\left(_{44}C_1\right)}{_{52}C_5} \right] = \dfrac{1584}{2598960} = \dfrac{33}{54,145}$

P(2 aces/2 8's/other card   ace or 8) $= \dfrac{33}{54,145}$

b) P(aces of spades and clubs/8's of spades and clubs/9 of diamonds) =

$\dfrac{1}{_{52}C_5} = \dfrac{1}{2,598,960}$

44. $\left(\dfrac{3}{6}\right)\left(\dfrac{2}{5}\right)\left(\dfrac{1}{4}\right)\left(\dfrac{3}{3}\right)\left(\dfrac{2}{2}\right)\left(\dfrac{1}{1}\right) = \dfrac{1}{20}$

2 ways: $\dfrac{1}{20} + \dfrac{1}{20} = \dfrac{2}{20} = \dfrac{1}{10}$

45. a) $\left(\dfrac{1}{15}\right)\left(\dfrac{1}{14}\right)\left(\dfrac{1}{13}\right)\left(\dfrac{5}{12}\right)\left(\dfrac{4}{11}\right)\left(\dfrac{3}{10}\right)\left(\dfrac{2}{9}\right)\left(\dfrac{1}{8}\right)$

$= \dfrac{120}{259459200} = \dfrac{1}{2,162,160}$

b) P(any 3 of 8 for officers) $= \dfrac{(8)(7)(6)}{2162160} = \dfrac{1}{6435}$

46. Given any four different numbers, there are (4)(3)(2)(1) = 24 different ways they can be arranged. One of these is in ascending order. Thus, the probability of the numbers being in ascending order is 1/24.

47. Since there are more people than hairs, 2 or more people must have the same number of hairs.

Exercise Set 12.11

1. A probability distribution shows the probability associated with each specific outcome of an experiment. In a probability distribution every possible outcome must be listed and the sum of all the probabilities must be 1.

2. Each trial has two possible outcomes, success and failure. There are n repeated independent trials.

3. $P(x) = {_nC_x}\, p^x q^{n-x}$

4. a) p is the probability of success, $q = 1 - p$ is the probability of failure.
   b) $q = 1 - p = 1 - 0.7 = 0.3$
   c) $q = 1 - p = 1 - 0.25 = 0.75$

5. $P(3) = {_5C_3}(0.2)^3(0.8)^{5-3}$

$= \dfrac{5!}{2!3!}(0.008)(0.64) = 0.0512$

6. $P(2) = {_3C_2}(0.6)^2(0.4)^{3-2} = \dfrac{3!}{2!1!}(.36)(.4) = 0.4320$

7. $P(2) = {_5C_2}(0.4)^2(0.6)^{5-2}$

$= \dfrac{5!}{2!3!}(0.16)(0.216) = 0.3456$

8. $P(3) = {_3C_3}(0.8)^3(0.2)^{3-3} = \dfrac{3!}{3!}(0.512)(1) = 0.512$

9. $P(0) = {}_6C_0 (0.5)^0 (0.5)^{6-0}$

$= \dfrac{6!}{0!6!}(1)(.0156252) = 0.015625$

10. $P(3) = {}_5C_3 (0.4)^3 (0.6)^{5-3} = \dfrac{5!}{3!2!}(.064)(.36) = 0.2304$

11. $p = 0.14, \quad q = 1 - p = 1 - 0.14 = 0.86$

a) $P(x) = {}_nC_x (0.14)^x (0.86)^{n-x}$

b) $n = 12, x = 2, p = 0.14, q = 0.86$

$P(2) = {}_{12}C_2 (0.14)^2 (0.86)^{12-2}$

12. a) $P(x) = {}_nC_x (0.0077)^x (0.9963)^{n-x}$

b) $P(5) = {}_{20}C_5 (0.0077)^5 (0.9963)^{15}$

13. $P(4) = {}_6C_4 (0.8)^4 (0.2)^{6-4}$

$= \dfrac{6!}{4!2!}(0.4096)(0.04) = 0.24576$

14. $P(5) = {}_8C_5 (0.6)^5 (0.4)^{8-5}$

$= \dfrac{8!}{5!3!}(.07776)(.064) = 0.27869$

15. $P(5) = {}_8C_5 (0.7)^5 (0.3)^{8-5}$

$= \dfrac{8!}{3!5!}(0.16807)(0.027) = 0.25412$

16. $P(4) = {}_7C_4 (0.8)^4 (0.2)^{7-4}$

$= \dfrac{7!}{3!4!}(0.4096)(0.008) = 0.11469$

17. $P(4) = {}_6C_4 (0.92)^4 (0.08)^{6-4}$

$= \dfrac{6!}{4!2!}(.7164)(.0064) = 0.06877$

18. $P(2) = {}_6C_2 (0.01)^2 (0.99)^{6-2}$

$= \dfrac{6!}{4!2!}(0.0001)(0.96059601) = 0.00144$

19. $P(4) = {}_5C_4 (.8)^4 (.2)^{5-4}$

$= \dfrac{5!}{1!4!}(.4096)(.2) \doteq 0.4096$

20. a) $P(0) = {}_4C_0 (.25)^0 (.75)^{4-0}$

$= \dfrac{4!}{4!}(1)(.3164) = 0.3164$

b) $P(\text{at least } 1) = 1 - P(0) = 1 - 0.3164 = 0.6836$

21. a) $P(\text{all five}) = {}_5C_5 (0.25)^5 (0.75)^{5-5}$

$= \dfrac{5!}{5!}(0.0009765625)(1) \approx 0.00098$

b) $P(\text{exactly three}) = {}_5C_3 (0.25)^3 (0.75)^{5-3}$

$= \dfrac{5!}{2!3!}(0.015625)(0.5625) \approx 0.08789$

c) $P(\text{at least } 3) = P(3) + P(4) + P(5)$

$P(4) = {}_5C_4 (0.25)^4 (0.75)^{5-1}$

$= \dfrac{5!}{1!4!}(0.00390625)(0.75) \approx 0.01465$

$P(\text{at least } 3) = 0.08789 + 0.01465 + 0.00098$

$= 0.10352$

22. a) $P(3) = {}_5C_3 \left(\dfrac{40}{80}\right)^3 \left(\dfrac{40}{80}\right)^2$

$= \dfrac{5!}{3!2!}(.125)(.25) = 0.3125$

b) $P(3) = {}_5C_3 \left(\dfrac{20}{80}\right)^3 \left(\dfrac{60}{80}\right)^2$

$= \dfrac{5!}{3!2!}(.015625)(.5625) = 0.08789$

23. a) $P(3) = {}_6C_3 \left(\dfrac{12}{52}\right)^3 \left(\dfrac{40}{52}\right)^3$

$\dfrac{6!}{3!3!}(.01229)(.45517) = 0.11188$

b) $P(2) = {}_6C_2 \left(\dfrac{13}{52}\right)^2 \left(\dfrac{39}{52}\right)^4$

$= \dfrac{6!}{2!4!}(.0625)(.3164) = 0.29663$

24. a) $P(3) = {}_5C_3 (0.7)^3 (0.3)^2$

$= \dfrac{5!}{3!2!}(.343)(.09) = 0.3087$

b) $P(\text{at least } 3) = P(3) + P(4) + P(5)$

$= 0.3087 + 0.3602 + 0.1681$

$= 0.8370$

25. The probability that the sun would be shining would equal 0 because 72 hours later would occur at midnight.

Review Exercises

1. Relative frequency over the long run can accurately be predicted, not individual events or totals.

2. Roll the die many times then compute the relative frequency of each outcome and compare with the expected probability of 1/6.

4. Answers will vary.

3. $P(SUV) = \dfrac{8}{40} = \dfrac{1}{5}$

5. $P(\text{watches ABC}) = \dfrac{80}{200} = \dfrac{2}{5}$

6. $P(\text{even}) = \dfrac{5}{10} = \dfrac{1}{2}$

7. $P(\text{odd or} > 5) = \dfrac{5}{10} + \dfrac{4}{10} - \dfrac{2}{10} = \dfrac{7}{10}$

8. $P(> 3 \text{ or} < 6) = \dfrac{6}{10} + \dfrac{6}{10} - \dfrac{2}{10} = \dfrac{10}{10} = 1$

9. $P(\text{even and} > 6) = \dfrac{1}{10}$

10. $P(\text{Jack}) = \dfrac{14}{50} = \dfrac{7}{25}$

11. $P(\text{Muenster}) = \dfrac{11}{50}$

12. $P(\text{Cheddar or Colby}) =$
$\dfrac{18}{50} + \dfrac{14}{50} = \dfrac{32}{50} = \dfrac{16}{25}$

13. $P(\text{not Swiss}) = \dfrac{50 - 7}{50} = \dfrac{43}{50}$

14. a) 69:31   b) 31:69

15. 5:3

16. $P(\text{wins Triple Crown}) = \dfrac{3}{85}$

17. 7:3

18. a) $E = P(\text{win \$200}) \bullet \$198 + P(\text{win \$100}) \bullet \$98$
$+ P(\text{lose}) \bullet (-\$2)$
$= (.003)(198) + (.002)(98) - (.995)(2)$
$= .594 + .196 - 1.990 = -1.200 \rightarrow -\$1.20$

    b) The expectation of a person who purchases three tickets would be $3(-1.20) = -\$3.60$.

    c) Expected value = Fair price – Cost
$-1.20 = $ Fair price $- 2.00$ $\$.80 = $ Fair price

19. a) $E_{\text{Cameron}} = P(\text{pic. card})(\$9) +$
$P(\text{not pic. card})(-\$3)$
$= \left(\dfrac{12}{52}\right)(9) - \left(\dfrac{40}{52}\right)(3) = \approx -\$0.23$

    b) $E_{\text{Lindsey}} = P(\text{pic. card})(-\$9) + P(\text{not pic. card})(\$3)$
$= \dfrac{-27}{13} + \dfrac{30}{13} = \dfrac{3}{13} \approx \$0.23$

    c) Cameron can expect to lose $(100)\left(\dfrac{3}{13}\right) \approx \$23.08$

20. $E = P(\text{sunny})(1000) + P(\text{cloudy})(500) + P(\text{rain})(100) = 0.4(1000) + 0.5(500) + 0.1(100) = $
$400 + 250 + 10 = 660$ people

21. a)

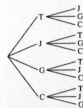

    b) Sample space:
    {TJ,TG,TC,JT,JG,JC,GT,GJ,GC,CT,CJ,CG}

    c) P(Gina is Pres. and Jake V.P.) = 1/12

22. a)

    b) Sample space:
    {H1,H2,H3,H4,T1,T2,T3,T4}

    c) P(heads and odd) = (1/2)(2/4) = 2/8 = ¼

    d) P(heads or odd) = (1/2)(2/4) + (1/2)(2/4)
                 = 4/8 + 2/8 = 6/8 = 3/4

23. P(even and even) = (4/8)(4/8) = 16/64 = 1/4

24. P(outer is greater than 5 and inner is greater than 5)

$$= \text{P(outer is} > 5) \cdot \text{P(inner is} > 5) = \frac{3}{8} \cdot \frac{3}{8} = \frac{9}{64}$$

25. P(outer odd and inner < 6)

$$= \text{P(outer odd) P(inner} < 6) = \frac{4}{8} \cdot \frac{5}{8} = \frac{1}{2} \cdot \frac{5}{8} = \frac{5}{16}$$

26. P(outer is even or less than 6)

$$= \text{P(even)} + \text{P(} < 6) - \text{P(even and} < 6)$$

$$= \frac{4}{8} + \frac{5}{8} - \frac{2}{8} = \frac{7}{8}$$

27. P(inner even and not green) =

$$\frac{1}{2} + \frac{6}{8} - \frac{2}{8} = \frac{1}{2} + \frac{4}{8} = 1$$

28. P(outer gold and inner not gold)

$$= \left(\frac{2}{8}\right)\left(\frac{6}{8}\right) = \left(\frac{1}{4}\right)\left(\frac{3}{4}\right) = \frac{3}{16}$$

29. P(all 3 are GM) = $\dfrac{5}{12} \cdot \dfrac{4}{11} \cdot \dfrac{3}{10} = \dfrac{60}{1320} = \dfrac{1}{22}$

30. P(none are Kellogg's) =

$$\frac{8}{12} \cdot \frac{7}{11} \cdot \frac{6}{10} = \frac{336}{1320} = \frac{14}{55}$$

31. P(at least one is Kellogg's) = 1 – P(none are Kellogg's)

$$= 1 - \frac{14}{55} = \frac{55}{55} - \frac{14}{55} = \frac{41}{55}$$

32. P(GM, GM, Post)

$$= \frac{5}{12} \cdot \frac{4}{11} \cdot \frac{3}{10} = \frac{60}{1320} = \frac{1}{22}$$

33. P(yellow) = 1/4

34. Odds against yellow   3:1
    Odds for yellow   1:3

35. $5 for red; $10 for yellow; $20 for green
    P(green) = ½; P(yellow) = ¼; P(red) = ¼
    EV = (1/4)(5) + (1/4)(10) + (1/2)(20) = $13.75

36. P(red, then green) = P(red)P(green)
    = (1/4)(1/2) = 1/8

37. P(not green) = 1/4 + 1/4 + 1/8 = 5/8

38. Odds in favor of green   3:5
    Odds against green   5:3

39. E = P(green)($10) + P(red)($5) + P(yellow)(–$20)
    = (3/8)(10) + (1/2)(5) – (1/8)(20)
    = (15/4) + (10/4) – (10/4) = 15/4 → $3.75

40. P(at least one red) = 1 – P(none are red)
    = 1 – (1/2)(1/2)(1/2) = 1-1/8 = 7/8

41. P(rated good) = 150/170 = 15/17.

42. P(good | dinner) = 85/95 = 17/19

43. P(poor | lunch) = 10/75 = 2/15

44. P(dinner | poor) = 10/20 = 1/2

45. P(right handed) = $\dfrac{230}{400} = \dfrac{23}{40}$

46. P(left brained | left handed) = $\dfrac{30}{170} = \dfrac{3}{17}$

47. P(right handed | no predominance) = $\dfrac{60}{80} = \dfrac{3}{4}$

48. P(right brained | left handed) = $\dfrac{120}{170} = \dfrac{12}{17}$

49. a) 4! = (4)(3)(2)(1) = 24
    b) E = (1/4)(10K) + (1/4)(5K) + (1/4)(2K) + (1/4)(1K) = (1/4)(18K) = $4,500.00

50. # of possible arrangements = $(_5C_2)(_3C_2)(_1C_1)$

$$= \left(\frac{5!}{3!2!}\right)\left(\frac{3!}{1!2!}\right)\left(\frac{1!}{1!}\right) = \frac{(5)(4)(3)}{(2)(1)} = 30$$

51. $_{10}P_3 = \dfrac{10!}{7!} = (10)(9)(8) = 720$

52. $_9P_3 = \dfrac{9!}{6!} = \dfrac{(9)(8)(7)(6!)}{6!} = (9)(8)(7) = 504$

53. $6C3 = \dfrac{6!}{3!3!} = \dfrac{(6)(5)(4)}{(3)(2)(1)} = 20$

54. a) $15C_{10} = \dfrac{15!}{5!10!} = \dfrac{(15)(14)(13)(12)(11)}{(5)(4)(3)(2)(1)} = 3003$

b) number of arrangements = $10! = 3{,}628{,}800$

55. a) P(match 5 numbers) = $\dfrac{1}{56C_5}$

$= \dfrac{1}{\dfrac{56!}{51!5!}} = \dfrac{51!5!}{56!} = \dfrac{1}{3{,}819{,}816}$

b) P(Big game win) = P(match 5 #s and Big #)
= P(match 5 #s) • P(match Big #)

$= \left(\dfrac{1}{3{,}819{,}816}\right)\left(\dfrac{1}{46}\right) = \dfrac{1}{175{,}711{,}536}$

56. $(10C_2)(12C_5) =$

$\left(\dfrac{10!}{8!2!}\right)\left(\dfrac{12!}{7!5!}\right)$

$= \dfrac{(10)(9)(12)(11)(10)(9)(8)}{(2)(1)(5)(4)(3)(2)(1)}$

$= 35{,}640$ possible committees

57. $(8C_3)(5C_2) =$

$\left(\dfrac{8!}{5!3!}\right)\left(\dfrac{5!}{2!3!}\right) = \dfrac{(8)(7)(6)(5)(4)}{(3)(2)(1)(2)(1)} = 560$

58. P(two aces) = $\dfrac{4C_2}{52C_2} = \dfrac{\dfrac{4!}{2!2!}}{\dfrac{52!}{50!2!}}$

$= \left(\dfrac{4!}{2!2!}\right)\left(\dfrac{50!2!}{52!}\right) = \dfrac{1}{221}$

59. P(all three are red) = $\left(\dfrac{5}{10}\right)\left(\dfrac{4}{9}\right)\left(\dfrac{3}{8}\right) = \dfrac{1}{12}$

60. P(1st 2 are red/3rd is blue) = $\left(\dfrac{5}{10}\right)\left(\dfrac{4}{9}\right)\left(\dfrac{2}{8}\right) = \dfrac{1}{18}$

61. P(1st red, 2nd white, 3rd blue)

$= \left(\dfrac{5}{10}\right)\left(\dfrac{3}{9}\right)\left(\dfrac{2}{8}\right) = \dfrac{1}{24}$

62. P(at least one red) = 1 − P(none are red)

$= 1 - \left(\dfrac{5}{10}\right)\left(\dfrac{4}{9}\right)\left(\dfrac{3}{8}\right) = 1 - \dfrac{1}{12} = \dfrac{11}{12}$

63. P(3 N&WRs) =

$\dfrac{5C_3}{14C_3} = \dfrac{\dfrac{5!}{3!2!}}{\dfrac{14!}{3!11!}} = \dfrac{5!3!11!}{3!2!14!} = \dfrac{(5)(4)(3)}{(14)(13)(12)} = \dfrac{5}{182}$

64. P(2 NWs & 1 Time) =

$\dfrac{(6C_2)(3C_1)}{14C_3} = \dfrac{\left(\dfrac{6!}{2!4!}\right)\left(\dfrac{3!}{1!2!}\right)}{\dfrac{14!}{3!11!}}$

$= \dfrac{(6)(5)(3)(3)(2)(1)}{(2)(1)(14)(13)(12)} = \dfrac{45}{364}$

65. $\dfrac{8C_3}{14C_3} = \dfrac{\dfrac{8!}{3!5!}}{\dfrac{14!}{3!11!}} = \dfrac{8!3!11!}{3!5!14!}$

$= \dfrac{(8)(7)(6)}{(14)(13)(12)} = \dfrac{336}{2184} = \dfrac{2}{13}$

66. $1 - \dfrac{2}{13} = \dfrac{11}{13}$

67. a) $P(x) = {}_nC_x (0.6)^x (0.4)^{n-x}$

b) $P(75) = {}_{100}C_{75}(0.6)^{75}(0.4)^{25}$

68. n = 5, x = 3, p = 1/5, q = 4/5

$P(3) = {}_5C_3\left(\dfrac{1}{5}\right)^3\left(\dfrac{4}{5}\right)^2 = 10 \cdot \left(\dfrac{1}{5}\right)^3\left(\dfrac{4}{5}\right)^2 =$
0.0512

69. a) n = 5, p = 0.6, q = 0.4

$P(0) = {}_5C_0(0.6)^0(0.4)^5$

$= (1)(1)(0.4)^5 = 0.01024$

b) P(at least 1) = 1 − P(0) = 1 − 0.01024 = 0.98976

Chapter Test

1. P(fishing for tuna) = $\dfrac{22}{40} = \dfrac{11}{20}$

2. $(P > 7) = \dfrac{2}{9} \approx 0.22$

3. P(odd) = $\dfrac{5}{9} \approx 0.55$

4. $P(\geq 4) = \dfrac{7}{9} \approx 0.78$

5. P(odd and > 4) = $\dfrac{3}{9} = \dfrac{1}{3} \approx 0.33$

6. P(both > 5) = $\dfrac{4}{9} \cdot \dfrac{3}{8} = \dfrac{12}{72} = \dfrac{1}{6}$

7. P(both even) = $\dfrac{4}{9} \cdot \dfrac{3}{8} = \dfrac{1 \cdot 1}{3 \cdot 2} = \dfrac{1}{6}$

8. P(1st odd, 2nd even) = $\dfrac{5}{9} \cdot \dfrac{4}{8} = \dfrac{5}{9} \cdot \dfrac{1}{2} = \dfrac{5}{18}$

9. P(neither > 6) = $\dfrac{6}{9} \cdot \dfrac{5}{8} = \dfrac{1 \cdot 5}{3 \cdot 4} = \dfrac{5}{12}$

10. P(red or picture)

   = P(red) + P(picture) – P(red and picture)

   = $\dfrac{26}{52} + \dfrac{12}{52} - \dfrac{6}{52} = \dfrac{32}{52} = \dfrac{8}{13}$

11. 1 die   (6)(3) = 18

12.

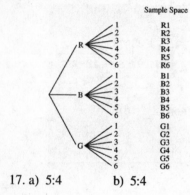

Sample Space

13. P(green and 2) = $\dfrac{1}{18}$

14. P(red or 1) = $\dfrac{6}{18} + \dfrac{3}{18} - \dfrac{1}{18} = \dfrac{8}{18} = \dfrac{4}{9}$

15. P(not red or even) = $\dfrac{12}{18} + \dfrac{9}{18} - \dfrac{6}{18} = \dfrac{15}{18} = \dfrac{5}{6}$

16. Number of codes = (26)(9)(10)(26)(26)
    = 1,581,840

17. a) 5:4   b) 5:4

18. odds against Mark winning are 7:2 or

   $\dfrac{7}{2} = \dfrac{7/9}{2/9} = \dfrac{\text{P(not winning)}}{\text{P(winning)}}$

   Therefore, P(Mark wins) = 2/9

19. E = P(club) ($8) + P(heart) ($4)
      + P(spade or diamond) (–$6)

   = $\left(\dfrac{1}{4}\right)(8) + \left(\dfrac{1}{4}\right)(4) + \left(\dfrac{2}{4}\right)(-6)$

   = $\dfrac{8}{4} + \dfrac{4}{4} - \dfrac{12}{4} = \$0.00$

20. a) P(car) = $\dfrac{214}{456} = \dfrac{107}{228}$

   b) P(Golden Gate) = $\dfrac{230}{456} = \dfrac{115}{228}$

   c) P(SUV | Golden Gate) = $\dfrac{136}{230} = \dfrac{68}{115}$

20. d) P(GW Bridge | car) = $\dfrac{120}{214} = \dfrac{60}{107}$

21. $_6P_3 = \dfrac{6!}{(6-3)!} = \dfrac{6!}{3!} = 6 \cdot 5 \cdot 4 = 120$

22. P(neither is good) = $\dfrac{6}{20} \cdot \dfrac{5}{19} = \dfrac{3}{38}$

23. P($\geq$ 1 good) = 1 – P(neither -good) =
    $1 - \dfrac{3}{38} = \dfrac{35}{38}$

24. $_7C_3 = \dfrac{7!}{4!3!} = \dfrac{(7)(6)(5)}{(3)(2)(1)} = 35$

$_5C_2 = \dfrac{5!}{3!2!} = \dfrac{(5)(4)}{(2)(1)} = 10$

$_{12}C_5 = \dfrac{12!}{7!5!} = \dfrac{(12)(11)(10)(9)(8)}{(5)(4)(3)(2)(1)} = 792$

P(3 red and 2 green) $= \dfrac{(35)(10)}{792} = \dfrac{350}{792} = \dfrac{175}{396}$

25. $(0.3)(0.3)(0.3) = 0.027$

$(0.3)(0.3)(0.3)(0.7)(0.7) = 0.01323$

$_5C_3 = \dfrac{5!}{3!2!} = \dfrac{(5)(4)}{(2)(1)} = 10$

$(10)(.01323) = 0.1323$

Group Projects

1. 0 because no measurement is exact.

2. a) 0.30199   b) 0.10737   c) 0.89263   d) 0.00000   e) 0.30199   f) They should be the same.

3. a) $10^5 = 100,000$ b) $5^5 = 3125$ c) $\dfrac{1}{3125}$ d) 3125   e) 3125

f) $\dfrac{1}{3125}$ g) same likelihood   h) More 5 digit codes are available.

CHAPTER THIRTEEN

STATISTICS

Exercise Set 13.1

1. **Statistics** is the art and science of gathering, analyzing, and making inferences (predictions) from numerical information obtained in an experiment.

2. **Descriptive statistics** is concerned with the collection, organization, and analysis of data.
   Inferential statistics is concerned with making generalizations or predictions from the data collected.

3. Answers will vary.   4. Answers will vary.

5. Insurance companies, sports, airlines, stock market, medical profession

6. **Probability** is used to compute the chance of occurrence of a particular event when all possible outcomes are known. **Statistics** is used to draw conclusions about possible outcomes through observations of only a few particular events.

7. a) A **population** consists of all items or people of interest.   b) A **sample** is a subset of the population.

8. a) A **random sample** is a sample drawn in such a way that each item in the population has an equal chance of being selected.
   b) Number each item in the population. Write each number on a piece of paper and put each numbered piece of paper in a hat. Select pieces of paper from the hat and use the numbered items selected as your sample.

9. a) A **systematic sample** is a sample obtained by selecting every n^{th} item on a list or production line.
   b) Use a random number table to select the first item, then select every n^{th} item after that.

10. a) A **convenience sample** uses data that is easily or readily obtained.
    b) For example, select the first 20 students entering a classroom.

11. a) A **cluster sample** is a random selection of groups of units.
    b) Divide a geographic area into sections. Randomly select sections or clusters. Either each member of the selected cluster is included in the sample or a random sample of the members of each selected cluster is used.

12. a) A **stratified sample** is one that includes items from each part (or strata) of the population.
    b) First identify the strata you are interested in. Then select a random sample from each strata.

13. a) An **unbiased sample** is one that is a small replica of the entire population with regard to income, education, gender, race, religion, political affiliation, age, etc.

14. a) No, the method used to obtain the sample is biased. In classes where students are seated alphabetically, brothers and sisters could be selected from different classes.
    b) The mean will be greater. Families with many children are more likely to be selected.

15. Stratified sample   16. Systematic sample
17. Cluster sample   18. Random sample
19. Systematic sample   20. Stratified sample
21. Convenience sample   22. Cluster sample
23. Random sample   24. Convenience sample

25. a) – c) Answers will vary.

26. Biased because the subscribers of *Consumer Reports* are not necessarily representative of the entire population.

27. President; four out of 42 U.S. presidents have been assassinated (Lincoln, Garfield, McKinley, Kennedy).

28. Answers will vary.

Exercise Set 13.2

1. Answers will vary.

2. Yes, the sum of its parts is 119%. The sum of the parts of a circle graph should be 100%. When the total percent of responses is more than 100%, a circle graph is not an appropriate graph to display the data. A bar graph is more appropriate in this situation.

3. Not all people who request a brochure will purchase a travel package.

4. Mama Mia's may have more empty spaces and more cars in the parking lot than Shanghi's due to a larger parking lot or because more people may walk to Mama Mia's than to Shanghi's.

5. Although the cookies are fat free, they still contain calories. Eating many of them may still cause you to gain weight.

6. More people drive on Saturday evening. Thus, one might expect more accidents.

7. The fact that Morgan's is the largest department store does not imply it is inexpensive.

8. Most driving is done close to home. Thus, one might expect more accidents close to home.

9. People with asthma may move to Arizona because of its climate. Therefore, more people with asthma may live in Arizona.

10. We don't know how many of each professor's students were surveyed. Perhaps more of Professor Malone's students than Professor Wagner's students were surveyed. Also, because more students prefer a teacher does not mean that he or she is a better teacher. For example, a particular teacher may be an easier grader and that may be why that teacher is preferred.

11. The quality of a steak does not necessarily depend on the price of the steak.

12. Just because they are more expensive does not mean they will last the longer.

13. There may be deep sections in the pond, so it may not be safe to go wading.

14. Men may drive more miles than women and men may drive in worse driving conditions (like snow).

15. Half the students in a population are expected to be below average.

16. Not all candidates who apply for a position will be accepted.

17. a)   b)

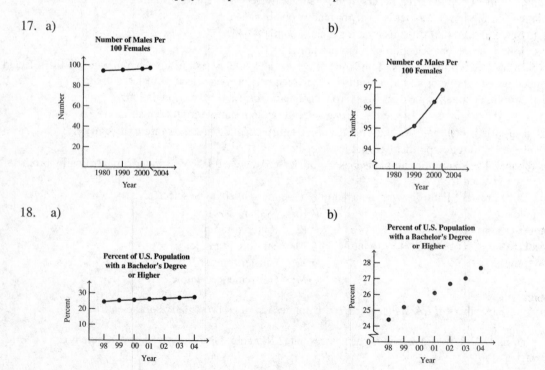

18. a)   b)

19. a)

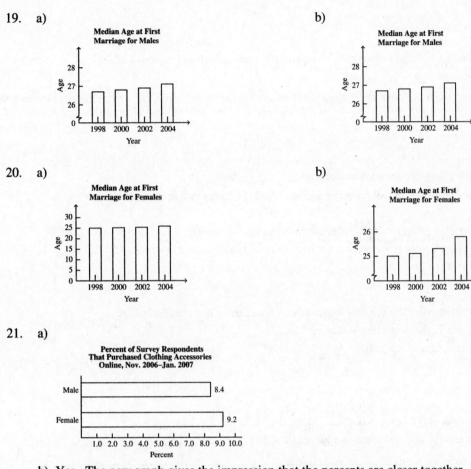

b)

20. a)

b)

21. a)

   b) Yes. The new graph gives the impression that the percents are closer together.

22. a) $\dfrac{394,000,000 - 275,000,000}{275,000,000} = \dfrac{119,000,000}{275,000,000}$

   $= 0.43\overline{27} \approx 43.3\%$ increase

   b) Radius $= \dfrac{1}{4}$ in. $= 0.25$ in.

   $A = \pi r^2 = \pi(0.25)^2 = 0.0625\pi = 0.196349541$

   ≈ 0.196 in.^{2}

   c) Radius $= \dfrac{3}{8}$ in. $= 0.375$ in.

   $A = \pi r^2 = \pi(0.375)^2 = 0.140625\pi = 0.441786467$

   ≈ 0.442 in.^{2}

   d) $\dfrac{0.442 - 0.196}{0.196} = \dfrac{0.246}{0.196} = 1.255102041$

   $\approx 125.5\%$ increase

   e) Yes, the percent increase in the size of the area from the first circle to the second is greater than the percent increase in population.

23. A decimal point

Exercise Set 13.3

1. A **frequency distribution** is a listing of observed values and the corresponding frequency of occurrence of each value.

2. Subtract a lower class limit from the next lower class limit or subtract an upper class limit from the next upper class limit.

3. a) 7   b) 16-22   c) 16   d) 22
4. a) 9   b) 21-29   c) 21   d) 29

5. The **modal class** is the class with the greatest frequency.

6. The **class mark** is another name for the midpoint of a class. Add the lower and upper class limits and divide the sum by 2.

7. a) Number of observations = sum of frequencies = 20
    b) Width = $16 - 9 = 7$
    c) $\dfrac{16+22}{2} = \dfrac{38}{2} = 19$
    d) The modal class is the class with the greatest frequency. Thus, the modal class is 16 - 22.
    e) Since the class widths are 7, the next class would be 51 - 57.

8. a) Number of observations = sum of frequencies = 25
    b) Width = 50 - 40 = 10
    c) $\dfrac{50+59}{2} = \dfrac{109}{2} = 54.5$
    d) 40 - 49 and 80 - 89 both contain 7 pieces of data. Thus, they are both modal classes.
    e) Since the class widths are 10, the next class would be 100 - 109.

9.

Number of Visits	Number of Students
0	3
1	8
2	3
3	5
4	2
5	7
6	2
7	3
8	4
9	1
10	2

10.

Number Sold	Number of Days
15	3
16	2
17	0
18	3
19	4
20	3
21	5
22	2
23	2
24	1
25	2
26	1
27	2
28	1
29	1

11.

I.Q.	Number of Students
78 - 86	2
87 - 95	15
96 - 104	18
105 - 113	7
114 - 122	6
123 - 131	1
132 - 140	1

12.

I.Q.	Number of Students
80 - 88	4
89 - 97	17
98 - 106	15
107 - 115	8
116 - 124	4
125 - 133	1
134 - 142	1

13.

I.Q.	Number of Students
80 - 90	8
91 - 101	22
102 - 112	11
113 - 123	7
124 - 134	1
135 - 145	1

14.

I.Q.	Number of Students
80 - 92	11
93 - 105	24
106 - 118	9
119 - 131	5
132 - 144	1

15.

Placement test scores	No. of Students
472 - 492	9
493 - 513	9
514 - 534	5
535 - 555	2
556 - 576	3
577 - 597	2

16.

Placement test scores	No. of Students
470 - 486	4
487 - 503	9
504 - 520	8
521 - 537	2
538 - 554	2
555 - 571	2
572 - 588	2
589 - 605	1

17.

Placement test scores	No. of Students
472 - 487	4
488 - 503	9
504 - 519	7
520 - 535	3
536 - 551	2
552 - 567	2
568 - 583	2
584 - 599	1

18.

Placement test scores	No. of Students
472 - 496	9
497 - 521	12
522 - 546	4
547 - 571	2
572 - 596	3

19.

Circulation (10,000's)	Number of Magazines
157 - 306	34
307 - 456	9
457 - 606	2
607 - 756	1
757 - 906	1
907 - 1056	1

20.

Circulation (10,000's)	Number of Magazines
150 - 296	32
297 - 436	11
437 - 576	2
577 - 716	0
717 - 856	2
857 - 996	0
997 - 1136	1

21.

Circulation (10,000's)	Number of Magazines
157 - 256	29
257 - 356	8
357 - 456	6
457 - 556	2
557 - 656	0
657 - 756	1
757 - 856	1
857 - 956	0
957 - 1056	1

22.

Circulation (10,000's)	Number of Magazines
157 - 234	22
235 - 319	13
320 - 404	5
405 - 489	4
490 - 574	1
575 - 659	0
660 - 744	1
745 - 829	1
830 - 914	0
915 - 999	0
1000 - 1084	1

23.

Population (millions)	Number of Cities
6.0 - 6.9	2
7.0 - 7.9	5
8.0 - 8.9	6
9.0 - 9.9	2
10.0 - 10.9	3
11.0 - 12.0	2

24.

Population (millions)	Number of Cities
5.5 - 6.4	2
6.5 - 7.4	3
7.5 - 8.4	4
8.5 - 9.4	5
9.5 - 10.4	3
10.5 - 11.4	2
11.5 - 12.4	1

25.	Population (millions)	Number of Cities
	5.5 - 6.6	2
	6.6 - 7.6	4
	7.7 - 8.7	6
	8.8 - 9.9	3
	9.9 - 10.9	3
	11.0 – 12.0	2

26.	Population (millions)	Number of Cities
	6.0 - 6.4	2
	6.5 - 6.9	0
	7.0 - 7.4	3
	7.5 - 7.9	2
	8.0 - 8.4	2
	8.5 - 8.9	4
	9.0 - 9.4	1
	9.5 - 9.9	1
	10.0 - 10.4	2
	10.5 - 10.9	1
	11.0 - 11.4	1
	11.5 - 11.9	1

27.	Percent	Number of States
	5.6 -7.5	2
	7.6 - 9.5	8
	9.6 - 11.5	16
	11.6 - 13.5	10
	13.6 - 15.5	6
	15.6 - 17.5	8

28.	Percent	Number of States
	5.6 - 8.2	4
	8.3 - 10.9	17
	11.0 - 13.6	15
	13.7 - 16.3	9
	16.4 - 19.0	5

29.	Percent	Number of States
	5.6 - 7.0	1
	7.1 - 8.5	4
	8.6 - 10.0	13
	10.1 - 11.5	8
	11.6 - 13.0	9
	13.1 - 14.5	3
	14.6 - 16.0	7
	16.1 - 17.5	5

30.	Percent	Number of States
	5.6 - 8.0	2
	8.1 - 10.5	16
	10.6 - 13.0	17
	13.1 - 15.5	7
	15.6 - 18.0	8

31. February, since it has the fewest number of days

32. a) **Did You Know?, page 845:** There are 6 F's.

    b) Answers will vary.

Exercise Set 13.4

1. Answers will vary.

3. Answers will vary.

5. a) Answers will vary.

    b)

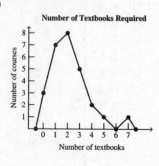

2. a) Observed values

    b) Frequency

4. Answers will vary.

6. a) Answers will vary.

 b)

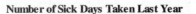

Number of Sick Days Taken Last Year

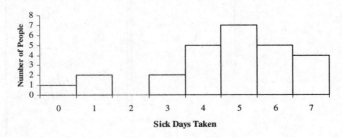

7. a) Answers will vary.

 b)

Observed Values	Frequency
45	3
46	0
47	1
48	0
49	1
50	1
51	2

8.

Observed Values	Frequency
16	1
17	2
18	1
19	1
20	0
21	1
22	2
23	1
24	1
25	2

9. Tuition: $0.721(32,235) = \$23,241$

 Room: $0.151(32,235) = \$4867$

 Board: $0.111(32,235) = \$3578$

 Fees: $0.017(32,235) = \$548$

10. Contact lenses: $0.30(2200) = \$660$ million

 Pharmaceuticals: $0.24(2200) = \$528$ million

 Lens care products: $0.23(2200) = \$506$ million

 Cataract/vitreoretinal: $0.16(2200) = \$352$ million

 Refracting products: $0.07(2200) = \$154$ million

11. Breakfast: $\dfrac{46}{600} \approx 0.077 = 7.7\%$

 Dinner: $\dfrac{190}{600} \approx 0.317 = 31.7\%$

 Lunch: $\dfrac{293}{600} \approx 0.488 = 48.8\%$

 Snack: $\dfrac{71}{600} \approx 0.118 = 11.8\%$

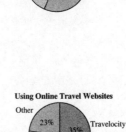

12. Travelocity: $\dfrac{175}{500} = 0.35 = 35\%$

 Expedia: $\dfrac{125}{500} = 0.25 = 25\%$

 Priceline: $\dfrac{85}{500} = 0.17 = 17\%$

 Other: $\dfrac{115}{500} = 0.23 = 23\%$

13.   a) and b)

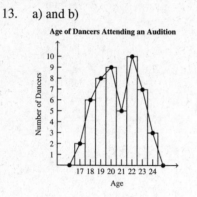

Age of Dancers Attending an Audition

14.   a) and b)

Height of Male High School Seniors

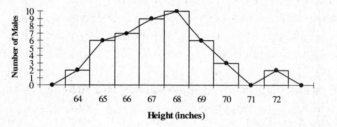

15.   a) and b)

DVDs Owned

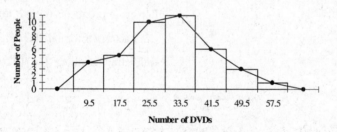

16.   a) and b)

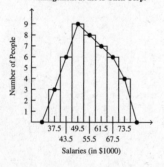

Annual Salaries of People in
Management at the X-Chek Corp.

17. a) $2+4+8+6+4+3+1=28$

b) 4

c) 2

d) $2(0)+1(4)+2(8)+6(3)+4(4)+3(5)+1(6)=75$

e)

Number of TVs	Number of homes
0	2
1	4
2	8
3	6
4	4
5	3
6	1

18) a) The total number of students surveyed: $2 + 4 + 6 + 8 + 7 + 3 + 1 = 31$

b) Since there are 51 units between class midpoints, each class width must also be 51 units.

650 is the midpoint of the first class and there must be 25 units below it and 25 units above it.

Therefore, the first class is 625 - 675. The second class will be 676 - 726.

c) Six

d) The class mark of the modal class is $803 because more students had an annual car insurance premium of $778 - $828 than any other annual car insurance premium.

e)

Price	Number of Students
625 - 675	2
676 - 726	4
727 - 777	6
778 - 828	8
829 - 879	7
880 - 930	3
931 - 981	0
982 - 1032	1

19. a) 7 messages

b) Adding the number of people who sent 6, 5, 4, or 3 messages gives: $4 + 7 + 3 + 2 = 16$ people

c) The total number of people in the survey: $2 + 3 + 7 + 4 + 3 + 8 + 6 + 3 = 36$

d)

Number of Messages	Number of People
3	2
4	3
5	7
6	4
7	3
8	8
9	6
10	3

e)

Number of Text Messages Sent

20. a) 8 families

b) At least six times means six or more times. Adding the families that went 6, 7, 8, 9, or 10 times
gives $11 + 9 + 3 + 0 + 1 = 24$ families

c) Total number of families surveyed: $4 + 2 + 8 + 8 + 6 + 11 + 9 + 3 + 0 + 1 = 52$ families

d)

Number of Visits	Number of Families
1	4
2	2
3	8
4	8
5	6
6	11
7	9
8	3
9	0
10	1

e)

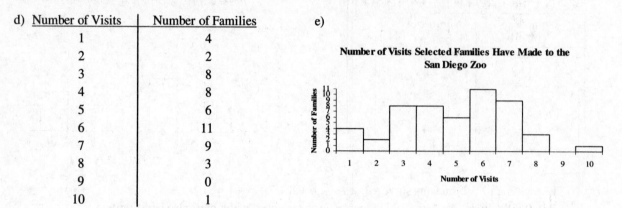

21.

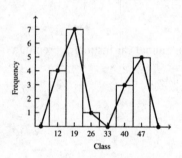

22.

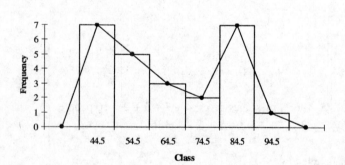

23. 1 | 2 represents 12

```
0 | 4 6 7 8
1 | 2 2 3 5 6 7 8 9
2 | 1 2 3 5 7
3 | 3 4
4 | 0
```

24. 1 | 5 represents 15

```
1 | 0 5 7
2 | 4 4
3 | 6 0 3
4 | 8 5 2 5 8
5 | 3 4
6 | 0 2 0
```

25. a)

Salaries (in $1000)	Number of Social Workers
27	1
28	7
29	4
30	3
31	2
32	3
33	3
34	2

b) and c)

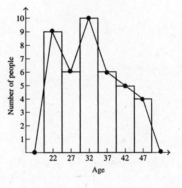

Starting Salaries for 25 Different Social Workers

d) 2 | 8 represents 28

    2 | 7 8 8 8 8 8 8 8 9 9 9 9
    3 | 0 0 0 1 1 2 2 2 3 3 3 4 4

26. a)

Age	Number of People
20 - 24	9
25 - 29	6
30 - 34	10
35 - 39	6
40 - 44	5
45 - 49	4

b) and c)

Age of 40 People Attending a Broadway Show

d) 2 | 3 represents 23

    2 | 0 1 1 2 3 3 3 4 4 5 5 6 7 8 8
    3 | 0 0 0 1 1 2 3 4 4 4 5 5 5 7 8 9
    4 | 0 0 0 2 4 5 5 6 7

27. a)

Number of Performances	Number of Shows
1508 - 2548	33
2549 - 3589	7
3590 - 4630	4
4631 - 5671	1
5672 - 6712	3
6713 - 7753	1
7754 - 8794	1

b) and c)

Number of Performances for the 50 Longest Running Broadway Shows

28. a)

Age	Number of Presidents
42 - 47	5
48 - 53	11
54 - 59	17
60 - 65	8
66 - 71	2

b) and c)

Age of U.S. Presidents at Their First Inauguration

29. a) – e) Answers will vary.

30. a) – e) Answers will vary.

Exercise Set 13. 5

1. a) The **mean** is the balancing point of a set of data. It is the sum of the data divided by the number of pieces of data.

   b) The **median** is the value in the middle of a set of ranked data. To find the median, rank the data and select the value in the middle.

2. a) The **midrange** is the value half way between the lowest and highest values. To find the midrange, add the lowest and highest values and divide the sum by 2.

   b) The **mode** is the most common piece of data. The piece of data that occurs most frequently is the mode.

3. The median should be used when there are some values that differ greatly from the rest of the values in the set, for example, salaries.

4. The mode may be used when you are primarily interested in the most popular value, or the one that occurs most often, for example, when buying clothing for a store.

5. The midrange should be used when the item being studied is constantly fluctuating, for example, daily temperature.

6. The mean is used when each piece of data is to be considered and "weighed" equally, for example, weights of adult males.

7. a) $\bar{x}$ b) μ

8. **Ranked data** are data listed from the lowest value to the highest value or from the highest value to the lowest value.

9. The second quartile is the median; the first and third quartiles are the medians of the lower and upper halves of the data

10. a) First quartile, or Q_1

   b) Second quartile, Q_2, or median

   c) Third quartile, or Q_3

	mean	median	mode	midrange
11.	$\dfrac{117}{9} = 13$	12	12	$\dfrac{7+25}{2} = 16$
12.	$\dfrac{79}{7} \approx 11.3$	11	11	$\dfrac{8+15}{2} = 11.5$
13.	$\dfrac{555}{7} \approx 79.3$	82	none	$\dfrac{52+100}{2} = 76$
14.	$\dfrac{501}{10} = 50.1$	10	10	$\dfrac{4+365}{2} = 184.5$
15.	$\dfrac{64}{8} = 8$	$\dfrac{7+9}{2} = 8$	none	$\dfrac{1+15}{2} = 8$
16.	$\dfrac{510}{7} \approx 72.9$	60	none	$\dfrac{30+140}{2} = 85$
17.	$\dfrac{118}{9} \approx 13.1$	11	1	$\dfrac{1+36}{2} = 18.5$
18.	$\dfrac{92}{14} \approx 6.6$	$\dfrac{4+4}{2} = 4$	1 and 4	$\dfrac{1+21}{2} = 11$
19.	$\dfrac{95}{8} \approx 11.9$	$\dfrac{12+13}{2} = 12.5$	13	$\dfrac{6+17}{2} = 11.5$
20.	$\dfrac{60}{6} = 10$	$\dfrac{5+15}{2} = 10$	5 and 15	$\dfrac{5+15}{2} = 10$
21.	$\dfrac{35}{10} = 3.5$ weeks	3 weeks	3 weeks	$\dfrac{1+7}{2} = 4$ weeks
22.	$\dfrac{\$434}{7} = \$62$	$61	none	$\dfrac{\$25+\$102}{2} = \$63.50$
23. a)	$\dfrac{34}{7} \approx 4.9$	5	5	$\dfrac{1+11}{2} = 6$
b)	$\dfrac{37}{7} \approx 5.3$	5	5	$\dfrac{1+11}{2} = 6$
c)	Only the mean			
d)	$\dfrac{33}{7} \approx 4.7$	5	5	$\dfrac{1+10}{2} = 5.5$

   The mean and the midrange

24. Answers will vary. The National Center for Health uses the median for averages in this exercise.

25. A 79 mean average on 10 quizzes gives a total of 790 points. An 80 mean average on 10 quizzes requires a total of 800 points. Thus, Jim missed a B by 10 points not 1 point.

26. a) Mean: $\dfrac{\$361,000}{10} = \$36,100$

    b) Median: $\dfrac{\$27,000 + \$28,000}{2} = \$27,500$

    c) Mode: $26,000

    d) Midrange: $\dfrac{\$24,000 + \$81,000}{2} = \$52,500$

    e) The median, since it is lower

    f) The mean, since it is higher

27. a) Mean: $\dfrac{528.7}{10} \approx 52.9$ million

    b) Median: $\dfrac{43.3 + 44.3}{2} = 43.8$ million

    c) Mode: none

    d) Midrange: $\dfrac{37.6 + 85.9}{2} \approx 61.8$ million

28. a) Mean: $\dfrac{\$14,810}{12} \approx \$1234.17$

    b) Median: $\dfrac{\$1230 + \$1250}{2} = \$1240$

    c) Mode: $850

    d) Midrange: $\dfrac{\$850 + \$1900}{2} = \$1375$

29. a) Mean: $\dfrac{107.5}{10} \approx 10.8$ million

    b) Median: $\dfrac{9.9 + 10.2}{2} \approx 10.1$ million

    c) Mode: none

    d) Midrange: $\dfrac{7.8 + 15.1}{10} \approx 11.5$ million

30. Let $x =$ the sum of his scores

$$\frac{x}{5} = 81$$

$$x = 81(5) = 405$$

31. Let $x =$ the sum of his scores

$$\frac{x}{6} = 92$$

$$x = 92(6) = 552$$

32. One example is 1, 1, 2, 5, 6. Mode = 1, Median = 2, Mean $= \dfrac{15}{5} = 3$

33. One example is 72, 73, 74, 76, 77, 78.

Mean: $\dfrac{450}{6} = 75$, Median: $\dfrac{74 + 76}{2} = 75$, Midrange: $\dfrac{72 + 78}{2} = 75$

34. One example is 81, 82, 83, 85, 86, 87.

35. a) Yes

    b) Cannot be found since we do not know the middle two numbers in the ranked list

    c) Cannot be found without knowing all of the numbers

    d) Yes

36. A total of $80 \times 5 = 400$ points are needed for a grade of B. Jorge earned $73 + 69 + 85 + 80 = 307$ points on his first four exams. Thus, he needs $400 - 307 = 93$ or higher to get a B.

37. a) For a mean average of 60 on 7 exams, she must have a total of $60 \times 7 = 420$ points. Sheryl presently has $51 + 72 + 80 + 62 + 57 + 69 = 391$ points. Thus, to pass the course, her last exam must be $420 - 391 = 29$ or greater.

    b) A C average requires a total of $70 \times 7 = 490$ points. Sheryl has 391. Therefore, she would need $490 - 391 = 99$ or greater on her last exam.

    c) For a mean average of 60 on 6 exams, she must have a total of $60 \times 6 = 360$ points. If the lowest score on an exam she has already taken is dropped, she will have a total of $72 + 80 + 62 + 57 + 69 = 340$ points. Thus, to pass the course, her last exam must be $360 - 340 = 20$ or greater.

    d) For a mean average of 70 on 6 exams, she must have a total of $70 \times 6 = 420$ points. If the lowest score on an exam she has already taken is dropped, she will have a total of 340 points. Thus, to obtain a C, her last exam must be $420 - 340 = 80$ or greater.

38. The mode is the only measure which must be an actual piece of data since it is the most frequently occurring piece of data.

39. One example is 1, 2, 3, 3, 4, 5 changed to 1, 2, 3, 4, 4, 5.

    First set of data: Mean: $\dfrac{18}{6} = 3$, Median: $\dfrac{3+3}{2} = 3$, Mode: 3

    Second set of data: Mean: $\dfrac{19}{6} = 3.1\overline{6}$, Median: $\dfrac{3+4}{2} = 3.5$, Mode: 4

40. The mean changes from $\dfrac{9}{6} = 1.5$ to $\dfrac{10}{6} = 1.\overline{6}$. The mode changes from 1 and 2 to a mode of 1.

    The midrange changes from $\dfrac{3}{2} = 1.5$ to $\dfrac{4}{2} = 2$.

41. No, by changing only one piece of the six pieces of data you cannot alter both the median and the midrange.

42. Let $x = $ sum of the values

    $\dfrac{x}{12} = 85.20$

    $x = 85.20(12) = \$1022.40$

    $\$1022.40 - \$47 + \$74 = \$1049.40$

    $\dfrac{1049.40}{12} = \$87.45$ is the correct mean

43. The data must be arranged in either ascending or descending order.

44. She scored above approximately 73% of all the students who took the test.

45. He is taller than approximately 35% of all kindergarten children.

46. About 25% of the workers earn \$20,750 or less.

47. a) $Q_2 = $ Median $= \$25$

    b) $Q_1 = $ Median of the first 10 data values $= \$22$

    c) $Q_3 = $ Median of the last 10 data values $= \$34$

48. a) $Q_2 = $ Median $= \dfrac{600+700}{2} = \$650$

    b) $Q_1 = $ Median of the first 10 data values $= \$500$

    c) $Q_3 = $ Median of the last 10 data values $= \dfrac{800+830}{2} = \$815$

49. Second quartile, median

50. a) No, the percentile only indicated relative position of the score and not the value of it.

    b) Yes, a higher percentile indicates a higher relative position in the respective population.

    Thus, Kendra was in a better relative position.

51. a) \$530   b) \$540   c) 25%   d) 25%   e) 17%   f) $100 \times \$550 = \$55,000$

52. a) $\dfrac{56}{7} = 8$, $\dfrac{26}{4} = 6.5$, $\dfrac{10}{5} = 2$, $\dfrac{50}{5} = 10$, $\dfrac{396}{6} = 66$

    b) $\dfrac{92.5}{5} = 18.5$ c) $\dfrac{538}{27} \approx 19.926$ d) No

53. a) Ruth: ≈ 0.290, 0.359, 0.301, 0.272, 0.315

    Mantle: ≈ 0.300, 0.365, 0.304, 0.275, 0.321

  b) Mantle's is greater in every case.

  c) Ruth: $\dfrac{593}{1878} \approx 0.316$; Mantle: $\dfrac{760}{2440} \approx 0.311$; Ruth's is greater.

  d) Answers will vary.

  e) Ruth: $\dfrac{1.537}{5} \approx 0.307$; Mantle: $\dfrac{1.565}{5} = 0.313$; Mantle's is greater.

  f) and g) Answers will vary.

54. a) $\dfrac{707,000}{25} = \$28,280$

  b) $21,000

  c) $17,000

  d) $\dfrac{17,000 + 100,000}{2} = \$58,500$

  e) The median because there are pieces of data that are much greater and much smaller than the rest of the data.

55. $\Sigma xw = 84(0.40) + 94(0.60) = 33.6 + 56.4 = 90$

   $\Sigma w = 0.40 + 0.60 = 1.00$

   weighted average $= \dfrac{\Sigma xw}{\Sigma w} = \dfrac{90}{1.00} = 90$

56. $\Sigma xw = 3.0(4) + 4.0(3) + 2.0(3) + 4.0(3) = 12 + 12 + 6 + 12 = 42$

   $\Sigma w = 4 + 3 + 3 + 3 = 13$

   weighted average $= \dfrac{\Sigma xw}{\Sigma w} = \dfrac{42}{13} = 3.230769231 \approx 3.23$

57. a) – c) Answers will vary.

58. a) Answers will vary. One example is 2, 3, 5, 7, 7.

  b) Answers will vary. The answers for the example given in part a) above are as follows:

   Mean: $\dfrac{24}{5} = 4.8$, Median = 5, Mode = 7

Exercise Set 13.6

1. To find the **range**, subtract the lowest value in the set of data from the highest value.

2. The **standard deviation** measures the spread of the data about the mean.

3. Answers will vary.

4. It may be important to determine the consistency of the data.

5. Zero since the mean is the same value as all of the data values. The spread about the mean is 0.

6. s

7. σ

8. Where one expects to find a large variability such as test scores

9. In manufacturing or anywhere else where a minimum variability is desired

10. The first set of data will have the greater standard deviation because the scores have a greater spread about the mean.

11. They would be the same since the spread of data about each mean is the same.

12. The sum of the values in the (Data − Mean)^2 column will always be greater than or equal to 0.

13. a) The grades will be centered about the same number since the mean, 75.2, is the same for both classes.

    b) The spread of the data about the mean is greater for the evening class since the standard deviation is greater for the evening class.

14. Answers will vary.

15. Range = 17 − 6 = 11

$\bar{x} = \dfrac{55}{5} = 11$

x	$x - \bar{x}$	$(x - \bar{x})^2$
11	0	0
9	−2	4
6	−5	25
12	1	1
17	6	36
	0	66

$\dfrac{66}{4} = 16.5, s = \sqrt{16.5} \approx 4.06$

16. Range = 21 − 13 = 8

$\bar{x} = \dfrac{96}{6} = 16$

x	$x - \bar{x}$	$(x - \bar{x})^2$
15	−1	1
15	−1	1
19	3	9
21	5	25
13	−3	9
13	−3	9
	0	54

$\dfrac{54}{5} = 10.8, s = \sqrt{10.8} \approx 3.29$

17. Range = 136 − 130 = 6

$\bar{x} = \dfrac{931}{7} = 133$

x	$x - \bar{x}$	$(x - \bar{x})^2$
130	−3	9
131	−2	4
132	−1	1
133	0	0
134	1	1
135	2	4
136	3	9
	0	28

$\dfrac{28}{6} \approx 4.67, s = \sqrt{4.67} \approx 2.16$

18. Range = 12 − 0 = 12

$\bar{x} = \dfrac{70}{10} = 7$

x	$x - \bar{x}$	$(x - \bar{x})^2$
3	−4	16
7	0	0
8	1	1
12	5	25
0	−7	49
9	2	4
11	4	16
12	5	25
6	−1	1
2	−5	25
	0	162

$\dfrac{162}{9} = 18, s = \sqrt{18} \approx 4.24$

19. Range = 15 − 4 = 11

$$\overline{x} = \frac{60}{6} = 10$$

x	$x - \overline{x}$	$(x - \overline{x})^2$
4	−6	36
8	−2	4
9	−1	1
11	1	1
13	3	9
15	5	25
	0	76

$$\frac{76}{5} = 15.2, \ s = \sqrt{15.2} \approx 3.90$$

20. Range = 9 − 9 = 0

Since all pieces of data are identical,

the standard deviation is 0.

21. Range = 12 − 7 = 5

$$\overline{x} = \frac{63}{7} = 9$$

x	$x - \overline{x}$	$(x - \overline{x})^2$
7	−2	4
9	0	0
7	−2	4
9	0	0
9	0	0
10	1	1
12	3	9
	0	18

$$\frac{18}{6} = 3, s = \sqrt{3} \approx 1.73$$

22. Range = 72 − 48 = 24

$$\overline{x} = \frac{488}{8} = 61$$

x	$x - \overline{x}$	$(x - \overline{x})^2$
60	−1	1
58	−3	9
62	1	1
67	6	36
48	−13	169
51	−10	100
72	11	121
70	9	81
	0	518

$$\frac{518}{7} = 74, s = \sqrt{74} \approx 8.60$$

23. Range = 80 − 48 = $32

$$\overline{x} = \frac{660}{10} = \$66$$

x	$x - \overline{x}$	$(x - \overline{x})^2$
58	−8	64
58	−8	64
80	14	196
75	9	81
60	-6	36
75	9	81
78	12	144
48	−18	324
75	9	81
53	−13	169
	0	1240

$$\frac{1240}{9} \approx 137.78, s = \sqrt{137.78} \approx \$11.74$$

24. Range = 28 − 1 = 27 years

$$\overline{x} = \frac{84}{7} = 12$$

x	$x - \overline{x}$	$(x - \overline{x})^2$
10	−2	4
23	11	121
28	16	256
4	−8	64
1	−11	121
6	-6	36
12	0	0
	0	602

$$\frac{602}{6} \approx 100.33, \ s = \sqrt{100.33} \approx 10.02 \text{ years}$$

25. Range = 200 − 50 = $150

$$\overline{x} = \frac{1100}{10} = \$110$$

x	$x - \overline{x}$	$(x - \overline{x})^2$
50	−60	3600
120	10	100
130	20	400
60	−50	2500
55	−55	3025
75	−35	1225
200	90	8100
110	0	0
125	15	225
175	65	4225
	0	23,400

$$\frac{23,400}{9} = 2600, \ s = \sqrt{2600} \approx \$50.99$$

26. Range = 850 − 100 = $750

$$\overline{x} = \frac{2590}{7} = \$370$$

x	$x - \overline{x}$	$(x - \overline{x})^2$
600	230	52,900
100	−270	72,900
850	480	230,400
350	−20	400
250	−120	14,400
140	−230	52,900
300	−70	4900
	0	428,800

$$\frac{428,800}{6} \approx 71,467, \ s = \sqrt{71,467} \approx \$267.33$$

27. a) Range = 68 - 5 = $63

$$\overline{x} = \frac{204}{6} = \$34$$

x	$x - \overline{x}$	$(x - \overline{x})^2$
32	−2	4
60	26	676
14	−20	400
25	−9	81
5	−29	841
68	34	1156
	0	3158

$$\frac{3158}{5} = 631.6, s = \sqrt{631.6} \approx \$25.13$$

b) New data: 42, 70, 24, 35, 15, 78
The range and standard deviation will be the same. If each piece of data is increased by the same number, the range and standard deviation will remain the same.

c) Range = 78 - 15 = $63

$$\overline{x} = \frac{264}{6} = \$44$$

x	$x - \overline{x}$	$(x - \overline{x})^2$
42	−2	4
70	26	676
24	−20	400
35	−9	81
15	−29	841
78	34	1156
	0	3158

$$\frac{3158}{5} = 631.6, s = \sqrt{631.6} \approx \$25.13$$ The answers remain the same.

28. a) - c) Answers will vary.

d) If each piece of data is increased, or decreased, by n, the mean is increased, or decreased, by n. The standard deviation remains the same.

e) The mean of the first set of numbers is 11. The mean of the second set is 651. In each set the values of $(x-\overline{x})^2$ in the standard deviation calculation will be 9, 4, 1, 0, 4, 1, and 9 and $\sqrt{\dfrac{28}{6}} \approx 2.16$.

29. a) - c) Answers will vary.

d) If each number in a distribution is multiplied by n, both the mean and standard deviation of the new distribution will be n times that of the original distribution.

e) The mean of the second set is $4 \times 5 = 20$, and the standard deviation of the second set is $2 \times 5 = 10$.

30. a) Same   b) More

31. a) The standard deviation increases. There is a greater spread from the mean as they get older.

b) ≈ 133 lb

c) $\dfrac{175 - 90}{4} = 21.25 \approx 21$ lb

d) The mean weight is about 100 pounds and the normal range is about 60 to 140 pounds.

e) The mean height is about 62 inches and the normal range is about 53 to 68 inches.

f) 100% - 95% = 5%

32. a) and b) Answers will vary.

c) Baseball: $\dfrac{187.9}{10} = \$18.79$ million

NFL: $\dfrac{153.6}{10} = \$15.36$ million

d) Baseball Mean $\approx \$18.8$ million

NFL Mean $\approx \$15.4$ million

Baseball

x	$x-\overline{x}$	$(x-\overline{x})^2$
21.7	2.9	8.41
20.6	1.8	3.24
20.4	1.6	2.56
19.4	0.6	0.36
19.3	0.5	0.25
19.0	0.2	0.04
18.3	−0.5	0.25
16.6	−2.2	4.84
16.4	−2.4	5.76
16.2	−2.6	6.76
		32.47

NFL

x	$x-\overline{x}$	$(x-\overline{x})^2$
23.1	7.7	59.29
19.0	3.6	12.96
18.0	2.6	6.76
17.7	2.3	5.29
15.7	0.3	0.09
13.5	−1.9	3.61
12.3	−3.1	9.61
12.0	−3.4	11.56
11.6	−3.8	14.44
10.7	−4.7	20.09
		145.70

$\dfrac{32.47}{9} \approx 3.61$, $s = \sqrt{3.61} \approx \$1.90$ million

$\dfrac{145.70}{9} \approx 16.19$, $s = \sqrt{16.19} \approx \$4.02$ million

33. a)

East		West	
Number of oil changes made	Number of days	Number of oil changes made	Number of days
15-20	2	15-20	0
21-26	2	21-26	0
27-32	5	27-32	6
33-38	4	33-38	9
39-44	7	39-44	4
45-50	1	45-50	6
51-56	1	51-56	0
57-62	2	57-62	0
63-68	1	63-68	0

b)

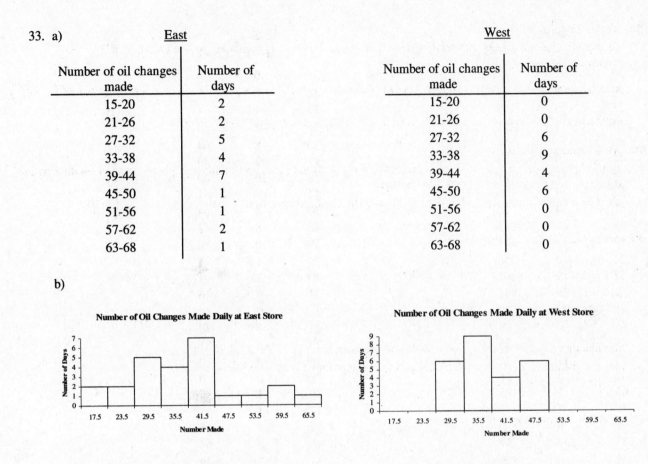

c) They appear to have about the same mean since they are both centered around 38.

d) The distribution for East is more spread out. Therefore, East has a greater standard deviation.

e) East: $\frac{950}{25} = 38$, West: $\frac{950}{25} = 38$

33. f)

East				West		
x	$x-\bar{x}$	$(x-\bar{x})^2$		x	$x-\bar{x}$	$(x-\bar{x})^2$
33	−5	25		38	0	0
30	−8	64		38	0	0
25	−13	169		37	−1	1
27	−11	121		36	−2	4
40	2	4		30	−8	64
44	6	36		45	7	49
49	11	121		28	−10	100
52	14	196		47	9	81
42	4	16		30	−8	64
59	21	441		46	8	64
19	−19	361		38	0	0
22	−16	256		39	1	1
57	19	361		40	2	4
67	29	841		34	−4	16
15	−23	529		31	−7	49
41	3	9		45	7	49
43	5	25		29	−9	81
27	−11	121		38	0	0
42	4	16		38	0	0
43	5	25		39	1	1
37	−1	1		37	−1	1
38	0	0		42	4	16
31	−7	49		46	8	64
32	-6	36		31	−7	49
35	−3	9		48	10	100
	0	3832			0	858

$$\frac{3832}{24}\approx159.67, \quad s=\sqrt{159.67}\approx12.64$$

$$\frac{858}{24}=35.75, \quad s=\sqrt{35.75}\approx5.98$$

34. Answers will vary.

35. 6, 6, 6, 6, 6

Exercise Set 13.7

1. A **rectangular distribution** is one where all the values have the same frequency.
2. A **J-shaped distribution** is one where the frequency is either constantly increasing or constantly decreasing.
3. A **bimodal distribution** is one where two nonadjacent values occur more frequently than any other values in a set of data.
4. A **distribution skewed to the right** is one that has "a tail" on its right.
5. A **distribution skewed to the left** is one that has "a tail" on its left.
6. A **normal distribution** is a bell-shaped distribution.
7. A z-score measure how far, in terms of standard deviations, a given score is from the mean
8. Subtract the mean from the given data value and divide the result by the standard deviation of the data set.
9. a) Below the mean
   b) Above the mean
10. 0

11. a) *B*   b) *C*   c) *A*
12. a) Yes, 36
      b) *B*, since curve *B* is more spread out it has the higher standard deviation.
13. The distribution of outcomes from the roll of a die
14. Skewed left – a listing of test scores where most of the students did well and a few did poorly;
      Skewed right – number of cans of soda consumed in a day where most people consumed a few
      cans and a few people consumed many cans
15. J shaped right – consumer price index; J shaped left – value of the dollar
16. The distribution of heights of an equal number of males and females
17. Normal
18. Rectangular
19. Skewed right
20. Bimodal
21. The mode is the lowest value, the median is greater than the mode, and the mean is greater than
      the median. The greatest frequency appears on the left side of the curve. Since the mode is the
      value with the greatest frequency, the mode would appear on the left side of the curve (where the
      lowest values are). Every value in the set of data is considered in determining the mean. The
      values on the far right of the curve would increase the value of the mean. Thus, the value of the
      mean would be farther to the right than the mode. The median would be between the mode
      and the mean.
22. The mode is the highest value. The median is lower than the mode. The mean is the lowest value.
23. Answers will vary.
24. Answers will vary.
25. In a normal distribution the mean, median, and the mode all have the same value.
26.   a) $\approx 68\%$ b) $\approx 95\%$
27.   0.5000
28.   0.5000
29.   (area to the left of 1) – (area to the left of -2)
        $= 0.8413 - 0.0228 = 0.8185$
30.   (area to the left of 1.70) – (area to the left of 1.10)
        $= 0.9554 - 0.8643 = 0.0911$
31.   area to the right of 1.34
        $= 1 -$ (area to the left of 1.34)
        $= 1 - 0.9099 = 0.0901$
32.   0.9474
33.   area to the left of -1.78
      0.0375
34.   area to the right of -1.78
        $=$ area to the left of $1.78 = 0.9625$
35. area between -1.32 and -1.64
      $0.0934 - 0.0505 = 0.0429$
36.   0.9671
37. area to the left of -1.62
      0.0536
38. area to the left of -0.92
      0.1788
39. $0.7611 = 76.11\%$
40. area less than -0.82
      $0.2061 = 20.61\%$
41. (area to the left of 2.24) – (area to the left of -1.34)
      $= 0.9875 - 0.0901 = 0.8974 = 89.74\%$
42. (area to the left of -1.90) – (area to the left of -2.18)
      $= 0.0287 - 0.0146 = 0.0141 = 1.41\%$
43.   area greater than -1.90
        $=$ area less than $1.90 = 0.9713 = 97.13\%$
44. area greater than 2.66 $= 1 -$ (area less than 2.66)
        $= 1 - 0.9961 = 0.0039 = 0.39\%$

45. area less than $1.96 = 0.9750 = 97.50\%$

46. (area to the left of -1.53) $-$ (area to the left of -1.82)
$= 0.0630 - 0.0344 = 0.0286 = 2.86\%$

47. (area to the left of 2.14) $-$ (area to the left of 0.72)
$= 0.9838 - 0.7642 = 0.2196 = 21.96\%$

48. (area to the left of 3.31) $-$ (area to the left of -2.15)
$= 0.9995 - 0.0158 = 0.9837 = 98.37\%$

49. a) Emily, Sarah, and Carol are taller than the mean because their z-scores are positive.

b) Jason and Juan are at the mean because their z-scores are zero.

c) Omar, Heather, and Kim are shorter than the mean because their z-scores are negative.

50. a) Sarah is the tallest because she had the highest z-score.

b) Heather is the shortest because she had the lowest z-score.

51. $0.5000 = 50\%$

52. $z_{14} = \dfrac{14 - 18}{4} = \dfrac{-4}{4} = -1.00$

$z_{26} = \dfrac{26 - 18}{4} = \dfrac{8}{4} = 2.00$

$0.9772 - 0.1587 = 0.8185 = 81.5\%$

53. $z_{23} = \dfrac{23 - 18}{4} = \dfrac{5}{4} = 1.25$

$1.000 - 0.8944 = 0.1056 = 10.56\%$

54. 10.56% of college students work at least 23 hours per week. (See Exercise 53.)

$0.1056(500) = 53$ students ; the average for random samples will be close to 53

55. $z_{550} = \dfrac{550 - 500}{100} = \dfrac{50}{100} = 0.50$

area less than $0.5 = 0.6915 = 69.15\%$

56. $z_{550} = \dfrac{650 - 500}{100} = \dfrac{150}{100} = 1.50$

area greater than $1.50 = 1 - 0.9332 = 0.0668 = 6.68\%$

57. $z_{550} = \dfrac{550 - 500}{100} = \dfrac{50}{100} = 0.50$

$z_{650} = \dfrac{650 - 500}{100} = \dfrac{150}{100} = 1.50$

area between 1.5 and 0.5
$= 0.9332 - 0.6915 = 0.2417 = 24.17\%$

58. $z_{300} = \dfrac{300 - 500}{100} = \dfrac{-200}{100} = -2.00$

area less than -2.00
$0.0228 = 2.28\%$

59. $z_{525} = \dfrac{525 - 500}{100} = \dfrac{25}{100} = 0.25$

$z_{400} = \dfrac{400 - 500}{100} = \dfrac{-100}{100} = -1.00$

area between -1.00 and 0.25
$= 0.5987 - 0.1587 = 0.4400 = 44.00\%$

60. $z_{380} = \dfrac{380 - 500}{100} = \dfrac{-120}{100} = -1.20$

area greater than -1.20
$=$ area less than $1.20 = 0.8849 = 88.49\%$

61. $z_{7.4} = \dfrac{7.4 - 7.6}{0.4} = \dfrac{-0.2}{0.4} = -0.50$

$z_{7.7} = \dfrac{7.7 - 7.6}{0.4} = \dfrac{0.1}{0.4} = 0.25$

$0.5987 - 0.3085 = 0.2902 = 29.02\%$

62. $z_{7.0} = \dfrac{7.0 - 7.6}{0.4} = \dfrac{-0.6}{0.4} = -1.50$

$0.0668 = 6.68\%$

63. $z_{7.7} = \dfrac{7.7 - 7.6}{0.4} = \dfrac{0.1}{0.4} = 0.25$

$0.5987 = 59.87\%$

64. The 8-oz cup will overflow when the machine dispenses more than 8 oz of coffee.

$$z_{8.0} = \frac{8.0 - 7.6}{0.4} = \frac{0.4}{0.4} = 1$$

$$(1 - 0.8413) = 0.1587 = 15.87\%$$

65. $0.5000 = 50.00\%$

66. $z_{58} = \frac{58 - 62}{5} = \frac{-4}{5} = -0.80$

$$z_{66} = \frac{66 - 62}{5} = \frac{4}{5} = 0.80$$

$$0.7881 - 0.2119 = 0.5762 = 57.62\%$$

67. $z_{56} = \frac{56 - 62}{5} = \frac{-6}{5} = -1.20$

$$0.1151 = 11.51\%$$

68. $z_{70} = \frac{70 - 62}{5} = \frac{8}{5} = 1.6$

$$1 - 0.9452 = 0.0548 = 5.48\%$$

69. 11.51% of cars are traveling slower than 56 mph. (See Exercise 67.)

$$(0.1151)(200) \approx 23 \text{ cars}$$

70. 5.48% of cars are traveling faster than 70 mph. (See Exercise 68.)

$$(0.0548)(200) \approx 11 \text{ cars}$$

71. $z_{15.83} = \frac{15.83 - 16}{0.1} = -1.70$

$$z_{16.32} = \frac{16.32 - 16}{0.1} = 3.2$$

$$0.9993 - 0.0446 = 0.9547 = 95.47\%$$

72. $z_{16.6} = \frac{16.16 - 16}{0.1} = 1.6$

$$1 - 0.9452 = 0.0548 = 5.48\%$$

73. $z_{15.83} = \frac{15.83 - 16}{0.1} = -1.70$

$$1 - 0.9554 = 0.0446$$

$$(0.0446)(300,000) = 13,380 \text{ boxes}$$

74. 5.48% of boxes contain more than 16.16 oz. (See Exercise 72.)

$$(0.0548)(300,000) = 16,440 \text{ boxes}$$

75. $z_{3.1} = \frac{3.1 - 3.7}{1.2} = \frac{-0.6}{1.2} = -0.50$

area greater than $-0.50 =$ area less than 0.50

$$0.6915 = 69.15\%$$

76. $z_{2.5} = \frac{2.5 - 3.7}{1.2} = \frac{-1.2}{1.2} = -1.00$

$$z_{4.3} = \frac{4.3 - 3.7}{1.2} = \frac{0.6}{1.2} = 0.50$$

$$0.6915 - 0.1587 = 0.5328 = 53.28\%$$

77. $z_{6.7} = \frac{6.7 - 3.7}{1.2} = \frac{3}{1.2} = 2.5$

$$1 - 0.9938 = 0.0062 = 0.62\%$$

78. $z_{6.7} = \frac{6.7 - 3.7}{1.2} = \frac{3}{1.2} = 2.5$

$$0.9938 = 99.38\%$$

79. 69.15% of the children are older than 3.1 years. (See Exercise 75.)

$$(0.6915)(120) \approx 83 \text{ children}$$

80. 53.28% of the children are between 2.5 and 4.3 years. (See Exercise 76.)

$$(0.5328)(120) \approx 64 \text{ children}$$

81. We need the percentage of customers with a weight loss of less than 5 lb.

$$z_5 = \frac{5 - 6.7}{0.81} = \frac{-1.7}{0.81} = -2.10$$

$$1 - 0.9821 = 0.0179 = 1.79\%$$

82. We need the percentage of batteries lasting less than 36 months.

$$z_{36} = \frac{36 - 46}{8} = \frac{-10}{8} = -1.25$$

$$0.1056 = 10.56\%$$

83. The standard deviation is too large. There is too much variation.

84. The percentages for each cutoff point are:

1.8: 96.41%

1.1: 86.43%

−1.2: 11.51%

−1.9: 2.87%

The percentages for each grade are:

A: $100 - 96.41 = 3.59\%$

B: $96.41 - 86.43 = 9.98\%$

C: $86.43 - 11.51 = 74.92\%$

D: $11.51 - 2.87 = 8.64\%$

F: 2.87%

85. a) Katie: $z_{28,408} = \dfrac{28,408 - 23,200}{2170} = \dfrac{5208}{2170} = 2.4$

Stella: $z_{29,510} = \dfrac{29,510 - 25,600}{2300} = \dfrac{3910}{2300} = 1.7$

b) Katie. Her z-score is higher than Stella's z-score. This means her sales are further above the mean than Stella's sales.

86. a) $\bar{x} = \dfrac{160}{30} = 5.\overline{3} \approx 5.33$

b)

x	$x-\bar{x}$	$(x-\bar{x})^2$	x	$x-\bar{x}$	$(x-\bar{x})^2$	x	$x-\bar{x}$	$(x-\bar{x})^2$
1	−4.33	18.75	4	−1.33	1.77	7	1.67	2.79
1	−4.33	18.75	4	−1.33	1.77	8	2.67	7.13
1	−4.33	18.75	4	−1.33	1.77	8	2.67	7.13
1	−4.33	18.75	5	−0.33	0.11	8	2.67	7.13
2	−3.33	11.09	6	0.67	0.45	8	2.67	7.13
2	−3.33	11.09	6	0.67	0.45	9	3.67	13.47
2	−3.33	11.09	6	0.67	0.45	9	3.67	13.47
2	−3.33	11.09	7	1.67	2.79	9	3.67	13.47
3	−2.33	5.43	7	1.67	2.79	10	4.67	21.81
3	−2.33	5.43	7	1.67	2.79	10	4.67	21.81
								260.70

$260.70 \div 29 \approx 8.99$ $s = \sqrt{8.99} \approx 3.00$

c)

$\bar{x} + 1.1s = 5.33 + 1.1(3) = 8.63$

$\bar{x} + 1.5s = 5.33 + 1.5(3) = 9.83$

$\bar{x} + 2.0s = 5.33 + 2.0(3) = 11.33$

$\bar{x} + 2.5s = 5.33 + 2.5(3) = 12.83$

$\bar{x} - 1.1s = 5.33 - 1.1(3) = 2.03$

$\bar{x} - 1.15s = 5.33 - 1.5(3) = 0.83$

$\bar{x} - 2.0s = 5.33 - 2.0(3) = -0.67$

$\bar{x} - 2.5s = 5.33 - 2.5(3) = -2.17$

d) Between -1.1s and 1.1s or between scores of 2.03 and 8.63, there are 17 scores.

$\dfrac{17}{30} = 0.5\overline{6} \approx 56.7\%$

Between -1.5s and 1.5s, or between scores of 0.83 and 9.83, there are 28 scores.

$\dfrac{28}{30} = 0.9\overline{3} \approx 93.3\%$

Between -2.0s and 2.0s, or between scores of -0.67 and 11.33, there are 30 scores.

$\dfrac{30}{30} = 1 = 100\%$

Between -2.5s and 2.5s, or between scores of -2.17 and 12.83, there are 30 scores.

$\dfrac{30}{30} = 1 = 100\%$

e)

Minimum %	K = 1.1	K = 1.5	K = 2.0	K = 2.5
(For any distribution)	17.4%	55.6%	75%	84%
Normal distribution	72.8%	86.6%	95.4%	99.8%
Given distribution	56.7%	93.3%	100%	100%

f) The percent between -1.1s and 1.1s is too low to be considered a normal distribution, and the percentages for K = 1.5 and K = 2 are too high for a normal distribution.

87. Answers will vary.

88. Using Table 13.7, the answer is 1.96.

89. Using Table 13.7, the answer is −1.18.

90. Answers will vary.

91. $\dfrac{0.77}{2} = 0.385$

Using the table in Section 13.7, an area of 0.385 has a z-score of 1.20.

$$z = \frac{x - \overline{x}}{s}$$

$$1.20 = \frac{14.4 - 12}{s}$$

$$1.20 = \frac{2.4}{s}$$

$$\frac{1.20s}{1.20} = \frac{2.4}{1.20}$$

$$s = 2$$

Exercise Set 13.8

1. The **correlation coefficient** measures the strength of the linear relationship between the quantities.

2. The purpose of **linear regression** is to determine the linear relationship between two variables.

3. 1   4. −1   5. 0

6. a) A negative correlation indicates that as one quantity increases, the other quantity decreases.
   b) Answers will vary.

7. a) A positive correlation indicates that as one quantity increases, the other quantity increases.
   b) Answers will vary.

8. The **line of best fit** represents the line such that the sum of the squares of the vertical distances between the points and the line is a minimum.

9. The **level of significance** is used to identify the cutoff between results attributed to chance and results attributed to an actual relationship between the two variables.

10. A **scatter diagram** is a plot of data points.

11. No correlation   12. Weak negative

13. Strong positive   14. Strong negative

15. Yes, $\mid 0.82 \mid > 0.684$

16. No, $\mid 0.51 \mid < 0.537$

17. Yes, $\mid -0.73 \mid > 0.707$

18. No, $\mid -0.49 \mid < 0.602$

19. No, $\mid -0.23 \mid < 0.254$

20. No, $\mid -0.49 \mid < 0.590$

21. No, $\mid 0.75 \mid < 0.917$

22. Yes, $\mid 0.96 \mid > 0.959$

Note: The answers in the remainder of this section may differ slightly from your answers, depending upon how your answers are rounded and which calculator you used.

23. a)

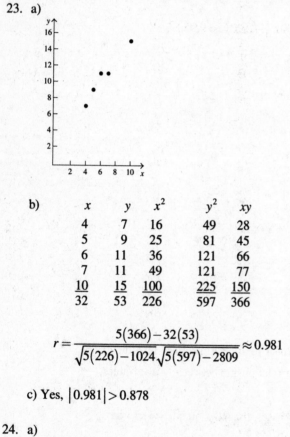

b)

x	y	x^2	y^2	xy
4	7	16	49	28
5	9	25	81	45
6	11	36	121	66
7	11	49	121	77
10	15	100	225	150
32	53	226	597	366

$$r = \frac{5(366) - 32(53)}{\sqrt{5(226) - 1024}\sqrt{5(597) - 2809}} \approx 0.981$$

c) Yes, $\mid 0.981 \mid > 0.878$

d) Yes, $\mid 0.981 \mid > 0.959$

24. a)

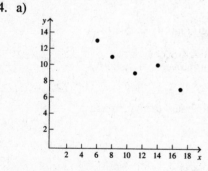

24. b)

x	y	x^2	y^2	xy
6	13	36	169	78
8	11	64	121	88
11	9	121	81	99
14	10	196	100	140
17	7	289	49	119
56	50	706	510	524

$$r = \frac{5(524) - 56(50)}{\sqrt{5(706) - 3136}\sqrt{5(520) - 2500}} \approx -0.907$$

c) Yes, $|-0.907| > 0.878$

d) No, $|-0.907| < 0.959$

25. a)

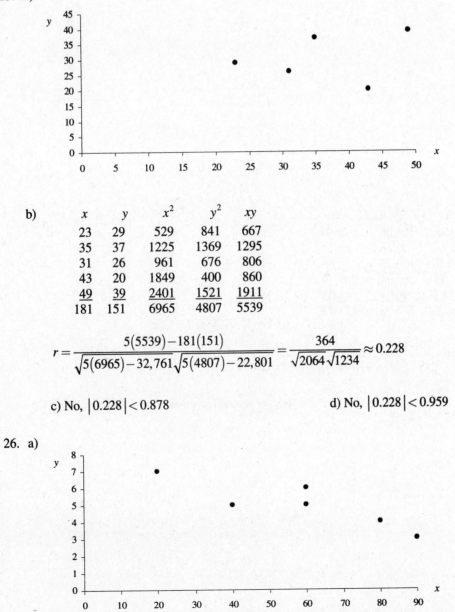

b)

x	y	x^2	y^2	xy
23	29	529	841	667
35	37	1225	1369	1295
31	26	961	676	806
43	20	1849	400	860
49	39	2401	1521	1911
181	151	6965	4807	5539

$$r = \frac{5(5539) - 181(151)}{\sqrt{5(6965) - 32,761}\sqrt{5(4807) - 22,801}} = \frac{364}{\sqrt{2064}\sqrt{1234}} \approx 0.228$$

c) No, $|0.228| < 0.878$

d) No, $|0.228| < 0.959$

26. a)

26. b)

x	y	x^2	y^2	xy
90	3	8100	9	270
80	4	6400	16	320
60	6	3600	36	360
60	5	3600	25	300
40	5	1600	25	200
20	7	400	49	140
350	30	23,700	160	1590

$$r = \frac{6(1590) - 350(30)}{\sqrt{6(23,700) - 122,500}\sqrt{6(160) - 900}} = \frac{-960}{\sqrt{19,700}\sqrt{60}} \approx -0.883$$

c) Yes, $|-0.883| > 0.811$ d) No, $|-0.883| < 0.917$

27. a)

b)

x	y	x^2	y^2	xy
5.3	10.3	28.09	106.09	54.59
4.7	9.6	22.09	92.16	45.12
8.4	12.5	70.56	156.25	105
12.7	16.2	161.29	262.44	205.74
4.9	9.8	24.01	96.04	48.02
36	58.4	306.04	712.98	458.47

$$r = \frac{5(458.47) - 36(58.4)}{\sqrt{5(306.04) - 1296}\sqrt{5(712.98) - 3410.56}} = \frac{189.95}{\sqrt{234.2}\sqrt{154.34}} \approx 0.999$$

c) Yes, $|0.999| > 0.878$ d) Yes, $|0.999| > 0.959$

28. a)

28. b)

x	y	x^2	y^2	xy
12	15	144	225	180
16	19	256	361	304
13	45	169	2025	585
24	30	576	900	720
100	60	10,000	3600	6000
50	28	2500	784	1400
215	197	13,645	7895	9189

$$r = \frac{6(9189) - 215(197)}{\sqrt{6(13,645) - 46,225}\sqrt{6(7895) - 38,809}} = \frac{12,779}{\sqrt{35,645}\sqrt{8561}} \approx 0.732$$

c) No, $|0.732| < 0.811$ **d)** No, $|0.732| < 0.917$

29. a)

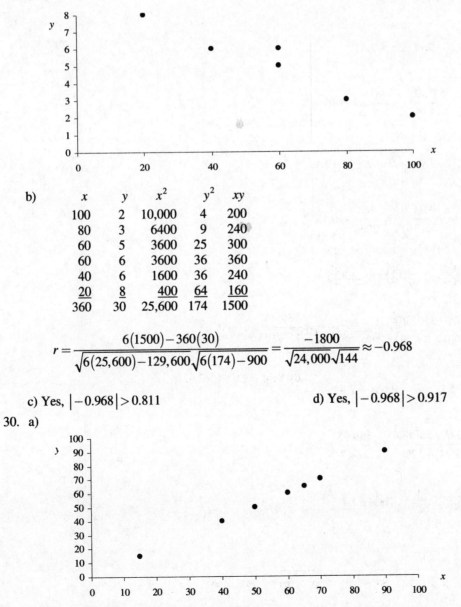

b)

x	y	x^2	y^2	xy
100	2	10,000	4	200
80	3	6400	9	240
60	5	3600	25	300
60	6	3600	36	360
40	6	1600	36	240
20	8	400	64	160
360	30	25,600	174	1500

$$r = \frac{6(1500) - 360(30)}{\sqrt{6(25,600) - 129,600}\sqrt{6(174) - 900}} = \frac{-1800}{\sqrt{24,000}\sqrt{144}} \approx -0.968$$

c) Yes, $|-0.968| > 0.811$ **d)** Yes, $|-0.968| > 0.917$

30. a)

30. b)

x	y	x^2	y^2	xy
90	90	8100	8100	8100
70	70	4900	4900	4900
65	65	4225	4225	4225
60	60	3600	3600	3600
50	50	2500	2500	2500
40	40	1600	1600	1600
15	15	225	225	225
390	390	25,150	25,150	25,150

$$r = \frac{7(25{,}150) - 390(390)}{\sqrt{7(25{,}150) - 152{,}100}\sqrt{7(25{,}150) - 152{,}100}} = \frac{23{,}950}{\sqrt{23{,}950}\sqrt{23{,}950}} = 1.00$$

c) Yes, $|1.00| > 0.754$ d) Yes, $|1.00| > 0.875$

31. From # 23: $m = \dfrac{5(366) - 32(53)}{5(226) - 1024} = \dfrac{67}{53} \approx 1.26$

$b = \dfrac{53 - \left(\dfrac{67}{53}\right)(32)}{5} \approx 2.51, \quad y = 1.26x + 2.51$

32. From # 24: $m = \dfrac{5(524) - 56(50)}{5(706) - 3136} = \dfrac{-90}{197} \approx -0.46$

$b = \dfrac{50 - \left(\dfrac{-90}{197}\right)(56)}{5} \approx 15.12, \quad y = -0.46x + 15.12$

33. From # 25: $m = \dfrac{5(5539) - 181(151)}{5(6965) - 32{,}761} = \dfrac{364}{2064} \approx 0.18$

$b = \dfrac{151 - \dfrac{364}{2064}(181)}{5} \approx 23.82, \quad y = 0.18x + 23.82$

34. From # 26: $m = \dfrac{6(1590) - 350(30)}{6(23{,}700) - 122{,}500} = \dfrac{-960}{19{,}700} \approx -0.05$

$b = \dfrac{30 - \dfrac{-960}{19{,}700}(350)}{6} \approx 7.84, \quad y = -0.05x + 7.84$

35. From # 27: $m = \dfrac{5(458.47) - 36(58.4)}{5(306.04) - 1296} = \dfrac{189.95}{234.2} \approx 0.81$

$b = \dfrac{58.4 - \dfrac{189.95}{234.2}(36)}{5} \approx 5.84, \quad y = 0.81x + 5.84$

36. From # 28: $m = \dfrac{6(9189)-215(197)}{6(13,645)-46,225} = \dfrac{12,779}{35,645} \approx 0.36$

    $b = \dfrac{197 - \dfrac{12,779}{35,645}(215)}{6} \approx 19.99, \quad y = 0.36x + 19.99$

37. From # 29: $m = \dfrac{6(1500)-360(30)}{6(25,600)-129,600} = \dfrac{-1800}{24,000} \approx -0.08$

    $b = \dfrac{30 - \dfrac{-1800}{24,000}(360)}{6} \approx 9.50, \quad y = -0.08x + 9.50$

38. From # 30: $m = \dfrac{7(25,150)-390(390)}{7(25,150)-152,100} = \dfrac{23,950}{23,950} = 1.00$

    $b = \dfrac{390 - 1(390)}{7} = 0, \quad y = 1.00x$

39.   a)

x	y	x^2	y^2	xy
50	40	2500	1600	2000
53	42	2809	1764	2226
60	45	3600	2025	2700
35	25	1225	625	875
43	34	1849	1156	1462
62	45	3844	2025	2790
303	231	15827	9195	12053

$r = \dfrac{6(12053)-(303)(231)}{\sqrt{6(15827)-91809}\sqrt{6(9195)-53361}} \approx 0.974$

b) Yes, $|\,0.974\,| > 0.811$

c) $m = \dfrac{6(12053)-(303)(231)}{(6)(15827)-91809} = \dfrac{775}{1051} \approx 0.74$,

   $b = \dfrac{231 - \dfrac{775}{1051}(303)}{6} \approx 1.26, \quad y = 0.74x + 1.26$

40. a)

x	y	x^2	y^2	xy
80	9	6400	81	720
70	8	4900	64	560
60	7	3600	49	420
40	4.5	1600	20.25	180
70	8	4900	64	560
50	5	2500	25	250
370	41.5	23900	303.25	2690

$$r = \frac{6(2690)-(370)(41.5)}{\sqrt{6(23900)-136900}\sqrt{6(303.25)-1722.25}} = 0.98734 \approx 0.987$$

b) Yes, $|\,0.987\,| > 0.811$

c) $m = \dfrac{6(2690)-(370)(41.5)}{6(23900)-136900} = 0.12077 \approx 0.12$,

$b = \dfrac{41.5-(0.12077)(370)}{6} \approx -0.53$, $\quad y = 0.12x - 0.53$

41. a)

x	y	x^2	y^2	xy
20	40	400	1600	800
40	45	1600	2025	1800
50	70	2500	4900	3500
60	76	3600	5776	4560
80	92	6400	8464	7360
100	95	10,000	9025	9500
350	418	24,500	31,790	27,520

$$r = \frac{6(27,520)-350(418)}{\sqrt{6(24,500)-122,500}\sqrt{6(31,790)-174,724}} = \frac{18,820}{\sqrt{24,500}\sqrt{16,016}} \approx 0.950$$

b) Yes, $|0.950| > 0.917$

c) $m = \dfrac{6(27,520)-350(418)}{6(24,500)-122,500} = \dfrac{18,820}{24,500} \approx 0.77$, $\quad b = \dfrac{418-\dfrac{18,820}{24,500}(350)}{6} \approx 24.86$, $\quad y = 0.77x + 24.86$

42. a)

x	y	x^2	y^2	xy
765	119	585,225	14,161	91,035
926	127	857,476	16,129	117,602
1145	150	1,311,025	22,500	171,750
842	119	708,964	14,161	100,198
1485	153	2,205,225	23,409	227,205
1702	156	2,896,804	24,336	265,512
6865	824	8,564,719	114,696	973,302

$$r = \frac{6(973,302)-6865(824)}{\sqrt{6(8,564,719)-47,128,225}\sqrt{6(114,696)-678,976}} = \frac{183,052}{\sqrt{4,260,089}\sqrt{9200}} \approx 0.925$$

42. b) Yes, $\mid 0.925 \mid > 0.811$

c) $m = \dfrac{6(973,302) - 6865(824)}{6(8,564,719) - 47,128,225} = \dfrac{183,052}{4,260,089} \approx 0.04$,

$$b = \dfrac{824 - \dfrac{183,052}{4,260,089}(6865)}{6} \approx 88.17, \quad y = 0.04x + 88.17$$

d) $y = 0.04(1500) + 88.17 = 148.17 \approx 148$ mountain lions

43. a)

x	y	x^2	y^2	xy
6.5	27	42.25	729	175.5
7	30	49	900	210
6	25	36	625	150
2	10	4	100	20
6.4	28	40.96	784	179.2
6	24	36	576	144
33.9	144	208.21	3714	878.7

$$r = \dfrac{6(878.7) - (33.9)(144)}{\sqrt{6(208.21) - 1149.21}\sqrt{6(3714) - 20736}} = 0.99252 \approx 0.993$$

b) Yes, $\mid 0.993 \mid > 0.811$

c) $m = \dfrac{6(878.7) - (33.9)(144)}{6(208.21) - 1149.21} = 3.90405 \approx 3.90$,

$$b = \dfrac{144 - (3.90405)(33.9)}{6} \approx 1.94, \quad y = 3.90x + 1.94$$

d) $y = 3.90(5) + 1.94 \approx 21.4$ kilocalories

44. a)

x	y	x^2	y^2	xy
89	22	7921	484	1958
110	28	12,100	784	3080
125	30	15,625	900	3750
92	26	8464	676	2392
100	22	10,000	484	2200
95	21	9025	441	1995
108	28	11,664	784	3024
97	25	9409	625	2425
816	202	84,208	5178	20,824

$$r = \dfrac{8(20,824) - 816(202)}{\sqrt{8(84,208) - 665,856}\sqrt{8(5178) - 40,804}} = \dfrac{1760}{\sqrt{7808}\sqrt{620}} \approx 0.800$$

b) Yes, $\mid 0.800 \mid > 0.707$

44. c) $m = \dfrac{8(20,824) - 816(202)}{8(84,208) - 665,856} = \dfrac{1760}{7808} \approx 0.23$,

$b = \dfrac{202 - \dfrac{1760}{7808}(816)}{8} \approx 2.26$, $y = 0.23x + 2.26$

d) $y = 0.23(115) + 2.26 = 28.71 \approx 29$ units

45. a)

x	y	x^2	y^2	xy
27	23	729	529	621
31	22	961	484	682
35	20	1225	400	700
32	21	1024	441	672
30	24	900	576	720
30	22	900	484	660
185	132	5739	2914	4055

$r = \dfrac{6(4055) - (185)(132)}{\sqrt{6(5739) - 34225}\sqrt{6(2914) - 17424}} \approx -0.804$

b) No, $|-0.804| < 0.917$

c) $m = \dfrac{6(4055) - (185)(132)}{6(5739) - 34225} = -0.43063 \approx -0.43$

$b = \dfrac{132 - (-0.43063)(185)}{6} \approx 35.28$, $y = -0.43x + 35.28$

Note, however, that since we have not found a significant correlation between x and y, the line of best fit may not be very useful for predicting y given x.

d) $y = -0.43(33) + 35.28 \approx 21.1$ mpg

46. a)   For a data set of this size, use of a calculator is recommended.
The values in the last row of the calculation table are:

$\Sigma x = 129, \ \Sigma y = 85, \ \Sigma x^2 = 2221, \ \Sigma y^2 = 1023, \ \Sigma xy = 1269$

$r = \dfrac{8(1269) - (129)(85)}{\sqrt{8(2221) - (129)^2}\sqrt{8(1023) - (85)^2}} \approx -0.782$

b) Yes, $|-0.782| > 0.707$

c) $m = \dfrac{8(1269) - (129)(85)}{8(2221) - (129)^2} = -0.7214 \approx -0.72$

$b = \dfrac{85 - (-0.7214)(129)}{8} \approx 22.26$

d) $y = -0.72(14) + 22.26 \approx 12.2$ muggings

47. a)

x	y	x^2	y^2	xy
1	80.0	1	6400.0	80.0
2	76.2	4	5806.4	152.4
3	68.7	9	4719.7	206.1
4	50.1	16	2510.0	200.4
5	30.2	25	912.0	151.0
6	20.8	36	432.6	124.8
21	326	91	20,780.7	914.7

$$r = \frac{6(914.7) - 21(326)}{\sqrt{6(91) - 441}\sqrt{6(20,780.7) - 106,276}} = \frac{-1357.8}{\sqrt{105}\sqrt{18,408.2}} \approx -0.977$$

b) Yes, $|-0.977| > 0.917$

c) $m = \dfrac{6(914.7) - 21(326)}{6(91) - 441} = \dfrac{-1357.8}{105} \approx -12.93$, $b = \dfrac{326 - \frac{-1357.8}{105}(21)}{6} \approx 99.59$, $y = -12.93x + 99.59$

d) $y = -12.93(4.5) + 99.59 \approx 41.4\%$

48. Answers will vary.

49. a) and b) Answers will vary.

c)

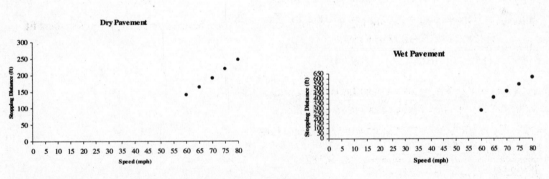

d) The values in the last row of the calculation table are:

$\Sigma x = 350$, $\Sigma y = 959$, $\Sigma x^2 = 24750$, $\Sigma y^2 = 191129$, $\Sigma xy = 68470$

$$r = \frac{5(68470) - (350)(959)}{\sqrt{5(24750) - (350)^2}\sqrt{5(191129) - (959)^2}} \approx 0.999$$

e) The values in the last row of the calculation table are:

$\Sigma x = 350$, $\Sigma y = 2328$, $\Sigma x^2 = 24750$, $\Sigma y^2 = 1151074$, $\Sigma xy = 167015$

$$r = \frac{5(167015) - (350)(2328)}{\sqrt{5(24750) - (350)^2}\sqrt{5(1151074) - (2328)^2}} \approx 0.990$$

f) Answers will vary.

49. g) $m = \dfrac{5(68470)-(350)(959)}{5(24750)-(350)^2} = 5.36$

$b = \dfrac{959-(5.36)(350)}{5} = -183.40$

$y = 5.36x - 183.40$

h) $m = \dfrac{5(167015)-(350)(2328)}{5(24750)-(350)^2} = 16.22$

$b = \dfrac{2328-(16.22)(350)}{5} = -669.80$

$y = 16.22x - 699.80$

i) Dry: $y = 5.36(77)-183.40 \approx 229.3\,\text{ft}$ ft

   Wet: $y = 16.22(77)-669.80 = 579.1\,\text{ft}$ ft

50. a) The correlation coefficient will not change because $\sum xy = \sum yx$, $\left(\sum x\right)\left(\sum y\right) = \left(\sum y\right)\left(\sum x\right)$, and the square roots in the denominator will be the same.

   b) Answers will vary.

51. Answers will vary.

52. Answers will vary.

53. a) The values in the last row of the calculation table are:

   $\Sigma x = 12015$, $\Sigma y = 1097.4$, $\Sigma x^2 = 24060055$, $\Sigma y^2 = 201062.56$, $\Sigma xy = 2197621$

   $r = \dfrac{6(2197621)-(12015)(1097.4)}{\sqrt{6(24060055)-(12015)^2}\,\sqrt{6(201062.56)-(1097.4)^2}} \approx 0.993$

   b) Should be the same.

   c) The values in the last row of the calculation table are:

   $\Sigma x = 15$, $\Sigma y = 1097.4$, $\Sigma x^2 = 55$, $\Sigma y^2 = 201062.56$, $\Sigma xy = 2821$

   $r = \dfrac{6(2821)-(15)(1097.4)}{\sqrt{6(55)-(15)^2}\,\sqrt{6(201062.56)-(1097.4)^2}} \approx 0.993$

54. a) $SS(xy) = \sum xy - \dfrac{\left(\sum x\right)\left(\sum y\right)}{n} = 387 - \dfrac{17(106)}{6} = 86.67$

   $SS(x) = \sum x^2 - \dfrac{\left(\sum x\right)^2}{n} = 75 - \dfrac{289}{6} = 26.83$

   $SS(y) = \sum y^2 - \dfrac{\left(\sum y\right)^2}{n} = 2202 - \dfrac{11236}{6} = 329.33$

   $r = \dfrac{86.67}{\sqrt{(26.83)(329.33)}} \approx 0.922$

   b) Should be the same.

Review Exercises

1. a) A **population** consists of all items or people of interest.

   b) A **sample** is a subset of the population.

2. A **random sample** is one where every item in the population has the same chance of being selected.

3. The candy bars may have lots of calories, or fat, or sodium. Therefore, it may not be healthy to eat them.

4. Sales may not necessarily be a good indicator of profit. Expenses must also be considered.

5. a)   b)

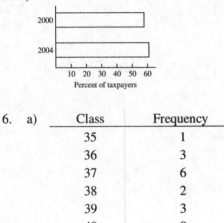   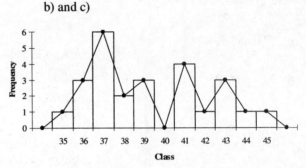

6. a)

Class	Frequency
35	1
36	3
37	6
38	2
39	3
40	0
41	4
42	1
43	3
44	1
45	1

   b) and c)

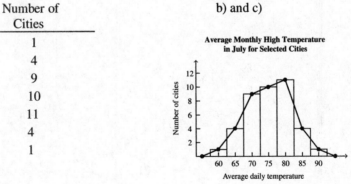

7. a)

High Temperature	Number of Cities
58 - 62	1
63 - 67	4
68 - 72	9
73 - 77	10
78 - 82	11
83 - 87	4
88 - 92	1

   b) and c)

Average Monthly High Temperature in July for Selected Cities

   d) 6 | 5 represents 65

```
5 | 8
6 | 3 6 6 7 8 8 9
7 | 0 1 1 1 2 2 3 3 3 4 5 5 5 6 6 7 9 9 9
8 | 0 0 0 0 1 2 2 2 3 4 4 7
9 | 1
```

8. $\bar{x} = \dfrac{480}{6} = 80$

9. $\dfrac{79+83}{2} = 81$

10. None

11. $\dfrac{65+93}{2} = 79$

12. $93 - 65 = 28$

13.

x	$x - \bar{x}$	$(x-\bar{x})^2$
65	-15	225
76	-4	16
79	-1	1
83	3	9
84	4	16
93	13	169
	0	520

$\dfrac{436}{5} = 87.2$, $s = \sqrt{87.2} \approx 9.34$

14. $\bar{x} = \dfrac{156}{12} = 13$

15. $\dfrac{12+14}{2} = 13$

16. 12 and 7

17. $\dfrac{4+23}{2} = 13.5$

18. $23 - 4 = 19$

19.

x	$x - \bar{x}$	$(x-\bar{x})^2$
4	-9	81
5	-8	64
7	-6	36
7	-6	36
12	-1	1
12	-1	1
14	1	1
15	2	4
17	4	16
19	6	36
21	8	64
23	10	100
	0	440

$\dfrac{440}{11} = 40$, $s = \sqrt{40} \approx 6.32$

20. $z_7 = \dfrac{7-9}{2} = \dfrac{-2}{2} = -1.00$

$z_{11} = \dfrac{11-9}{2} = \dfrac{2}{2} = 1.00$

$0.8413 - 0.1587 = 0.6826 = 68.26\%$

21. $z_5 = \dfrac{5-9}{2} = \dfrac{-4}{2} = -2.00$

$z_{13} = \dfrac{14-9}{2} = \dfrac{4}{2} = 2.00$

$0.9772 - 0.0228 = 0.9544 = 95.44\%$

22. $z_{12.2} = \dfrac{12.2-9}{2} = \dfrac{3.2}{2} = 1.6$

$0.9452 = 94.52\%$

23. Subtract the answer for Exercise 22 from 1:

$1 - 0.9452 = 0.0548 = 5.48\%$

24. $z_{7.8} = \dfrac{7.8 - 9}{2} = -\dfrac{1.2}{2} = -0.6$

$1 - 0.2743 = 0.7257 = 72.57\%$

25. $z_{20} = \dfrac{20 - 20}{5} = \dfrac{0}{5} = 0$

$z_{25} = \dfrac{25 - 20}{5} = \dfrac{5}{5} = 1.00$

$0.341 = 34.1\%$

26. $z_{18} = \dfrac{18 - 20}{5} = \dfrac{-2}{5} = -0.40$

$0.500 - 0.155 = 0.345 = 34.5\%$

27. $z_{22} = \dfrac{22 - 20}{5} = \dfrac{2}{5} = 0.40$

$z_{28} = \dfrac{28 - 20}{5} = \dfrac{8}{5} = 1.60$

$0.445 - 0.155 = 0.29 = 29.0\%$

28. $z_{30} = \dfrac{30 - 20}{5} = \dfrac{10}{5} = 2.00$

$0.500 - 0.477 = 0.023 = 2.3\%$

29. a)

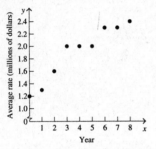

b) Yes; positive because generally as the year increases, the cost increases.

c) The values in the last row of the calculation table are:

$\Sigma x = 36, \; \Sigma y = 17.1, \; \Sigma x^2 = 204, \; \Sigma y^2 = 34.03, \; \Sigma xy = 77.6$

$r = \dfrac{9(77.6) - (36)(17.1)}{\sqrt{9(204) - (36)^2}\,\sqrt{9(34.03) - (17.1)^2}} \approx 0.957 \, .$

d) Yes, $\left|\, 0.957 \,\right| > 0.666$

e) $m = \dfrac{9(77.6) - (36)(17.1)}{9(204) - (36)^2} = 0.1533 \approx 0.15$

$b = \dfrac{17.1 - (0.1533)(36)}{9} \approx 1.29, \quad y = 0.15x + 1.29$

f) $y = 0.15(13) + 1.29 \approx \$3.2$ million

30. a)

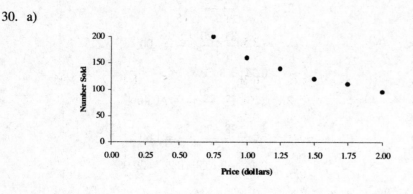

b) Yes; negative because generally as the price increases, the number sold decreases.

c)

x	y	x^2	y^2	xy
0.75	200	0.5625	40,000	150
1.00	160	1	25,600	160
1.25	140	1.5625	19,600	175
1.50	120	2.25	14,400	180
1.75	110	3.0625	12,100	192.5
2.00	95	4	9025	190
8.25	825	12.4375	120,725	1047.5

$$r = \frac{6(1047.5) - 8.25(825)}{\sqrt{6(12.4375) - 68.0625}\sqrt{6(120,725) - 680,625}} = \frac{-521.25}{\sqrt{6.5625}\sqrt{43,725}} \approx -0.973$$

d) Yes, $|-0.973| > 0.811$

e) $m = \dfrac{6(1047.5) - 8.25(825)}{6(12.4375) - 68.0625} = \dfrac{-521.25}{6.5625} \approx -79.4$

$b = \dfrac{825 - \dfrac{-521.25}{6.5625}(8.25)}{6} \approx 246.7, \quad y = -79.4x + 246.7$

f) $y = -79.4(1.60) + 246.7 = 119.66 \approx 120$ sold

31. 180 lb
32. 185 lb
33. 25%
34. 25%
35. 14%
36. $(100)(192) = 19,200$ lb
37. $192 + (2)(23) = 238$ lb
38. $192 - (1.8)(23) = 150.6$ lb
39. $\bar{x} = \dfrac{150}{42} \approx 3.57$
40. 2
41. $\dfrac{3+3}{2} = 3$
42. $\dfrac{0+14}{2} = 7$
43. $14 - 0 = 14$

44.

x	$x-\bar{x}$	$(x-\bar{x})^2$	x	$x-\bar{x}$	$(x-\bar{x})^2$	x	$x-\bar{x}$	$(x-\bar{x})^2$
0	−3.6	12.96	2	−1.6	2.56	4	0.4	0.16
0	−3.6	12.96	2	−1.6	2.56	5	1.4	1.96
0	−3.6	12.96	3	−0.6	0.36	5	1.4	1.96
0	−3.6	12.96	3	−0.6	0.36	5	1.4	1.96
0	−3.6	12.96	3	−0.6	0.36	6	2.4	5.76
0	−3.6	12.96	3	−0.6	0.36	6	2.4	5.76
1	−2.6	6.76	3	−0.6	0.36	6	2.4	5.76
1	−2.6	6.76	3	−0.6	0.36	6	2.4	5.76
2	−1.6	2.56	4	0.4	0.16	6	2.4	5.76
2	−1.6	2.56	4	0.4	0.16	7	3.4	11.56
2	−1.6	2.56	4	0.4	0.16	8	4.4	19.36
2	−1.6	2.56	4	0.4	0.16	10	6.4	40.96
2	−1.6	2.56	4	0.4	0.16	14	10.4	108.16
2	−1.6	2.56	4	0.4	0.16			332.32
2	−1.6	2.56						

$$\frac{332.32}{41} \approx 8.105, \quad s = \sqrt{8.105} \approx 2.85$$

45.

# of Children	# of Presidents
0 - 1	8
2 - 3	15
4 - 5	10
6 - 7	6
8 - 9	1
10 - 11	1
12 - 13	0
14 - 15	1

46. and 47.

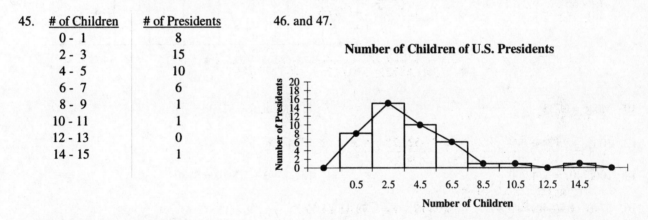

Number of Children of U.S. Presidents

48. No, it is skewed to the right.

49. No, some families have no children, more have one child, the greatest percent may have two children, fewer have three children, etc.

50. No, the number of children per family has decreased over the years.

Chapter Test

1. $\bar{x} = \dfrac{210}{5} = 42$

2. 43

3. 43

4. $\dfrac{27 + 52}{2} = 39.5$

5. $52 - 27 = 25$

6.

x	$x - \bar{x}$	$(x - \bar{x})^2$
27	–15	225
43	1	1
43	1	1
45	3	9
52	10	100
	0	336

$\dfrac{336}{4} = 84, \ s = \sqrt{84} \approx 9.17$

7.

Class	Frequency
25 - 30	7
31 - 36	5
37 - 42	1
43 - 48	7
49 - 54	5
55 - 60	3
61 - 66	2

8. and 9.

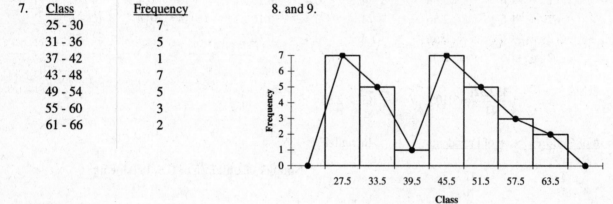

10. Mode = $735

11. Median = $710

12. $100\% - 25\% = 75\%$

13. 79%

14. $100(740) = \$74,000$

15. $\$740 + 1(\$40) = \$780$

16. $\$740 - 1.5(\$40) = \$680$

17. $z_{36} = \dfrac{36 - 42}{5} = \dfrac{-6}{5} = -1.20$

$z_{53} = \dfrac{53 - 42}{5} = \dfrac{11}{5} = 2.20$

$0.9861 - 0.1151 = 0.8710 = 87.10\%$

18. $z_{35.75} = \dfrac{35.75 - 42}{5} = -1.25$

$1 - 0.1056 = 0.8944 = 89.44\%$

19. $z_{48.25} = \dfrac{48.25 - 42}{5} = 1.25$

$1 - 0.8944 = 0.1056 = 10.56\%$

20. $z_{50} = \dfrac{50 - 42}{5} = 1.6$

$0.9452 = 94.52\%$

21. a)

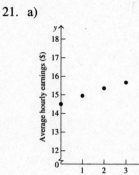

b) Yes

c) The values in the last row of the calculation table are:

$\Sigma x = 10,\ \Sigma y = 76.7,\ \Sigma x^2 = 30,\ \Sigma y^2 = 1178.11,\ \Sigma xy = 157.3$

$$r = \frac{5(157.3) - (10)(76.7)}{\sqrt{5(30) - (10)^2}\sqrt{5(1178.11) - (76.7)^2}} \approx 0.996$$

d) Yes, $|\,0.996\,| > 0.878$

e) $m = \dfrac{5(157.3) - (10)(76.7)}{5(30) - (10)^2} = 0.39$

$b = \dfrac{76.7 - (0.39)(10)}{5} = 14.56,\quad y = 0.39x + 14.56$

f) $y = 0.39(29) + 14.56 = \$25.87$

Group Projects

1. a) – j) Answers will vary.
2. a) – g) Answers will vary.

CHAPTER FOURTEEN

GRAPH THEORY

1. A **graph** is a finite set of points, called **vertices**, that are connected with line segments, called **edges**.

2.   3.

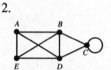

4. The **degree** of a vertex is the number of edges that connect to that vertex.

5. If the number of edges connected to the vertex is even, the vertex is **even**. If the number of edges connected to the vertex is odd, the vertex is **odd**.

6. Answers will vary. In the following graph, the edge *EF* is a bridge because if it were removed from the graph, the result would be a disconnected graph (i.e., there would be no path from vertices *A, B, E, H,* and *G* to vertices *C, D, J, I,* and *F*).

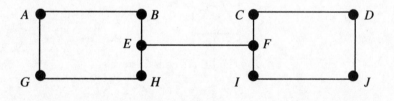

7. a) A **path** is a sequence of adjacent vertices and the edges connecting them.

   b) A **circuit** is a path that begins and ends at the same vertex.

   c)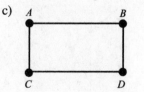

   The path *A, B, D, C* is a path that is not a circuit.
   The path *A, B, D, C, A* is a path that is also a circuit.

8. Answers will vary. In the graphs below, the graph on the right is disconnected since no path connects vertices *A*, *D*, and *E* to vertices *B* and *C*.

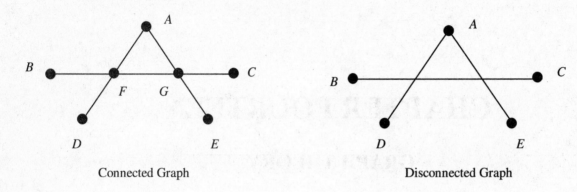

Connected Graph   Disconnected Graph

9.

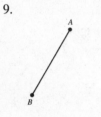

A and *B* are odd.

10.

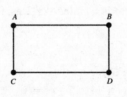

A, *B*, *C*, and *D* are all even.

11.

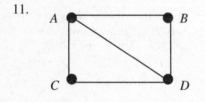

B and *C* are even. *A* and *D* are odd.

12.

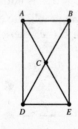

A, *B*, *D* and *E* are odd, *C* is even.

13.

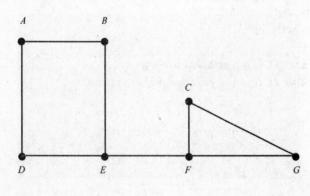

14.

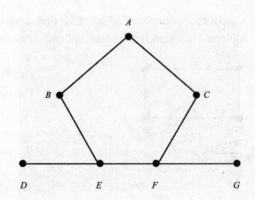

15. No. There is no edge connecting vertices B and C. Therefore, A, B, C, D, E is not a path.

16. Edge AC and edge CD

17. No.

18. Yes. One example is A, B, D, C, A.

19. Yes. One example is C, A, B, D, F, E, C, D.

20. Yes. One example is A, B, D, F, E, C, A.

21.

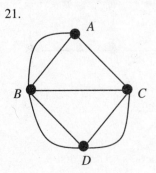

22.

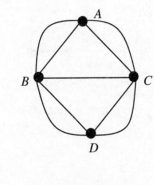

23.

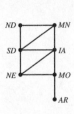

24.

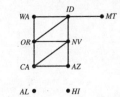

25.

26.

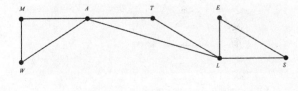

27.

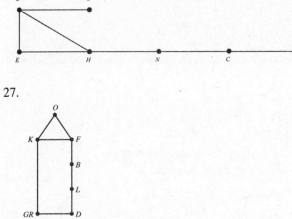

28.

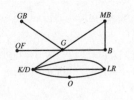

29.

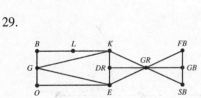

30.

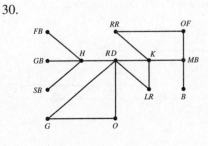

31.

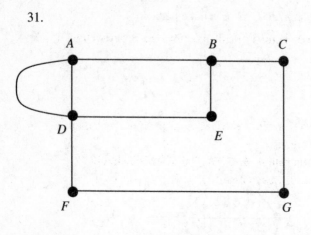

32.

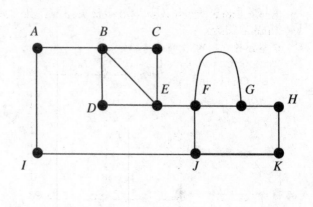

33. Disconnected. There is no path that connects
   A to C.

34. Connected

35. Connected

36. Disconnected. There is no path that
   connects A to B.

37. Edge AB

38. Edge BC

39. Edge EF

40. Edge FK and edge HL

41.

42. Answers will vary.

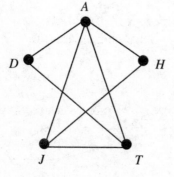

   Other answers are possible.

43. It is impossible to have a graph with an odd number of odd vertices.

44. a) - c) Answers will vary.

   d) The sum of the degrees is equal to twice the number of edges. This is true since each edge
   must connect two vertices. Each edge then contributes two to the sum of the degrees.

45. a) and b) Answers will vary.

Exercise Set 14.2

1. a) An **Euler path** is a path that must include each edge of a graph exactly one time.
   b) and c)

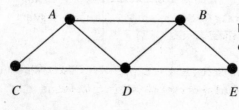

   b) The path A, B, E, D, C, A, D, B is an Euler path.
   c) The path A, B, E, D, C is a path that is not an Euler path.

2. a) An **Euler circuit** is a circuit that must include each edge of a graph exactly one time and return to the original vertex.

b) and c)

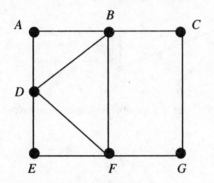

b)   The circuit *A, B, C, G, F, B, D, F, E, D, A* is an Euler circuit.

c)   The path *A, B, C, G, F, E, D, A* is a circuit but not an Euler circuit.

3. a) Yes, according to Euler's Theorem.
   b) Yes, according to Euler's Theorem.
   c) No, according to Euler's Theorem.

4. a) Yes, according to Euler's Theorem.
   b) No, according to Euler's Theorem.
   c) No, according to Euler's Theorem.

5. If all of the vertices are even, the graph has an Euler circuit.

6. a) If all the vertices are even, then start with any vertex. If there are two odd vertices, then start with one of the odd vertices. Move from vertex to vertex without tracing any bridges until you have traced each edge of the graph exactly one time. You will finish at the other odd vertex.

   b) If there are any odd vertices, then there is no Euler circuit. If there are all even vertices, then start with any vertex. Move from vertex to vertex without tracing any bridges until you have traced each edge of the graph exactly one time. You will finish at the vertex you started from.

7. *A, B, D, B, C, D, E, A, C*; other answers are possible.

8. *C, A, B, C, D, B, D, E, A*; other answers are possible.

9. No. This graph has exactly two odd vertices. Each Euler path must begin with an odd vertex. *B* is an even vertex.

10. No. A graph with exactly two odd vertices has no Euler circuits.

11. *A, B, A, C, B, E, C, D, A, D, E*; other answers are possible.

12. *E, D, A, B, E, C, D, A, B, C, A*; other answers are possible.

13. No. A graph with exactly two odd vertices has no Euler circuits.

14. No. This graph has exactly two odd vertices. Each Euler path must begin with an odd vertex. *C* is an even vertex.

15. *A, B, C, D, E, F, B, D, F, A*; other answers are possible.

16. *B, C, D, E, F, A, B, D, F, B*; other answers are possible.

17. *C, D, E, F, A, B, D, F, B, C*; other answers are possible.

18. *D, E, F, A, B, C, D, F, B, D*; other answers are possible.

19. *E, F, A, B, C, D, F, B, D, E*; other answers are possible.

20. *F, A, B, F, D, B, C, D, E, F*; other answers are possible.

21. a) Yes. There are zero odd vertices.
    b) Yes. There are zero odd vertices.

22. a) Yes. There are two or fewer odd vertices.
    b) No. There are more than zero odd vertices.

23. a) No. There are more than two odd vertices.
    b) No. There are more than zero odd vertices.

24. a) No. There are more than two odd vertices.
    b) No. There are more than zero odd vertices.

25. a) Yes. Each island would correspond to an odd vertex. According to item 2 of Euler's Theorem, a graph with exactly two odd vertices has at least one Euler path, but no Euler circuit.

    b) They could start on either island and finish at the other.

26. a) Yes. The land at the top and the island on the left would each correspond to an odd vertex. According to item 2 of Euler's Theorem, a graph with exactly two odd vertices has at least one Euler path, but no Euler circuits.

    b) They could start either on the land at the top of the picture or on the island on the left. If they started on the island, then they would end on the land at the top, and vice versa.

In Exercises 27-32, one graph is shown. Other graphs are possible.

27. a)

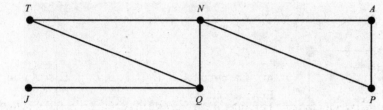

b) Vertices *J* and *Q* are both odd. According to item 2 of Euler's Theorem, since there are exactly two odd vertices, at least one Euler path, but no Euler circuits exist.

Yes; *J, Q, T, N, A, P, N, Q*

c) No. (See part b) above.)

28. a)

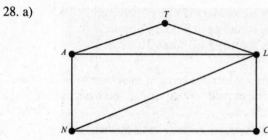

b) Vertices *A* and *N* are both odd. According to item 2 of Euler's Theorem, since there are exactly two odd vertices, at least one Euler path, but no Euler circuits exist.

Yes; *A, T, L, C, N, L, A, N*

c) No. (See part b) above.)

29. a)

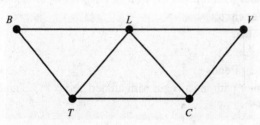

b) Vertices *T* and *C* are both odd. According to item 2 of Euler's Theorem, since there are exactly two odd vertices, at least one Euler path, but no Euler circuits exist.

Yes; *T, B, L, V, C, L, T, C*

c) No. (See part b) above.)

30. a)

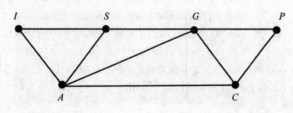

b) Vertices *S* and *C* are both odd. According to item 2 of Euler's Theorem, since there are exactly two odd vertices, at least one Euler path, but no Euler circuits exist.

Yes; *S, I, A, S, G, A, C, G, P, C*

c) No. (See part b) above.)

31. a)

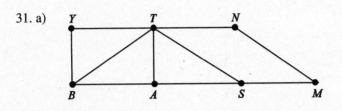

b) Vertices *A*, *S*, *T*, and *B* are odd. According to item 3 of Euler's Theorem there is neither an Euler path nor an Euler circuit.

c) No. (See part b) above.)

32. a)

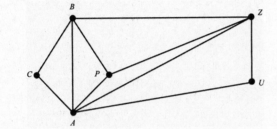

b) Vertices *A* and *P* are both odd. According to item 2 of Euler's Theorem, since there are exactly two odd vertices, at least one Euler path, but no Euler circuits exist.

Yes; *P, B, Z, P, A, B, C, A, U, Z, A*

c) No. (See part b) above.)

33. a) The graph representing the floor plan:

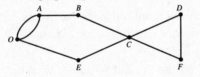

b) Yes
c) *O, A, B, C, D, F, C, E, O, A*

34. a) The graph representing the floor plan:

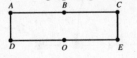

b) Yes
c) *O, E, C, B, A, D, O*

35. a) The graph representing the floor plan:

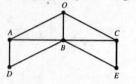

   b) No; the graph has four odd vertices, and by Euler's theorem a graph with more than two odd vertices has neither and Euler path nor an Euler circuit.

36. a) The graph representing the floor plan:

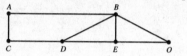

   b) Yes

   c) *D, C, A, B, D, E, B, O, E*

37. a) Yes. The graph representing the map:

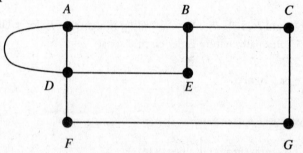

   They are seeking an Euler path or an Euler circuit. Note that vertices *A* and *B* are both odd. According to item 2 of Euler's Theorem; since there are exactly two odd vertices, at least one Euler path, but no Euler circuits exist.

   b) The residents would need to start at the intersection of Maple Cir., Walnut St., and Willow St. or at the intersection of Walnut St. and Oak St.

38. a) Yes. The graph representing the map:

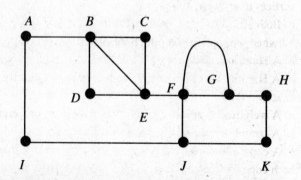

   They are seeking an Euler path or an Euler circuit. Note that vertices *G* and *J* are both odd. According to item 2 of Euler's Theorem, since there are exactly two odd vertices, at least one Euler path, but no Euler circuits exist.

   b) The residents would need to start at the intersection of Spring Blvd. and Lake St. or at the rightmost intersection of Stream Cir. and Ocean Blvd.

39. *B, E, D, A, B, C, A, D, C, E*; other answers are possible.
40. *C, A, D, B, E, G, D, F, C, D, E*; other answers are possible.
41. *H, I, F, C, B, D, G, H, E, D, A, B, E, F*; other answers are possible.
42. *D, A, B, E, I, H, D, C, G, K, L, H, M, I, N, O, J, F, E*; other answers are possible.
43. *A, E, B, F, C, G, D, K, G, J, F, I, E, H, A*; other answers are possible.
44. *A, B, C, F, I, H, G, D, H, E, F, B, E, D, A*; other answers are possible.
45. *A, C, D, G, H, F, C, F, E, B, A*; other answers are possible.
46. *A, B, C, D, F, C, B, E, F, H, G, E, A*; other answers are possible.
47. *A, B, C, E, B, D, E, F, I, E, H, D, G, H, I, J, F, C, A*; other answers are possible.
48. *A, B, C, E, B, D, E, F, D, A, C, A*; other answers are possible.
49. *OK, KS, CO, WY, UT, CO, NM, OK, CO*; other answers are possible.
50. *A, O, H, C, B, K, H, R, A, S, H, O*; other answers are possible.
51. *B, A, E, H, I, J, K, D, C, G, G, J, F, C, B, F, I, E, B*; other answers are possible.
52. *B, E, I, F, B, C, F, J, G, G, C, D, K, J, I, H, E, A, B*; other answers are possibe.
53. *J, G, G, C, F, J, K, D, C, B, F, I, E, B, A, E, H, I, J*; other answers are possible.
54. *J, F, C, B, F, I, E, B, A, E, H, I, J, G, G, C, D, K, J*; other answers are possible.
55. a) No.

    b) California, Nevada, and Louisiana (and others) have an odd number of states bordering them. Since a graph of the United States would have more than two odd vertices, no Euler path and no Euler circuit exist.
56. It is not possible to draw a graph with an Euler circuit that has a bridge. Therefore, a graph with an Euler circuit has no bridge.
57. a)   b)   c)

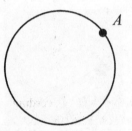

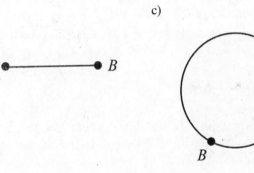

Exercise Set 14.3

1. a) A **Hamilton circuit** is a path that begins and ends with the same vertex and passes through all other vertices exactly one time.

    b) Both **Hamilton** and **Euler circuits** begin and end at the same vertex. A **Hamilton circuit** passes through all other *vertices* exactly once, while an **Euler circuit** passes through each *edge* exactly once.

2. a) A **Hamilton path** is a path that passes through each vertex exactly one time.

    b) A **Hamilton path** passes through each *vertex* exactly once; an **Euler path** passes through each *edge* exactly once.

3. a) A **weighted graph** is a graph with a number, or weight, assigned to each edge.

    b) A **complete graph** is a graph in which there is an edge between each pair of vertices.

    c) A **complete, weighted graph** is a graph in which there is an edge between each pair of vertices and each edge has a number, or weight, assigned to it.

4. a) The **factorial** of a number is computed by multiplying the given number by each natural number less than the given number.

    b) $4! = 4 \cdot 3 \cdot 2 \cdot 1 = 24$

    c) $6! = 6 \cdot 5 \cdot 4 \cdot 3 \cdot 2 \cdot 1 = 720$

    d) $8! = 8 \cdot 7 \cdot 6 \cdot 5 \cdot 4 \cdot 3 \cdot 2 \cdot 1 = 40,320$

5. a) The number of unique Hamilton circuits in a complete graph with n vertices is found by computing $(n-1)!$

   b) $n=6;(n-1)!=(7-1)!=6!=720$

   c) $n=10;(n-1)!=(10-1)!=9!=362,880$

6. a) The **optimal solution** to a traveling salesman problem is the least expensive or shortest way to visit each location exactly one time and return to the starting location.

   b) It is a solution that is close to optimal and can be used when determining the optimal solution is not feasible.

7. To find the optimal solution using the **Brute Force method**, write down all possible Hamilton circuits and then compute the cost or distance associated with each Hamilton circuit. The one with the lowest cost or shortest distance is the optimal solution to the traveling salesman problem.

8. Starting from your current position, choose the cheapest or shortest route to get to the next location. From there choose the cheapest or shortest route to a location you have not already visited. Continue this process until you have visited each location. The path found is the path found using the **Nearest Neighbor method** for approximating the optimal solution.

9. *A, E, F, B, C, D, G* and *G, D, C, F, E, A, B*; other answers are possible.

10. *A, C, D, H, E, F, B, G, I* and *B, G, I, F, E, A, D, H, C*; other answers are possible.

11. *A, B, C, D, G, F, E, H* and *E, H, F, G, D, C, A, B*; other answers are possible.

12. *A, B, C, D, H, G, F, E, I, J, K, L* and *A, E, I, J, F, B, C, G, K, L, H, D*; other answers are possible.

13. *A, B, C, E, D, F, G, H* and *F, G, H, E, D, A, B, C*; other answers are possible.

14. *A, D, F, G, H, E, B, C, I* and *I, C, B, A, D, E, F, H, G*; other answers are possible.

15. *A, B, C, F, I, H, E, G, D, A* and *E, H, I, F, C, B, A, D, G, E*; other answers are possible.

16. *A, B, C, D, H, L, K, G, F, J, I, E, A* and *A, E, I, J, K, L, H, D, C, G, F, B, A*; other answers are possible.

17. *A, B, C, F, I, E, H, G, D, A* and *A, E, B, C, F, I, H, G, D, A*; other answers are possible.

18. *D, H, G, F, C, E, B, A, D* and *A, B, C, E, F, G, H, D, A*; other answers are possible.

19.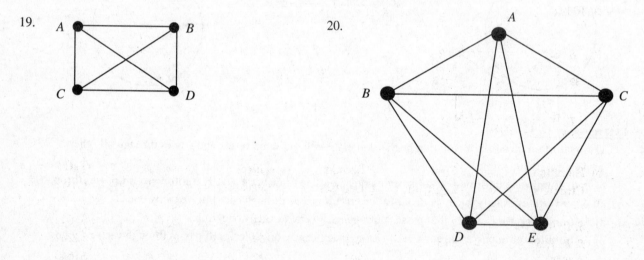

20.

21. The number of unique Hamilton circuits within the complete graph with 7 vertices representing this situation is $(7-1)!=6!=6\cdot5\cdot4\cdot3\cdot2\cdot1=720$ ways

22. The number of unique Hamilton circuits within the complete graph with eight vertices representing this situation is $(8-1)!=7!=7\cdot6\cdot5\cdot4\cdot3\cdot2\cdot1=5040$ ways

23. The number of unique Hamilton circuits within the complete graph with thirteen vertices representing this situation is $(13-1)!=12!=12\cdot11\cdot10\cdot9\cdot8\cdot7\cdot6\cdot5\cdot4\cdot3\cdot2\cdot1=479,001,600$ ways

24. The number of unique Hamilton circuits within the complete graph with eleven vertices representing
    this situation is $(11-1)! = 10! = 10 \cdot 9 \cdot 8 \cdot 7 \cdot 6 \cdot 5 \cdot 4 \cdot 3 \cdot 2 \cdot 1 = 3,628,800$ ways
    (The vertices are the 10 different farms he has to visit and his starting point.)

In Exercises 25-32, other graphs are possible.

25. a)

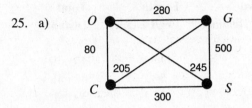

b)

Hamilton Circuit	First Leg/Distance	Second Leg/Distance	Third Leg/Distance	Fourth Leg/Distance	Total Distance
C, O, G, S, C	80	280	500	300	1160 miles
C, O, S, G, C	80	245	500	205	1030 miles
C, G, O, S, C	205	280	245	300	1030 miles
C, G, S, O, C	205	500	245	80	1030 miles
C, S, G, O, C	300	500	280	80	1160 miles
C, S, O, G, C	300	245	280	205	1030 miles

The shortest route is C, O, S, G, C or C, G, O, S, C or C, G, S, O, C or C, S, O, G, C

c) 1030 miles

26. a)

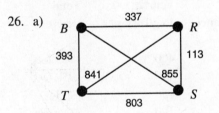

b)

Hamilton Circuit	First Leg/Cost	Second Leg/Cost	Third Leg/Cost	Fourth Leg/Cost	Total Cost
S, R, B, T, S	113	337	393	803	$1646
S, R, T, B, S	113	841	393	855	$2202
S, T, B, R, S	803	393	337	113	$1646
S, T, R, B, S	803	841	337	855	$2836
S, B, R, T, S	855	337	841	803	$2836
S, B, T, R, S	855	393	841	113	$2202

The least expensive route is S, R, B, T, S or S, T, B, R, S

c) $1646

27. a)

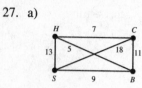

b)

Hamilton Circuit	First Leg/Distance	Second Leg/Distance	Third Leg/Distance	Fourth Leg/Distance	Total Distance
H, S, B, C, H	13	9	11	7	40 miles
H, S, C, B, H	13	18	11	5	47 miles
H, B, S, C, H	5	9	18	7	39 miles
H, B, C, S, H	5	11	18	13	47 miles
H, C, S, B, H	7	18	9	5	39 miles
H, C, B, S, H	7	11	9	13	40 miles

The shortest route is *H, C, S, B, H* or *H, B, S, C, H*

c) 39 miles

28. a)

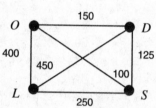

b)

Hamilton Circuit	First Leg/Distance	Second Leg/Distance	Third Leg/Distance	Fourth Leg/Distance	Total Distance
O, D, S, L, O	150	125	250	400	925 feet
O, D, L, S, O	150	450	250	100	950 feet
O, L, S, D, O	400	250	125	150	925 feet
O, L, D, S, O	400	450	125	100	1075 feet
O, S, D, L, O	100	125	450	400	1075 feet
O, S, L, D, O	100	250	450	150	950 feet

The shortest route is *O, D, S, L, O* or *O, L, S, D, O*

c) 925 feet (But note that if Mary goes back to her office from the library by revisiting the student center, her total trip will be 875 feet.)

29. a)
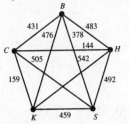

b) *S, B, C, H, K, S* for $1954
c) Answers will vary.

30. a)
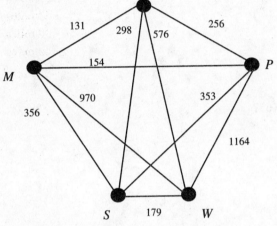

b) *B, M, P, S, W, B* for 131 + 154 + 353 + 179 + 576 = $1393
c) Answers will vary.

31. a)
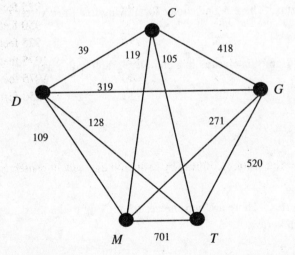

b) *C, D, M, G, T, C* for 39 + 109 + 271 + 520 + 105 = $1044
c) Answers will vary.

32. a)

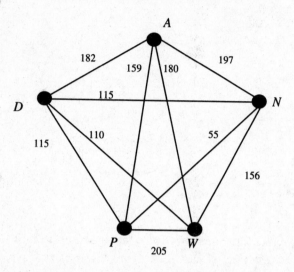

b) *N, P, D, W, A, N* for 55 + 115 + 110 + 180 + 197 = $657
c) Answers will vary.

33. a) – d) Answers will vary.

34. a)

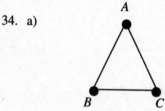

There are two choices for moving to the second vertex. There is one choice for moving to a third vertex.
2(1) = 2
(3 -1)! = 2! = 2(1) = 2
The number obtained is the same as the number of Hamilton circuits in a complete graph with 3 vertices.

b)

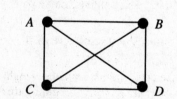

There are three choices for moving to the second vertex. There are two choices for moving to the third vertex. There is one choice for moving to the fourth vertex.
3(2)(1) = 6
(4 - 1)! = 3! = 3(2)(1) = 6
The number obtained is the same as the number of Hamilton circuits in a complete graph with 4 vertices.

34. c)

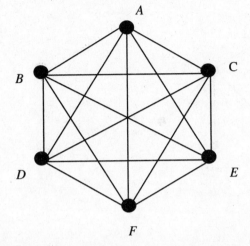

There are five choices for moving to the second vertex. There are four choices for moving to the third vertex. There are three choices for moving to the fourth vertex. There are two choices for moving to the fifth vertex. There is one choice for moving to the sixth vertex.

$5(4)(3)(2)(1) = 120$

$(6 - 1)! = 5! = 5(4)(3)(2)(1) = 120$

The number obtained is the same as the number of Hamilton circuits in a complete graph with 6 vertices.

d) When starting at a vertex in a complete graph with n vertices, you have $n-1$ choices. At your second vertex, you have one less choice, or $n-2$ choices. This process continues until you only have one vertex to choose from.

35. *A, E, D, N, O, F, G, Q, P, T, M, L, C, B, J, K, S, R, I, H, A*; other answers are possible.

Exercise Set 14.4

1. A **tree** is a connected graph in which each edge is a bridge.

2. In a tree, each edge is a bridge. In a graph that is not a tree, there is at least one edge that is not a bridge.

3. Yes, because removing the edge would create a disconnected graph.

4. A **spanning tree** is obtained by removing the edges of a graph one at a time, while maintaining a path to each vertex, until the graph is reduced to a tree.

5. A **minimum-cost spanning tree** is a spanning tree that has the lowest cost or shortest distance of all spanning trees for a given graph.

6. To find a minimum-cost spanning tree from a weighted graph, choose the edge with the smallest weight first. Continue to choose the edge with the smallest weight that does not lead to a circuit until a spanning tree is found.

7.

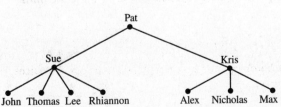

8.

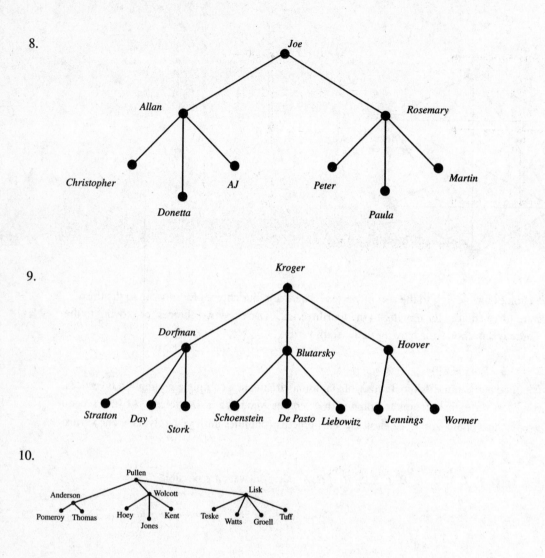

9.

10.

11.

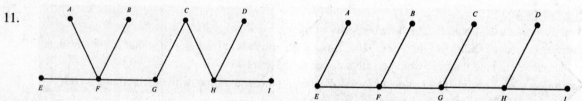

Other answers are possible.

12.

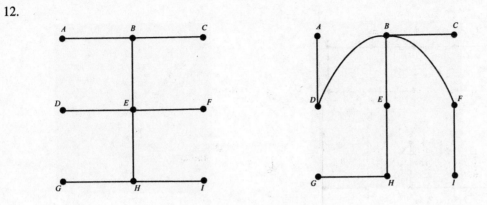

Other answers are possible.

13.

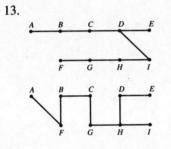

Other answers are possible.

14.

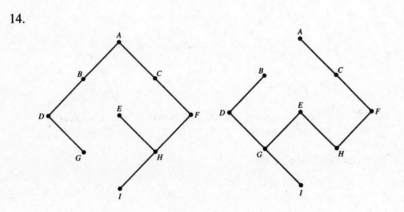

Other answers are possible.

15.

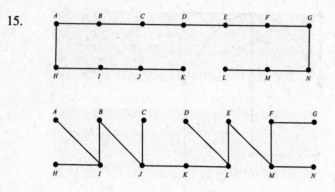

Other answers are possible.

16.

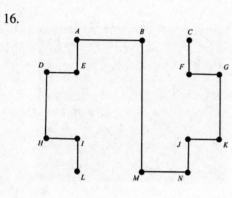
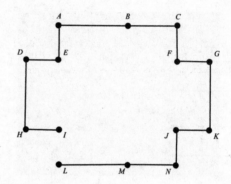

Other answers are possible.

17.

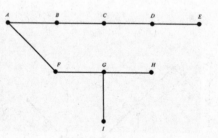

Other answers are possible.

18.

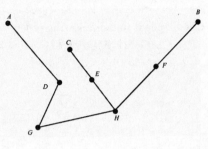 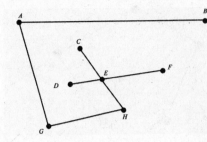

Other answers are possible.

19.

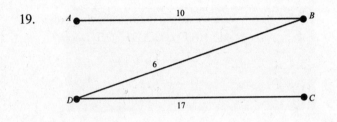

Choose edges in the following order:
DB, BA, DC

20.

Choose edges in the following order:
CD, AE, EC, AB

21.

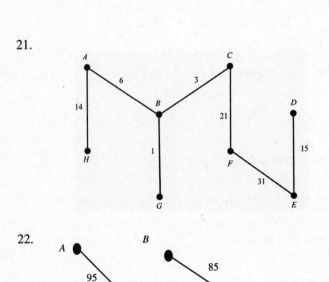

Choose edges in the following order:
GB, BC, BA, AH, DE, CF, FE

22.

Choose edges in the following order:
EF, FD, FC, BD, AC

23.

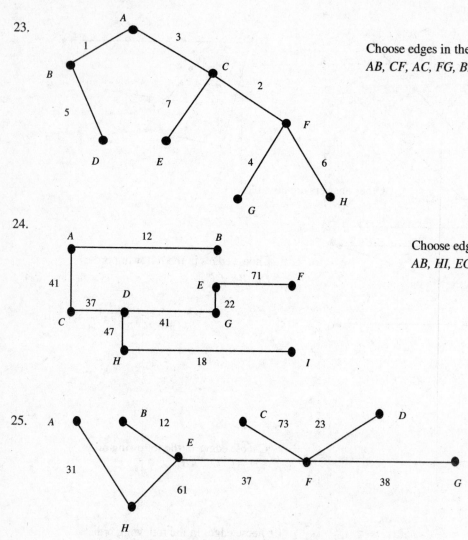

Choose edges in the following order:
AB, CF, AC, FG, BD, FH, EC

24.

Choose edges in the following order:
AB, HI, EG, CD, AC, DG, DH, EF

25.

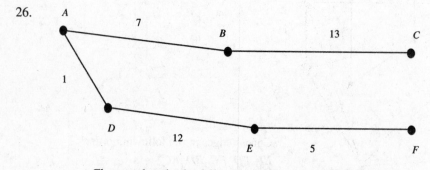

Choose edges in the following order: *BE*, FD, AH, EF, FG, HE, CF

26.

Choose edges in the following order: *AD, EF, AB, DE, BC*

27. a)

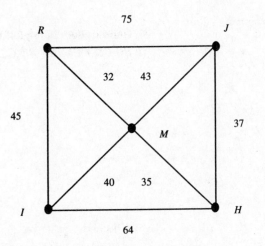

75

R   J

32   43

45   37

M

40   35

I   H

64

Other answers are possible.

27. b)

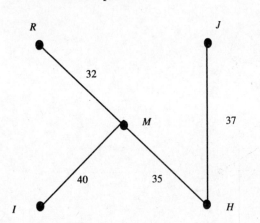

R   J

32

M

37

40   35

I   H

Choose edges in the following order:
RM, MH, JH, IM

c) 25(32 + 35 + 37 + 40) = 25(144) = $3600

28. a)

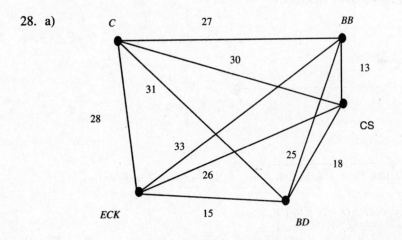

C   27   BB

30

13

31

28

CS

33

25

26   18

ECK   15   BD

Other answers are possible.

28.   b)

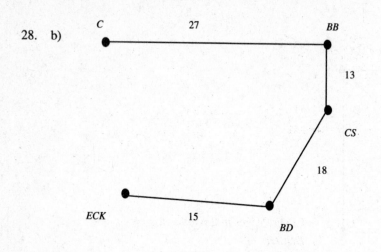

Choose edges in the following order:
BB CS, ECK BD, BD CS, C BB

c) $0.75(13 + 15 + 18 + 27) = 0.75(73) = \$54.75$

29.   a)

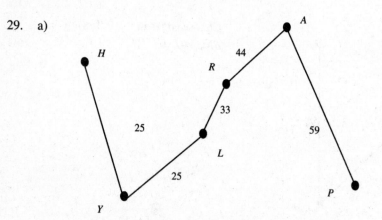

Choose edges in the following order: *HY, YL, LR, RA, AP*

b) $6800(25 + 25 + 33 + 44 + 59) = 6800(186) = \$1,264,800$

30. a)

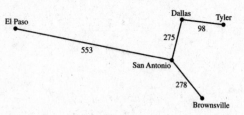

Choose edges in the following order: Dallas-Tyler, Dallas-San Antonio, San Antonio-Brownsville, and San Antonio-El Paso.

b) $1700(98 + 275 + 278 + 553) = 1700(1204) = \$2,046,800$

31. a)

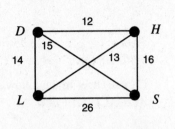

Other answers are possible.

b)

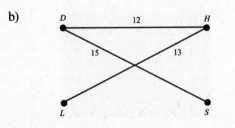

Choose edges in the following order:
DH, HL, DS

c) 3500 (12 + 13 + 15) = 3500 (40) = $140,000

32. a)

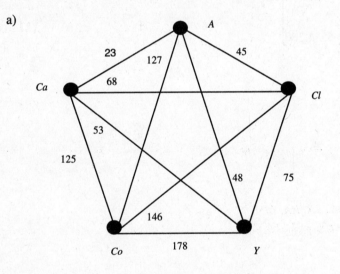

Other answers are possible.

32. b)

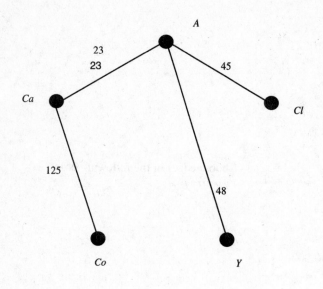

Choose edges in the following order:
ACa, ACl, AY, CaCo

c) 2300(23 + 45 + 48 + 125) = 2300(241) = $554,300

33. a)

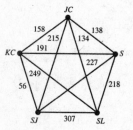

Other answers are possible.

b)

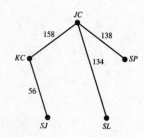

Choose edges in the following order: *KC-SJ, JC-SL, JC-SP, JC-KC*

c) 3700(56 + 134 + 138 + 158) = 3700(486) = $1,798,200

34. a)

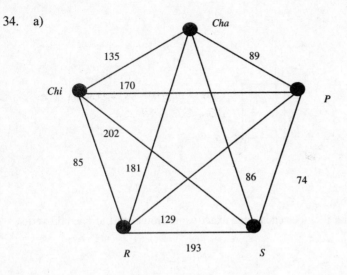

Other answers are possible.

b)

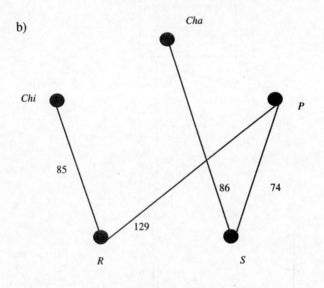

Choose edges in the following order: *PS, Chi R, Cha S, RP*

c) 74 + 85 + 86 + 129 = 374 miles

35. Answers will vary.
36. Answers will vary.
37. Answers will vary.

Review Exercises

1.

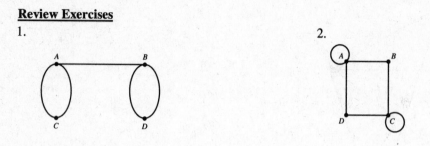

2.

3. *A, B, C, A, D, C, E, D*; other answers are possible.

4. No. The graph has two odd vertices, so a path that includes each edge exactly once must start at one odd vertex and end at the other; *B* is an even vertex.

5.

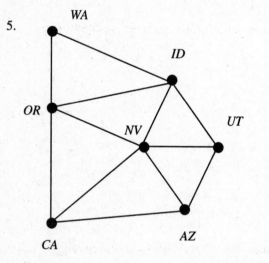

6.

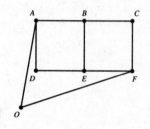

7. Connected

8. Disconnected. There is no path that connects *A* to *C*.

9. Edge *CD*

10. *D, A, B, C, E, H, G, F, D, B, E, G, D, E*; other answers are possible.

11. *E, D, B, E, G, D, A, B, C, E, H, G, F, D*; other answers are possible.

12. *B, C, A, D, F, E, C, D, E, B*; other answers are possible.

13. *E, F, D, E, C, D, A, C, B, E*; other answers are possible.

14. a)　　　　No.　The graph representing the map:

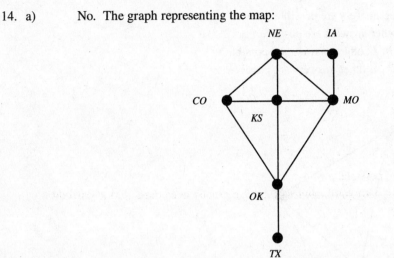

b) Vertices *CO* and *TX* are both odd.　According to item 2 of Euler's Theorem, since there are exactly two odd vertices, at least one Euler path, but no Euler circuits exist.

Yes; *CO, NE, IA, MO, NE, KS, MO, OK, CO, KS, OK, TX*; other answers are possible.

c) No.　(See part b) above.)

15. a)

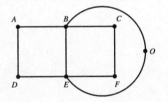

b) Yes; the graph has no odd vertices, so there is at least one Euler path, which is also an Euler circuit.

c) The person may start in any room or outside and will finish where he or she started.

16. a) Yes.　The graph representing the map:

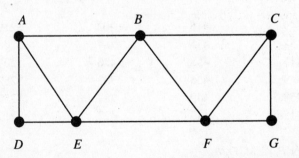

The officer is seeking an Euler path or an Euler circuit.　Note that vertices *A* and *C* are both odd. According to item 2 of Euler's Theorem, since there are exactly two odd vertices, at least one Euler path but no Euler circuits exist.

b) The officer would have to start at either the upper left-hand corner or the upper right-hand corner.

If the officer started in the upper left-hand corner, he or she would finish in the upper right-hand corner, and vice versa.

17. *A, B, F, E, H, G, D, C, A, D, E, B*; other answers are possible.
18. *A, B, C, D, H, G, C, F, G, B, F, E, A*; other answers are possible.
19. *A, C, B, F, E, D, G* and *A, C, D, G, F, B, E*; other answers are possible.
20. *A, B, C, D, F, E, A* and *A, E, F, B, C, D, A*; other answers are possible.

21.

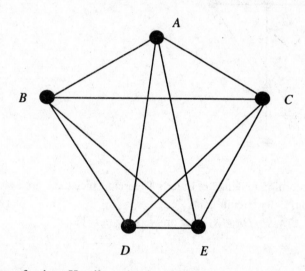

22. The number of unique Hamilton circuits within the complete graph with 5 vertices representing this situation is $(5-1)! = 4! = 4 \cdot 3 \cdot 2 \cdot 1 = 24$ ways

23. a)

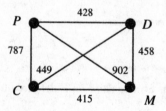

b)

Hamilton Circuit	First Leg/Cost	Second Leg/Cost	Third Leg/Cost	Fourth Leg/Cost	Total Cost
P, D, C, M, P	428	449	415	902	$2194
P, D, M, C, P	428	458	415	787	$2088
P, C, M, D, P	787	415	458	428	$2088
P, C, D, M, P	787	449	458	902	$2596
P, M, D, C, P	902	458	449	787	$2596
P, M, C, D, P	902	415	449	428	$2194

The least expensive route is *P, D, M, C, P* or *P, C, M, D, P*

c) $2088

24. a)

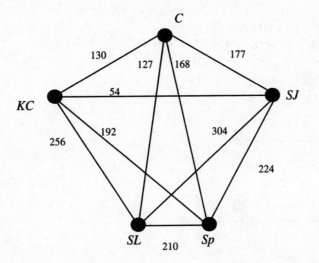

b) *SJ, KC, C, SL, Sp, SJ* traveling a total of 54 + 130 + 127 + 210 + 224 = 745 miles

c) *Sp, C, SL, KC, SJ, Sp* traveling a total of 168 + 127 + 256 + 54 + 224 = 829 miles

25.

26.

Other answers are possible

27.

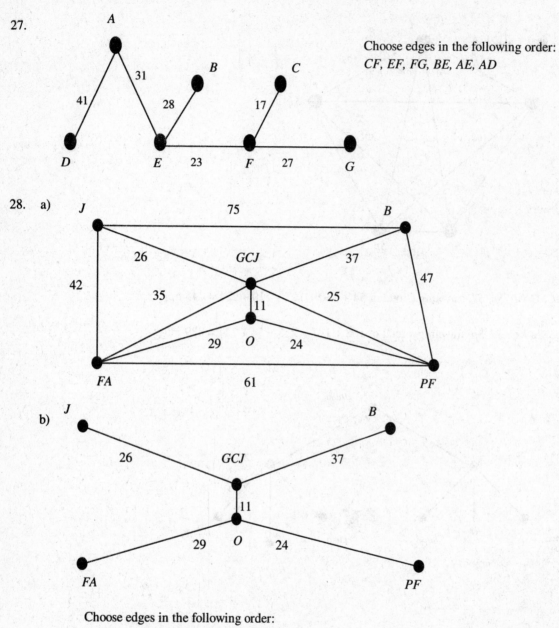

Choose edges in the following order:
CF, EF, FG, BE, AE, AD

28. a)

b)

Choose edges in the following order:
O GCJ, O PF, J GCJ, FA O, GCJ B

c) 2.50 (11 + 24 + 26 + 29 + 37) = 2.50 (127) = $317.50

Chapter Test

1.

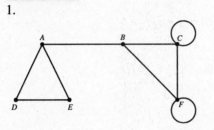

Edge *AB* is a bridge. There is a loop at vertex *G*.
Other answers are possible.

2.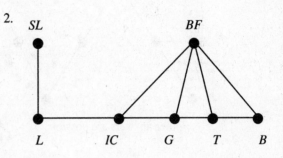

3. One example:

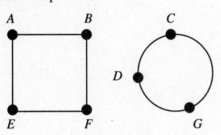

4. *A, B, C, F, H, G, E, F, B, E, D, A*;
other answers are possible.

5. Yes. The person may start in room *A* and end in room *B* or vice versa.
6. *A, D, E, A, F, E, H, F, I, G, F, B, G, C, B, A*; other answers are possible.
7. *A, B, C, G, E, D, H, I, K, J, F, A*; other answers are possible.
8. The number of unique Hamilton circuits within the complete graph with 5 vertices representing
this situation is $(5-1)! = 4! = 24$ ways

9. a)

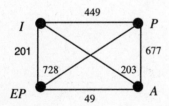

b)

Hamilton Circuit	First Leg/Cost	Second Leg/Cost	Third Leg/Cost	Fourth Leg/Cost	Total Cost
I, P, EP, A, I	449	728	49	203	$1429
I, P, A, EP, I	449	677	49	201	$1376
I, A, P, EP, I	203	677	728	201	$1809
I, A, EP, P, I	203	49	728	449	$1429
I, EP, A, P, I	201	49	677	449	$1376
I, EP, P, A, I	201	728	677	203	$1809

The least expensive route is *I, P, A, EP, I* or *I, EP, A, P, I* for $1376.

c) *I, EP, A, P, I* for $1376

10.

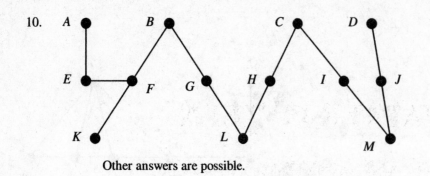

Other answers are possible.

11.

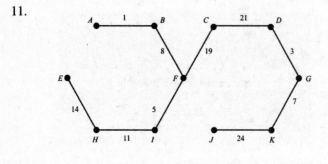

Choose edges in the following order:
AB, DG, FI, KG, BF, HI, EH, FC, CD, JK

12. a)

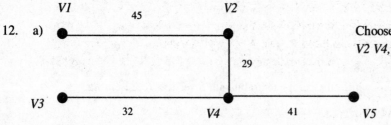

Choose edges in the following order:
V2 V4, V3 V4, V4 V5, V1 V2

b) 1.25 (29 + 32 + 41 + 45) = 1.25 (147) = $183.75

Group Projects
1. Answers will vary.
2. a) – d) Answers will vary.
3. a) – d) Answers will vary.
4. Answers will vary.

CHAPTER FIFTEEN

VOTING AND APPORTIONMENT

Exercise Set 15.1

1. When a candidate receives more than 50% of the votes.
2. Each voter votes for one candidate. The candidate receiving the most votes is declared the winner.
3. Voters rank candidates from most favorable to least favorable. Each last place vote is awarded one point, each next to last place vote is awarded two points, each third from last place vote is awarded three points, etc. The candidate receiving the most points is the winner.
4. Each voter votes for one candidate. If a candidate receives a majority of votes, that candidate is declared the winner. If no candidate receives a majority, eliminate the candidate with the fewest votes. (If there is a tie for the fewest votes, eliminate all tied candidates.) Repeat this process until a candidate receives a majority.
5. Voters rank the candidates. A series of comparisons in which each candidate is compared to each of the other candidates follows. If candidate A is preferred to candidate B, then A receives one point. If candidate B is preferred to candidate A, then B receives one point. If the candidates tie, each receives ½ point. The candidate receiving the most points is declared the winner.
6. Different systems can lead to a different winner.
7. A preference table summarizes the results of an election.

8. a) The number of comparisons will be $_nC_2 = \dfrac{n(n-1)}{2}$

   b)

   $3+2+1 = 6$ groupings

   c)

   $5+4+3+2+1 = 15$ groupings

9. By ranking their choices, voters are able to provide more information with the Borda count method.
10. One way to settle a tie is to bring in an additional voter.
11. a) Jeter is the winner; he received the most votes using the plurality method.

   b) No. $\dfrac{265128}{192827+210361+265128} = \dfrac{265128}{668316} \approx 0.40$ is not a majority.   Majority is > 334,158 votes.

12. a) Felicia is the winner. Felicia received the most votes using the plurality method.

   b) No. $\dfrac{2863}{2192+2562+1671+2863+1959} = \dfrac{2863}{11247} \approx 0.25$ is not a majority.   Majority is > 5,624 votes.

13.

Number of votes	3	1	2	2	1
First	H	G	S	S	G
Second	G	H	H	G	S
Third	S	S	G	H	H

14.

Number of votes	2	3	2	1
First	D	C	B	C
Second	B	D	D	B
Third	C	B	C	D

15. $10 + 5 + 4 + 2 = 21$ employees

16. No. Wrench had the most with 9 votes, but $10/21 = 0.48$ which is not a majority. Majority is ≥ 11.

17. Wrench wins with the most votes (10).

18. W: 10 1st place votes = $(10)(3) = 30$
    5 2nd place votes = $(5)(2) = 10$
    6 3rd place votes = $(6)(1) = 6$
    H: 9 1st place votes = $(9)(3) = 27$
    12 2nd place votes = $(12)(2) = 24$
    F: 2 1st place votes = $(2)(3) = 6$
    4 2nd place votes = $(4)(2) = 8$
    15 3rd place votes = $(15)(1) = 14$
    W = 46 points; H = 51 points; F = 28 points
    Water heater wins with 51 points.

19. A majority out of 21 votes is 11 or more votes.
    First choice votes: (W) 10, (H) 9, (F) 2
    None receives a majority, thus F with the least votes is eliminated.
    Second round: (W) 10, (H) 5+4+2 = 11
    Water heater wins with a majority of 11 votes.

20. W vs. H: W = 10   H = 5+4+2 = 11   H gets 1 pt.
    W vs. F: W = 10+5 = 15   F = 4+2 = 6
               W gets 1 pt.
    H vs. F: H = 10+5+4 = 19   F = 2   H gets 1 pt.
    Water heater wins with 2 points.

21. Y: 4 1st place votes = $(4)(3) = 12$
    2 2nd place votes = $(2)(2) = 4$
    3 3rd place votes = $(3)(1) = 3$
    R: 2 1st place votes = $(2)(3) = 6$
    4 2nd place votes = $(4)(2) = 8$
    3 3rd place votes = $(3)(1) = 3$
    S: 3 1st place votes = $(3)(3) = 9$
    3 2nd place votes = $(3)(2) = 6$
    3 3rd place votes = $(3)(1) = 3$
    Y = 19 points; R = 17 points; S = 18 points
    Yellowstone wins with 19 points.

22. Votes – (Y): 3+1 = 4, (R): 2, (S): 2+1 = 3
    Yellowstone wins with the most votes.

23. Y vs. R: Y = 3+2+1 = 6   R = 2+1 = 3
    Y gets 1 pt.
    Y vs. S: Y = 3+1 = 4   S = 2+2+1 = 5
    S gets 1 pt.
    R vs. S: R = 3+2 = 5   S= 2+1+1 = 4
    R gets 1 pt.
    All get 1 point, which indicates no winner.

24. A majority out of 9 votes is 5 or more votes.
    First choice votes: (Y) 4, (R) 2, (S) 3
    None receives a majority, thus R with the least
    votes is eliminated.
    Second round: (Y) 4, (S) 2+2+1 = 5
    Smoky Mountains wins with a majority of 5 votes.

25. Votes: (S) 8+3+2 = 13   (L) 6+3 = 9
    (H) 4+3+2 = 9   (T) 1
    San Antonio wins with the most votes.

26. S: 13 1st place votes = (13)(4) = 52
    5 2nd place votes = (5)(3) = 15
    4 3rd place votes = (4)(2) = 8
    10 4th place votes = (10)(1) = 10
    L: 9 1st place votes = (9)(4) = 36
    18 2nd place votes = (18)(3) = 54
    4 3rd place votes = (4)(2) = 8
    1 4th place vote = (1)(1) = 1
    H: 9 1st place votes = (9)(4) = 36
    9 2nd place votes = (9)(3) = 27
    11 3rd place votes = (11)(2) = 22
    3 4th place votes = (3)(1) = 3
    T: 1 1st place votes = (1)(4) = 4
    0 2nd place votes = 0
    13 3rd place votes = (13)(2) = 26
    18 4th place vote = (18)(1) = 18

    S = 85 points; L = 99 points;
    H = 88 points; T = 48 points
    Los Angeles wins with 99 points.

27. A majority out of 32 votes is 17 or more votes.
    First choice votes: (S) 13, (L) 9, (H) 9, (T) 1
    None receives a majority, thus T with the least
    votes is eliminated.
    Second round: (S) 13, (L) 9, (H) 10
    No majority, thus eliminate L.
    Third round: (S) 16, (H) 16
    Since S and H tied, there is no winner.

28. S vs. L: S = 8+3+2+1+2 = 16
    L = 6+3+4+3 = 16   S / L get 0.5 pt.
    S vs. H: S = 8+3+3+2 = 16
    H = 6+4+3+1+2 = 16   S / H get 0.5 pt.
    S and T: S = 8+3+2+1+2 = 16
    T = 6+4+1 = 11   S gets 1 pt.
    L and H: L = 8+6+3+3 = 20
    H = 4+3+2+1+2 = 12   L gets 1 pt.
    L and T: L = 8+6+3+4+3+3+2+2 = 31
    T = 1   L gets 1 pt.
    H and T: H = 8+6+3+4+3+2+2 = 28
    T = 4   H gets 1 pt.
    S = 2   H = 1.5   L = 2.5   T = 0   LA wins.

29. W: 5 1st place votes = (5)(3) = 15
    4 2nd place votes = (4)(2) = 8
    3 3rd place votes = (3)(1) = 3
    D: 1 1st place votes = (1)(3) = 3
    7 2nd place votes = (7)(2) = 14
    4 3rd place votes = (4)(1) = 4
    J: 6 1st place votes = (6)(3) = 18
    1 2nd place votes = (1)(2) = 2
    5 3rd place votes = (5)(1) = 5
    W = 26 points; D = 21 points; J = 25 points
    Williams wins with 26 points.

30. Votes: (W): 5, (D): 1, (J): 4 + 2 = 6
    Johnson wins with the most votes.

31. W vs. D: W = 5+4 = 9   D = 1+2 = 3
    W gets 1 pt.
    W vs. J: W = 5   J = 1+4+2 = 7
    J gets 1 pt.
    D vs. J: D = 5+1 = 6   J = 4+2 = 6
    D and J get 0.5 pt.
    W = 1 pt.   D = 0.5 pt.   J = 1.5 pts.
    Johnson wins with 1.5 points.

32. A majority out of 12 votes is 7 or more votes.
    First choice votes: (W) 5, (D) 1, (J) 6
    None receives a majority, thus D with the least
    votes is eliminated.
    Second round: (W) 5, (J) 1+4+2 = 7
    Johnson wins with a majority of 7 votes.

33. A majority out of 12 votes is 7 or more votes.
    Most last place votes: (W) 3, (D) 4, (J) 5
    Thus J with the most last place votes is eliminated.
    Second round using the most last place votes:
    (W) 1+2 = 3, (D) 5+4 = 9
    Williams wins with the least last place votes.

34. Votes: (L): 5, (E): 2, (O): 4.   Lehigh Road wins
    with the most votes.

35. L: 5 1st place votes = (5)(3) = 15
       6 3rd place votes = (6)(1) = 6
    E: 2 1st place votes = (2)(3) = 6
       9 2nd place votes = (9)(2) = 18
    O: 4 1st place votes = (4)(3) = 12
       2 2nd place votes = (2)(2) = 4
       5 3rd place votes = (5)(1) = 5
    L = 21 points; E = 24 points; O = 21 points
    Erie Road wins with 24 points.

36. A majority out of 11 votes is 6 or more votes.
    First choice votes: (L) 5, (E) 2, (O) 4
    None receives a majority, thus E with the least
    votes is eliminated.
    Second round: (L) 5, (O) 2+4 = 6
    Ontario Road wins with a majority of 6 votes.

37. L vs. E: L = 5   E = 2+4 = 6   E gets 1 pt.
    L vs. O: L = 5   O = 2+4 = 6   O gets 1 pt.
    E vs. O: E = 5+2 = 6   O = 4   E gets 1 pt.
    Erie Road wins with 2 points.

38. A majority out of 11 votes is 6 or more votes.
    Most last place votes: (L) 2+4 = 6, (E) 0, (O) 5
    Thus L with the most last place votes is eliminated.
    Second round using the most last place votes:
    (E) 0, (O) 4
    Erie Road wins with the least last place votes.

39. a) Votes: (B): 112, (L): 2, (D): 1
       Becker wins with the most votes.
    b) B: 12 1st place votes = (12)(4) = 48
         5 2nd place votes = (3)(3) = 9
      L: 3 1st place votes = (2)(4) = 8
         6 2nd place votes = (8)(3) = 24
         6 3rd place votes = (5)(2) = 10
      M: 9 3rd place votes = (10)(2) = 20
         6 4th place votes = (5)(1) = 5
      D: 1 1st place vote = (1)(4) = 4
         4 2nd place votes = (4)(3) = 12
         10 4th place votes = (10)(1) = 10
    B = 57 points; L = 42 points; M = 25 points,
    D = 26 points   B wins with 57 points.

39. c) A majority out of 15 votes is 8 or more votes.
      First choice votes: (B) 12, (L) 2
                  (M) 0, (D) = 2
      Because B already has a majority, B wins.
    d) B vs. L: B = 8+4+1 = 13   L = 2
      B gets 1 pt.
      B vs. M: B = 8+4+2+1 = 15   B gets 1 pt.
      B vs. D: B = 8+4+2 = 14   D = 1
      B gets 1 pt.
      L vs. M: L = 8+4+2+1 = 15   L gets 1 pt.
      L vs. D: L = 8+2 = 10   D = 4+1 = 5
      L = gets 1 pt.
      M vs. D: S = 8+2 = 10   D = 4+1 = 5
      M gets 1 pt.
      B wins with 3 points.

40. a) Votes: (L): 8, (C): 2, (S): 3, (H): 4
       I Love Lucy wins with the most votes.
   b) L: 8 1st place votes = (8)(4) = 32
        9 4th place votes = (9)(1) = 9
      C: 2 1st place votes = (2)(4) = 8
        15 2nd place votes = (15)(3) = 45
      S: 3 1st place votes = (3)(4) = 12
        2 2nd place votes = (2)(3) = 6
        12 3rd place votes = (12)(2) = 24
      H: 4 1st place votes = (4)(4) = 16
        5 3rd place votes = (5)(2) = 10
        8 4th place votes = (8)(1) = 8
      L= 41 points; C = 53 points; S = 42 points,
      H = 34 points   Cheers wins with 53 points.

40. c) A majority out of 17 votes is 9 or more votes.
       First choice votes: (L) 8, (C) 2
                           (S) 3, (H) = 4
       None receives a majority, thus M with the least
       votes is eliminated.
       Second round: (L) 8, (S) 5, (H) 4
       No majority, thus eliminate H.
       Third round: (L) 8, (S) 9
       Seinfeld wins with 9 votes.
    d) L vs. C: L = 8 C = 9 C gets 1 pt.
       L vs. S: L = 8 S = 9 S gets 1 pt.
       L vs. H: L = 8 H = 9 H gets 1 pt.
       C vs. S: C = 14 S = 3 C gets 1 pt.
       C vs. H: C = 13 H = 4 C gets 1 pt.
       S vs. H: S = 13 H = 4 S gets 1 pt.
       Cheers wins with 3 points.

41. a) G: 8 1st place votes = (8)(4) = 32
        3 2nd place vote = (3)(3) = 9
        4 3rd place votes = (4)(2) = 8
        14 4th place votes = (14)(1) = 14
      I: 3 1st place votes = (3)(4) = 12
        7 2nd place vote = (7)(3) = 21
        19 3rd place votes = (19)(2) = 38
      P: 14 1st place votes = (14)(4) = 56
        8 2nd place votes = (8)(3) = 24
        3 3rd place votes = (3)(2) = 6
        4 4th place votes = (4)(1) = 4
      Z: 4 1st place votes = (4)(4) = 16
        11 2nd place vote = (11)(3) = 33
        3 3rd place votes = (3)(2) = 6
        11 4th place votes = (11)(1) = 11
      G = 63 points; I = 71 points; P = 91 points;
      Z = 66 points
      P wins with 91 points.

41. b) Votes: (G): 8, (I): 3, (P): 14, (Z): 4
       P wins with the most votes.
    c) A majority out of 29 votes is 15 or more votes.
       First choice votes: (G) 8, (I) 3
                           (P) 14, (Z) = 4
       None receives a majority, thus I with the least
       votes is eliminated.
       Second round: (G) 11, (P) 14, (Z) 4
       No majority, thus eliminate Z.
       Third round: (G) 15, (P) 14
       G wins with 15 votes.
    d) G vs. P: G = 15 P = 14 G gets 1 pt.
       G vs. Z: G= 11 Z = 18 Z gets 1 pt.
       G vs. I: G = 8 I = 21 I gets 1 pt.
       P vs. Z: P = 25 Z = 4 P gets 1 pt.
       P vs. I: P = 22 I = 7 P gets 1 pt.
       Z vs. I: Z = 15 I = 14 Z gets 1 pt.
       P and Z tie with 2 points.

42. a) G vs. A: G = 69 A = 73 A gets 1 pt.
       G vs. C: G = 43 C = 99 C gets 1 pt.
       G vs. D: G = 43 D = 99 D gets 1 pt.
       A vs. C: A = 73 C = 69 A gets 1 pt.
       A vs. D: A = 73 D = 69 A gets 1 pt.
       C vs. D: C = 72 D = 70 C gets 1 pt.

       Apple wins with 3 points.

42. b) A majority out of 142 votes is 72 or more votes.
       First choice votes: G=43, A=30, C=29, D=40
       None receives a majority, thus C with the least
       votes is eliminated.
       Second round: (G) 43, (A) 30, (D) 69
       No majority, thus eliminate A.
       Third round: (G) 43, (D) 99
       Dell wins with 99 votes.

42. c) G: 43 1st place votes = (43)(4) = 172
    26 3rd place votes = (26)(2) = 52
    73 4th place votes = (73)(1) = 73
    A: 30 1st place vote = (30)(4) = 120
    43 2nd place vote = (43)(3) = 129
    43 3rd place votes = (43)(2) = 86
    26 4th place vote = (26)(1) = 26
    C: 29 1st place votes = (29)(4) = 116
    40 2nd place vote = (40)(3) = 120
    73 3rd place vote = (73)(2) = 146
    D: 40 1st place votes = (40)(4) = 160
    59 2nd place vote = (59)(3) = 177
    43 4th place votes = (43)(1) = 43
    G = 297 points;   A = 361 points;
    C = 382 points;   D = 380 points
    Compaq wins with 382 points.

42. d) Votes: (G): 43, (A): 30, (C): 29, (D): 40
    Gateway wins with the most votes.
    e) You must choose the voting method prior to
    the election.

43. a) If there were only two columns then only two of
    the candidates were the first choice of the
    voters. If each of the 15 voters cast a ballot,
    then one of the voters must have received a
    majority of votes because 15 cannot be split
    evenly.
    b) An odd number cannot be divided evenly so one
    of the two first choice candidates must receive
    more than half of the votes.

44. a) A: 1 + 2 + 3 + 2 = 8
    B. 3 + 1 + 4 + 3 = 11
    C: 4 + 4 + 1 + 1 = 10
    D: 2 + 3 + 2 + 4 = 11
    B and D tie with 11 points.
    b) A: 0 + 1 + 3 + 1 = 5
    B: 3 + 0 + 5 + 3 = 11
    C: 5 + 5 + 0 + 0 = 10
    D: 1 + 3 + 1 + 5 = 10
    B wins with 11 points.

45. a) C: 4 + 1 + 1 = 6   R: 4 + 4 + 3 = 11
    W: 3 + 3 + 2 + 2 + 1 + 1 = 12
    T: 4 + 3 + 2 + 2 = 11
    The Warriors finished 1st, the Rams and the
    Tigers tied for 2nd , and the Comets were 4th.
    b) C: 5 + 0 = 5   R: 5 + 5 + 3 = 13
    W: 3 + 3 + 1 + 1 + 0 + 0 = 8
    T: 5 + 3 + 1 1 = 10
    Rams - 1st, Tigers - 2nd, Warriors - 3rd, and
    Comets - 4th.

46. a) Each voter casts 3+2+1 = 6 votes.
    (20)(6) = 120 votes
    b) 120 − (55+25) = 120 − 80 = 40 votes
    c) No. Candidate B cannot win because the votes
    for Candidate A > votes for Candidate B.

47. a) Each voter casts 4+3+2+1 = 10 votes.
    (15)(10) = 150 votes
    b) 150 − (35+40+25) = 150 − 100 = 50 votes
    c) Yes. Candidate D has more votes than each
    of the other 3 candidates.

48. A = 10   B = 7   C = 5   D = 9
    Candidates A and D will win.

49. Answers will vary.

Exercise Set 15.2

1. If a candidate receives a majority of first place votes, then that candidate should be declared the winner.
2. A candidate who wins a first election and then gains additional support without losing any of the original support should also win a second election.
3. If a candidate is favored when compared individually with every other candidate, then that candidate should be declared the winner.
4. If a candidate is declared the winner of an election, and in a second election, one or more of the other candidates is removed, then the previous winner should still be declared the winner

5. A candidate that is preferred to all others will win each pairwise comparison and be selected with the pairwise comparison method.

6. A candidate that holds a majority of first place votes wins each pairwise comparison and is selected with the pairwise comparison method.

7. If a candidate receives a majority of first place votes, then that candidate should be declared the winner. Plurality counts only the 1st place votes.

8. If a majority is not reached on the 1st vote, then the candidate with the lowest vote total is eliminated and successive votes are taken until one of the candidates achieves a majority vote.

9. The plurality method yields Tampa is the winner with a majority of 10 1st place votes. However, if the Borda count method is used:
   Tampa $(10)(3) + (3)(2) + (6)(1) = 30 + 6 + 6 = 42$
   Portland $(6+3)(3) + (10)(2) = 27 + 20 = 47$
   SA $(6)(2) + (10+3)(1) = 12 + 13 = 19$
   The winner is Portland using the Borda count method, thus violating the majority criterion.

10. a) Total votes = $2+4+2+3 = 11$
    A vs. B: A = $4+2 = 6$ B = $2+3 = 5$ A gets 1 pt.
    A vs. C: A = $2+4 = 6$ C = $2+3 = 5$ A gets 1 pt.
    B vs. C: B = $2+4 = 6$ C = $2+3 = 5$ B gets 1 pt.
    Plan A wins all head-to-head comparisons.

    b) C wins by a plurality of 5 votes. No, the head-to-head criterion is not satisfied.

11. Total votes = $3+2+1+1 = 7$ Candidates A is the candidate of choice with a majority of 5 votes.
    A: 5 1st place votes = $(5)(4) = 20$
        4 4th place votes = $(4)(1) = 4$
    B: 4 1st place vote = $(4)(4) = 16$
        5 2nd place vote = $(5)(3) = 15$
    S: 3 2nd place vote = $(3)(3) = 9$
        5 3rd place vote = $(5)(2) = 10$
        1 4th place vote = $(1)(1) = 1$
    Y: 1 2nd place vote = $(1)(3) = 3$
        4 3rd place votes = $(4)(2) = 8$
        4 4th place votes = $(4)(1) = 4$

    A gets 24 pts., B gets 31 pts., S gets 20 pts., and Y gets 15 pts. Candidate B wins by the Borda count method.

12. a) Total votes = $12+6+4+3 = 25$
    B vs. W: B = $12+6+4 = 22$ W = 3 B gets 1 pt.
    B vs. S: B= $12+3 = 15$ S = 10   B gets 1 pt.
    B vs. R: B = $12+6 = 18$ R = 7   B gets 1 pt.
    W vs. S: W = $12+3 = 15$ S = 10   W gets 1 pt.
    W vs. R: W = $12+6+3 = 21$ R = 4   W gets 1 pt.
    S vs. R: S = $12+6 = 18$ S = 7   S gets 1 pt.
    Beach wins all head-to-head comparisons.

    b) B wins by a plurality of 12 votes. Yes, the head-to-head criterion is satisfied.

13. P: 4 1st place votes = $(4)(3) = 12$
        2 2nd place votes = $(2)(2) = 4$
        3 3rd place votes = $(3)(1) = 3$
    L: 3 1st place vote = $(3)(3) = 9$
        5 2nd place vote = $(5)(2) = 10$
        1 3rd place vote = $(1)(1) = 1$
    S: 2 1st place votes = $(2)(3) = 6$
        2 2nd place vote = $(2)(2) = 4$
        5 3rd place vote = $(5)(1) = 5$
    P = 19 votes;   L = 20 votes;   S = 15 votes
    P vs. L: P = $4+1 = 5$ L = 4   P gets 1 pt.
    P vs. S: P = $4+1 = 5$ S = 4   P gets 1 pt.
    L vs. S: L = $4+1+2 = 7$ S = 2   L gets 1 pt.
    Because Parking wins its head-to-head comparisons and the Lounge Areas win by Borda count method, the head-to-head criterion is not satisfied.

14. A: 2 1st place votes = (2)(3) = 6
    $7 2^{nd}$ place votes = (7)(2) = 14
    B: 2 1st place vote = (2)(3) = 6
    2 2nd place vote = (2)(2) = 4
    5 3rd place vote = (5)(1) = 5
    C: 5 1st place votes = (5)(3) = 15
    4 3rd place vote = (4)(1) = 4
    A = 20 votes;   B = 15 votes;   C = 19 votes
    A vs. B: A = 2+2 = 4   B = 5   B gets 1 pt.
    A vs. C: A = 2+2 = 4   C = 5   C gets 1 p
    B vs. C: B = 2+2 = 4   C = 5   C gets 1 pt.
    Because C wins its head-to-head comparisons
    and the A wins by the Borda count method,
    the head-to-head criterion is not satisfied.

16. A majority out of 25 votes is 13 or more votes.
    First choice votes: (A) 10, (B) 2, (C) 8, (D) = 5
    None receives a majority, thus B with the least
    votes is eliminated.
    Second round: (A) 10, (C) 10, (D) 5
    Still no majority, thus eliminate D.
    Third round: (A) 10, (C) 15
    C wins with a majority of 15 votes.
    A vs. B: A = 10   B = 15   B gets 1 pt.
    A vs. C: A = 10   C = 15   C gets 1 pt.
    A vs. D: A = 12   D = 13   D gets 1 pt.
    B vs. C: B = 17   C = 8   B gets 1 pt.
    B vs. D: B = 20   D = 5   B gets 1 pt.
    C vs. D: C = 10   D = 15   D gets 1 pt.
    B wins all head-to-head comparisons. Therefore,
    the head-to-head criterion is not satisfied.

20. A receives 38 points, B receives 35 points, C
    receives 35 points. Thus, A wins using the Borda
    count method. If B drops out we get the following:
    A receives 25 points, and C receives 29 points.
    Thus, C wins the second vote.

    The irrelevant alternatives criterion is not satisfied.

15. A majority out of 21 votes is 11 or more votes.
    Plurality with elimination:
    First choice votes: A = 6, B = 8, C = 7
    Eliminate A. B = 8, C = 13; C wins

    Pairwise comparison:
    A vs. B: A = 7+6 = 13   B = 8   A gets 1 pt.
    A vs. C: A = 8+6 = 14   C = 7   A gets 1 pt.
    B vs. C: B = 8   C = 7+6=13   C gets 1 pt.

    No, because C wins by plurality with elimination
    but A wins using head-to-head comparison.

17. Votes: A: 12,   B: 4,   C: 9; thus, A wins.
    If B drops out, we get the following:
    Votes: A: 12,   C: 9 + 4 = 13, thus C would win.
    The irrelevant alternatives criterion is not satisfied.

18. Votes: A: 3,   B: 4,   C: 5; thus B wins
    If C drops out, we get the following:
    Votes: A: 3 + 5 = 8,   B:6, thus A would win.
    The irrelevant alternatives criterion is not satisfied.

19. A receives 53 points, B receives 56 points, and
    C receives 53 points. Thus, B wins using the
    Borda count method. If C drops out, we get the
    following: B receives 46 points, and C receives
    35 points. Thus, B still wins. The
    irrelevant alternatives criterion is satisfied.

21. A majority out of 32 voters is 17 or more votes.
    Votes: A: 8 + 3 = 11, B: 9, C: 12; none has a
    majority, thus eliminate B.
    Votes: A:8 + 3 = 11,   C: 9 +12 = 21, thus C
    wins. If the three voters who voted for A,C,B
    change to C,A,B, the new set of votes becomes:
    Votes: A: 8, B: 9, C: 15; none has a
    majority, thus eliminate A.
    Votes: B: 17, C:15, B wins.
    Thus, the monotonicity criterion is not satisfied.

22. A majority out of 21 voters is 11 or more votes.
    Votes: A: 6, B: 7, C: 8; none has a majority,
    thus eliminate A.
    Votes: B: 7 + 6 = 13, C: 8, thus B wins.
    After the three votes change their votes, the
    the new set of votes is A: 6, B: 10., C: 5;
    none has a majority, thus eliminate C.
    Votes: A: 6 + 5 = 11, B: 10; thus A wins.
    Thus, the monotonicity criterion is not satisfied.

23. A vs. B: A = 13 B = 13 A gets .5, B gets .5.
    A vs. C: A = 13 C = 13 A gets .5, C gets .5.
    A vs. D: A = 13 D = 13 A gets .5, D gets .5.
    B vs. C: B = 13 C = 13 B gets .5, C gets .5.
    B vs. D: B = 13 D = 13 B gets .5, D gets .5.
    C vs. D: C = 12 D = 14 D gets 1 pt.
    D wins with 2 pts.
    After the change in votes:
    A vs. B: A = 8 B = 16 B gets 1 pt.
    A vs. C: A = 13 C = 13 A gets .5, C gets .5.
    A vs. D: A = 13 D = 13 A gets .5, D gets .5.
    B vs. C: B = 18 C = 6 B gets 1 pt.
    B vs. D: B = 13 D = 13 B gets .5, D gets .5.
    C vs. D: C = 15 D = 11 C gets 1 pt.
    B wins with 2.5 pts.
    The monotonicity criterion is not satisfied.

24. Original Borda count:
    $A = (8)(4) + (8)(3) + (7)(1) = 63$
    $B = (7)(4) + (8)(3) + (8)(1) = 60$
    $C = (3)(4) + (20)(2) = 52$
    $D = (5)(4) + (7)(3) + (3)(2) + (8)(1) = 55$
    A wins.
    After vote changes:
    $A = (16)(4) + (7)(1) = 71$
    $B = (7)(4) + (16)(3) = 76$
    $C = (18)(2) + (5)(1) = 41$
    $D = (7)(3) + (5)(2) + (11)(1) = 42$
    B wins.
    The monotonicity criterion is not satisfied.

25. A receives 2 points, B receives 3 point, C receives
    2 points, D receives 1 point, and E receives 2 pts.
    B wins by pairwise comparison.
    After A, C and E drop out, the new set of votes is
    B: 2 D: 3, thus D wins. The irrelevant
    alternatives criterion is not satisfied.

26. A receives 3 points, B receives 1 point, C receives 3 points, D receives 1 point, and E receives 2 points. A and C tie, but when A vs. C, C wins and thus we declare C the winner. After A, B and E drop out, the new set of votes is table is C: 2 + 1 = 3, D: 4, thus D wins.
The irrelevant alternatives criterion is not satisfied.

27. Total votes = 7   A wins with a majority of 4 votes.
    A: 4 1st place votes = (4)(3) = 12
       3 3rd place votes = (3)(1) = 3
    B: 2 1st place vote = (2)(3) = 6
       5 2nd place vote = (5)(2) = 10
    C: 1 1st place votes = (1)(3) = 3
       2 2nd place votes = (2)(2) = 4
       4 3rd place vote = (4)(1) = 4
    A = 15 points;   B = 16 points;   C = 11 points
    B wins with 16 points. No. The majority criterion is not satisfied.

28. Total votes = 11   B wins with a majority of 6 votes.
    A: 1 1st place votes = (1)(3) = 3
       5 2nd place votes = (5)(2) = 10
       5 3rd place votes = (5)(1) = 5
    B: 6 1st place vote = (6)(3) = 18
       5 3rd place votes = (5)(1) = 5
    C: 4 1st place votes = (4)(3) = 12
       6 2nd place votes = (6)(2) = 12
       1 3rd place vote = (1)(1) = 1
    A = 18 points;   B = 23 points;   C = 25 points
    C wins with 25 points. No. The majority criterion is not satisfied.

29. a) Washington, with 12 out of 23 votes
    b) Again, Washington, since it has a majority.
    c) N = (20)(3) + (3)(1) = 63
       W = (12)(4) + (3)(3) + (8)(1) = 65
       P = (8)(4) + (15)(2) = 62
       B = (3)(4) + (8)(2) + (12)(1) = 40
       Washington wins.
    d) Again, Washington, since it has a majority.

e) N vs. W: N = 8   W = 15, W gets 1 pt.
   N vs. P: N= 12   P = 11, N gets 1 pt.
   N vs. B: N= 20   B = 3, N gets 1 pt.
   W vs. P: W = 15   P = 8, W gets 1 pt.
   W vs. B: W= 15   B = 8, W gets 1 pt.
   P vs. B: P = 20   B = 3, P gets 1 pt.
   Washington wins with 3 pts.
f) None of them.

30. a) B and E have two points and C and D are tied with 3 points, but D wins the head-to-head competition with C so Dow Chemical wins.
    b) After C is eliminated, B wins with 2.5 ponts.
    c) Yes.

31. a) A majority out of 82 votes is 42 or more votes.
    First choice votes: (A) 28, (L) 30, (W) 24
    None receives a majority, thus D with the least votes is eliminated.
    Second round: (A) 52, (L) 30
    Thus, Jennifer Aniston is selected..
    b) No majority on the 1st vote; C is eliminated with the fewest votes.
    Second round: (A) 38, (W) 44
    Denzel Washington is chosen.
    c) Yes.

32. a) A receives 650 points, B receives 980 points C receives 880 points, D receives 1040 points, and E receives 950 points; Stacy Davis wins.
    b) A receives 500 points, B receives 850 points D receives 840 points, and E receives 820 points; Brac Brady wins.
    c) Yes

33. A candidate who holds a plurality will only gain strength and hold and even larger lead if more favorable votes are added.

34. Answers will vary (AWV).   35. AWV
38. A majority out of 11 voters is 6 or more votes.
    a) Votes: A: 9,   B: 2; thus A wins.
    b) Votes: A: 4 + 2 = 6,   C: 5;   Yes, A wins.
    c) The five voters who favor C should vote C, B, A instead of C, A, B.

36. AWV   37. AWV
39. AWV

Exercise Set 15.3

1. If we divide the total population by the number of items to be apportioned we obtain a number called the standard divisor.
2. The standard quota is found by dividing each group's population by the standard divisor.
3. The standard quota rounded down to the nearest whole number.
4. The standard quota rounded up to the nearest whole number.
5. An apportionment should always be either the upper quota or the lower quota.
6. Hamilton's method
7. Jefferson's method, Webster's method, Adams's method
8. a) Jefferson's method   b) Adams's method   c) Webster's method
9. a) Webster's method   b) Adams's method   c) Jefferson's method
10. Jefferson's method, Webster's method, Adams's method

11. a) $\dfrac{8000000}{160} = 50,000$ = standard divisor

b)

State	A	B	C	D	Total
Population	1,345,000	2,855,000	982,000	2,818,000	8,000,000
Standard Quota	26.9	57.1	19.64	56.36	

12.

State	A	B	C	D	Total
Standard Quota	26.9	57.1	19.64	56.36	
Lower Quota	26	57	19	56	158
Hamilton's Apportionment	27	57	20	56	150

13. a) and b) Modified divisor: 49,300

State	A	B	C	D	Total
Population	1,345,000	2,855,000	982,000	2,818,000	8,000,000
Modified Quota	27.31	57.97	19.939	57.218	
Jefferson's Apportionment (round down)	27	57	19	57	160

14. a) and b) Modified divisor: 49,250

State	A	B	C	D	Total
Population	1,345,000	2,855,000	982,000	2,818,000	8,000,000
Modified Quota	27.31	57.97	19.939	57.218	
Jefferson's Apportionment (round down)	27	57	19	57	160

15. a) and b) Modified divisor: 50,700

State	A	B	C	D	Total
Population	1,345,000	2,855,000	982,000	2,818,000	8,000,000
Modified Quota	26.529	56.312	19.369	55.582	
Adams's Apportionment (round up)	27	57	20	56	160

16. a) and b) Modified divisor: 50,600

State	A	B	C	D	Total
Population	1,345,000	2,855,000	982,000	2,818,000	8,000,000
Modified Quota	26.581	56.423	19.407	55.692	
Adams's Apportionment (round up)	27	57	20	56	160

17. a) and b) Standard divisor: 50,000

State	A	B	C	D	Total
Population	1,345,000	2,855,000	982,000	2,818,000	8,000,000
Standard Quota	26.9	57.1	19.64	56.36	
Webster's Apportionment (standard rounding)	27	57	20	56	160

18. a) and b) Modified divisor: 50,100

State	A	B	C	D	Total
Population	1,345,000	2,855,000	982,000	2,818,000	8,000,000
Modified Quota	26.846	56.986	19.601	56.248	
Webster's Apportionment	27	57	20	56	160

19. a) Standard divisor $= \dfrac{\text{total}}{25} = \dfrac{675}{25} = 27$

b)

Hotel	A	B	C	Total
Amount	306	214	155	675
Standard Quota	11.33	7.93	5.74	

20.

Hotel	A	B	C	Total
Amount	306	214	155	675
Standard Quota	11.33	7.93	5.74	
Hamilton's Apportionment	11	8	6	25

21. a) and b)

Hotel	A	B	C	Total
Amount	306	214	155	675
Modified Quota	11.86	8.29	6.01	
Jefferson's Apportionment (rounded down)	11	8	6	25

22. a) and b)

Hotel	A	B	C	Total
Amount	306	214	155	675
Modified Quota	11.91	8.33	6.03	
Jefferson's Apportionment	11	8	6	25

23. a) and b)

Hotel	A	B	C	Total
Amount	306	214	155	675
Modified Quota	10.55	7.38	5.34	
Adams's Apportionment (rounded up)	11	8	6	25

24. a) and b)

Hotel	A	B	C	Total
Amount	306	214	155	675
Modified Quota	10.93	7.64	5.54	
Adams's Apportionment (rounded up)	11	8	6	25

25. a) and b)

Store	A	B	C	Total
Amount	306	214	155	675
Standard Quota	11.33	7.93	5.74	
Webster's Apportionment (standard rounding)	11	8	6	25

26. a) and b)

Store	A	B	C	Total
Amount	306	214	155	675
Modified Quota	10.89	7.62	5.52	
Webster's Apportionment	11	8	6	25

27. a) A standard divisor $= \dfrac{\text{total}}{50} = \dfrac{550}{50} = 11$

b) and c)

Resort	A	B	C	D	Total
Rooms	86	102	130	232	550
Standard Quota	7.82	9.27	11.82	21.09	
Lower Quota	7	9	11	21	48
Hamilton's Method	8	9	12	21	50

28. Using a divisor of 10.7:

Resort	A	B	C	D	Total
Rooms	86	102	130	232	550
Modified Quota	8.04	9.53	12.15	21.68	
Jeffereson's Method	8	9	12	21	50

29. Using a divisor of 11.4:

Resort	A	B	C	D	Total
Rooms	86	102	130	232	550
Modified Quota	7.54	8.95	11.40	20.35	
Adams's Method	8	9	12	21	50

30. Using a divisor of 10.8:

Resort	A	B	C	D	Total
Rooms	86	102	130	232	550
Modified Quota	7.96	9.44	12.04	21.48	
Adams's Method	8	9	12	21	50

31. a) Standard divisor $= \dfrac{\text{total}}{250} = \dfrac{13000}{250} = 52$

   b) and c)

School	LA	Sci.	Eng.	Bus.	Hum	Total
Enrollment	1746	7095	2131	937	1091	13000
Standard Quota	33.58	136.44	40.98	18.02	20.98	
Lower Quota	33	136	40	18	20	247
Hamilton's Apportionment	34	136	41	18	21	250

32. A divisor of 52.5 was used.

School	LA	Sci.	Eng.	Bus.	Hum	Total
Enrollment	1746	7095	2131	937	1091	13000
Modified Quota	33.26	135.14	40.59	17.85	20.78	
Adams's Apportionment (round up)	34	136	41	18	21	250

33. A divisor of 51.5 was used.

School	LA	Sci.	Eng.	Bus.	Hum	Total
Enrollment	1746	7095	2131	937	1091	13000
Modified Quota	33.90	137.77	41.38	18.19	21.18	
Jefferson's Apportionment (round down)	33	137	41	18	21	250

34.

School	LA	Sci.	Eng.	Bus.	Hum	Total
Enrollment	1746	7095	2131	937	1091	13000
Standard Quota	33.58	136.44	40.98	18.02	20.98	
Webster's Apportionment (standard rounding)	34	136	41	18	21	250

35. a) A standard divisor $= \dfrac{\text{total}}{150} = \dfrac{13500}{150} = 90$

   b) and c)

Dealership	A	B	C	D	Total
Annual Sales	4800	3608	2990	2102	13500
Standard Quota	53.33	40.09	33.22	23.36	150.00
Hamilton's Apportionment	53	40	33	24	150

36. A divisor of 88.5 was used.

Dealership	A	B	C	D	Total
Annual Sales	4800	3608	2990	2102	13500
Modified Quota	54.24	40.77	33.79	23.75	
Jefferson's Apportionment	54	40	33	23	150

37. A divisor of 89.5 was used.

Dealership	A	B	C	D	Total
Annual Sales	4800	3608	2990	2102	13500
Modified Quota	53.63	40.31	33.41	23.47	
Webster's Apportionment	54	40	33	23	150

38. A divisor of 91 was used.

Dealership	A	B	C	D	Total
Annual Sales	4800	3608	2990	2102	13500
Modified Quota	52.75	39.65	32.86	23.10	
Adams's Apportionment	53	40	33	24	150

39. a) Standard divisor $= \dfrac{75,000}{100} = 750$

   b) and c)

Route	A	B	C	D	E	F	Total
Passengers	9070	15,275	12,810	5720	25,250	6875	75,000
Standard Quota	12.09	20.37	17.08	7.63	33.67	9.17	
Lower Quota	12	20	17	7	33	9	98
Hamilton's Method	12	20	17	8	34	9	100

40. The divisor 725 was used.

Route	A	B	C	D	E	F	Total
Passengers	9070	15,275	12,810	5720	25,250	6875	75,000
Modified Quota	12.51	21.07	17.67	7.89	34.83	9.48	
Jefferson's Method	12	21	17	7	34	9	100

41. The divisor 765 was used.

Route	A	B	C	D	E	F	Total
Passengers	9070	15,275	12,810	5720	25,250	6875	75,000
Modified Quota	11.86	19.97	16.75	7.48	33.01	8.99	
Adams's Method	12	20	17	8	34	9	100

42. The divisor 753 was used.

Route	A	B	C	D	E	F	Total
Passengers	9070	15,275	12,810	5720	25,250	6875	75,000
Modified Quota	12.05	20.29	17.01	7.60	33.53	9.13	
Webster's Method	12	20	17	8	34	9	100

43 a) Standard divisor $= \dfrac{\text{total}}{200} = \dfrac{2400}{200} = 12$

b) and c)

Shift	A	B	C	D	Total
Room calls	751	980	503	166	2400
Standard Quota	62.58	81.67	41.92	13.83	
Lower Quota	62	81	41	13	197
Hamilton's Method	62	82	42	14	200

44. The divisor 12.1 was used.

Shift	A	B	C	D	Total
Room calls	751	980	503	166	2400
Modified Quota	62.07	80.99	41.57	13.72	
Adams's Apportionment (round up)	63	81	42	14	200

45. The divisor 11.9 was used.

Shift	A	B	C	D	Total
Room calls	751	980	503	166	2400
Modified Quota	63.11	82.35	42.27	13.95	
Jefferson's Apportionment (round down)	63	82	42	13	200

46. The divisor 12.02 was used.

Shift	A	B	C	D	Total
Room calls	751	980	503	166	2400
Modified Quota	62.48	81.53	41.85	13.81	
Webster's Apportionment (standard rounding)	62	82	42	14	200

47. Standard divisor $= \dfrac{3615920}{105} = 34437.33$

   a) Hamilton's Apportionment: 7, 2, 2, 2, 8, 14, 4, 5, 10, 10, 13, 2, 6, 2, 18

   b) Jefferson's Apportionment: 7, 1, 2, 2, 8, 14, 4, 5, 10, 10, 13, 2, 6, 2, 19

   c) States that Benefited: Virginia   States Disadvantaged: Delaware

48. One possible answer is A: 3,250,000, B: 1,750,000, C: 2,265,000, D: 2,735,000

49. One possible answer is A; 734, B: 367, C: 432, D: 491, E: 519, F: 388

Exercise Set 15.4

1. The Alabama paradox occurs when an increase in the total # of items results in a loss of items for a group.

2. The new-states paradox occurs when the addition of a new group changes the apportionment of another group.

3. The population paradox occurs when group A loses items to group B, although group A's population grew at a higher rate than group B's.

4. Yes, it can produce the Alabama paradox, population paradox, and new-states paradox.

5. Adams's, Webster's

6. Hamilton's, Jefferson's

7. New divisor = $\dfrac{1080}{61} = 17.71$

Office	A	B	C	D	E	Total
Employees	246	201	196	211	226	1080
Standard Quota	13.98	11.35	11.07	11.91	12.76	
Lower Quota	13	11	11	11	12	58
Hamilton's Apportionment	14	11	11	12	13	61

No. No office suffers a loss so the Alabama paradox does not occur.

8. a) Standard divisor = $\dfrac{2592}{144} = 18$

Office	A	B	C	D	Total
Employees	739	277	618	958	2592
Standard Quota	41.06	15.39	34.33	53.22	
Hamilton's Apportionment	41	16	34	53	144

b) New divisor = $\dfrac{2592}{145} = 17.88$

Office	A	B	C	D	Total
Employees	739	277	618	958	2592
Standard Quota	41.33	15.49	34.56	53.57	
Hamilton's Apportionment	41	15	35	54	145

Yes. Office B loses a chair while offices C and D each gain a chair.

9. a) Standard divisor = $\dfrac{900}{30} = 30$

State	A	B	C	Total
Population	161	250	489	900
Standard Quota	5.37	8.33	16.30	
Hamilton's Apportionment	6	8	16	30

b) New divisor = $\dfrac{900}{31} = 29.03$

State	A	B	C	Total
Population	161	250	489	900
Standard Quota	5.55	8.61	16.84	
Hamilton's Apportionment	5	9	17	31

Yes, state A loses 1 seat and states B and C each gain 1 seat.

10. a) Standard divisor $= \dfrac{1000000}{200} = 5000$

State	A	B	C	Total
Population	247,100	481,900	271,000	1,000,000
Standard Quota	49.42	96.38	54.20	
Lower Quota	49	96	54	199
Hamilton's Apportionment	50	96	54	200

b) New divisor $= \dfrac{1000000}{201} = 4975.12$

State	A	B	C	Total
Population	247,100	481,900	271,000	1,000,000
Standard Quota	49.67	96.86	54.47	
Lower Quota	49	96	54	199
Hamilton's Apportionment	50	97	54	201

No. None of the States lost a seat.

11. a) Standard divisor $= \dfrac{25000}{200} = 125$

City	A	B	C	Total
Population	8130	4030	12,840	25,000
Standard Quota	65.04	32.24	102.72	
Hamilton's Apportionment	65	32	103	200

b) New divisor $= \dfrac{25125}{200} = 125.625$

City	A	B	C	Total
New Population	8150	4030	12,945	25,125
Standard Quota	64.88	32.08	103.04	
Hamilton's Apportionment	65	32	103	200

No. None of the Cities loses a bonus.

12. a) Standard divisor $= \dfrac{990}{30} = 33$

Clinic	A	B	C	Total
Patients	217	436	337	990
Standard Quota	6.58	13.21	10.21	
Lower Quota	6	13	10	29
Hamilton's Method	7	13	10	30

b) New divisor $= \dfrac{1042}{30} = 34.73$

Clinic	A	B	C	Total
Patients	230	450	362	965
Standard Quota	6.62	12.96	10.42	
Lower Quota	6	12	10	28
Hamilton's Method	7	13	10	30

No. The apportionment is the same.

13. a) Standard divisor = $\dfrac{5400}{54} = 100$

Division	A	B	C	D	E	Total
Population	733	1538	933	1133	1063	5400
Standard Quota	7.33	15.38	9.33	11.33	10.63	
Lower Quota	7	15	9	11	10	52
Hamilton's Apportionment	7	16	9	11	11	54

b) New divisor = $\dfrac{5454}{54} = 101$

Division	A	B	C	D	E	Total
Population	733	1539	933	1133	1116	
Standard Quota	7.26	15.24	9.24	11.22	11.05	
Lower Quota	7	15	9	11	11	53
Hamilton's Apportionment	8	15	9	11	11	54

Yes. Division B loses an internship to Division A even though the population of division B grew faster than the population of division A.

14. a) Standard divisor = $\dfrac{30000}{250} = 120$

State	A	B	C	Total
Population	459	10551	18990	30000
Standard Quota	3.83	87.93	158.25	
Hamilton's Apportionment	4	88	158	250

b) New divisor = $\dfrac{30110}{250} = 120.44$

State	A	B	C	Total
Population	464	10551	19100	30115
Standard Quota	3.85	87.60	158.59	
Hamilton's Apportionment	4	88	158	250

No. The apportionment is the same.

15. a) Standard divisor = $\dfrac{4800}{48} = 100$

Tech. Data	A	B	Total
Employees	844	3956	4800
Standard Quota	8.44	39.56	
Lower Quota	8	39	47
Hamilton's Apportionment	8	40	48

b) New divisor = $\dfrac{5524}{55} = 100.44$

Tech. Data	A	B	C	Total
Employees	844	3956	724	5524
Standard Quota	8.40	39.39	7.21	
Lower Quota	8	39	7	54
Hamilton's Apportionment	9	39	7	55

Yes. Group B loses a manager.

16. a) Standard divisor = $\dfrac{10,000}{25} = 40$

Park	A	B	Total
Visitors	3750	6250	10000
Standard Quota	9.37	15.63	
Hamilton's Apportionment	9	16	25

b) New divisor = $\dfrac{12,100}{30} = 403.33$

Park	A	B	C	Total
Visitors	3750	6250	2100	10625
Standard Quota	9.38	15.63	5.25	
Hamilton's Apportionment	9	16	5	30

No.

17. a) Standard divisor = $\dfrac{990000}{66} = 15,000$

State	A	B	C	Total
Population	68970	253770	667260	990000
Standard Quota	4.60	16.92	44.48	
Hamilton's Apportionment	5	17	44	66

b) New divisor = $\dfrac{1075800}{71} = 15,152.11$

State	A	B	C	D	Total
Population	68970	253770	667260	85800	1075800
Standard Quota	4.55	16.75	44.04	5.66	
Hamilton's Apportionment	4	17	44	6	71

Yes. State A loses a seat.

18. a) Standard divisor = $\dfrac{3300}{33} = 100$

State	A	B	Total
Population	744	2556	3300
Standard Quota	7.44	25.56	
Lower Quota	7	25	32
Hamilton's Apportionment	7	26	33

b) New divisor = $\dfrac{4010}{40} = 100.25$

State	A	B	C	Total
Population	744	2556	710	4010
Standard Quota	7.42	25.50	7.08	
Lower Quota	7	25	7	39
Hamilton's Apportionment	7	26	7	40

No. The apportionment is the same.

Review Exercises

1. a) Robert Rivera wins with the most votes (15).

   b) A majority out of 34 voters is 18 or more votes. Robert Rivera does not have a majority.

2. a) Michelle MacDougal wins with the most votes (231).

   b) Yes. A majority out of 413 voters is 207 or more votes.

3.

# of votes	3	2	1	3	1
First	B	A	D	C	D
Second	A	C	C	B	A
Third	C	D	A	A	B
Fourth	D	B	B	D	C

4.

# of votes	2	2	2	1
First	C	B	A	C
Second	A	A	C	B
Third	B	C	B	A

5. Number of votes = 8 + 5 + 4 + 2 + 1 = 20

6. DVD player wins with a plurality of 8 votes.

7. I: 59 points,   D: 48 points,   C: 53 points,
   N: 40 points. iPod wins with 59 points.

8. A majority out 20 voters is 11 or more votes.
   Votes: I: 4, D: 8, C:7, N: 1.
   None has a majority, thus eliminate N.
   Votes: I: 4, D: 9, C: 7
   None has a majority, thus eliminate I
   Votes: D: 9, D: 11
   The digital camera wins.

9. The camera and iPod tie with 2 points each.
   D and N each have 1 point.

10. Votes: Votes: I: 4, D: 8, C:7, N: 1   None has a
    majority, thus eliminate D with most last place
    votes. Votes: I: 12, C: 7, N: 1; the iPod wins.

11. 38+30+25+7+10 = 110 students voted

12. Volleyball wins with a plurality of 40 votes.

13. S: 223 pts., V: 215 pts., B: 222 pts.
    Soccer wins.

14. A majority out of 110 voters is 56 or more votes.
    Votes: S: 38, V: 40, B: 32; None has a majority,
    thus eliminate B. Votes: S: 45, V: 65
    Volleyball wins.

15. S: 1 pt.,   V: 1 pt.,   B: 1 pt.   A 3-way tie

16. Votes: S: 38,   V: 40,   B: 32   None has a
    majority, thus eliminate V with the most last place
    votes. Votes: S: 68, B: 42.   Soccer wins.

17. a) Votes: A: 161+134 = 295,   F: 45,   M: 12,
       P: 0   AARP wins.

   b) Yes. A majority out of 372 voters is 187 or more
      votes. AARP receives a majority.

   c) A: 1387 pts.,   F: 740 pts.,   M: 741 pts.,
      P: 852 pts.   AARP wins.

   d) 187 or more votes is needed for a majority.
      Votes: A: 295,   F: 45,   M: 12,   P: 0
      AARP wins.

   e) A: 3 pts.,   F: 1 pt.,   M: 1 pt.,   P: 1 pt.
      AARP wins.

18. Votes: C: 25, S: 80, D: 45, L: 50

   a) A majority out of 200 voters is 101 or more
      votes. None of the cities has a majority.

   b) Seattle, with a plurality of 80 votes.

   c) C: 480, S: 440, D: 490, L: 590; Las Vegas wins.

   d) C: 25, S: 80, D: 45, L: 50; no city has a majority
      so eliminate C.
      S: 80, D: 45, L: 75; no city has a majority so
      eliminate D.
      S: 80, L: 120; Las Vegas wins.

   e) Las Vegas wins with 3 points; Dallas has 2 and
      Chicago 1.

19. a) A majority out of 16 voters is 9 or more votes.
    Votes: (EB): 4+3+ = 7,   (FW): 1+1 = 2,
    (G): 0,   (WB): 6+1 = 7   None has a majority,
    thus eliminate G.   Votes: (EB): 4+3 = 7,
    (FW): 1+1 = 2,   (WB): 6 + 1 = 7   None has a
    majority, thus eliminate FW
    Votes: (EB): 4+3+1 = 8,   (WB): 6+1+1 = 8.
    Thus, EB and WB tie.

    b) Use the Borda count method to break the tie.
    (EB) = 46 points,   (WB) = 50 points;
    World Book wins.

22. a) A majority out of 42 voters is 21 or more votes.
    Votes: A: 12,   B: 10+6 = 16,   C: 14
    None has the majority, thus eliminate A.
    Votes: B :10+6 = 16,   C: 14+12 = 26   C wins.

    b) The new preference table is

Number of votes	10	14	6	12
First	B	C	C	A
Second	A	B	B	C
Third	C	A	A	B

    Votes: A: 12,   B: 10,   C: 20;   None has a
    majority, thus eliminate B.
    Votes: A: 22,   C: 20   A wins.   When the
    order is changed A wins.   Therefore, the
    monotonicity criterion is not satisfied.

23. a) B to O: 59 to 55, B to N: 58 to 56,
    B to H: 58 to 56, so Ball Park wins the
    head-to-head comparison.

    b) Oscar Mayer with a plurality of 34.

    c) B; 289, O: 237, N: 307, H: 307; a tie between
    Nathan's and Hebrew National.

    d) In the first round N is eliminated, then B is
    eliminated, and Hebrew National wins with
    80 votes.

    e) Ball Park wins with 3 points.

    f) Plurality, Borda count, and plurality with
    elimination all violate the head-to-head criterion.

19. c) (EB) vs. (WB): EB: 4+3+1 = 8 points,
    (WB): 6+1+1 = 8 points.
    EB and WB tie again.

20. A: 44 pts.,   B: 53 pts,   C: 46 pts.,   D: 27 pts.
    Using the Borda count, candidate B wins.
    However, B only has 2 first place votes, thus the
    majority criterion is not satisfied.

21. A wins all its head-to-head comparisons but B
    wins using the Borda count method.
    The head-to-head criterion is not satisfied.

22. c) If B drops out the new table is

Number of votes	10	14	6	12
First	A	C	C	A
Second	C	A	A	C

    Votes: A: 10+12 = 22,   C: 14+6 = 20   A wins.
    Since C won the first election and then after B
    dropped out A won, the irrelevant criterion is
    not satisfied.

24. a) Yes. Fleetwood Mac is favored when
    compared to each of the other bands.

    b) Votes: R: 15,   B: 34,   J: 9+4 = 13,
    F: 25   Boston wins.

    c) R: 217 points,   B: 198 points,   J: 206 points,
    F: 249 points   Fleetwood Mac wins.

    d) A majority out of 87 voters is 44 or more votes.
    Votes: R: 15,   B: 34,   J: 13,   F:25
    None has a majority, thus eliminate J.
    Votes: R: 15+9+4 = 28,   B: 34,   F: 25
    None has a majority, thus eliminate F.
    Votes: R: 28+25 = 53,   B: 34   REO wins.

    e) R = 2 pts.,   B = 0 pts.,   J = 1 pt.,   F = 3 pts.
    Thus, Fleetwood Mac wins.

    f) Plurality and plurality w/elimination methods

25. The Borda count method

26. Plurality and plurality w/elimination methods

27. Pairwise comparison and Borda count methods

28. Standard divisor $= \dfrac{6000}{10} = 600$

Region	A	B	C	Total
Number of Houses	2592	1428	1980	6000
Standard Quota	4.32	2.38	3.30	
Lower Quota	4	2	3	9
Hamilton's Apportionment	4	3	3	10

29. Using the modified divisor 500.

Region	A	B	C	Total
Number of Houses	2592	1428	1980	6000
Modified Quota	5.18	2.86	3.96	
Jefferson's Apportionment (rounded down)	5	2	3	10

30. Using the modified divisor 700.

Region	A	B	C	Total
Number of Houses	2592	1428	1980	6000
Modified Quota	3.70	2.04	2.83	
Adams's Apportionment (rounded up)	4	3	3	10

31. Using the modified divisor 575.

Region	A	B	C	Total
Number of Houses	2592	1428	1980	6000
Modified Quota	4.51	2.48	3.4	
Webster's Apportionment (normal rounding)	5	2	3	10

32. Yes. Hamilton's Apportionment becomes 5, 2, 4.   Region B loses one truck.

33. Standard divisor $= \dfrac{870}{29} = 30$

Course	A	B	C	Total
Number of Students	371	279	220	870
Standard Quota	12.37	9.30	7.33	
Lower Quota	12	9	7	28
Hamilton's Apportionment	13	9	7	29

34. Use the modified divisor 28.

Course	A	B	C	Total
Number of Students	371	279	220	870
Modified Quota	13.25	9.96	7.86	
Jefferson's Apportionment (round down)	13	9	7	29

35. Use the modified divisor 31.2

Course	A	B	C	Total
Number of Students	371	279	220	870
Modified Quota	11.89	8.94	7.05	
Adams's Apportionment (round up)	12	9	8	29

36. Use the modified divisor 29.5

Course	A	B	C	Total
Number of Students	371	279	220	870
Modified Quota	12.58	9.46	7.46	
Webster's Apportionment (standard rounding)	13	9	7	29

37. The new divisor is $\dfrac{877}{29} = 30.24$

Course	A	B	C	Total
Number of Students	376	279	222	698
Standard Quota	12.75	9.46	7.53	
Lower Quota	12	9	7	28
Hamilton's Apportionment	13	9	7	29

No. The apportionment remains the same.

38. The Standard divisor $= \dfrac{55000}{55} = 1000$

State	A	B	Total
Population	4862	50138	55,000
Standard Quota	4.86	50.14	
Hamilton's Apportionment	5	50	55

39. The apportionment is 4, 51.

40. The apportionment is 5, 50.

41. The apportionment is 5, 50.

42. The new divisor is $\dfrac{60940}{60} = 1015.67$

State	A	B	C	Total
Population	4862	50138	5940	60940
Standard Quota	4.79	49.36	5.85	
Hamilton's Apportionment	5	49	6	60

Yes. State B loses a seat.

Chapter Test

1. $7 + 6 + 6 + 5 = 24$ members voted.

2. No candidate has a majority of ≥ 13 votes.

3. Pizza wins with a plurality of 11 votes.

4. T: 49, P: 53, B: 42; pizza wins.

5. B is eliminated and T then has a plurality of 13; tacos wins.

6. T: 1.5 pts., P 1 pt., B 0.5 pt.; Tacos wins.

7. a) Votes: H: 26+14 = 40, I: 29, L: 30, S: 43
   Thus, the salamander wins.

   b) (H) 1st $(40)(4) = 160$
   2nd $(59)(3) = 177$
   3rd $(0)(2) = 0$
   4th $(43)(1) = 43$ H receives 380 points.

   (I) 1st $(29)(4) = 116$
   2nd $(40)(3) = 120$
   3rd $(73)(2) = 146$
   4th $(0)(1) = 0$ I receives 382 points

   (L) 1st $(30)(4) = 120$
   2nd $(43)(3) = 129$
   3rd $(43)(2) = 86$
   4th $(26)(1) = 26$ ·L receives 361 points

7. b) (S) 1st $(43)(4) = 172$
   2nd $(0)(3) = 0$
   3rd $(26)(2) = 52$
   4th $(73)(1) = 73$ S receives 297 points.
   The iguana (I) wins with the most points.

   c) A majority out of 142 voters is 72 or more votes.
   Votes: H: 40, I: 29, L: 30, S: 43; None has a majority, thus eliminate I. Votes: H: 69, L: 30, S: 43 None has a majority, thus eliminate L. Votes: H: 99, S: 43
   The hamster wins.

   d) H vs. I: I gets 1 pt. H vs. L: L gets 1 pt.
   H vs. S: H gets 1 pt. I vs. L: L gets 1 pt.
   I vs. S: I gets 1 pt. L vs. S: L gets 1 pt.
   The lemming wins with 3 points.

8. Plurality: Votes: W: 86, X: 52+28 = 80, Y: 60, Z: 58 W wins.
   Borda count: W gets 594 points, X gets 760 points, Y gets 722 points, Z gets 764 points Z wins
   Plurality with elimination: A majority out of 284 voters is 143 or more votes.
   Votes: W: 86, X: 80, Y: 60, Z: 58
   None has a majority, thus eliminate Z.
   Votes: W: 86, X: 80+58 = 138, Y: 60
   None has a majority, thus eliminate Y.
   Votes: W: 86, X: 138+60 = 198 X wins.

8. Head-to-Head: When Y is compared to each of the others, Y is favored. Thus Y wins the head-to-head comparison.
   Plurality, Borda count and Plurality with elimination each violate the head-to-head criterion. The pairwise method never violates the head-to-head criterion.

9. A majority out of 35 voters is 18 or more votes.
   El Capitan (E) has a majority.
   However, the mule deer (M) wins using the Borda count method with 115 points. Thus the majority criterion is violated.

10. a) The standard divisor $= \dfrac{33000}{30} = 1100$

State	A	B	C	Total
Population	6933	9533	16534	33,000
Standard Quota	6.30	8.67	15.03	
Hamilton's Apportionment	6	9	15	30

   b) The divisor 1040 was used.

State	A	B	C	Total
Population	6933	9533	16534	33,000
Modified Quota	6.67	9.17	15.90	
Jefferson's Apportionment (round down)	6	9	15	30

10. c) The divisor used was 1160

State	A	B	C	Total
Population	6933	9533	16534	33,000
Standard Quota	5.98	8.22	14.25	
Adams's Apportionment	6	9	15	30

d) The divisor 1100 was used.

State	A	B	C	Total
Population	6933	9533	16534	33,000
Modified Quota	6.30	8.67	15.03	
Webster's Apportionment	6	9	15	30

e) The new divisor 1064.52

State	A	B	C	Total
Population	6933	9533	16534	33,000
Standard Quota	6.51	8.96	15.53	
Hamilton's Apportionment	6	9	16	31

The Alabama paradox does not occur, since none of the states loses a seat.

f) The divisor $= \dfrac{33826}{30} = 1127.53$

State	A	B	C	Total
Population	7072	9724	17030	33,826
Standard Quota	5.98	8.62	15.10	
Hamilton's Apportionment	6	9	15	30

The Alabama paradox does not occur, since none of the states loses a seat.

g) The new divisor is $\dfrac{38100}{36} = 1058.33$

State	A	B	C	D	Total
Population	6933	9533	16534	5100	38100
Standard Quota	6.55	9.01	15.62	4.82	
Hamilton's Apportionment	6	9	16	5	36

The new states paradox does not occur, since none of the existing states loses a seat.

APPENDIX

GRAPH THEORY

Exercise Set

1. A **vertex** is a designated point.
2. An **edge** (or an **arc**) is any line, either straight or curved, that begins and ends at a vertex.
3. To determine whether a vertex is odd or even, count the number of edges attached to the vertex. If the number of edges is odd, the vertex is **odd**. If the number of edges is even, the vertex is **even**.
4. Answers will vary.

5. 5 vertices, 7 edges
6. 6 vertices, 8 edges
7. 7 vertices, 11 edges
8. 5 vertices, 6 edges
9. Each graph has the same number of edges from the corresponding vertices.
10. Each graph has the same number of edges from the corresponding vertices.
11. Odd vertices: *C, D*
    Even vertices: *A, B*
12. Odd vertices: *A, C, E, F*
    Even vertices: *B, D*

13. Yes. The figure has exactly two odd vertices, namely *C* and *D*. Therefore, the figure is traversable. You may start at *C* and end at *D*, or start at *D* and end at *C*.
14. No. All four vertices are odd. There are more than two odd vertices. Therefore, the figure is not traversable.
15. Yes. The figure has no odd vertices. Therefore, the figure is traversable. You may start at any point and end where you started.
16. Yes. The figure has no odd vertices. Therefore, the figure is traversable. You may start at any point and end where you started.
17. No. The figure has four odd vertices, namely *A, B, E,* and *F*. There are more than two odd vertices. Therefore, the figure is not traversable.
18. Yes. The figure has exactly two odd vertices, namely *C* and *G*. Therefore, the figure is traversable. You may start at *C* and end at *G*, or start at *G* and end at *C*.
19. Yes. The figure has exactly two odd vertices, namely *A* and *C*. Therefore, the figure is traversable. You may start at *A* and end at *C*, or start at *C* and end at *A*.
20. Yes. The figure has no odd vertices. Therefore, the figure is traversable. You may start at any point and end where you started.
21. a) 0 rooms have an odd number of doors.
    5 rooms have an even number of doors.
    b) Yes because the figure would have no odd vertices.
    c) Start in any room and end where you began. For example: *A* to *D* to *B* to *C* to *E* to *A*.
22. a) 4 rooms have an odd number of doors.
    1 room has an even number of doors.
    b) No because the figure would have more than two odd vertices.

23. a) 2 rooms have an odd number of doors.

4 rooms have an even number of doors.

b) Yes because the figure would have exactly two odd vertices.

c) Start at *B* and end at *F*, or start at *F* and end at *B*.

For example: *B* to *C* to *F* to *E* to *D* to *A* to *B* to *E* to *F*

24. a) 2 rooms have an odd number of doors.

4 rooms have an even number of doors.

b) Yes because the figure would have exactly two odd vertices.

c) Start at *B* and end at *E*, or start at *E* and end at *B*. For example: *B* to *A* to *D* to *E* to *F* to *C* to *B* to *E*

25. a) 4 rooms have an odd number of doors.

1 room has an even number of doors.

b) No because the figure would have more than two odd vertices.

26. a) 5 rooms have an odd number of doors.

1 room has an even number of doors.

b) No because the figure would have more than two odd vertices.

27. a) 3 rooms have an odd number of doors.

2 rooms have an even number of doors.

b) No because the figure would have more than two odd vertices.

28. a) 3 rooms have an odd number of doors.

4 rooms have an even number of doors.

b) No because the figure would have more than two odd vertices.

29. The door must be placed in room *D*. Adding a door to any other room would create two rooms with an odd number of vertices. You would then be unable to enter the building through the door marked "enter" and exit through the new door without going through a door at least twice.

30. The door must be placed in room *D*. Adding a door to any other room would create two rooms with an odd number of vertices. You would then be unable to enter the building through the door marked "enter" and exit through the new door without going through a door at least twice.

31. Yes because the figure would have exactly two odd vertices. Begin at either the island on the left or on the right and end at the other island.

32. Yes because the figure would have exactly two odd vertices. Begin at the island on the right and end on the land below the island, or vice versa.

33.

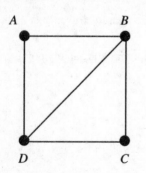

34.

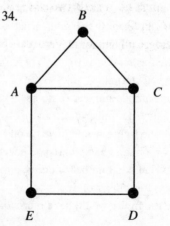

35. a) Kentucky, Virginia, North Carolina, Georgia, Alabama, Mississippi, Arkansas, Missouri
    b) Illinois, Arkansas, Tennessee

36. a) French Guiana, Surinam, Guyana, Venezuela, Columbia, Peru, Bolivia, Paraguay, Argentina, Uruguay
    b) Peru, Chile, Argentina, Paraguay, Brazil

37. a) 4
    b) 4
    c) 11

38.

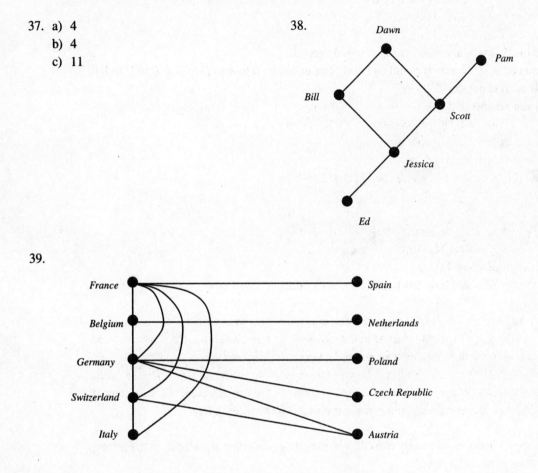

39.

40. No, it is not possible, assuming that your starting and ending points are considered vertices.

41. a) Yes, the graph has exactly two odd vertices, namely *C* and *G*.
    b) *C, A, B, E, F, D, G, C*

42. Number of Edges = Number of Vertices + Number of Regions − 2